D1030377

ELEMENTS OF COMPLEX VARIABLES

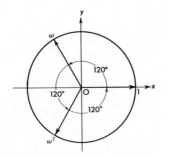

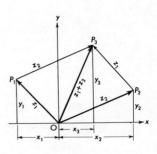

Elements of

LOUIS L. PENNISI

University of Illinois, Chicago

With the Collaboration of

LOUIS I. GORDON
and SIM LASHER

University of Illinois, Chicago

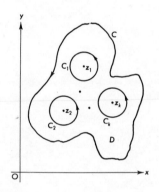

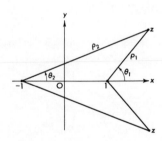

COMPLEX VARIABLES

HOLT, RINEHART AND WINSTON
New York – Chicago – San Francisco – Toronto – London

03-011450-0

Copyright © 1963 by Holt, Rinehart and Winston, Inc.
Library of Congress Catalog Card Number: 63-7619
All Rights Reserved
89012   22   987
Printed in the United States of America

Preface

Students enrolled in a first course in the theory of functions of a complex variable usually present a variety of backgrounds and degrees of mathematical maturity. Consequently, the author has included a good deal of elementary material accessible to the student who is taking his first course beyond calculus. It seemed also desirable to present the material in sufficient detail in order to minimize a sense of vagueness which is apt to disturb the beginning student when only the highlights of the argument are given.

In undertaking to prove theorems in full detail there is, of course, the danger of the text becoming too ponderous. To circumvent this difficulty, the device of separating auxiliary arguments and stating them in the form of exercises has been used. These exercises, in turn, have been supplied with liberal hints or complete solutions.

Chapters 1, 3, and 4 are devoted to the algebraic properties of complex numbers, the notion of an analytic function, and an extensive treatment of elementary functions. Chapter 2 and the beginning of Chapter 3 contain a presentation of those basic concepts associated with the notions of limit and continuity that are used in later chapters. The latter part of Chapter 5 and Chapters 6 and 7 deal mainly with the Cauchy integral formula and its consequences, the Taylor and Laurent expansions and the residue theorem together with its applications. The first part of Chapter 5 is devoted to contour integration and a proof of the Cauchy integral theorem based on the concept of winding number. Chapter 8 contains a discussion of the mapping properties of analytic functions and some examples of conformal mapping. Chapter 9 deals with application of analytic functions to the theory of flows.

In a one-semester course, Chapters 1, 3, 4, 5, 6, and 7 would constitute the main part, and the remaining chapters may be dealt with more lightly.

To provide an opportunity for the student to assimilate and familiarize himself with the subject matter, a considerable number of examples have been incorporated into the body of the text, and a large variety of exercises have been placed at the end of various sections. Answers and hints to many of these exercises will be found in the back of the book.

The numbering system is according to chapter and section. For example, the sixth section of Chapter 3 is designated by 3.6; the second theorem of

Section 3.6 is designated by Theorem 3.6.2, and so on. In general, in order to facilitate references, results are stated as theorems.

The author wishes to acknowledge his indebtedness to his colleagues Roger G. Hill, Lawrence R. Sjoblom, and Nicholas C. Scholomiti, whose counsel he has enjoyed during the writing of this book and who have read the manuscript making valuable suggestions and contributions. Also, he wishes to express his appreciation to Professor Haim Reingold of Illinois Institute of Technology for making possible the use of the text in mimeographed form during the evening classes. While acknowledging the contributions of his collaborators and his colleagues, the author assumes full responsibility for the contents of the book.

November 1962   L.L.P.
Chicago, Illinois

Contents

ELEMENTS OF COMPLEX VARIABLES

1

Complex Numbers and Their Geometrical Representation

1.1. COMPLEX NUMBERS. An approach to complex numbers is to consider the properties of expressions of the form $a + bi$, where a and b are real numbers and i is one of the *imaginary* roots of $x^2 + 1 = 0$. We shall approach the subject of complex numbers, however, by considering the set of all ordered pairs of real numbers. An ordered pair of real numbers will be denoted by the symbol $[a, b]$. When we say the number pairs are ordered, we mean $[a, b]$ and $[b, a]$ are to be considered different unless $a = b$.

Definition 1.1.1.   The system of complex numbers is the *set of all ordered pairs $[a, b]$ of real numbers with two binary operations, addition, $+$, and multiplication, $\cdot$,* defined as follows:

$$[a, b] + [c, d] = [a + c, b + d],$$
$$[a, b] \cdot [c, d] = [ac - bd, ad + bc].$$

Two complex numbers $[a, b]$ and $[c, d]$ are *equal* if, and only if, $a = c$ and $b = d$.

Let us put $\alpha = [a, b]$, $\beta = [c, d]$, $\gamma = [e, f]$. From the above definition and from the properties of real numbers, we may establish the following

——*THEOREM* 1.1.1.

$\alpha + \beta = \beta + \alpha$.   Addition is commutative. $\hspace{2cm}$ (1.1.1)

$\alpha + (\beta + \gamma) = (\alpha + \beta) + \gamma$.   Addition is associative. $\hspace{1cm}$ (1.1.2)

There exists a complex number τ namely, $[0, 0]$, such that
$\alpha + \tau = \alpha = \tau + \alpha$, for all α. $\hspace{4cm}$ (1.1.3)

$\alpha \cdot \beta = \beta \cdot \alpha$. Multiplication is commutative. (1.1.4)

$\alpha \cdot (\beta \cdot \gamma) = (\alpha \cdot \beta) \cdot \gamma$. Multiplication is associative. (1.1.5)

$\alpha \cdot (\beta + \gamma) = \alpha \cdot \beta + \alpha \cdot \gamma$. Multiplication is distributive with respect to addition. (1.1.6)

Proof. We shall prove (1.1.2) and (1.1.5).

$$
\begin{aligned}
\alpha + (\beta + \gamma) &= [a, b] + \{[c, d] + [e, f]\} \\
&= [a, b] + [c + e, d + f] \\
&= [a + (c + e), b + (d + f)] \\
&= [(a + c) + e, (b + d) + f] \\
&= [a + c, b + d] + [e, f] \\
&= \{[a, b] + [c, d]\} + [e, f] = (\alpha + \beta) + \gamma,
\end{aligned}
$$

thus establishing (1.1.2).

$$
\begin{aligned}
\alpha \cdot (\beta \cdot \gamma) &= [a, b] \cdot \{[c, d] \cdot [e, f]\} \\
&= [a, b] \cdot [ce - df, cf + de] \\
&= [a(ce - df) - b(cf + de), a(cf + de) + b(ce - df)] \\
&= [(ac - bd) e - (ad + bc) f, (ac - bd) f + (ad + bc) e] \\
&= [ac - bd, ad + bc] \cdot [e, f] \\
&= \{[a, b] \cdot [c, d]\} \cdot [e, f] = (a \cdot \beta) \cdot \gamma,
\end{aligned}
$$

thus establishing (1.1.5).

Note that the number τ in (1.1.3) is necessarily unique, for, suppose that another number $\delta = [g, h]$ exists such that $[a, b] + [g, h] = [a, b]$. Then $a + g = a$ and $b + h = b$. Hence $g = 0$ and $h = 0$. Consequently $\delta = [0, 0]$.

1.2. SUBTRACTION AND DIVISION OF COMPLEX NUMBERS

——**THEOREM** 1.2.1. Given two complex numbers $\alpha = [a, b]$ and $\beta = [c, d]$, there exists a unique complex number $\gamma = [e, f]$ such that $\alpha + \gamma = \beta$.

Proof. In view of Definition 1.1.1, $\alpha + \gamma = \beta$ if and only if $a + e = c$ and $b + f = d$; or equivalently, if and only if $e = c - a$ and $f = d - b$. Thus γ exists and is unique.

Definition 1.2.1. *Subtraction.* Given two complex numbers α and β, we define the *difference* γ, denoted by $\beta - \alpha$, to be a complex number such that $\beta = \alpha + \gamma$.

It follows at once from Theorem 1.2.1 that γ exists and is unique. Also note that

$$
\tau - \alpha = [0, 0] - [a, b] = [- a, - b].
$$

We denote

$$\tau - \alpha \qquad \text{by} - \alpha.$$

Numbers of the form $[a, 0]$ can be set up in a one-to-one correspondence with the real numbers a: $[a, 0] \leftrightarrow a$. In view of Definition 1.1.1, we have

$$[a, 0] \leftrightarrow a,$$
$$[a, 0] + [b, 0] = [a + b, 0] \leftrightarrow a + b,$$
$$[a, 0] \cdot [b, 0] = [ab, 0] \leftrightarrow ab.$$

The above three conditions establish what is known as an *isomorphism* between the set of ordered pairs of the form $[a, 0]$ and the set of real numbers. Because of these three conditions we can replace $[a, 0]$ by a, and, in particular, $\tau = [0, 0]$ by 0. Therefore, in practice it is convenient to write $[a, 0] = a$, and to regard the real numbers as a subset of the complex numbers. If we denote $[0, 1]$ by i, we see that

$$i^2 \equiv i \cdot i = [0, 1] \cdot [0, 1] = [-1, 0] = -1. \qquad (1.2.1)$$

Hence i is a square root of -1. Also, in view of Definition 1.1.1

$$[a, 0] + [0, 1] \cdot [b, 0] = [a, 0] + [0, b] = [a, b],$$

hence

$$[a, b] = a + ib. \qquad (1.2.2)$$

Thus $[a, b]$ may be denoted by $a + ib$ with the understanding that a is $[a, 0]$, b is $[b, 0]$, and $a + ib$ is a plus i times b. In the complex number $[a, b]$, a is called the *real part* and b the *imaginary part*. Also a and b are known, respectively, as the *real* and the *imaginary components* of the complex number $[a, b]$. Complex numbers of the form $[0, b] = 0 + ib$ are known as *pure imaginary numbers*. In practice, it is convenient to write $0 + ib$ as ib. The complex number $a + ib$ is *imaginary* if $b \neq 0$. It is easy to verify that

$$0 \cdot [a, b] = 0, \qquad (1.2.3)$$
$$k \cdot [a, b] = [ka, kb], \qquad (k \text{ is any real number}). \qquad (1.2.4)$$

For any complex number α, it follows from (1.2.4) that $1 \cdot \alpha = \alpha$ and $(-1) \cdot \alpha = -\alpha$. From (1.2.2) we see that a complex number $a + ib = 0$ if, and only if, $a = 0$ and $b = 0$. Thus, $a + ib \neq 0$ if, and only if, $a^2 + b^2 \neq 0$.

We shall write $\alpha \cdot \beta$ as $\alpha\beta$, aa as a^2, a^3 as aa^2, and so forth.

——**THEOREM** 1.2.2.   Given two complex numbers $\alpha = [a, b]$ and $\beta = [c, d]$, $\beta \neq 0$, there exists a unique complex number $\delta = [g, h]$ such that $\beta\delta = \alpha$.

Proof. In view of Definition 1.1.1, $\beta\delta = \alpha$ if, and only if, $cg - dh = a$ and $ch + dg = b$. Since $\beta \neq 0$, $c^2 + d^2 \neq 0$. Solving for g and h, we obtain

$$g = \frac{ac + bd}{c^2 + d^2} \quad \text{and} \quad h = \frac{bc - ad}{c^2 + d^2}.$$

Hence $\delta = [g, h]$ is uniquely determined.

Definition 1.2.2. **Division.** Given two complex numbers α and β, $\beta \neq 0$, we define the *quotient* δ, denoted by α/β, to be a complex number such that $\alpha = \beta\delta$.

It follows at once from Theorem 1.2.2 that δ exists and is unique. Moreover if $\alpha = [a, b]$ and $\beta = [c, d]$, then

$$\delta = \frac{\alpha}{\beta} = \left[\frac{ac + bd}{c^2 + d^2}, \frac{bc - ad}{c^2 + d^2} \right]. \tag{1.2.5}$$

Remark 1.2.1. Complex numbers expressed as in (1.2.2) may be added, subtracted, multiplied, and divided formally as in the algebra of real numbers provided i^2, when it occurs, is replaced by -1; for example,

$$(a + ib) + (c + id) = a + c + i(b + d), \tag{1.2.6}$$

$$(a + ib) - (c + id) = a - c + i(b - d), \tag{1.2.7}$$

$$(a + ib) \cdot (c + id) = ac - bd + i(ad + bc), \tag{1.2.8}$$

$$\frac{(a + ib)}{(c + id)} = \frac{(a + ib)(c - id)}{(c + id)(c - id)} = \frac{ac + bd}{c^2 + d^2} + i\frac{bc - ad}{c^2 + d^2} \tag{1.2.9}$$

give the results required by Definitions 1.1.1, 1.2.1, and 1.2.2. Also in (1.2.9) we assume that $c + id \neq 0$. It is now clear why Definition 1.1.1 implies the commutative, associative, and distributive laws; for these laws are valid in the algebra of real numbers and will remain valid after we put $i^2 = -1$.

The converse of (1.2.3) also holds: if the product of two complex numbers is zero, then at least one of the factors must be zero. In fact, if $\alpha \cdot \beta = 0$ and $\beta \neq 0$, then by (1.2.3)

$$\alpha = (\alpha\beta)\left(\frac{1}{\beta}\right) = 0 \cdot \left(\frac{1}{\beta}\right) = 0.$$

EXERCISES 1.2

In Exercises 1-7 reduce the number to the form $a + ib$.

 1. $(3 + 6i) + (5 - 2i) + (4 - 5i)$.

 2. $(2 - 3i) - (5 + 4i) - (-2 - 5i)$.

 3. $(3 + 5i)(-4 - 2i)(-1 + 4i)$.

4. $\dfrac{4 + 2i}{1 - 2i} + \dfrac{3 + 4i}{2 + 3i}$.

5. $i^{18} - 3i^7 + i^2(1 - i^4) - (-i)^{26}$.

6. $(1 - i)^3 (1 + i)$.

7. $\left[\dfrac{2i}{1 + i}\right]^4$.

8. Show that the number $z = \dfrac{1 - i\sqrt{3}}{2}$ satisfies the equation $\dfrac{3}{z + 1} - \dfrac{1}{z} = 1$.

Also show that $\left(\dfrac{1 - i\sqrt{3}}{2}\right)^6 = 1$.

9. Prove (1.1.1).

10. Prove (1.1.4) and (1.1.6).

11. Prove (1.2.3) and (1.2.4).

12. Using the ordered pair representation for i and b, show by a direct calculation that $ib = bi$.

1.3. CONJUGATE AND ABSOLUTE VALUE OF A COMPLEX NUMBER

Definition 1.3.1.   The *conjugate* $\bar{\alpha}$ of a complex number $\alpha = [a, b] = a + ib$, is given by $\bar{\alpha} = [a, -b] = a - ib$.

Using the above definition, one can verify that the conjugate of the sum, difference, product, and quotient of two complex numbers is equal, respectively, to the sum, difference, product, and quotient of their conjugates; that is,

$$\overline{\alpha + \beta} = \bar{\alpha} + \bar{\beta}. \tag{1.3.1}$$

$$\overline{\alpha - \beta} = \bar{\alpha} - \bar{\beta}. \tag{1.3.2}$$

$$\overline{\alpha\beta} = \bar{\alpha}\bar{\beta}. \tag{1.3.3}$$

$$\overline{\left(\dfrac{\alpha}{\beta}\right)} = \dfrac{\bar{\alpha}}{\bar{\beta}}, \qquad (\beta \neq 0). \tag{1.3.4}$$

We shall verify (1.3.1) and (1.3.3). Let $\alpha = a + ib$ and $\beta = c + id$. Then

$$\overline{\alpha + \beta} = (a + c) - i(b + d) = (a - ib) + (c - id) = \bar{\alpha} + \bar{\beta}.$$

$$\overline{\alpha\beta} = (ac - bd) - i(ad + bc) = \bar{\alpha}\bar{\beta}.$$

Also observe that $\bar{\bar{\alpha}} = \alpha$.

Remark 1.3.1.   It follows from (1.3.1)-(1.3.4) that if $R(\alpha, \beta, \gamma, \cdots)$ is a rational expression involving the complex numbers $\alpha, \beta, \gamma, \cdots$, then

$$\overline{R(\alpha, \beta, \gamma, \cdots)} = R(\bar{\alpha}, \bar{\beta}, \bar{\gamma}, \cdots).$$

Definition 1.3.2. The *modulus* or *absolute value* of a complex number $\alpha = [a, b] = a + ib$, written $| \alpha |$, is given by $| \alpha | = \sqrt{a^2 + b^2}$.

Note that the absolute value of a complex number is a nonnegative real number.

Suppose that $z = [x, y] = x + iy$.* Let us denote by $\mathscr{R}(z)$ and $\mathscr{I}(z)$, respectively, the real part x and the imaginary part y of the complex number z. We shall establish the following simple but useful

——*THEOREM* 1.3.1.   If $z = x + iy$, then we have

$$| z | = | \bar{z} | \quad \text{and} \quad | z |^2 = z\bar{z}. \tag{1.3.5}$$

$$2\mathscr{R}(z) = z + \bar{z} \quad \text{and} \quad 2i\mathscr{I}(z) = z - \bar{z}. \tag{1.3.6}$$

$$| \mathscr{R}(z) | \leq | z | \quad \text{and} \quad | \mathscr{I}(z) | \leq | z |. \tag{1.3.7}$$

Proof.

$$| z | = \sqrt{x^2 + y^2} = \sqrt{x^2 + (-y)^2} = | \bar{z} |.$$
$$z\bar{z} = (x + iy)(x - iy) = x^2 + y^2 = | z |^2.$$
$$z + \bar{z} = (x + iy) + (x - iy) = 2x = 2\mathscr{R}(z).$$
$$z - \bar{z} = (x + iy) - (x - iy) = 2iy = 2i\mathscr{I}(z).$$

Since $| z |^2 = | \mathscr{R}(z) |^2 + |\mathscr{I}(z) |^2$, it follows that $| \mathscr{R}(z) | \leq | z |$ and $|\mathscr{I}(z) | \leq | z |$.

——*THEOREM* 1.3.2.   The absolute value of the product of two complex numbers is the product of the absolute values of the factors; that is,

$$| z_1 z_2 | = | z_1 | | z_2 |. \tag{1.3.8}$$

Proof.   Utilizing (1.3.3) and Theorems 1.1.1 and 1.3.1, we have

$$| z_1 z_2 |^2 = (z_1 z_2)(\overline{z_1 z_2}) = (z_1 z_2)(\bar{z}_1 \bar{z}_2) = (z_1 \bar{z}_1)(z_2 \bar{z}_2) = | z_1 |^2 | z_2 |^2,$$

from which equation (1.3.8) follows, since the absolute value of a complex number is nonnegative.

——*THEOREM* 1.3.3.   The absolute value of the sum of two complex numbers cannot exceed the sum of their absolute values; that is,

$$| z_1 + z_2 | \leq | z_1 | + | z_2 |. \tag{1.3.9}$$

---

* It is to be understood, even when it is not explicitly stated, that when we write z, we mean that z is a complex number equal to $x + iy$, x and y real.

Proof. Utilizing (1.3.1) and Theorems 1.1.1, 1.3.1, and 1.3.2, we have

$$
\begin{aligned}
| z_1 + z_2 |^2 &= (z_1 + z_2)\,(\overline{z_1 + z_2}) = (z_1 + z_2)\,(\bar{z}_1 + \bar{z}_2) \\
&= z_1 \bar{z}_1 + z_1 \bar{z}_2 + \bar{z}_1 z_2 + z_2 \bar{z}_2 \\
&= | z_1 |^2 + 2\mathscr{R}(z_1 \bar{z}_2) + | z_2 |^2 \\
&\leqq | z_1 |^2 + 2\,| z_1 \bar{z}_2 | + | z_2 |^2 \\
&= | z_1 |^2 + 2\,| z_1 |\,| z_2 | + | z_2 |^2 \\
&= (| z_1 | + | z_2 |)^2,
\end{aligned}
$$

from which inequality (1.3.9) follows.

The above result can be extended by mathematical induction to any finite number of complex numbers. The following theorem is left as an exercise for the reader.

——**THEOREM** 1.3.4. The absolute value of the sum of n complex numbers cannot exceed the sum of their absolute values; that is,

$$
\left| \sum_{k=1}^{n} z_k \right| \leqq \sum_{k=1}^{n} | z_k |. \tag{1.3.10}
$$

——**THEOREM** 1.3.5. If z_1 and z_2 are any two complex numbers, then the absolute value of $| z_1 | - | z_2 |$ does not exceed the absolute value of $z_1 - z_2$; that is,

$$
\Big|\, | z_1 | - | z_2 | \,\Big| \leqq | z_1 - z_2 |. \tag{1.3.11}
$$

Proof. Utilizing (1.3.2) and Theorems 1.1.1, 1.3.1, and 1.3.2, we have

$$
\begin{aligned}
| z_1 - z_2 |^2 &= (z_1 - z_2)\,(\overline{z_1 - z_2}) \\
&= z_1 \bar{z}_1 - z_1 \bar{z}_2 - z_2 \bar{z}_1 + z_2 \bar{z}_2 \\
&= | z_1 |^2 - 2\mathscr{R}(z_1 \bar{z}_2) + | z_2 |^2 \\
&\geqq | z_1 |^2 - 2\,| z_1 z_2 | + | z_2 |^2 = (| z_1 | - | z_2 |)^2,
\end{aligned}
$$

from which inequality (1.3.11) may now be deduced.

Inequality (1.3.11) may also be derived directly from (1.3.9) and vice versa. (See Exercises 1.3.10 and 1.3.11.)

EXAMPLE 1.3.1. Let us show that if $z_1 + z_2$ and $z_1 z_2$ are both real, then either z_1 and z_2 are both real or $z_1 = \bar{z}_2$.

Solution. Let $z_1 + z_2 = r_1$ and $z_1 z_2 = r_2$, where r_1 and r_2 are real numbers. It is sufficient to prove the results for the case when z_1 and z_2 are not both zero—for example, $z_2 \neq 0$. Then

$$
z_1 = \frac{r_2}{z_2} = \frac{r_2 \bar{z}_2}{z_2 \bar{z}_2} = r_3 \bar{z}_2,
$$

where $r_3 = r_2/|z_2|^2$ is real. Thus

$$r_3\bar{z}_2 + z_2 = r_1.$$

Since $\mathscr{I}(\bar{z}_2) = -\mathscr{I}(z_2)$ and $\mathscr{I}(r_1) = 0$, we obtain (see Exercise 1.3.2)

$$-r_3\mathscr{I}(z_2) + \mathscr{I}(z_2) = 0, \quad \text{or} \quad (1 - r_3)\mathscr{I}(z_2) = 0.$$

Therefore, either $r_3 = 1$ and hence $z_1 = \bar{z}_2$, or $\mathscr{I}(z_2) = 0$ from which it follows that z_2 is real and, consequently, z_1 is also real.

EXERCISES 1.3

1. Prove (1.3.2) and (1.3.4).

2. Prove that if z_1 and z_2 are any complex numbers, then

(a) $\mathscr{R}(z_1 + z_2) = \mathscr{R}(z_1) + \mathscr{R}(z_2)$,

(b) $\mathscr{I}(z_1 + z_2) = \mathscr{I}(z_1) + \mathscr{I}(z_2)$,

(c) $\mathscr{R}(z_1 z_2) = \mathscr{R}(z_1)\, \mathscr{R}(z_2) - \mathscr{I}(z_1)\, \mathscr{I}(z_2)$,

(d) $\mathscr{I}(z_1 z_2) = \mathscr{R}(z_1)\, \mathscr{I}(z_2) + \mathscr{I}(z_1)\, \mathscr{R}(z_2)$.

3. Prove that if $z_2 \neq 0$, then $|z_1/z_2| = |z_1|/|z_2|$.

4. Find the absolute value of $(3z + i)/(3z - i)^2$ in terms of x and y.

5. Prove that if $z^2 = (\bar{z})^2$, then z is either real or pure imaginary.

6. Prove that $|(1 - z)/(\bar{z} - 1)| = 1$, provided that $z \neq 1$.

7. Prove that

$$\mathscr{R}\left(\frac{z_1}{z_1 + z_2}\right) + \mathscr{R}\left(\frac{z_2}{z_1 + z_2}\right) = 1.$$

8. Prove that if $z_1 + z_2$ and $z_1\bar{z}_2$ are both real, then either z_1 and z_2 are both real or $z_1 = -z_2$.

9. Prove that if $z + 1/z$ is real, then either $\mathscr{I}(z) = 0$ or $|z| = 1$.

10. Let z_1 and z_2 be any complex numbers. Proceeding directly from Theorem 1.3.3, show that

$$|z_1| - |z_2| \leqq |z_1 - z_2|$$

and

$$|z_1| - |z_2| \geqq -|z_1 - z_2|.$$

Use this to infer (1.3.11).

11. Derive (1.3.9) directly from (1.3.11).

12. Derive the result of Example 1.3.1 by using the identity

$$(z_1 - z_2)^2 = (z_1 + z_2)^2 - 4z_1 z_2.$$

13. Prove that $\overline{\left(\sum_{k=1}^{n} z_k\right)} = \sum_{k=1}^{n} \overline{z_k}.$

14. Prove that $\overline{\left(\prod_{k=1}^{n} z_k\right)} = \prod_{k=1}^{n} \overline{z_k}.$

(The symbol $\prod$ stands for product.)

15. Prove that $\left| \sum_{k=1}^{n} z_k \right| \leq \sum_{k=1}^{n} |z_k|.$

16. Prove *Lagrange's identity* in the complex form:

$$\left| \sum_{j=1}^{n} \alpha_j \beta_j \right|^2 = \sum_{j=1}^{n} |\alpha_j|^2 \sum_{j=1}^{n} |\beta_j|^2 - \sum_{1 \leq j < k \leq n} |\alpha_j \overline{\beta_k} - \alpha_k \overline{\beta_j}|^2.$$

17. Prove *Cauchy's inequality* in the complex form:

$$\left| \sum_{j=1}^{n} \alpha_j \beta_j \right|^2 \leq \sum_{j=1}^{n} |\alpha_j|^2 \sum_{j=1}^{n} |\beta_j|^2.$$

18. Prove the *triangle* or *Minkowski inequality* in the complex form:

$$\left[\sum_{j=1}^{n} |\alpha_j + \beta_j|^2 \right]^{1/2} \leq \left[\sum_{j=1}^{n} |\alpha_j|^2 \right]^{1/2} + \left[\sum_{j=1}^{n} |\beta_j|^2 \right]^{1/2}.$$

1.4. GEOMETRIC REPRESENTATION OF COMPLEX NUMBERS.

According to Gauss, complex numbers may be interpreted as points in a two-dimensional plane. We introduce in this plane a rectangular coordinate system, and the complex number $z = x + iy$ is made to correspond to the point $P = (x, y)$ with the real component x of z as abscissa and imaginary component y of z as ordinate. We call this plane the *complex plane* or the z *plane*. The x axis and y axis are referred to as the *real axis* and the *imaginary axis*, respectively. Hereafter, we shall use the words "point" and "complex number" interchangeably. Also, at times, when referring to the complex plane, we shall omit the word "complex."

For example, the number $-3 + 2i$ is represented by the point $(-3, 2)$ as shown in Fig. 1.4.1.

Each point (different from the origin) of the complex plane determines a vector (directed line segment) from the origin to the point. If the point is the origin, the zero vector results. Thus a complex number may also be represented by a vector. Since addition of two complex numbers is performed by

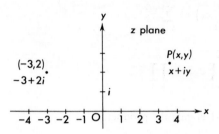

FIG. 1.4.1.   Complex Plane.

addition of their x and y components, it is seen that addition of complex numbers corresponds to geometric vector addition in the complex plane according to the parallelogram law as shown in Fig. 1.4.2.

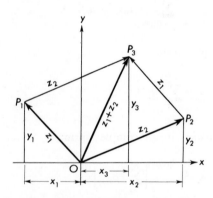

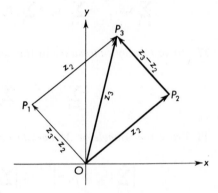

FIG. 1.4.2.   Addition of Complex Numbers.

FIG. 1.4.3.   Subtraction of Complex Numbers.

Let P_1 and P_2 be the points z_1 and z_2. Then addition is described as follows. Through P_1, draw $\overrightarrow{P_1P_3}$ equal and parallel to $\overrightarrow{OP_2}$. Then P_3 has coordinates $(x_1 + x_2, y_1 + y_2)$, and P_3 represents the point $z_1 + z_2$. In vectorial notation, we have

$$\overrightarrow{OP_3} = \overrightarrow{OP_1} + \overrightarrow{P_1P_3} = \overrightarrow{OP_1} + \overrightarrow{OP_2} = \overrightarrow{OP_2} + \overrightarrow{P_2P_3}.$$

Also, if P_3 is the point z_3, we have (see Fig. 1.4.3)

$$z_3 - z_2 = \overrightarrow{OP_3} - \overrightarrow{OP_2} = \overrightarrow{OP_3} + \overrightarrow{P_3P_1} = \overrightarrow{OP_1} = \overrightarrow{P_2P_3}.$$

We see that the difference $z_3 - z_2$ is represented by a vector from the point z_2 to the point z_3. Vectors with common length and direction are identified.

If $z = x + iy$, then $|z| = \sqrt{x^2 + y^2}$. Geometrically, the absolute value of z is the length of the vector z; it is the distance of the point z from the origin. The distance between the points z_2 and z_1 is

$$\sqrt{(x_2 - x_1)^2 + (y_2 - y_1)^2} = |z_2 - z_1|. \qquad (1.4.1)$$

From (1.4.1) one may readily verify that

$$|z_2 - z_1| \geqq |x_2 - x_1|, \qquad |z_2 - z_1| \geqq |y_2 - y_1| \qquad (1.4.2)$$

and

$$|z_2 - z_1| \leqq |x_2 - x_1| + |y_2 - y_1|. \qquad (1.4.3)$$

Remark 1.4.1. Inequality (1.3.9) is known as the *triangle inequality* and is of basic importance in analysis. Inequalities (1.3.9) and (1.3.11) may now be readily established by observing (see Figs. 1.4.2 and 1.4.3) that each side of a triangle is less than or equal to the sum of the other two sides; and that the difference of two sides of a triangle is less than or equal to the third side; the equalities holding only when the triangle is degenerate.

Remark 1.4.2. The reader should keep in mind that the complex numbers are not ordered. Thus, the expressions $z_1 > z_2$ or $z_1 < z_2$ have no meanings unless z_1 and z_2 are real numbers. However, the greater than or less than relation does hold between the absolute values of complex numbers, since the absolute values are real numbers. For example, to assert that $|z_2| > |z_1|$ means that the point z_2 is farther away from the origin than is the point z_1. Also when we write, for example, $z = k$, $k > 0$, it is then to be understood that z is a real positive number.

Remark 1.4.3. We shall mean by a *circle* of radius r and center z_0 the set of all points z satisfying $|z - z_0| = r$; by a *disk* of radius r and center z_0 the set of all points z satisfying $|z - z_0| < r$ together with none, some or all of the points of the circle $|z - z_0| = r$; and by the *unit circle*, the circle with radius $r = 1$ and center at the origin, where in all cases r is a positive number.

EXAMPLE 1.4.1. Suppose that z_1, z_2, z_3 are three complex numbers such that $|z_1| = |z_2| = |z_3| = 1$ and $z_1 + z_2 + z_3 = 0$. Show that z_1, z_2, z_3 are the vertices of an equilateral triangle inscribed in the unit circle.

Solution. In Fig. 1.4.4, let $z_k = \overrightarrow{OP_k}$, $k = 1, 2, 3$. Then in the triangle $P_1P_2P_3$ we have $\overrightarrow{P_1P_2} = z_2 - z_1$, $\overrightarrow{P_2P_3} = z_3 - z_2$, $\overrightarrow{P_3P_1} = z_1 - z_3$. We would like to show that $|z_2 - z_1| = |z_3 - z_2| = |z_1 - z_3|$. We shall first verify that $|z_2 - z_1| = |z_1 - z_3|$. Since $z_1 + z_2 + z_3 = 0$, then $z_1 = -(z_2 + z_3)$.

Thus $|z_2 - z_1| = |z_1 - z_3|$ is equivalent to $|2z_2 + z_3| = |2z_3 + z_2|$. However, this expression is equivalent to

$$(2z_2 + z_3)\,\overline{(2z_2 + z_3)} - (2z_3 + z_2)\,\overline{(2z_3 + z_2)} = 0,$$

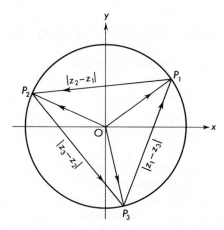

FIG. 1.4.4

which can be easily verified if we expand and use the fact that $z_2 \bar{z}_2 = z_3 \bar{z}_3 = 1$. In a similar manner, we verify that $|z_2 - z_1| = |z_3 - z_2|$. Hence triangle $P_1 P_2 P_3$ is equilateral. Since $|z_1| = |z_2| = |z_3| = 1$, the triangle $P_1 P_2 P_3$ can be inscribed in the unit circle.

EXERCISES 1.4

In Exercises 1-3, perform the additions and subtractions graphically, and check the results algebraically.

1. $(4 + 3i) + (2 + 5i)$.

2. $(-2 - 3i) - (4 - 2i)$.

3. $(2 + 4i) - (3 - 2i) + (-6 - 6i)$.

4. Show graphically that (a) the sum of a complex number and its conjugate is a real number, and (b) the difference between a complex number and its conjugate is a pure imaginary number.

5. Identify all the points in the complex plane which satisfy the following relations:

   (a) $z^2 = 2(z - 1)$,

   (b) $|z - 1| \leq 2\,|z + 1|$,

   (c) $|z + 1| \leq 4 - |z - 1|$.

6. Prove (1.4.2) and (1.4.3).

7. Prove that $|z_1 + z_2|^2 + |z_1 - z_2|^2 = 2|z_1|^2 + 2|z_2|^2$. How is this related to the geometrical theorem that the sum of the squares of the diagonals of a parallelogram is equal to the sum of the squares of the sides?

8. Prove that the equation of a circle in the z plane is given by

$$az\bar{z} + b\bar{z} + \bar{b}z + c = 0,$$

where $a \neq 0$ and c are real constants and b a complex constant.

9. Prove that if $|\alpha| = 1$ and $\alpha \neq \beta$, then $|(\alpha - \beta)/(1 - \bar{\beta}\alpha)| = 1$.

10. Show that if α is a complex number such that $|\alpha| < 1$, then $1 + \alpha$ lies to the right of the y axis.

11. Show that a straight line perpendicular to a complex vector α has an equation of the form

$$\alpha\bar{z} + \bar{\alpha}z + k = 0 \qquad (k \text{ real}).$$

12. Prove that $\sqrt{2}\,|x + iy| \geqq |x| + |y| \geqq |x + iy|$.

13. Prove that the vectors $z_1 = x_1 + iy_1$, $z_2 = x_2 + iy_2$ are perpendicular if, and only if,* $z_1\bar{z}_2 + \bar{z}_1z_2 = 0$.

14. Prove that the points z_1, z_2, z_3 in the complex plane are collinear if, and only if, the ratio $(z_3 - z_1)/(z_2 - z_1)$ is real.

15. Show that if the points z_1, z_2, z_3 in the complex plane are collinear, then there exist real numbers p, q, r, not all equal to zero, such that

$$p + q + r = 0 \quad \text{and} \quad pz_1 + qz_2 + rz_3 = 0.$$

16. Prove that three points z_1, z_2, z_3 in the complex plane cannot all lie on the same side of the real axis if $z_1 + z_2 + z_3 = z_1z_2z_3$.

17. Let $z, p,$ and q be complex numbers and k a real positive constant different from unity. Show that

$$\left|\frac{z - p}{z - q}\right| = k$$

can be expressed as

(a) $|z|^2 - 2\mathcal{R}(\bar{p}z) + |p|^2 = k^2[|z|^2 - 2\mathcal{R}(\bar{q}z) + |q|^2]$.

Show that (a) can be written as

(b) $|z|^2 - \dfrac{2\mathcal{R}[(\bar{p} - k^2\bar{q})\,z]}{1 - k^2} + \dfrac{|p|^2 - k^2\,|q|^2}{1 - k^2} = 0$.

Prove that

(c) $|p - k^2q|^2 - (1 - k^2)\,[|p|^2 - k^2\,|q|^2] = k^2\,|p - q|^2$.

---

* Let B and C be propositions. B if, and only if, C means that C implies B (if), and B implies C (only if).

Use (c) to show that (b) can be expressed as

(d) $\left| z - \dfrac{p - k^2 q}{1 - k^2} \right| = \dfrac{k\,|\,p - q\,|}{|\,1 - k^2\,|}.$

18. Suppose that $z_2 \neq 0$. (a) Show that if

$$| z_1 + z_2 | = | z_1 | + | z_2 | \text{ or if } | z_1 - z_2 | = \Big| \,| z_1 | - | z_2 |\, \Big|,$$

then $z_1 = r z_2$, $r \geq 0$.

(b) State and prove the converse of the assertion in (a) above.

19. (a) Show that if Γ is a circle passing through the points $z = \pm k$, $k > 0$, then a point z will be exterior to, on, or interior to Γ according as

$$z \bar{z} - 2b \mathscr{I}(z)$$

is greater than, equal to, or less than k^2, where b is real and $z = ib$ is the center of Γ.

(b) Show that for any complex number $z_1 = x_1 + iy_1$, $y_1 \neq 0$, the points $- k$, k, z_1 and k^2/z_1 lie on a circle.

(c) Prove that if a circle passes through the points $- k$, z_1 and k^2/z_1, it must also pass through the point $z = k$.

(d) Show that z is a point interior to the circle Γ given in (a) above if, and only if, the point k^2/z is exterior to Γ.

1.5. POLAR FORM OF COMPLEX NUMBERS. It is convenient to introduce in the z plane polar coordinates. We may recall that each point P of the plane and hence each complex number z is uniquely determined by two polar coordinates r and θ, where r is the (nonnegative) length of the segment $\overrightarrow{OP}$ joining the point P to the origin, while θ is the angle from the x axis to this segment (see Fig. 1.5.1). The polar coordinates (r, θ) of the point $z = x + iy$ can be determined from the equations

$$x = r \cos \theta, \qquad y = r \sin \theta, \qquad (1.5.1)$$

and we have

$$r = | z | = \sqrt{x^2 + y^2}, \qquad \tan \theta = \frac{y}{x}.$$

θ is called the *argument* or *amplitude* of z. We write

$$\theta = \arg z. \qquad (1.5.2)$$

Using these relations we may write $z = x + iy$ in its *polar form*:

$$z = r(\cos \theta + i \sin \theta). \qquad (1.5.3)$$

Note that any integral multiple of 2π may be added to θ, θ in radians, without changing the value of z. The *principal value* of arg z, denoted by Arg z, is that value which satisfies the inequality $-\pi < \arg z \leqq \pi$.

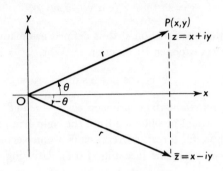

FIG. 1.5.1

The conjugate $\bar{z} = x - iy$ is simply the reflection in the real axis of the point z and we have

$$|\bar{z}| = |z| = r, \qquad \arg \bar{z} = -\arg z = -\theta. \qquad (1.5.4)$$

Thus the polar form of the conjugate z is

$$\bar{z} = r(\cos\theta - i\sin\theta). \qquad (1.5.5)$$

The polar representation of a complex number about a point other than the origin is given by

$$z - z_0 = \rho(\cos\phi + i\sin\phi) \qquad (1.5.6)$$

where ϕ is the angle of inclination of the vector $z - z_0$ with the positive x axis and ρ is the distance between z and z_0. (See Fig. 1.5.2.)

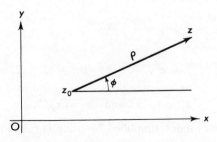

FIG. 1.5.2

1.6. PRODUCTS AND QUOTIENTS OF COMPLEX NUMBERS.

In Section 4.1 of Chapter 4, we shall define the function e^z, when z is a complex number, as follows

$$e^z = e^{x+iy} = e^x(\cos y + i \sin y),$$

and we shall prove that the function e^z thus defined has many of the properties associated with the real exponential function e^x. When $z = 0 + iy$, we have

$$e^{iy} = \cos y + i \sin y. \tag{1.6.1}$$

We shall, therefore, represent the expression $\cos \theta + i \sin \theta$ by the symbol $e^{i\theta}$.

Observe that $e^{i\theta}$ would be obtained from the right-hand member of (1.5.3) by taking $r = 1$. Thus, for θ real, $e^{i\theta}$ represents a unit vector which makes an angle θ with the positive x axis (see Fig. 1.6.1). Utilizing the trigonometric

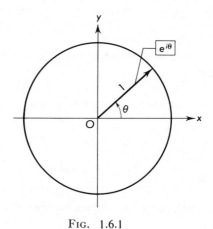

FIG. 1.6.1

identities, we leave it as an exercise for the reader to verify that the complex-valued function $e^{i\theta}$ has the following properties:

$$\begin{cases} e^{i\theta_1} e^{i\theta_2} = e^{i(\theta_1+\theta_2)}, \\[2mm] (e^{i\theta})^{-1} = e^{-i\theta}, \\[2mm] \dfrac{e^{i\theta_1}}{e^{i\theta_2}} = e^{i(\theta_1-\theta_2)}, \\[2mm] e^{i(\theta+2k\pi)} = e^{i\theta}, \qquad k = 0, \pm 1, \pm 2, \cdots. \end{cases} \tag{1.6.2}$$

Let

$$z_1 = r_1 e^{i\theta_1} \quad \text{and} \quad z_2 = r_2 e^{i\theta_2}. \tag{1.6.3}$$

Multiplication becomes much simplified by using (1.6.3) and (1.6.2):

$$z_1 z_2 = r_1 e^{i\theta_1} r_2 e^{i\theta_2} = r_1 r_2 e^{i(\theta_1+\theta_2)}. \tag{1.6.4}$$

Thus we have another verification of (1.3.8), namely,

$$|z_1 z_2| = r_1 r_2 = |z_1| \cdot |z_2|,$$

(see Fig. 1.6.2) and we also have that

$$\arg(z_1 z_2) = \arg z_1 + \arg z_2, \qquad (1.6.5)$$

up to a multiple of 2π, that is,

$$\arg(z_1 z_2) = \arg z_1 + \arg z_2 + 2k\pi,$$
$$k = 0, \pm 1, \cdots .$$

Hence, we have established the following

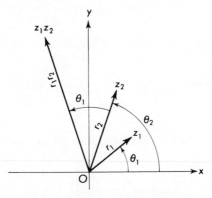

FIG. 1.6.2. Multiplication of Complex Numbers.

——*THEOREM* 1.6.1.   The product of two complex numbers is a complex number whose modulus is the product of the two moduli and whose argument is the sum of the two arguments (up to a multiple of 2π) of the two given complex numbers.

Suppose that $z_2 \neq 0$, then

$$\frac{z_1}{z_2} = \frac{r_1 e^{i\theta_1}}{r_2 e^{i\theta_2}} = \frac{r_1}{r_2} e^{i(\theta_1 - \theta_2)}. \qquad (1.6.6)$$

Thus

$$\left| \frac{z_1}{z_2} \right| = \frac{r_1}{r_2} = \frac{|z_1|}{|z_2|}, \qquad (1.6.7)$$

and $\arg(z_1/z_2) = \theta_1 - \theta_2 = \arg z_1 - \arg z_2$, up to a multiple of 2π. Hence, we have the following

——*THEOREM* 1.6.2.   The quotient of two complex numbers is a complex number whose modulus is the quotient of the two moduli and whose argument is the difference of the two arguments (up to a multiple of 2π) of the two given complex numbers, the denominator being nonzero.

Remark 1.6.1.   Any equality of the type arg z_1 = arg z_2 means that for any pair of values of arg z_1 and arg z_2, the equality holds, up to a multiple of 2π. Similarly, arg $z = \theta$ means that any value of arg z is equal to θ up to a multiple of 2π. Also note that *two complex numbers z_1 and z_2 are equal* if, and only if, $|z_1| = |z_2|$ and arg z_1 = arg z_2 (up to a multiple of 2π).

EXAMPLE 1.6.1.   Let us write

$$\frac{(1 + i)^3}{(\sqrt{3} + i)^2}$$

in polar form.

Solution.   Let

$$z_1 = 1 + i$$

and

$$z_2 = \sqrt{3} + i.$$

Then

$$\theta_1 = \arg z_1 = \tan^{-1}(1) = \frac{\pi}{4}, \qquad |z_1| = \sqrt{2},$$

and

$$\theta_2 = \arg z_2 = \tan^{-1}\left(\frac{1}{\sqrt{3}}\right) = \frac{\pi}{6}, \qquad |z_2| = 2.$$

Thus

$$z_1 = \sqrt{2}\left(\cos\frac{\pi}{4} + i\sin\frac{\pi}{4}\right) = \sqrt{2}e^{i(\pi/4)}$$

and

$$z_2 = 2\left(\cos\frac{\pi}{6} + i\sin\frac{\pi}{6}\right) = 2e^{i(\pi/6)}.$$

Consequently,

$$\frac{z_1^3}{z_2^2} = \frac{2\sqrt{2}\,e^{i(3\pi/4)}}{4e^{i(\pi/3)}} = \frac{\sqrt{2}}{2}\,e^{i(5\pi/12)} = \frac{\sqrt{2}}{2}\left(\cos\frac{5}{12}\pi + i\sin\frac{5}{12}\pi\right).$$

EXERCISES 1.6

In Exercises 1-5, write z in the polar form.

1. $z = -2 + 2i$.

2. $z = 1 - i\sqrt{3}$.

3. $z = -3$.

4. $z = 2i$.

5. $z = -\sqrt{7} + i\sqrt{21}$.

In Exercises 6-8, use the polar form to perform the indicated operations.

6. $(1 + i \sqrt{3})/(1 - i \sqrt{3})$.

7. $(1 + i \sqrt{3})^2$.

8. $[(- \sqrt{3} + i) (1 + i)]/(1 + i \sqrt{3})$.

9. Find the real and imaginary parts and the modulus of

$$\frac{1 + \cos \theta + i \sin \theta}{1 + \cos \phi + i \sin \phi}.$$

10. Verify (1.6.2).

11. Prove that $\arg z + \arg \bar{z} = 2n\pi$, where n is an integer.

12. Show that a circle with center at z_0 has an equation of the form

$$z\bar{z} - z_0\bar{z} - \bar{z}_0 z + k = 0 \qquad (k \text{ real}).$$

13. Show that the triangles whose vertices are z_1, z_2, z_3 and z_4, z_5, z_6 are similar if, and only if,

$$\begin{vmatrix} z_1 & z_4 & 1 \\ z_2 & z_5 & 1 \\ z_3 & z_6 & 1 \end{vmatrix} = 0.$$

14. The complex numbers z_1, z_2, z_3 are represented by the vertices A, B, C of an isosceles triangle, the angles at B, C being each $(\pi - \alpha)/2$. Prove that

$$(z_3 - z_2)^2 = 4(z_3 - z_1) (z_1 - z_2) \sin^2 \frac{\alpha}{2}.$$

15. Show that two lines joining the points z_1, z_2, and z_3, z_4 are perpendicular provided that $\arg [(z_1 - z_2)/(z_3 - z_4)] = \pm (\pi/2)$; that is, if

$$\frac{z_1 - z_2}{z_3 - z_4}$$

is pure imaginary.

16. Prove that the curves $| (z - 1)/(z + 1) | = k_1$ and $\arg [(z - 1)/(z + 1)] = k_2$, where $k_1 \neq 1$ and $k_2 \neq 0$ are real constants, are orthogonal circles.

17. Prove that if the points z_1, z_2, z_3 are vertices of an equilateral triangle, then

$$z_1^2 + z_2^2 + z_3^2 = z_1 z_2 + z_2 z_3 + z_3 z_1.$$

18. Show that a necessary and sufficient condition* that four points z_1, z_2, z_3, z_4 lie on a circle, in that order, is

$$| (z_1 - z_2) (z_3 - z_4) | + | (z_2 - z_3) (z_1 - z_4) | - | (z_3 - z_1) (z_4 - z_2) | = 0.$$

This is known as *Ptolemy's Theorem*.

---

* Let B and C be propositions. A necessary and sufficient condition for B is C means that B implies C (necessity), and C implies B (sufficiency).

1.7.   POWERS AND ROOTS OF COMPLEX NUMBERS. By repeated application of (1.6.4), one deduces the formula for the nth power of z:

$$z^n = (re^{i\theta})^n = r^n e^{in\theta} \qquad (n = 1, 2, \cdots).\qquad (1.7.1)$$

In particular, if we let $r = 1$ in (1.7.1), we obtain *DeMoivre's Theorem*:

$$(e^{i\theta})^n = e^{in\theta},$$

or

$$(\cos \theta + i \sin \theta)^n = \cos n\theta + i \sin n\theta \qquad (n = 1, 2, \cdots).\qquad (1.7.2)$$

Formula (1.7.2) enables us to find the nth roots of $z = re^{i\theta}$. For, if we have

$$z_0^n = z \quad \text{and} \quad z_0 = r_0 e^{i\theta_0},$$

then

$$r_0^n e^{in\theta_0} = re^{i\theta}.$$

Thus

$$r_0 = \sqrt[n]{r} \text{ (the real positive nth root), and}$$

$$n\theta_0 = \theta + 2k\pi \qquad (k = 0, \pm 1, \pm 2, \cdots).$$

Hence

$$z^{1/n} = \sqrt[n]{r} \; e^{i[(\theta/n)+k\cdot(2\pi/n)]} \qquad (k = 0, 1, \cdots, n - 1).\qquad (1.7.3)$$

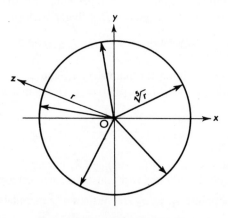

Fig. 1.7.1. Fifth Roots of z.

Remark 1.7.1.   It might appear in (1.7.3) that there are infinitely many complex numbers corresponding to the infinitely many possible values of k. However, we may show (see Exercise 1.8.13) that when $k = n + m$, we obtain the same complex number as when $k = m$. Thus we need only to take n consecutive values of k to obtain all the different nth roots of z. For convenience, we have taken $k = 0, 1, 2, \cdots, n - 1$. Observe that the nth roots of $re^{i\theta}$ lie on a circle centered at the origin O and having radius equal to $r_0 = \sqrt[n]{r}$. Also, one of the nth roots has an argument $\theta_0 = \theta/n$ and the others are uniformly spaced around the circumference of the circle, each being separated from its neighbors by an angle equal to $2\pi/n$. Fig. 1.7.1 illustrates the case for the fifth roots of z.

Summarizing, we may say that there are n nth roots of any complex number $z \neq 0$. They all have the same modulus and their arguments are equally spaced.

If m and n are relatively prime positive integers (that is, have no common factors), then it follows from formulas (1.7.3) and (1.7.1) that

$$z^{m/n} = \sqrt[n]{r^m}\, e^{i[(m/n)\theta + k\cdot(2m\pi/n)]}, \qquad k = 0, 1, \cdots, n-1. \qquad (1.7.4)$$

One may verify that (1.7.2) is also valid when n is a negative integer. Also (1.7.4) holds when m/n is negative.

1.8. THE NTH ROOTS OF UNITY.

In virtue of the formula

$$1 = \cos 0 + i \sin 0 = e^0,$$

it follows from (1.7.3) that the nth roots of unity are given by

$$e^{i(2k\pi/n)}, \qquad k = 0, 1, \cdots, n-1. \qquad (1.8.1)$$

For example, when $n = 3$, there are three cube roots, namely,

$$e^{i(2k\pi/3)}, \qquad k = 0, 1, 2. \qquad (1.8.2)$$

When $k = 0$, (1.8.2) gives 1. The values $k = 1, 2$ give, respectively,

$$e^{i(2/3)\pi} = \tfrac{1}{2}(-1 + i\sqrt{3}), \qquad e^{i(4/3)\pi} = \tfrac{1}{2}(-1 - i\sqrt{3}).$$

These complex cube roots of unity are usually denoted by the symbols ω, ω^2, either being the square of the other. They are also connected by the relation

$$1 + \omega + \omega^2 = 0. \qquad (1.8.3)$$

For, $\omega^3 = 1$ implies that $(\omega - 1)(\omega^2 + \omega + 1) = 0$. But $\omega \neq 1$, hence (1.8.3) follows. The cube roots of unity are illustrated in Fig. 1.8.1.

Similarly, we denote by ω_n the root corresponding to $k = 1$ in (1.8.1):

$$\omega_n = e^{i(2\pi/n)}. \qquad (1.8.4)$$

Using (1.7.2) we write the n roots of unity as

$$1, \omega_n, \omega_n^2, \cdots, \omega_n^{n-1}. \qquad (1.8.5)$$

By Remark 1.7.1, the nth roots of unity are the vertices of a regular n-sided polygon inscribed in the circle $|z| = 1$ with one vertex at the point $z = 1$.

Also, the complex nth roots of unity are connected by the relation

$$1 + \omega_n + \omega_n^2 + \cdots + \omega_n^{n-1} = 0. \qquad (1.8.6)$$

For, $\omega_n^n = 1$ implies that

$$(\omega_n - 1)(\omega_n^{n-1} + \omega_n^{n-2} + \cdots + \omega_n^2 + \omega_n + 1) = 0.$$

But $\omega_n \neq 1$, hence (1.8.6) follows.

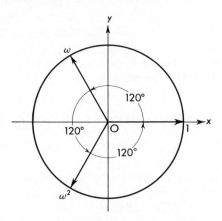

FIG. 1.8.1.   Cube Roots of Unity.

Remark 1.8.1.   Observe that if z_0 is any nth root of z, then

$$z_0, \; z_0\omega_n, \; z_0\omega_n^2, \; \cdots, \; z_0\omega_n^{n-1} \qquad (1.8.7)$$

are the nth roots of z.

EXAMPLE 1.8.1.   Denote the roots of the equation $(z + 1)^5 + z^5 = 0$ by z_k, $k = 0, 1, \cdots, 4$. Show that $\mathscr{R}(z_k) = -\frac{1}{2}$, $k = 0, 1, \cdots, 4$, that is, all the roots lie on a line $(x = -\frac{1}{2})$ which is parallel to the imaginary axis.

Solution.   Observe that $(z + 1)^5 + z^5 = 0$ may be written as

$$[-(z + 1)/z]^5 = 1.$$

Hence by (1.8.1), we obtain

$$-(z + 1)/z = e^{i(2k\pi/5)}, \qquad k = 0, 1, \cdots, 4.$$

Let $\frac{2}{5}\pi = \lambda$ and solve for z. We find the roots to be

$$z_k = -\frac{1}{1 + e^{i\lambda k}} \qquad (k = 0, 1, \cdots, 4)$$

$$= -\frac{1}{1 + \cos \lambda k + i \sin \lambda k} = -\frac{(1 + \cos \lambda k) - i \sin \lambda k}{2(1 + \cos \lambda k)}$$

$$= -\frac{1}{2} + \frac{i \sin \lambda k}{2(1 + \cos \lambda k)}.$$

Hence, $\mathscr{R}(z_k) = -\frac{1}{2}$, $k = 0, 1, \cdots, 4$, and the roots lie on the line $(x = -\frac{1}{2})$ which is parallel to the imaginary axis.

EXAMPLE 1.8.2. Suppose that the points P and Q represent the complex numbers z and z^2, respectively, in the complex plane. Suppose that P lies on a circle with unit radius and center at $z = 1$. Show geometrically that $|z^2 - z| = |z|$ and that $3 \arg (z - 1) = 3 \arg z^2 = 2 \arg (z^2 - z)$.

Solution. In Fig. 1.8.2, let C denote the center of the circle. We have $P = z$, $Q = z^2$ and $|z| = OP$. Thus $OQ/OP = OP/1 = OP/OC$. Let $\arg z = \theta$. Since $\angle xOQ = 2\theta$ and $\angle xOP = \theta$, it follows that $\angle POQ = \theta$. Hence triangles OPQ and OCP are similar. Since $OC = CP$, we see that $OP = PQ$. Therefore, $|z| = |z^2 - z|$.

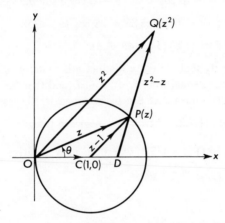

FIG. 1.8.2

Since $\angle xCP = 2\theta$ and $\angle CPD = \theta$, we have $\angle xDQ = 3\theta$. Thus

$$\arg (z - 1) = \arg z^2 = 2\theta \quad \text{and} \quad \arg (z^2 - z) = 3\theta.$$

Therefore, $3 \arg (z - 1) = 3 \arg z^2 = 2 \arg (z^2 - z)$.

EXERCISES 1.8

1. Find the square roots of i.

2. Find the fourth roots of 1.

3. Find the fifth roots of -32.

4. Find the fourth roots of $-2 - 2i\sqrt{3}$ and check graphically.

5. Find the values of $(\sqrt{3}/2 + i/2)^{2/3}$.

6. Evaluate $(3 + 4i)^{30}/(1 + 2i)^{50}$ in the form $x + iy$, obtaining each of the real numbers x, y correct to two significant figures.

7. Solve: $z^4 + 1 = 0$.

8. Find the three roots of the equation $z^3 + z^2 + z + 1 = 0$.

9. Show that the equation $32z^5 = (z + 1)^5$ has four imaginary roots, two of which lie in the second quadrant and two in the third. Also show that all of the roots lie on the circle:

$$\left(x - \frac{1}{3}\right)^2 + y^2 = \left(\frac{2}{3}\right)^2.$$

In Exercises 10-12, use DeMoivre's theorem [see formula (1.7.2)], to prove the following results:

10. $\cos 5\theta = \cos^5 \theta - 10 \cos^3 \theta \sin^2 \theta + 5 \cos \theta \sin^4 \theta$.

11. $\cos^8 \theta + \sin^8 \theta = (1/64)(\cos 8\theta + 28 \cos 4\theta + 35)$.

12. $\sin^6 \theta + \cos^6 \theta = (1/8)(3 \cos 4\theta + 5)$.

13. In (1.7.3), verify that we get n distinct nth roots, which are determined by placing k in turn equal to $0, 1, \cdots, n - 1$, and that for k equal to any other integer, we get values that can be obtained by the earlier substitutions.

14. Verify formula (1.7.2) when n is a negative integer.

15. Let $x_n + iy_n = (1 + i\sqrt{3})^n$ where n is a positive integer. Prove that

$$x_{n-1}y_n - x_n y_{n-1} = 2^{2n-2}\sqrt{3}.$$

16. Prove that

$$\left(\frac{1 + \sin \theta + i \cos \theta}{1 + \sin \theta - i \cos \theta}\right)^n = \cos\left[n\left(\frac{\pi}{2} - \theta\right)\right] + i \sin\left[n\left(\frac{\pi}{2} - \theta\right)\right].$$

17. Prove that the real values of $\sqrt[n]{z} + \sqrt[n]{\bar{z}}$, where $z = re^{i\theta}$, are given by $2\sqrt[n]{r} \cos\left(\frac{\theta}{n} + \frac{2k\pi}{n}\right)$, $k = 0, 1, \cdots, n - 1$. Find the real values of

$$\sqrt[3]{1 + i\sqrt{3}} + \sqrt[3]{1 - i\sqrt{3}}.$$

18. The points z_1, z_2, z_3 form an equilateral triangle in the complex plane with $z_1 = 4 + 6i$ and $z_2 = (1 - i)z_1$. Determine the two possible values of z_3.

19. The three points in the complex plane which correspond to the roots of the equation

$$z^3 - 3pz^2 + 3qz - r = 0$$

are the vertices of a triangle ABC. Prove that the centroid of the triangle is the point corresponding to p. If the triangle ABC is equilateral, prove that $p^2 = q$.

20. Observe that

$$(1 + z + z^2 + \cdots + z^n)(1 - z) = 1 - z^{n+1}.$$

For $z \neq 1$, we have

$$1 + z + z^2 + \cdots + z^n = \frac{1 - z^{n+1}}{1 - z}.$$

Using this formula, derive the following formulas:

$$\sum_{k=0}^{n} \cos k\theta = \frac{1}{2} + \frac{\sin [(n + 1/2)\,\theta]}{2 \sin (\theta/2)},$$

$$\sum_{k=1}^{n} \sin k\theta = \frac{1}{2} \cot \frac{\theta}{2} - \frac{\cos [(n + 1/2)\,\theta]}{2 \sin (\theta/2)}, \text{ where } 0 < \theta < 2\pi.$$

21. Let $z = \cos \theta + i \sin \theta = e^{i\theta}$. Establish the results given below.
(a) $z^n + 1/z^n = 2 \cos n\theta$ and $z^n - 1/z^n = 2i \sin n\theta$.
When n is a positive odd integer:

(b) $\cos^n \theta = \dfrac{1}{2^{n-1}} \displaystyle\sum_{r=0}^{(n-1)/2} \binom{n}{r} \cos (n - 2r)\,\theta,$

(c) $\sin^n \theta = \dfrac{(-1)^{(n-1)/2}}{2^{n-1}} \displaystyle\sum_{r=0}^{(n-1)/2} (-1)^r \binom{n}{r} \sin (n - 2r)\,\theta,$

where

$$\binom{n}{r} = \frac{n(n-1)(n-2)\cdots(n-r+1)}{r!} \text{ for } r > 0, \binom{n}{0} = 1.$$

When n is a positive even integer:

(d) $\cos^n \theta = \dfrac{1}{2^{n-1}} \displaystyle\sum_{r=0}^{(n-2)/2} \binom{n}{r} \cos (n - 2r)\,\theta + \dfrac{1}{2^n} \binom{n}{n/2},$

(e) $\sin^n \theta = \dfrac{(-1)^{n/2}}{2^{n-1}} \displaystyle\sum_{r=0}^{(n-2)/2} (-1)^r \binom{n}{r} \cos (n - 2r)\,\theta + \dfrac{1}{2^n} \binom{n}{n/2}.$

22. Show by expanding $(\cos \theta + i \sin \theta)^n$ and equating the real and imaginary parts that

(a) $\cos n\theta = \displaystyle\sum_{r=0}^{k} (-1)^r \binom{n}{2r} \cos^{(n-2r)} \theta \sin^{2r} \theta,$

(b) $\sin n\theta = \displaystyle\sum_{r=0}^{m} (-1)^r \binom{n}{2r + 1} \cos^{(n-2r-1)} \theta \sin^{(2r+1)} \theta,$

where

$$\binom{n}{2r} = \frac{n(n-1)(n-2)\cdots(n-2r+1)}{(2r)!} \text{ for } r > 0, \binom{n}{0} = 1,$$

$$k = \frac{(2n-1)+(-1)^n}{4} = \left[\frac{n}{2}\right] \text{ and } m = \left[\frac{n-1}{2}\right].$$

Here $[x]$ means the greatest integer less than or equal to the real number x. That is, $[x]$ is that integer p which satisfies the inequalities

$$p \leqq x < p + 1.$$

Thus, we have

$$x - 1 < [x] \leqq x.$$

For example, $[.5] = 0$, $[1.58] = 1$, $[8] = 8$, $[-.578] = -1$, $[-4.997] = -5$. The symbol $[x]$ is to be read: the greatest integer in x, or bracket x. $f(x) = [x]$ is called the *bracket function*.

23. Show that when n is a positive odd integer

(a) $\cos n\theta = \sum_{r=1}^{k+1} \frac{(-1)^{k+r-1}\, n2^{2r-2}}{2r-1}\binom{n/2+r-3/2}{2r-2}\cos^{(n+2r-2k-2)}\theta,$

and when n is a positive even integer

(b) $\cos n\theta = (-1)^k \cos^{(n-2k)}\theta$

$$+ \sum_{r=2}^{k+1} \frac{(-1)^{k+r-1}\, n2^{2r-4}}{r-1}\binom{n/2+r-2}{2r-3}\cos^{(n+2r-2k-2)}\theta,$$

where

$$k = \frac{(2n-1)+(-1)^n}{4} = \left[\frac{n}{2}\right],$$

and the bracket function is defined in Exercise 22 above.

24. The *Tchebycheff polynomials* are defined by

$$T_n(x) = 2^{1-n}\cos n\theta, \qquad n = 1, 2, \cdots,$$

where $\theta = \arccos x$ or $x = \cos\theta$, and further we define $T_0(x) = 1$. Use the result of Exercise 23 above to show that if n is a positive odd integer, then

(a) $T_n(x) = \frac{n}{2^{n+1}} \sum_{r=1}^{(n+1)/2} \frac{(-1)^{(n+1)/2+r}\, 4^r}{2r-1}\binom{n/2+r-3/2}{2r-2} x^{2r-1},$

and if n is a positive even integer, then

(b) $T_n(x) = (-1)^{n/2} 2^{1-n} + \dfrac{n}{2^{n+3}} \displaystyle\sum_{r=2}^{n/2+1} \dfrac{(-1)^{n/2+r-1} 4^r}{r-1} \binom{n/2+r-2}{2r-3} x^{2r-2}.$

Verify that

(c) $T_1(x) = x, \qquad T_2(x) = -\dfrac{1}{2} + x^2, \qquad T_3(x) = -\dfrac{3}{4} x + x^3,$

$\qquad T_4(x) = \dfrac{1}{8} - x^2 + x^4, \qquad T_5(x) = \dfrac{5}{16} x - \dfrac{5}{4} x^3 + x^5.$

Note that originally $|x| \leq 1$, since $x = \cos\theta$. However, the polynomials given in (a), (b), and (c) are defined for all x, $-\infty < x < \infty$.

25. Consider the set of complex numbers $z = x + iy$, the set of matrices of the form

$$A = \begin{pmatrix} x & y \\ -y & x \end{pmatrix},$$

and the one-to-one correspondence

$$x + iy \leftrightarrow \begin{pmatrix} x & y \\ -y & x \end{pmatrix}.$$

Denote this correspondence by $A = z^*$. Let $z_k = x_k + iy_k$ and

$$A_k = \begin{pmatrix} x_k & y_k \\ -y_k & x_k \end{pmatrix}, \qquad k = 1,2.$$

Define $A_1 + A_2$, $A_1 A_2$, aA, a real, as follows:

$$A_1 + A_2 = \begin{pmatrix} x_1 + x_2 & y_1 + y_2 \\ -y_1 - y_2 & x_1 + x_2 \end{pmatrix}, \quad A_1 A_2 = \begin{pmatrix} x_1 x_2 - y_1 y_2 & x_1 y_2 + x_2 y_1 \\ -x_1 y_2 - x_2 y_1 & x_1 x_2 - y_1 y_2 \end{pmatrix},$$

$$aA = \begin{pmatrix} ax & ay \\ -ay & ax \end{pmatrix}.$$

Show that

(1) $\qquad (z_1 + z_2)^* = z_1^* + z_2^*, \quad (z_1 z_2)^* = z_1^* z_2^*, \quad (az)^* = az^*.$

Note: The complex numbers form what is known as a *linear algebra* of order two over the field of real numbers. In view of relations (1), we say that the linear algebra of complex numbers is isomorphic to the linear algebra of matrices of the form A.

2

Point Sets,
Sequences, and
Mappings

2.1. POINT SETS ON THE REAL LINE AND IN THE COMPLEX PLANE. The correspondence between the complex numbers and the points in the plane, as well as the correspondence between the real numbers and the points on the real line, is of importance in the theory of functions. In the ensuing discussion, the concepts of *point set* and *set of numbers* will be used interchangeably. Sets of real and complex numbers will constantly be considered as point sets on the line and in the plane, and vice versa. We shall now take up briefly a few basic properties of point sets on the line and in the plane that will be utilized in the forthcoming chapters.*

The terms *aggregate*, *class*, *collection*, and *family* are used synonymously with the term *set*. The points of these sets will also be referred to as the elements of the sets. A set S is a *subset* of a set T, written $S \subseteq T$, if every element of S is an element of T. The expression $S \subseteq T$ is also read S is *contained* or *included* in T. A nonempty set S is a *proper* subset of a set T, written $S \subset T$, if S is contained in T and there exists at least one element of T that is not an element of S. The expression $S \subset T$ is also read S is *properly contained* or *properly included* in T.

Two sets, R and S, are said to be *equal*, and we write $R = S$ if, and only if, every element of R is an element of S and every element of S is an element of R. Thus $R = S$ if, and only if, $R \subseteq S$ and $S \subseteq R$.

If S is a subset of T, then the set of all points of T that are not in S is called the *complement* of S with respect to T. For example, if the set S consists of all real numbers x such that $|x| \leq 1$, then the complement of S, with respect to the set T of all real numbers, consists of all real x such that $|x| > 1$. However, the complement of the same set S, with respect to the set T of all complex

* Much of the content of the next few paragraphs applies also to sets in general.

numbers, consists of the set of all real x such that $|x| > 1$ and, in addition, all z such that $\mathscr{I}(z) \neq 0$.

The *union* of two sets, S and T, written $S \cup T$, is the set of all elements which belong either to S or to T (or to both S and T). The *intersection* of two sets, S and T, written $S \cap T$, is the set of all elements which belong to both S and T. For example, let S be the set of all real x such that $0 \leq x \leq 2$, and let T be the set of all real x such that $1/2 < x \leq 3$. Then $S \cup T$ is the set of all real x such that $0 \leq x \leq 3$, and $S \cap T$ is the set of all real x such that $1/2 < x \leq 2$.

Since there may not be any elements belonging to both of two arbitrary sets S and T, it is convenient to speak of the *null* or *void* set, which has no elements whatever.*

The following observations are left as exercises for the reader. For sets R, S, and T, we have

COMMUTATIVE LAWS. $S \cup T = T \cup S$ and $S \cap T = T \cap S$.

ASSOCIATIVE LAWS. $R \cup (S \cup T) = (R \cup S) \cup T$ and
$R \cap (S \cap T) = (R \cap S) \cap T$.

DISTRIBUTIVE LAWS. $R \cap (S \cup T) = (R \cap S) \cup (R \cap T)$ and
$R \cup (S \cap T) = (R \cup S) \cap (R \cup T)$.

If $\{S_\alpha\}$ is a family of sets, that is, α varies and for each α there is a set of the family, then by the union of the sets $\{S_\alpha\}$, written $\cup S_\alpha$, we mean the set of all points z contained in at least one of the S_α. By the intersection of the sets $\{S_\alpha\}$, written $\cap S_\alpha$, we mean the set of all points z such that z is contained in all the S_α where α varies over a given index set A.

Two sets S and T are said to be *disjoint* if their intersection is the null set. For example, if S is the set of all z such that $|z| \leq 1$ and T is the set of all points z such that $|z - 2| < 1$, then S and T are disjoint.

The set of all points t on the real line such that $\alpha < t < \beta$ (where we may have $\alpha = -\infty, \beta = \infty$, or both) is called an *open interval* and is denoted by (α, β). In case α and β are finite, they are called the *boundary points* of the interval. The set of all points t, $\alpha \leq t \leq \beta$, α and β finite, consisting of the open interval $\alpha < t < \beta$ together with its boundary points α and β is called a *closed interval*, and is denoted by $[\alpha, \beta]$. In the sequel, when we write $\alpha \leq t \leq \beta$, we understand that α and β are finite and $\alpha < \beta$. The word *interval* will be used to designate the set consisting of an open interval with both, one, or none of its boundary points. For example, the set of all real points t such that $0 < t < 1$ is an open interval. Similarly, the set of all real t such that $-\infty < t < 5$ is also an open interval.

---

* The sets considered in the sequel are nonvoid except where the context clearly indicates otherwise.

By an *open interval in the complex plane*: $I = (a_1, a_2; b_1, b_2)$ where a_1, a_2, b_1, and b_2 are finite, we mean the set of all points $z = x + iy$ such that $a_1 < x < a_2$ and $b_1 < y < b_2$. It consists of all z interior to the rectangle formed by the lines $x = a_j$, $y = b_j$ $(j = 1, 2)$. By the *boundary* of an interval, we mean the set of all points z on the sides of the rectangle. An open interval I with its boundary is called a *closed interval*. It consists of all $z = x + iy$ such that $a_1 \leq x \leq a_2$, $b_1 \leq y \leq b_2$. The word *interval* is used to denote an open interval with none, some, or all of its boundary points.

Let S be any point set on the real line. A point t_1 is said to be a *lower bound* of S, if $t_1 \leq t$ for all t in S. A point t_1 is said to be the *greatest lower bound* of S when the following two conditions are fulfilled: (1) t_1 is a lower bound of S and (2) if $t_0 > t_1$, then t_0 is not a lower bound of S. The latter condition can also be stated as follows: for any $t_0 > t_1$, there exists a t in S such that $t < t_0$. A point t_2 is said to be an *upper bound* of S if $t_2 \geq t$ for all t in S. A point t_2 is said to be the *least upper bound* of S when the following two conditions are satisfied: (1) t_2 is an upper bound of S and (2) if $t_0 < t_2$, then t_0 is not an upper bound. Again, this latter condition is equivalent to the following: if $t_0 < t_2$, then there exists a t in S such that $t_0 < t$. For example, if S is the set of all real t such that $t^2 < 3$, then $t = 2$ is an upper bound while $t = \sqrt{3}$ is the least upper bound. Similarly, $t = -2$ is a lower bound, while $t = -\sqrt{3}$ is the greatest lower bound.

If a set S of points on the real line has no finite upper bound, we say that the least upper bound is equal to ∞. Similarly, if S has no finite lower bound, then the greatest lower bound of S is said to be equal to $-\infty$. If the set S has finite lower and upper bounds, then S is said to be *bounded*, otherwise, S is said to be *unbounded*. A set S is bounded if, and only if, there exists a constant K such that $|x| < K$ for all x in S. A set of complex numbers S is said to be bounded if there exists a constant K such that $|z| < K$ for all z in S. In other words, all points of S lie within a circle with center at the origin and radius K.

By the *diameter* of a set S of complex numbers we mean the least upper bound of the set $r_{\alpha\beta} = |z_\alpha - z_\beta|$ for all z_α and z_β in S. If a set is bounded, then its diameter is finite.

2.2. OPEN, CLOSED, AND CONNECTED SETS

Definition 2.2.1. A *neighborhood* of a point z_0 in the complex plane is the set of all points z such that

$$|z - z_0| < \epsilon,$$

where ϵ is any given positive real number.

We observe that this definition asserts that a neighborhood of the point z_0 is given by the set of all points z whose distance from z_0 is less than ϵ, that is, the set of all points z interior to a circle with center at z_0 and radius ϵ; it includes the point z_0 and excludes the points on the circumference.

We shall have occasion to consider a *neighborhood* of a point z_0 with respect to a set S. By this we shall mean the set of all points z of S such that $|z - z_0| < \epsilon$ for some $\epsilon > 0$. Thus, if t_0 is a point on the real line, then a neighborhood of t_0 with respect to the real line is the set of all real t such that $|t - t_0| < \epsilon$ for some $\epsilon > 0$. Similarly, if t_0 is a point in a closed interval $I = [t_1, t_2]$ on the real line, then by a neighborhood of t_0 with respect to I we shall mean the set of all real t in I such that $|t - t_0| < \epsilon$ for some $\epsilon > 0$.

In the remainder of this chapter, we shall state our definitions for point sets in the plane. Similar definitions may be formulated for points on the real line.

A set S is said to be *open* (relative to the complex plane) if each point z of S has a neighborhood which lies entirely in S. For example, the interior of a circle forms an open set. Also, the entire complex plane, each of the half planes $\mathscr{R}(z) > 0$, $\mathscr{R}(z) < 0$, $\mathscr{I}(z) > 0$ or $\mathscr{I}(z) < 0$ forms an open set. On the other hand, the interior of a circle plus the circumference does not form an open set, since no neighborhood of a point on the circumference lies entirely within the set. Observe that a set of real numbers may be open relative to the real line but not with respect to the complex plane; for example, the set of all real t in the open interval $(0, 1)$. (See Exercise 2.2.1.)

Definition 2.2.2.   A point z_0 is said to be an *accumulation point* of a set S, if every neighborhood of z_0 contains infinitely many points of S.

The point z_0 itself may or may not belong to the set S. For example, suppose that S consists of the set of real points $\{1, 1/2, \cdots, 1/n, \cdots\}$, then $z_0 = 0$ is an accumulation point of S but does not belong to S. Again, each point on the circle $|z| = M$ is an accumulation point of the set of points $|z| < M$, but does not belong to that set. On the other hand, each point interior to the circle $|z| = M$ is an accumulation point of the set of interior points, and belongs to the set of interior points.

Observe that in the above definition of an accumulation point all that is really required is that every neighborhood of z_0 contains at least one point of S distinct from z_0. For, if this condition is satisfied, then the neighborhood $|z - z_0| < \epsilon$ contains a point $z_1 \neq z_0$ belonging to S. Similarly, the neighborhood of all z such that $|z - z_0| < |z_1 - z_0|$ contains a point z_2 belonging to S which is different from z_0 and z_1. This process may be carried out indefinitely. It follows that the neighborhood $|z - z_0| < \epsilon$ contains an infinite number of points of S.

A set S is said to be *closed* (relative to the complex plane) if every accumulation point of S is itself in S. For example, the set of all points for which $|z| = M$, $|z| \leq M$, or $|z| \geq M$ ($M \geq 0$) all form closed sets. In particular, the complex plane is closed. The set of numbers $x + iy$ with x and y rational is not closed. The set of all points consisting of the point $z = 2$, with all the points for which $|z| < 2$ is neither open nor closed. Also one may easily verify that the null set is both closed and open. The union of a set S with the set of accumulation points of S is called the *closure* of S.

A *boundary point* of a set S is a point, every neighborhood of which contains at least one point of S and at least one point not in S. The boundary points of the set consisting of all points z such that $|z| < M$, $M > 0$ are the points on the circle $|z| = M$. Observe that no boundary point of an open set can belong to the set; however, every boundary point of a closed set belongs to the set.

A point z_0 is said to be an *interior point* of a set S if there exists a neighborhood of z_0 contained in S. The *interior* of a set S is the set consisting of the interior points of S.

Definition 2.2.3.   A set S is said to be *separated* into the sets S_1 and S_2 if (1) S_1 and S_2 are nonvoid, (2) S is the union of S_1 and S_2, (3) S_1 and S_2 have no points in common, (4) S_1 contains no accumulation point of S_2, and (5) S_2 contains no accumulation point of S_1.

Definition 2.2.4.   A set S is said to be *connected* if it cannot be separated into two sets satisfying conditions (1)-(5) of Definition 2.2.3.

Definition 2.2.5.   An open connected set together with some, none, or all of its boundary points will be called a *region*. If none of the boundary points are included, the region will be called an *open region* or a *domain*. If all the boundary points are included, it will be called a *closed region*.

EXAMPLE 2.2.1.   Describe geometrically the region in the z plane determined by $|z + i| < |z - 1|$, where $z = x + iy$.

Solution.

$|z + i|^2 = (z + i)\,\overline{(z + i)} = (z + i)(\bar{z} - i) = z\bar{z} - i(z - \bar{z}) + 1 = z\bar{z} + 2y + 1$. Similarly, $|z - 1|^2 = z\bar{z} - 2x + 1$. Hence $|z + i| < |z - 1|$ is equivalent to $y < -x$. Thus the region lies to the left of the line $y = -x$ as shown in Fig. 2.2.1.

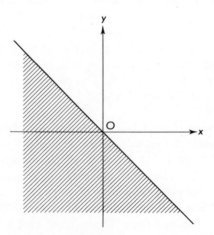

FIG. 2.2.1.   Region $y < -x$.

EXERCISES 2.2

1. Show that the set of all real t such that $0 < t < 1$ is open relative to the real line, but not open relative to the complex plane.

2. Show that the set consisting of all the complex numbers is both open and closed.

3. Prove that the complement of an open set is closed, and the complement of a closed set is open.

4. Prove that the interior of a set is an open set, and that the closure of a set is a closed set.

5. Prove that the union of any family of open sets is open.

6. Show that the intersection of any family of closed sets is closed.

7. Let S_n be the open interval $(-1/n, 1 + 1/n)$. Show that the intersection $\bigcap_{n=1}^{\infty} S_n$ is the closed interval $[0, 1]$. Prove that the intersection of a finite number of open sets is open.

8. Let S_n be the closed interval $[1/n, 1 - 1/n]$. Show that $\bigcup_{n=3}^{\infty} S_n$ is the open interval $(0, 1)$. Prove that the union of a finite number of closed sets is closed.

9. Suppose that $\{S_\alpha\}$ is a family of connected sets having a common point z_0. Show that the union $S = \cup S_\alpha$ is also connected.

10. Let E be a connected set, and let F consist of the set E together with some of the accumulation points of E. Show that F is a connected set.

Describe geometrically the regions in the z plane determined by the following inequalities.

11. $|z - 1| \leq 1$.

12. $|z - 1| \geq 1$.

13. $\mathcal{R}(z) > 0$.

14. $0 < \mathcal{I}(z) < 2\pi$.

15. $|z^2 - 1| \leq 1$.

16. $|z^2 - 1| \leq 5$.

17. $\mathcal{R}(z^2) \geq 9$.

18. $\mathcal{I}(z^2) \geq 9$.

19. $2 \leq |z - 1| \leq 4$.

20. $|z - 1| \leq 4|z - 2|$.

21. $\mathcal{R}(z - 1) \leq |z|$.

22. $|z - 1| + |z + 1| \leq 4$.

23. $0 < \arg z \leq \pi/4$.

24. $0 \leq \mathcal{R}(z) < 2\pi$.

25. $|z^2 - z| \leq 1$.

26. $|z - 2| \leq |z + 2|$.

27. $|1 - z| \leq 3(1 - |z|)$.

28. $|z - 1 - 2i| \leq 3$.

29. $|z - 2| \leq 2|z - 2i|$.

30. $\mathcal{R}[1/(z - 1)] \leq 1, z \neq 1$.

2.3. SEQUENCES. A *sequence* $\{z_n\}$ of complex numbers is defined by assigning to each integer n $(n = 1, 2, \cdots)$ a complex number z_n. The point z_n is called the nth term of the sequence. Two sequences $\{z_n\}$ and $\{w_n\}$ are the *same* if, and only if, $z_n = w_n$ for all n. For example, the sequences $\{1, 2, 3, 4, \cdots\}$

and $\{1, 1, 2, 3, 4, \cdots\}$ are not the same, even though the set of points S involved in the sequence is the same in each case, namely, the set of all positive integers.

A *subsequence* of a sequence $\{z_n\}$ is a sequence $\{z'_m\}$ whose terms are selected from the terms of the original sequence and are arranged in the same order. That is, (1) to each term z'_m of the subsequence $\{z'_m\}$, there corresponds a term z_n of the original sequence $\{z_n\}$ such that $z'_m = z_n$ and (2) if z_j and z_k, $j < k$, correspond, respectively, to z'_p and z'_q, then $p < q$.

Remark 2.3.1.   Observe that if $\{z'_m\}$ is a subsequence of $\{z_n\}$, then for each m, $z'_m = z_n$ for some $n \geq m$.

Definition 2.3.1.   A sequence $\{z_n\}$ is said to be a *Cauchy sequence* if, for every $\epsilon > 0$, there exists an integer N (depending upon ϵ) such that

$$|z_n - z_m| < \epsilon$$

for all $m > N$ and $n > N$.

Definition 2.3.2.   A sequence of complex numbers $\{z_n\}$ is said to *converge to z_0 or to have the limit z_0*, and we write

$$\lim_{n \to \infty} z_n = z_0 \quad \text{or} \quad z_n \to z_0 \tag{2.3.1}$$

if for every $\epsilon > 0$, there exists an integer N such that

$$|z_n - z_0| < \epsilon \quad \text{for} \quad n > N. \tag{2.3.2}$$

Geometrically this means that all points z_n, $n > N$, lie within a circle of radius ϵ and center at z_0 as shown in Fig. 2.3.1.

If the sequence fails to converge, it is said to *diverge*.

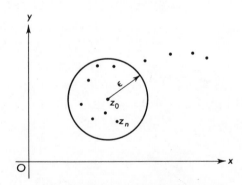

FIG. 2.3.1

——***THEOREM*** 2.3.1.   If a sequence $\{z_n\}$ has a limit z_0, then for every subsequence $\{z'_m\}$ of $\{z_n\}$, we have

$$\lim_{m \to \infty} z'_m = z_0. \tag{2.3.3}$$

Proof. Suppose that $\epsilon > 0$. Then since the sequence $\{z_n\}$ has a limit, there exists an N such that $|z_n - z_0| < \epsilon$ for all $n > N$. Consequently, $|z'_m - z_0| < \epsilon$ for all $m > N$.

Definition 2.3.3. A sequence $\{z_n\}$ is said to be *bounded* if for some constant M, $|z_n| \leq M$ for all n.

A bounded sequence need not converge. For example, $\{(-1)^n\}$ is a bounded sequence which does not converge. However, the converse of this proposition is true.

——**THEOREM 2.3.2.** If $\{z_n\}$ is a convergent sequence of complex numbers, then $\{z_n\}$ is bounded.

The proof is left as an exercise for the reader.

Definition 2.3.4. A sequence $\{z_n\}$ is said to have an *accumulation point* z_0 if given any neighborhood $N(z_0)$ of z_0, an infinite number of terms of the sequence are contained in $N(z_0)$.

Observe that a sequence may have an accumulation point and yet it may not have a limit. For example, the point $z_0 = 1$ is an accumulation point of the sequence

$$\left\{1 + \frac{1}{2}, 2 + \frac{1}{2}, 1 + \frac{1}{3}, 2 + \frac{1}{3}, 1 + \frac{1}{4}, 2 + \frac{1}{4}, 1 + \frac{1}{5}, 2 + \frac{1}{5}, \cdots\right\}.$$

This sequence, however, has no limit since the terms $1 + (1/n)$ $(n = 2, 3, \cdots)$ approach 1 while the terms $2 + (1/n)$ $(n = 2, 3, \cdots)$ approach 2.

Observe also that a sequence may have accumulation points, although the set of points used in the sequence has no accumulation points. For example, the sequence $\{1, 2, 1, 2, 1, 2, \cdots\}$ has 1 and 2 as accumulation points. However, the point set $\{1, 2\}$, consisting of all the points used in the sequence is a finite set and hence does not have an accumulation point.

——**THEOREM 2.3.3.** Let $\{z_n\}$ be a sequence of complex numbers, where $z_n = x_n + iy_n$ $(n = 1, 2, \cdots)$. A necessary and sufficient condition that $\{z_n\}$ converge to the limit $z_0 = x_0 + iy_0$ is that

$$\lim_{n\to\infty} x_n = x_0, \qquad \lim_{n\to\infty} y_n = y_0. \tag{2.3.4}$$

Proof. Necessity. Suppose that the sequence has a limit z_0. Then from Definition 2.3.2, we have for any given $\epsilon > 0$

$$|z_n - z_0| < \epsilon \quad \text{for} \quad n > N.$$

Using (1.4.2) we obtain

$$|x_n - x_0| \leqq |z_n - z_0| < \epsilon, \quad |y_n - y_0| \leqq |z_n - z_0| < \epsilon \quad \text{for} \quad n > N.$$

Hence

$$\lim_{n \to \infty} x_n = x_0, \qquad \lim_{n \to \infty} y_n = y_0.$$

Sufficiency. Suppose that the two limits in (2.3.4) exist. Then for a given $\epsilon > 0$, N can be chosen sufficiently large so that

$$|x_n - x_0| < \epsilon/2, \qquad |y_n - y_0| < \epsilon/2 \quad \text{for} \quad n > N.$$

Using (1.4.3) we obtain

$$|z_n - z_0| \leqq |x_n - x_0| + |y_n - y_0| < \epsilon \quad \text{for} \quad n > N.$$

Therefore the given sequence $\{z_n\}$ has the limit z_0 as the theorem requires.

EXERCISES 2.3

1. Show that if a sequence of complex numbers $\{z_n\}$ has an accumulation point z_0, then there exists a subsequence $\{z'_m\}$ of $\{z_n\}$ such that $\lim\limits_{m \to \infty} z'_m = z_0$.

2. Show that a point z_0 is an accumulation point of a set S of complex numbers if, and only if, there exists a sequence $\{z_n\}$ of distinct points in S such that $\lim\limits_{n \to \infty} z_n = z_0$.

3. Let $S_1, S_2, S_3, \cdots$ be a sequence of sets such that diameter $(S_n) \to 0$ as $n \to \infty$. Show that there cannot be more than one point common to all the sets of the sequence.

4. Show that if a sequence $\{z_n\}$ has a limit, then it is a Cauchy sequence.

5. Show that if a set S is not bounded, then there exists a sequence $\{z_n\}$ of points in S such that $|z_n - z_m| \geqq 1$ for all m and n, $m \neq n$.

6. Show that any sequence $\{z_n\}$ such that $|z_n - z_m| \geqq 1$ for all m and n, $m \neq n$, cannot have an accumulation point.

7. Show that if a sequence $\{z_n\}$ converges to z_0, then the sequence $\{\zeta_n\}$, where

$$\zeta_n = \frac{1}{n} \sum_{k=1}^{n} z_k$$

also converges to z_0.

8. Prove Theorem 2.3.2.

2.4. SOME FUNDAMENTAL PROPERTIES OF THE REAL AND COMPLEX NUMBER SYSTEMS.

We shall state without proof five fundamental properties of the real number system.*

* See L. Graves, *The Theory of Functions of Real Variables*, 2d ed., Chaps. II-III. New York: McGraw-Hill, 1956.

(1) DEDEKIND CUT PROPERTY. If the real line is decomposed into two non-empty sets S_1 and S_2 such that $t_1 < t_2$ for every point t_1 in S_1 and t_2 in S_2, then either S_1 has a least upper bound in S_1 or S_2 has a greatest lower bound in S_2.

This implies the existence of a point t_0 in S_1 or S_2 such that t_0 is simultaneously the least upper bound of S_1 and the greatest lower bound of S_2. All points t_1 less than t_0 are in S_1 and all points t_2 greater than t_0 are in S_2.

(2) THE DEDEKIND PROPERTY. Every bounded set of real numbers has a least upper bound and a greatest lower bound.

(3) THE COMPLETENESS PROPERTY. Every Cauchy sequence of real numbers has a limit.

(4) THE BOLZANO-WEIERSTRASS PROPERTY. Every bounded set of real numbers containing an infinite number of points has an accumulation point.

(5) THE NESTED INTERVAL PROPERTY. Given a nested sequence of closed intervals,* that is, a sequence of closed intervals $I_1, I_2, I_3, \cdots$, such that $I_{n+1} \subseteq I_n$ ($n = 1, 2, \cdots$), then there exists at least one point common to all of the intervals.

These five properties can be shown to be equivalent, that is, any one of them can be derived from any one of the others. In view of Remark 1.4.2, analogs of properties (1) and (2) for complex numbers do not exist. On the other hand, we shall see that properties (3), (4) and (5) may be extended without difficulty to the system of complex numbers.

——*THEOREM* 2.4.1. Every Cauchy sequence of complex numbers has a limit.

Proof. Let $\{z_n\}$ be a Cauchy sequence of complex numbers, where

$$z_n = x_n + iy_n \qquad (n = 1, 2, \cdots).$$

By (1.4.2) $|x_m - x_n| \leq |z_m - z_n|$, and hence for any $\epsilon > 0$, there exists an integer N such that $|x_m - x_n| < \epsilon$ when $m > N$ and $n > N$. Consequently, $\{x_n\}$ is a Cauchy sequence, and by the Completeness Property for real numbers, has a limit x_0.

Similarly, $\{y_n\}$ has a limit y_0. By Theorem 2.3.3, the sequence $\{z_n\}$ has the limit $z_0 = x_0 + iy_0$.

——*THEOREM* 2.4.2. Every bounded set S of complex numbers containing an infinite number of points has an accumulation point.

---

* According to the convention made in Section 2.1, closed intervals are bounded.

Proof. Let S be the given set of complex numbers and let $\{z_n\}$ be a sequence of distinct points in S. Since S is bounded, there exists a constant M such that $|z_n| < M$ for all n. By (1.4.2), we have also $|x_n| < M$ and $|y_n| < M$, where $z_n = x_n + iy_n$. Thus, $\{x_n\}$ and $\{y_n\}$ are bounded sequences. Consequently (see Exercise 2.4.4) the sequence $\{x_n\}$ has an accumulation point x_0. Hence (see Exercise 2.3.1) there exists a subsequence $\{x'_m\}$ of $\{x_n\}$ such that $x'_m \to x_0$.

Let $\{z'_m\}$ and $\{y'_m\}$ denote the corresponding subsequences of $\{z_n\}$ and $\{y_n\}$. Since the subsequence $\{y'_m\}$ is bounded, it has an accumulation point y_0. Hence, there exists a subsequence $\{y''_k\}$ of $\{y'_m\}$ such that $y''_k \to y_0$. Let $\{x''_k\}$ and $\{z''_k\}$ be the corresponding subsequences of $\{x'_m\}$ and $\{z'_m\}$. Since $x'_m \to x_0$, it follows from Theorem 2.3.1 that $x''_k \to x_0$, and consequently

$$z''_k = x''_k + iy''_k \to x_0 + iy_0 = z_0.$$

Since the terms of the sequence $\{z_n\}$ are all distinct, so are those of the subsequence $\{z''_k\}$, and hence (see Exercise 2.3.2) z_0 is an accumulation point of S.

——**THEOREM** 2.4.3. Let $\{I^{(n)}\}$ be a sequence of closed intervals in the plane such that $I^{(n+1)} \subseteq I^{(n)}$ ($n = 1, 2, \cdots$). Then there exists at least one point common to all the intervals of the sequence.

Proof. Suppose that $I^{(n)}$ consists of all $z = x + iy$ such that

$$a_1^{(n)} \leq x \leq a_2^{(n)} \quad \text{and} \quad b_1^{(n)} \leq y \leq b_2^{(n)}.$$

Since $I^{(n+1)} \subseteq I^{(n)}$ ($n = 1, 2, \cdots$), it follows that

$$a_1^{(n)} \leq a_i^{(n+1)} \leq a_2^{(n)} \quad \text{and} \quad b_1^{(n)} \leq b_i^{(n+1)} \leq b_2^{(n)} \qquad (i = 1, 2).$$

Let $J^{(n)}$ denote the set of all x such that $a_1^{(n)} \leq x \leq a_2^{(n)}$. Then $\{J^{(n)}\}$ is a nested sequence of intervals on the real line, and by the Nested Interval Property for real numbers, there exists a real number x_0 such that $a_1^{(n)} \leq x_0 \leq a_2^{(n)}$ for all n.

Similarly, there exists a real number y_0 such that $b_1^{(n)} \leq y_0 \leq b_2^{(n)}$ for all n. Consequently, the point $z_0 = x_0 + iy_0$ is contained in every interval $I^{(n)}$.

EXERCISES 2.4

1. Show that every set S of real numbers has a least upper bound and greatest lower bound, finite or infinite.

2. Suppose that A is a set of points on the real line. Show that A is an interval if, and only if, it has the following property: Given any two points t_1 and t_2 in A, then the set of points t such that $t_1 \leq t \leq t_2$ is also in A.

3. Suppose that $I_1, I_2, I_3, \cdots$ is a sequence of closed intervals in the plane such that $I_{n+1} \subseteq I_n$ and diameter $(I_n) \to 0$ as $n \to \infty$. Show that there exists a unique point z_0 common to all I_n.

4. Prove that if a sequence $\{x_n\}$ of real numbers is bounded, then it has an accumulation point.

5. Show that if S is a bounded set of complex numbers, then any sequence $\{z_n\}$ in S has an accumulation point.

6. Show that a bounded sequence of complex numbers $\{z_n\}$ has only one accumulation point z_0 if, and only if, $\lim\limits_{n \to \infty} z_n = z_0$.

7. Show that a set I of points on the real line is connected if, and only if, I is an interval.

2.5. COMPACT SETS. An especially important role in the theory of functions is played by sets that are both <u>bounded and closed</u>. Such sets are called *compact* sets. For example, a closed interval $I = [\alpha, \beta]$ on the real line is compact; and so is the set of all complex numbers z such that $|z| \leq M$ (M constant).

————*THEOREM* 2.5.1 (*Heine-Borel*). Let S be a compact set. Suppose there is a family $\{G_\alpha\}$ of open sets such that each point of S is contained in at least one of the G_α. Then there exists a finite subfamily $\{G_{\alpha_j}\}$ $(j = 1, 2, \cdots, n)$ of $\{G_\alpha\}$ such that every point of S is in at least one of the G_{α_j}.

Proof. Suppose that no finite subfamily of $\{G_\alpha\}$ covers S. (That is, there is no finite subfamily $\{G_{\alpha_j}\}$, $j = 1, 2, \cdots, n$ of the G_α such that every point of S is in at least one of the G_{α_j}.) Since S is a bounded set, it is contained in some closed square Q whose sides have length k. Subdivide Q into four closed congruent squares, the length of whose sides is $k/2$. Then there must be at least one of these, say Q_1, such that no finite subfamily of $\{G_\alpha\}$ covers $S \cap Q_1$ (that is, the part of S contained in Q_1). Subdividing Q_1 into four closed congruent squares with sides of length $k/2^2$, then for at least one of these squares, denoted by Q_2, there is no finite subfamily of $\{G_\alpha\}$ which covers $S \cap Q_2$.

Continuing this process, we obtain an infinite nested sequence of closed squares $Q \supset Q_1 \supset Q_2 \supset \cdots$, such that diameter $(Q_n) \to 0$ and no finite subfamily of $\{G_\alpha\}$ covers $S \cap Q_n$. By Theorem 2.4.3, there is a point z_0 common to all the squares Q_n. This point is in S and hence contained in one of the sets of $\{G_\alpha\}$, say G_{α_p}. Since G_{α_p} is an open set, there exists an $\epsilon > 0$ such that all z satisfying $|z - z_0| < \epsilon$ are contained in G_{α_p}. Furthermore, since z_0 is contained in all the Q_n and diameter $(Q_n) \to 0$, it follows that for n sufficiently large, $|z - z_0| < \epsilon$ for every z in Q_n, and thus Q_n is contained in G_{α_p}. Hence G_{α_p} covers $S \cap Q_n$. This contradicts the condition that no finite subfamily of $\{G_\alpha\}$ covers the part of S contained in any Q_n. Thus the theorem is established.

————*THEOREM* 2.5.2 (*Bolzano-Weierstrass*). A set S is compact if, and only if, every infinite subset of S has an accumulation point in S.

Proof. The theorem holds trivially for sets containing only a finite number of points, since such sets are compact. (See Exercise 2.5.1.) For the remainder of the proof, let S contain an infinite number of points.

Suppose that S is compact, and let S_1 be a subset of S containing infinitely many points. Clearly S_1 is bounded, and by Theorem 2.4.2 it has an accumulation point z_0. Since z_0 is also an accumulation point of S and S is closed, z_0 must be in S.

Conversely, we shall show that if S is a set such that every infinite subset of S has an accumulation point in S, then S is compact.

We shall first show that S is bounded. For, if S were not bounded, there would exist a sequence $\{z_n\}$ of points in S such that $|z_m - z_n| \geqq 1$ for all m and n, $m \neq n$ (see Exercise 2.3.5) and, consequently, this infinite set of points in S would not have an accumulation point. (See Exercise 2.3.6.)

Next we shall show that S is closed. If there were an accumulation point z_0 of S which is not contained in S, there would exist a sequence $\{z_n\}$ of distinct points in S such that $z_n \to z_0$. (See Exercise 2.3.2.) This sequence cannot have an accumulation point other than z_0. (See Exercise 2.4.6.) Thus, the infinite set of points z_n in S would have no accumulation point in S. The theorem is now established.

EXERCISES 2.5

1. Let S be a set consisting of a finite number of points. Show that S is bounded and closed, and hence compact.

2. Let $\{S_\alpha\}$ be a family of compact sets having at least one point in common. Show that their intersection $\cap S_\alpha$ is also compact.

3. Show that if S is a compact set of real numbers, then it contains its greatest lower bound and least upper bound.

4. Let $\{R_n\}$ be a sequence of compact sets such that $R_{n+1} \subseteq R_n$ $(n = 1, 2, \cdots)$. Show that there exists at least one point z_0 common to all the R_n.

5. Show that if a point set S has the Heine-Borel Property described in Theorem 2.5.1, then it is bounded and closed.

6. Let $I = [t_1, t_2]$ be a closed interval on the real line. Suppose that each point t in I is contained in a neighborhood $N(t)$ belonging to a given family $\{N(t)\}$ of neighborhoods with respect to I. Show that there exists a finite subfamily $\{N(t_k)\}$, $k = 1, 2, \cdots, n$, of $\{N(t)\}$ covering I.

7. Let S be a bounded and closed set. Show that any sequence $\{z_n\}$ in S has an accumulation point in S.

8. Show that the union of a finite number of compact sets is compact.

2.6. ALGEBRAIC OPERATIONS WITH SEQUENCES

Definition 2.6.1. Given two sequences $\{z_n\}$ and $\{w_n\}$, then by the sum, difference, product, and quotient of the two sequences we mean the sequence obtained by adding, subtracting, multiplying, and dividing, respectively, the corresponding terms of the two given sequences.

In particular, if one of the two given sequences has all its terms equal to a constant c, we obtain the sum, difference, product, and quotient of the other sequence and the constant c. Thus, if α and β denote, respectively, the sequences $\{z_1, z_2, \cdots, z_n, \cdots\}$ and $\{w_1, w_2, \cdots, w_n, \cdots\}$, then

$$\left\{ \begin{array}{l} \alpha + \beta = \{z_1 + w_1, z_2 + w_2, \cdots, z_n + w_n, \cdots\}, \\[2mm] \alpha\beta = \{z_1 w_1, z_2 w_2, \cdots, z_n w_n, \cdots\}, \\[2mm] \dfrac{\alpha}{\beta} = \left\{ \dfrac{z_1}{w_1}, \dfrac{z_2}{w_2}, \cdots, \dfrac{z_n}{w_n}, \cdots \right\} \quad (w_n \neq 0,\, n = 1, 2, \cdots), \\[3mm] c\alpha = \{cz_1, cz_2, \cdots, cz_n, \cdots\}, \\[2mm] \text{and so on.} \end{array} \right. \qquad (2.6.1)$$

Strictly speaking, the quotient of two sequences has a meaning only when the divisor sequence contains no zero terms. However, when the divisor sequence, for example, $\{w_n\}$, contains only a finite number of zero terms and if w_N is the last zero term in the sequence, then by the quotient of $\{z_n\}$ by $\{w_n\}$ we mean the sequence $\{z_{N+m}/w_{N+m}\}$, $m = 1, 2, \cdots$.

Definition 2.6.2. A sequence which has a limit equal to zero is called a *null sequence*.

If the sequence $\{z_n\}$ converges to z_0, then the sequence $\{z_n - z_0\}$ is a null sequence. We may write $\{z_n\} = z_0 + \{z_n - z_0\}$, which shows that any convergent sequence may be written as the sum of a fixed number and a null sequence. Conversely, if $\{z_n\}$ can be written as $\{z_n\} = z_0 + \{\alpha_n\}$, where $\{\alpha_n\}$ is a null sequence, then $|z_n - z_0| = |\alpha_n| < \epsilon$ for $n > N(\epsilon)$ and the sequence $\{z_n\}$ is convergent. Here $N(\epsilon)$ means that N depends on ϵ.

We shall utilize the concept of null sequence to establish Theorem 2.6.1 below. We first prove the following

LEMMA 2.6.1. (1) The product of a null sequence by a bounded sequence is a null sequence. (2) The sum of two null sequences is a null sequence.

Proof. (1) Let the null and bounded sequences be denoted by $\{\alpha_n\}$ and $\{a_n\}$, respectively. Then there exists a constant M such that $|a_n| < M$ for all n. Also, given an $\epsilon > 0$, there exists an N such that $|\alpha_n| < \epsilon/M$ for $n > N$. Thus

$$|a_n \alpha_n| < M |\alpha_n| < M \frac{\epsilon}{M} = \epsilon \quad \text{for} \quad n > N.$$

Hence $\{a_n \alpha_n\}$ is a null sequence.

(2) Let $\{\beta_n\}$ be a null sequence also. Then for n sufficiently large we have

$$|\,\alpha_n\,| < \frac{\epsilon}{2} \text{ for } n > N_1(\epsilon) \quad \text{and} \quad |\,\beta_n\,| < \frac{\epsilon}{2} \text{ for } n > N_2(\epsilon).$$

Hence for $n > N(\epsilon) = \max\,[N_1(\epsilon), N_2(\epsilon)]$, we have using (1.3.9)

$$|\,\alpha_n + \beta_n\,| \leqq |\,\alpha_n\,| + |\,\beta_n\,| < \frac{\epsilon}{2} + \frac{\epsilon}{2} = \epsilon.$$

Thus $\{\alpha_n + \beta_n\}$ is a null sequence, and the lemma is established.

Remark 2.6.1.   From the above lemma and Theorem 2.3.2 it also follows that the product and difference of two null sequences is a null sequence.

——**THEOREM** 2.6.1.   The sum or difference of two convergent sequences is convergent, and the limit of the sum or difference of the two sequences is the sum or difference of their limits; that is, if $\lim\limits_{n\to\infty} z_n = z_0$ and $\lim\limits_{n\to\infty} w_n = w_0$, then

$$\lim_{n\to\infty} (z_n \pm w_n) = z_0 \pm w_0. \tag{2.6.2}$$

The product of two convergent sequences is convergent, and the limit of the product is the product of the limits; that is,

$$\lim_{n\to\infty} (z_n \cdot w_n) = z_0 \cdot w_0. \tag{2.6.3}$$

The quotient of two convergent sequences is convergent, provided the sequence by which we are dividing is not null, and the limit of the quotient is the quotient of the limits; that is,

$$\lim_{n\to\infty} \frac{z_n}{w_n} = \frac{z_0}{w_0} \qquad (w_0 \neq 0). \tag{2.6.4}$$

Proof.   The verification of (2.6.2) will be left as an exercise for the reader. Concerning (2.6.3). Let $\{z_n\} = z_0 + \{\alpha_n\}$ and $\{w_n\} = w_0 + \{\beta_n\}$, where $\{\alpha_n\}$ and $\{\beta_n\}$ are null sequences. Then

$$\{z_n w_n\} = z_0 w_0 + \{z_0 \beta_n + w_0 \alpha_n + \alpha_n \beta_n\}.$$

By Lemma 2.6.1 and Remark 2.6.1, $\{z_0 \beta_n + w_0 \alpha_n + \alpha_n \beta_n\}$ is a null sequence. Hence (2.6.3) is established.

Concerning (2.6.4). Since $w_0 \neq 0$, we may take $\epsilon = |\,w_0/2\,|$ and we have $\epsilon > 0$. Since $w_n \to w_0$, it follows that $|\,w_n - w_0\,| < \epsilon$ for $n > N(\epsilon)$. Utilizing (1.3.11) we have for $n > N(\epsilon)$

$$|\,w_n\,| = |\,w_0 + (w_n - w_0)\,| \geqq |\,w_0\,| - |\,w_n - w_0\,| > |\,w_0\,| - \epsilon$$

$$= |\,w_0\,| - \left|\frac{w_0}{2}\right| = \left|\frac{w_0}{2}\right|.$$

Hence, the sequence $\{1/w_n\}$ is bounded. Since $z_n = z_0 + \alpha_n$ and $w_n = w_0 + \beta_n$, where $\{\alpha_n\}$ and $\{\beta_n\}$ are null sequences, we have

$$\frac{z_n}{w_n} - \frac{z_0}{w_0} = \frac{z_0 + \alpha_n}{w_0 + \beta_n} - \frac{z_0}{w_0} = \frac{w_0\alpha_n - z_0\beta_n}{w_0(w_0 + \beta_n)}.$$

Since $w_0 \neq 0$ and the sequence $\{1/w_n\}$ is bounded, we see that

$$\left\{\frac{1}{w_0(w_0 + \beta_n)}\right\} = \left\{\frac{1}{w_0 w_n}\right\}$$

is a bounded sequence. By Lemma 2.6.1, $\{w_0\alpha_n - z_0\beta_n\}$ is a null sequence and

$$\left\{\frac{1}{w_0(w_0 + \beta_n)} \cdot (w_0\alpha_n - z_0\beta_n)\right\}$$

is also a null sequence. Thus

$$\left\{\frac{z_n}{w_n}\right\} = \frac{z_0}{w_0} + \text{null sequence,}$$

from which (2.6.4) now follows.

Definition 2.6.3. A sequence of complex numbers $\{z_n\}$ is said to *diverge to the limit* ∞, and we write

$$\lim_{n \to \infty} z_n = \infty \quad \text{or} \quad z_n \to \infty \tag{2.6.5}$$

if, given any real number K, there exists a number N such that

$$|z_n| > K \quad \text{for} \quad n > N.$$

Geometrically, this means that given any circle with center at $z = 0$, all the points z_n, for n sufficiently large, lie outside this circle.

Remark 2.6.2. In Section 2.12, we shall add a new point to the complex plane called "the point at infinity," and we shall denote this point by the symbol ∞. We shall also define a system of neighborhoods at this point. It will then be seen that if $z_n \to \infty$ in the sense of our present definition, then given any neighborhood of the "point at infinity," there exists a number N such that when $n > N$, z_n will be in that neighborhood.

2.7. SERIES OF COMPLEX NUMBERS. Let $z_1, z_2, \cdots, z_n, \cdots$ be a sequence of complex numbers. The symbol

$$z_1 + z_2 + \cdots + z_n + \cdots, \tag{2.7.1}$$

denotes an *infinite series* of complex numbers. For convenience, we shall use the equivalent symbol

$$\sum_{n=1}^{\infty} z_n \tag{2.7.2}$$

to represent the series (2.7.1). We shall denote the nth term of the infinite series (2.7.1) by z_n.

The sum indicated in (2.7.1), which involves the addition of an infinite number of complex numbers has, in itself, no meaning. In order to assign a meaning to the sum of such an infinite series, we consider the associated sequence of partial sums $S_1, S_2, \cdots, S_n, \cdots$, where

$$
\left\{
\begin{array}{l}
S_1 = z_1 \\
S_2 = z_1 + z_2 \\
\quad \cdots \quad \cdots \\
S_n = z_1 + z_2 + \cdots + z_n \\
\quad \cdots \quad \cdots \quad \cdots
\end{array}
\right. \tag{2.7.3}
$$

The series $\sum_{n=1}^{\infty} z_n$ may be defined as the pair of sequences $\{z_n\}$ and $\{S_n\}$.

Definition 2.7.1. The series $\sum_{n=1}^{\infty} z_n$ of complex numbers is said to be *convergent*, or to *converge*, if there exists a finite number S such that

$$
\lim_{n \to \infty} S_n = S. \tag{2.7.4}
$$

S is then called the *sum* of the series, and we write

$$
\sum_{n=1}^{\infty} z_n = S. \tag{2.7.5}
$$

The series is said to be *divergent*, or to *diverge*, if $\lim_{n \to \infty} S_n$ either does not exist or is infinite.

——**THEOREM** 2.7.1. A necessary and sufficient condition for the series $\sum_{n=1}^{\infty} z_n$ to converge to the sum S is that

$$
\sum_{n=1}^{\infty} \mathcal{R}(z_n) = \mathcal{R}(S) \quad \text{and} \quad \sum_{n=1}^{\infty} \mathcal{I}(z_n) = \mathcal{I}(S). \tag{2.7.6}
$$

The proof is left as an exercise for the reader.

——**THEOREM** 2.7.2. If

$$
\sum_{n=1}^{\infty} z_n = S \quad \text{and} \quad \sum_{n=1}^{\infty} w_n = T,
$$

then

$$
\sum_{n=1}^{\infty} (z_n \pm w_n) = S \pm T \quad \text{and} \quad \sum_{n=1}^{\infty} k z_n = kS \quad (k \text{ constant}). \tag{2.7.7}
$$

Proof. From (2.7.4) and (2.7.5) we have

$$\sum_{n=1}^{\infty} z_n = \lim_{n\to\infty} S_n = S \quad \text{and} \quad \sum_{n=1}^{\infty} w_n = \lim_{n\to\infty} T_n = T,$$

where $S_n = z_1 + z_2 + \cdots + z_n$ and $T_n = w_1 + w_2 + \cdots + w_n$. From Theorem 2.6.1 we obtain

$$\sum_{n=1}^{\infty} (z_n \pm w_n) = \lim_{n\to\infty} (S_n \pm T_n) = S \pm T.$$

Also

$$\sum_{n=1}^{\infty} k z_n = \lim_{n\to\infty} (k S_n) = k \lim_{n\to\infty} S_n = kS.$$

——**THEOREM** 2.7.3. A necessary and sufficient condition for a series $\sum_{n=1}^{\infty} z_n$ of complex numbers to converge is that for every $\epsilon > 0$ there exists an integer N such that

$$| S_m - S_n | = | z_{n+1} + z_{n+2} + \cdots + z_m | < \epsilon \quad \text{for} \quad m > n > N. \quad (2.7.8)$$

Proof. The theorem states that a sequence $\{S_n\}$ of partial sums has a limit if, and only if, it is a Cauchy sequence. Now, if $\{S_n\}$ is a Cauchy sequence, then by Theorem 2.4.1 $\{S_n\}$ converges. Conversely, if the sequence $\{S_n\}$ has a limit, then it is not difficult to show that it is a Cauchy sequence. (See Exercise 2.3.4.)

——**THEOREM** 2.7.4. A necessary (but not sufficient) condition for a series $\sum_{n=1}^{\infty} z_n$ of complex numbers to converge is that

$$\lim_{n\to\infty} z_n = 0. \quad (2.7.9)$$

Proof. Suppose that the series converges to S, that is,

$$\lim_{n\to\infty} S_n = S.$$

Then

$$\lim_{n\to\infty} z_n = \lim_{n\to\infty} (S_n - S_{n-1}) = S - S = 0.$$

Note that condition (2.7.9) is not sufficient to guarantee convergence. For, we need only observe that the harmonic series $\sum_{n=1}^{\infty} 1/n$ satisfies this condition, yet is not convergent.

Remark 2.7.1. The above theorem may also be interpreted as saying that if the nth term of the series $\sum_{n=1}^{\infty} z_n$ as $n \to \infty$ does not converge to zero, then the series $\sum_{n=1}^{\infty} z_n$ diverges.

Definition 2.7.2. A series $\sum_{n=1}^{\infty} z_n$ of complex numbers is said to *converge absolutely* or be *absolutely convergent* if the series $\sum_{n=1}^{\infty} |z_n|$ is convergent.

——*THEOREM* 2.7.5. If the series $\sum_{n=1}^{\infty} z_n$ of complex numbers converges absolutely, then $\sum_{n=1}^{\infty} z_n$ converges.

Proof. The theorem follows from the Cauchy criterion (Theorem 2.7.3). For, using (1.3.10), we have

$$| z_{n+1} + \cdots + z_m | \leq | z_{n+1} | + \cdots + | z_m |.$$

If the series $\sum z_n$ converges absolutely, then for each $\epsilon > 0$ an N, depending upon ϵ, can be found such that

$$| z_{n+1} | + \cdots + | z_m | < \epsilon \qquad \text{for } m > n > N,$$

and, a fortiori, we have

$$| z_{n+1} + \cdots + z_m | < \epsilon \qquad \text{for } m > n > N.$$

Thus the series $\sum z_n$ converges.

Note that the converse of the above theorem is false. We need only to observe that the series $\sum_{n=1}^{\infty} (-1)^{n+1}/n$ is convergent, but not absolutely.

Other useful tests for convergence of infinite series of complex numbers will now be given.

——*THEOREM* 2.7.6 (*Comparison test for convergence*). If $| z_n | \leq | w_n |$ for all $n > N_0$ and the series $\sum_{n=1}^{\infty} | w_n |$ converges, then the series $\sum_{n=1}^{\infty} z_n$ is absolutely convergent.

Proof.   Given $\epsilon > 0$, there exists an integer $N \geq N_0$ such that

$$| z_{n+1} | + \cdots + | z_m | \leq | w_{n+1} | + \cdots + | w_m | < \epsilon \qquad \text{for } n > N,$$

since the series $\sum w_n$ converges absolutely. Hence, the series $\sum z_n$ also converges absolutely.

——*THEOREM* 2.7.7 (*Ratio test*). If

$$\lim_{n \to \infty} \left| \frac{z_{n+1}}{z_n} \right| = L,$$

then

$$\text{if } L < 1, \sum_{n=1}^{\infty} z_n \text{ is absolutely convergent, and}$$

(2.7.10)

$$\text{if } L > 1, \sum_{n=1}^{\infty} z_n \text{ is divergent.}$$

The proof is similar to that given in elementary calculus, and will be left as an exercise for the reader.

Remark 2.7.2. In case $L = 1$, the given series may converge or diverge. Consider the harmonic series of order p: $\sum_{n=1}^{\infty} 1/n^p$. Observe that the limit of the ratio is 1. One can easily verify that this series will converge for $p > 1$ and diverge for $p \leq 1$.

EXAMPLE 2.7.1. Test the series $\sum_{n=1}^{\infty} i^n/n!$ for absolute convergence.

Solution. $| z_{n+1}/z_n | = 1/(n + 1)$. Hence

$$\lim_{n \to \infty} \left| \frac{z_{n+1}}{z_n} \right| = 0,$$

and the series $\sum_{n=1}^{\infty} i^n/n!$ converges absolutely.

EXAMPLE 2.7.2. Test the series $\sum_{n=1}^{\infty} i^n/n$ for absolute convergence.

Solution. $| z_{n+1}/z_n | = n/(n + 1)$. Hence

$$\lim_{n \to \infty} \left| \frac{z_{n+1}}{z_n} \right| = 1,$$

and the test fails.

Let $z_n = x_n + iy_n$, where $z_n = i^n/n$. Then

$$\sum_{n=1}^{\infty} x_n = \sum_{n=1}^{\infty} \frac{(-1)^n}{2n} \quad \text{and} \quad \sum_{n=1}^{\infty} y_n = \sum_{n=1}^{\infty} \frac{(-1)^{n-1}}{(2n - 1)}.$$

Each of these alternating series is convergent, thus the given series is convergent; however, neither of the above two series converges absolutely, since they both form harmonic series. Hence, the given series does not converge absolutely.

Using the distributive law (1.1.6), we know that the product of two finite sums $\sum_{n=1}^{k} z_n$ and $\sum_{n=1}^{m} w_n$ can be obtained by multiplying the two sums term by term. To what extent is this true of infinite sums? An answer is given by the following theorem:*

———**THEOREM** 2.7.8. If the series $\sum_{n=1}^{\infty} z_n = S$ and $\sum_{n=1}^{\infty} w_n = T$ are absolutely convergent, then the series

$$\sum_{n=1}^{\infty} (z_1 w_n + z_2 w_{n-1} + \cdots + z_{n-1} w_2 + z_n w_1) \qquad (2.7.11)$$

also converges absolutely and has the sum $S \cdot T$.

* See K. Knopp, *Theory and Application of Infinite Series*, pp. 146-147. (London: Blackie, 1951).

The expression given in (2.7.11) is called the *Cauchy product* of the two given series.

So far, we have used the triangle inequality for finite sums. We would like to inquire whether inequality (1.3.10) can be extended to infinite series. An answer is given by the following

——*THEOREM* 2.7.9. If the series $\sum_{n=1}^{\infty} z_n$ of complex numbers converges absolutely, then

$$\left| \sum_{n=1}^{\infty} z_n \right| \leq \sum_{n=1}^{\infty} | z_n |. \tag{2.7.12}$$

The proof is left as an exercise for the reader.

EXERCISES 2.7

1. Show that for any positive integer N, the series $\sum_{n=1}^{\infty} x_n$ converges if, and only if, the series $\sum_{n=N}^{\infty} x_n$ converges.

2. Prove Theorem 2.7.1.

3. Prove Theorem 2.7.9.

2.8. UPPER AND LOWER LIMITS. In Chapter 6, we shall discuss the concept of the radius of convergence of a power series $\sum_{n=0}^{\infty} c_n(z - z_0)^n$. A very useful formula for evaluating the radius of convergence will be given in terms of the "upper limit" of a sequence of real numbers. If a sequence $\{x_n\}$ of real numbers is bounded from above and has one or more accumulation points, the least upper bound of all the accumulation points is called the *upper limit* or *limit superior* of the sequence $\{x_n\}$. Denoting it by β, we write

$$\overline{\lim_{n \to \infty}} \, x_n = \beta. \tag{2.8.1}$$

Similarly, if the sequence $\{x_n\}$ is bounded from below and has one or more accumulation points, the greatest lower bound of all the accumulation points is called the *lower limit* or *limit inferior* of the sequence $\{x_n\}$. Denoting it by α, we write

$$\underline{\lim_{n \to \infty}} \, x_n = \alpha. \tag{2.8.2}$$

If the sequence $\{x_n\}$ is unbounded from above or from below, we may extend the above definitions by introducing $+ \infty$ and $- \infty$ as possible limiting values. We say that

$$\overline{\lim_{n \to \infty}} \, x_n = + \infty, \tag{2.8.3}$$

provided that for every real number N, $x_n > N$ for infinitely many n. Also

$$\lim_{n \to \infty} x_n = -\infty, \tag{2.8.4}$$

provided that for every real number N, $x_n < N$ for infinitely many n.

EXAMPLE 2.8.1.   Let us verify that

$$\overline{\lim_{n \to \infty}} \left[1 + \sin\left(\frac{n\pi}{2}\right)\right] = 2, \qquad \underline{\lim_{n \to \infty}} \left[1 + \sin\left(\frac{n\pi}{2}\right)\right] = 0.$$

Solution.   Let $x_n = 1 + \sin(n\pi/2)$. Then

$$\begin{aligned}
x_{4k+1} &= 2, & k &= 0, 1, 2, \cdots, \\
x_{2k} &= 1, & k &= 1, 2, \cdots, \\
x_{4k+3} &= 0, & k &= 0, 1, 2, \cdots.
\end{aligned}$$

Hence

$$\overline{\lim_{n \to \infty}} x_n = \lim_{k \to \infty} x_{4k+1} = 2, \qquad \underline{\lim_{n \to \infty}} x_n = \lim_{k \to \infty} x_{4k+3} = 0.$$

EXAMPLE 2.8.2.   Let us verify that

$$\overline{\lim_{n \to \infty}} \left[(-1)^{n+1} n - n\right] = 0, \qquad \underline{\lim_{n \to \infty}} \left[(-1)^{n+1} n - n\right] = -\infty.$$

Solution.   Let $x_n = (-1)^{n+1}n - n$. Then

$$\begin{aligned}
x_{2k+1} &= 0, & k &= 0, 1, 2, \cdots, \\
x_{2k} &= -4k, & k &= 1, 2, \cdots.
\end{aligned}$$

Hence

$$\overline{\lim_{n \to \infty}} x_n = \lim_{k \to \infty} x_{2k+1} = 0, \qquad \underline{\lim_{n \to \infty}} x_n = \lim_{k \to \infty} x_{2k} = -\infty.$$

EXAMPLE 2.8.3.

$$\overline{\lim_{n \to \infty}} \left[n \sin\left(\frac{n\pi}{2}\right)\right] = \infty, \qquad \underline{\lim_{n \to \infty}} \left[n \sin\left(\frac{n\pi}{2}\right)\right] = -\infty.$$

The following theorem will be used in connection with evaluating the radius of convergence of a power series.

——**THEOREM** 2.8.1 (*Root test*).   Suppose that $\{z_n\}$ is a sequence of complex numbers and

$$\overline{\lim_{n \to \infty}} \sqrt[n]{|z_n|} = L.$$

Then

$$\text{if } L < 1, \sum_{n=1}^{\infty} z_n \text{ is absolutely convergent, and}$$

(2.8.5)

$$\text{if } L > 1, \sum_{n=1}^{\infty} z_n \text{ is divergent.}$$

Proof. Suppose that $L < 1$. Let r be a positive number such that $L < r < 1$. Then, except for, at most, a finite number of n, we have $\sqrt[n]{|z_n|} < r$. (See Exercise 2.8.1.) Hence

$$|z_n| < r^n \quad \text{when} \quad n \geq N \text{ for some } N.$$

Since the geometric series $r^N + r^{N+1} + r^{N+2} + \cdots$ converges, it follows from Theorem 2.7.6 that the series $|z_N| + |z_{N+1}| + |z_{N+2}| + \cdots$ also converges. Consequently, the series $\sum_{n=1}^{\infty} |z_n|$ also converges. (See Exercise 2.7.1.) Thus, the series $\sum_{n=1}^{\infty} z_n$ converges absolutely.

Suppose that $L > 1$. Hence there exist an infinite number of n's such that $\sqrt[n]{|z_n|} > 1$. (See Exercise 2.8.1.) Consequently, we have for an infinite number of n's, $|z_n| > 1$. Hence, by Theorem 2.7.4 the series $\sum_{n=1}^{\infty} z_n$ diverges.

Remark 2.8.1. When $L = 1$, the series may converge or diverge. For example, consider the series $\sum_{n=1}^{\infty} z_n$ where $z_n = 1/n^p$. Then

$$\lim_{n \to \infty} \sqrt[n]{|z_n|} = \lim_{n \to \infty} 1/\sqrt[n]{n^p} = 1.$$

Consequently, (see Exercise 2.8.5)

$$L = \overline{\lim_{n \to \infty}} \sqrt[n]{|z_n|} = 1.$$

This series, however, converges for $p > 1$ and diverges for $p \leq 1$.

EXERCISES 2.8

1. Suppose that the sequence $\{x_n\}$ of real numbers has a finite upper limit β. Show that for any given $\epsilon > 0$, we have (a) $x_n > \beta - \epsilon$ for an infinite number of n's and (b) except for, at most, a finite number of n's, we have $x_n < \beta + \epsilon$.

2. Formulate an assertion concerning the lower limit α of a sequence $\{x_n\}$ of real numbers similar to that of Exercise 1 above concerning the upper limit β.

3. Suppose that the sequence $\{x_n\}$ of real numbers has a finite upper limit β. Show that given any $\epsilon > 0$, $|x_n - \beta| < \epsilon$ for infinitely many values of n, and that no number larger than β has this property.

4. Suppose that the sequence $\{x_n\}$ of real numbers has a finite lower limit α. Show that given any $\epsilon > 0$, then $|x_n - \alpha| < \epsilon$ for infinitely many n, and no number less than α has this property.

5. Show that for a real number α and a sequence of real numbers $\{x_n\}$ we have $\lim_{n\to\infty} x_n = \alpha$ if, and only if, $\overline{\lim}_{n\to\infty} x_n = \underline{\lim}_{n\to\infty} x_n = \alpha$.

6. Suppose that $\lim_{n\to\infty} \sqrt[n]{|z_n|} = L$. Show that

$$\text{if } L < 1, \sum_{n=1}^{\infty} z_n \text{ is absolutely convergent;}$$

$$\text{if } L > 1, \sum_{n=1}^{\infty} z_n \text{ is divergent;}$$

$$\text{if } L = 1, \text{ the test fails.}$$

7. Evaluate the following limits when they exist:

(a) $\lim_{n\to\infty} i^n$

(b) $\lim_{n\to\infty} \dfrac{(n+i)^2}{3^{2n}}$

(c) $\lim_{n\to\infty} \left[(-1)^n + \dfrac{ni}{n+1}\right]$

(d) $\lim_{n\to\infty} \dfrac{n!\, i^n}{n^n}$

(e) $\lim_{n\to\infty} \dfrac{(1-i)\,n^4 + 2in^3 - 3n^2 + 5i}{in^4 + 5}$

(f) $\lim_{n\to\infty} \dfrac{i^n}{n^2}$.

8. Test for absolute convergence and for convergence:

(a) $\sum_{n=1}^{\infty} n^2 i^n$

(b) $\sum_{n=1}^{\infty} \dfrac{n!\, i^n}{n^n}$

(c) $\sum_{n=1}^{\infty} \dfrac{n^2 i^n}{n^3 + 1}$

(d) $\sum_{n=2}^{\infty} \dfrac{ni^n}{\log n}$

(e) $\sum_{n=1}^{\infty} \dfrac{i^n}{\log(n+1)}$

(f) $\sum_{n=1}^{\infty} \left(\dfrac{1+i}{3}\right)^n$

(g) $\sum_{n=1}^{\infty} \dfrac{i^n}{n^3}$

(h) $\sum_{n=1}^{\infty} \dfrac{3ni^n}{(n+2i)^3}$

(i) $\sum_{n=1}^{\infty} \dfrac{(3+2i)^n}{n+2}$

(j) $\sum_{n=1}^{\infty} \dfrac{\log n^n}{n!}\, i^n$

(k) $\sum_{n=1}^{\infty} \left(\dfrac{n}{2n+1}\right)^n i^n$

(l) $\sum_{n=1}^{\infty} \left(\dfrac{n}{n+1}\right)^{n^2} i^n$

(m) $\sum_{n=1}^{\infty} \left(\dfrac{n^2-1}{n^2+3n+2}\right)^n i^n$

(n) $\sum_{n=1}^{\infty} \dfrac{(n^3+3^n)\,i^n}{3^n n^3}$.

2.9. CONTINUOUS MAPPINGS. If to every point z of a set A there is assigned a unique point w in a set B, we say that we have a *mapping T of A into B*, and we write

$$T: A \to B. \tag{2.9.1}$$

If w is the point in B assigned by the mapping T to the point z in A, we say that z *is mapped into* w, and we write

$$w = T(z). \tag{2.9.2}$$

The point w is called the *image* of z, and the point z is called an *antecedent* of w. Observe that while each point z in A has only one image point, a point w in B may have more than one antecedent. This will occur when two distinct points z_1 and z_2 in A are mapped into the same point w in B. For example, if T assigns to every point z the point $w = z^2$, then the points $z = \pm 1$ both have the same image point $w = 1$. Note also that when T maps A into B, there may be points in B which have no antecedents in A. If every point w of B is the image under T of some point z of A, then we say that T maps A *onto* B. Note that when T maps A onto B, B as well as A is exhausted, that is, every point in B has at least one antecedent in A.

If any two distinct points in A are assigned distinct image points in B, then T is said to be a *one-to-one mapping* of A into B. If A_1 is a subset of A, then the set of all w in B such that w is the image of some z in A_1, is called the *image of A_1 under* T and is denoted by $T(A_1)$. In particular, the set of all w in B that are images of points in A is denoted by $T(A)$. Of special importance is the case when T maps A in one-to-one fashion onto B. Then we can form a mapping which assigns to every point w in B its unique antecedent z under the mapping T. This latter mapping, called the *inverse* of T, is denoted by T^{-1}, and we write

$$z = T^{-1}(w). \tag{2.9.3}$$

Clearly, T^{-1} maps B one-to-one onto A.

If T maps A onto a set B and B_1 is any subset of B, then the set of all z in A such that $T(z)$ is in B_1 is called the *inverse image* $T^{-1}(B_1)$ of B_1 under the mapping T. In particular, if B_1 consists of a single point w_0, then $T^{-1}(w_0)$ is the set of all z such that $T(z) = w_0$. Observe that the symbol T^{-1} has been used in two different but related senses.

Let T_1 be a mapping of a set A into a set B, and let T_2 be a mapping of the set B into a set C. Then, by the *product* $T_3 = T_2 T_1$ of the two mappings T_1 and T_2, we mean the mapping T_3 of the set A into the set C which assigns to each point z of A the point ζ in C obtained as follows: We take the point w in B, which is the image of z under T_1, and then find the image ζ in C of the point w under the mapping T_2. That is

$$\zeta = T_3(z) = T_2[T_1(z)]. \tag{2.9.4}$$

We shall need the following

LEMMA 2.9.1. Suppose that T maps a set A onto a set B. Let B_1 and B_2 be disjoint subsets of B, and let A_1 and A_2 be their respective inverse images under T. Then A_1 and A_2 are also disjoint.

Proof. If z were a point common to A_1 and A_2, then $w = T(z)$ would be both in B_1 and B_2, thus contradicting the hypothesis that B_1 and B_2 are disjoint.

Definition 2.9.1. A mapping T of a set A into a set B is said to be *continuous* if, for each point z_0 in A and any neighborhood $N(w_0)$ of its image point w_0 in B, there exists a neighborhood of z_0 which is mapped by T into $N(w_0)$.

If T is a continuous one-to-one mapping of a set A onto a set B such that the inverse mapping T^{-1} of B onto A is also continuous, then T is said to be a *homeomorphism*, a *bicontinuous mapping* or a *topological mapping* of A onto B. The sets A and B are said to be *homeomorphic*.

——THEOREM 2.9.1. Let T be a continuous mapping of a set A into a set B. If $\lim_{n\to\infty} z_n = z_0$, where the sequence of points $\{z_n\}$ and z_0 are in A, then

$$\lim_{n\to\infty} T(z_n) = T(z_0). \qquad (2.9.5)$$

Conversely, if T is a mapping of a set A into a set B and $\lim_{n\to\infty} T(z_n) = T(z_0)$ whenever $\lim_{n\to\infty} z_n = z_0$, with z_0 and z_n in A, then T is continuous.

Proof. Suppose that T is continuous. Let w_0 denote the image point of z_0 under T and let $N(w_0)$ be any neighborhood of w_0. By Definition 2.9.1, there exists a neighborhood $N(z_0)$ of z_0 which is mapped by T into $N(w_0)$. Thus, if z_n is in $N(z_0)$, then $T(z_n)$ is in $N(w_0)$. Since $z_n \to z_0$, z_n is in $N(z_0)$ for n sufficiently large. Consequently, $T(z_n)$ is in $N(w_0)$ for n sufficiently large. Thus $\lim_{n\to\infty} T(z_n) = T(z_0)$.

Conversely, suppose that $\lim_{n\to\infty} T(z_n) = T(z_0)$ whenever $\lim_{n\to\infty} z_n = z_0$. If T were not continuous, then there would be a point z_0 and a neighborhood N of $T(z_0)$ such that no neighborhood of z_0 is mapped entirely into N. Thus, for each n, the neighborhood of z_0 given by $|z - z_0| < 1/n$ would contain points whose images are not in N. Let z_n be such a point. Then $|z_n - z_0| < 1/n$ and, consequently, $z_n \to z_0$. Since $T(z_n)$ is outside of N, $T(z_n)$ does not approach $T(z_0)$. This contradiction shows that T must be continuous.

——THEOREM 2.9.2. Suppose that T is a continuous mapping of a set A onto a set B. If A is a connected set, then B is also a connected set.

Proof. We shall establish the theorem by showing that if B were not connected, then A would also be not connected.

Suppose that B is not connected. Then from Definition 2.2.4, B is the union of two nonempty disjoint sets B_1 and B_2 such that neither of them contains an accumulation point of the other. Let A_1 and A_2 be the respective inverse images of B_1 and B_2 under the mapping T. Since the image of any point z in A is either in B_1 or in B_2, z must be in A_1 or A_2, and, consequently, A is the union of A_1 and A_2. By Lemma 2.9.1, A_1 and A_2 are disjoint. We shall now show that neither A_1 nor A_2 contains an accumulation point of the other.

Suppose, for example, that the point z_0 in A_1 is an accumulation point of A_2. Then (see Exercise 2.3.2) there exists a sequence $\{z_n\}$ of points in A_2 such that $z_n \to z_0$. By Theorem 2.9.1, we have $T(z_n) \to T(z_0)$. But this is impossible, since $T(z_0)$ is in B_1 and $T(z_n)$ is in B_2. Thus, if B is not connected, A is also not connected, and the theorem is established.

——*THEOREM* 2.9.3. Let T be a continuous mapping of a compact set A onto a set B. Then B is also compact.

Proof. If B contains only a finite number of points, then B is compact. (See Exercise 2.5.1.) It is, therefore, sufficient to consider the case when B contains an infinite number of points. We shall show that every infinite subset B_1 of B contains an accumulation point in B. It will then follow by Theorem 2.5.2 that B is compact.

Let $\{w_n\}$ be any sequence of distinct points in B_1, and let $\{z_n\}$ be a sequence of points in A such that $w_n = T(z_n)$ for all n. Clearly, the z_n are distinct, and since the set A is compact, the sequence $\{z_n\}$ has by Theorem 2.5.2 an accumulation point z_0 in A. Consequently, by Exercise 2.3.1, there exists a subsequence $\{z'_m\}$ of $\{z_n\}$ such that $z'_m \to z_0$. It follows from Theorem 2.9.1 that the subsequence $\{w'_m\}$ of $\{w_n\}$, where $w'_m = T(z'_m)$, has a limit $w_0 = T(z_0)$ in B. Hence, the set B_1 has an accumulation point w_0 in B. The theorem is thus established.

——*THEOREM* 2.9.4. Let T be a continuous mapping of a compact set A into the real line, and let $T(A)$ denote the image of A under T. Then there exist points t_1 and t_2 in $T(A)$ such that $t_1 \leq t \leq t_2$ for all points t in $T(A)$.

Proof. By Theorem 2.9.3 $T(A)$ is bounded and closed. By the Dedekind Property of Section 2.4, $T(A)$ has a greatest lower bound t_1 and a least upper bound t_2. Since $T(A)$ is closed, it contains both t_1 and t_2. (See Exercise 2.5.3.)

A nonempty set G is called a *group* if the following four conditions are satisfied:

(1) There exists an operation that associates with each ordered pair of elements a, b of G a unique element c of G. (The element c is also defined when $a = b$.) This operation will be called *multiplication* and the element c will be called the *product* of a and b, and we write $c = ab$. (The product ab may depend upon the order of the factors a and b; ab, in general, may not be equal to ba.)

(2) The multiplication is *associative*, that is, if a, b, c are elements of G, then

$$(ab)\, c = a(bc).$$

(3) The set G contains an *identity* element, that is, an element e such that for every element a of G

$$ae = ea = a.$$

(4) For each element a of G there exists an *inverse* element, that is, an element a^{-1} such that

$$aa^{-1} = a^{-1}a = e.$$

(5) If besides the four conditions given above, the group also satisfies the commutative law, that is, if for any two elements a and b of G we have

$$ab = ba,$$

then the group is called *commutative* or *abelian*.

Remark 2.9.1.   It can be shown that in a group G each of the equations

$$ax = b \quad \text{and} \quad ya = b$$

has a unique solution with respect to the unknowns x and y. From this follows, in particular, the uniqueness of the identity and of the inverse element, since e is the solution of the equation $ax = a$, and the element a^{-1} is the solution of $ax = e$.

Let A be a nonempty set. We shall call any one-to-one mapping of the set A onto itself a *transformation** of the set A.

──**THEOREM** 2.9.5.   The collection G of all transformations of a nonempty set A forms a group under the operation defining the product of transformations.

Proof.   Let T_1 and T_2 be two transformations of A. It is easy to see that their product $T_3 = T_2 T_1$ is also a transformation of A.

Multiplication of transformations is associative, that is, $(T_3 T_2)T_1 = T_3(T_2 T_1)$. To prove this equality, we must show that $(T_3 T_2) T_1(z) = T_3(T_2 T_1)(z)$ for all elements z of A. Now

$$(T_3 T_2) T_1(z) = (T_3 T_2)(T_1(z)) = T_3(T_2(T_1(z)))$$

and

$$T_3(T_2 T_1)(z) = T_3(T_2 T_1(z)) = T_3(T_2(T_1(z))).$$

Thus, in both cases we get the same result.

The identity for G is the identity transformation I defined by $I(z) = z$ for all z in A. The inverse of a transformation T of A is the transformation T^{-1} which transforms every $T(z)$ of the set A into z. Hence, all the conditions for a group are satisfied and the theorem is thus established.

---

* In Section 8.1, however, *transformation* is used interchangeably with *mapping*.

EXERCISES 2.9

1. Suppose that T is a mapping of a set A onto a set B. Show that T is continuous if, and only if, for every subset B_1 of B, open with respect to B, the inverse image A_1 is open with respect to A.

2. Suppose that T is a continuous mapping of a connected set S into the real line R. Let α and β be image points under this mapping. Show that every point in R lying between α and β is also an image point.

3. Let H and G be continuous mappings of the set A into the set B and of the set B into the set C, respectively. Show that the product $F = GH$, mapping the set A into the set C, is also continuous.

4. Suppose that T_1 is a one-to-one mapping of a set S_1 onto a set S_2, and T_2 is a one-to-one mapping of S_2 onto a set S_3. Show that the product $T_3 = T_2 T_1$ is a one-to-one mapping of S_1 onto S_3 and that $T_3^{-1} = T_1^{-1} T_2^{-1}$.

5. Suppose that T_1 is a topological mapping of a set S_1 onto a set S_2, and T_2 is a topological mapping of S_2 onto a set S_3. Show that the product $T_3 = T_2 T_1$ is a topological mapping of S_1 onto S_3.

6. Show that if T is a topological mapping of a set A onto a set B, then a subset A_1 is open with respect to A if, and only if, its image $T(A_1)$ is open with respect to B.

7. Show that if T is a topological mapping of a set A onto a set B, then a subset A_1 of A is connected if, and only if, its image $T(A_1)$ is connected.

8. Suppose that T is a one-to-one mapping of a set A onto a set B. Suppose furthermore that if A_1 is a subset of A, open with respect to A, then the image B_1 of A_1 is open with respect to B. Show that the inverse mapping T^{-1} of B onto A is continuous.

9. Suppose that T is a continuous one-to-one mapping of a set A onto a set B. Suppose furthermore that if A_1 is any subset of A, open with respect to A, then its image is open with respect to B. Show that T is a topological mapping of A onto B.

10. Let $S = \bigcup_{j=1}^{k} S_j$ be the union of the disjoint subsets S_j, and let $S' = \bigcup_{j=1}^{k} S_j'$ be the union of the disjoint subsets S_j'. Suppose that T maps S one-to-one onto S'. Suppose further that each of the subsets S_j is mapped under T into S_j'. Show that T maps each S_j one-to-one onto S_j'.

11. Let S be separated into the connected sets D_1 and D_2, and let S' be separated into the connected sets D_1' and D_2'. Suppose that T is a continuous mapping of S onto S'. Show that T maps D_1 onto D_1' and D_2 onto D_2' or else T maps D_1 onto D_2' and D_2 onto D_1'.

12. Let S be a collection of transformations of a set A having the property that whenever T_1, T_2 are members of S, then T_1^{-1} and $T_2 T_1$ are also members of S. Show that S is a group. (It is assumed that both A and S are not empty.)

2.10. CONTINUOUS CURVES. Let $I = [t_1, t_2]$ be a closed interval on the real line, that is, I is the set of all t such that $t_1 \leq t \leq t_2$, with t_1 and t_2 finite. Let C be a continuous mapping of I into the complex plane. Then the mapping C is said to represent a *continuous curve or path in the plane.* The image z of any point t in I is given by

$$z = C(t).$$

However, we shall often write $z = C(t)$ as

$$z = z(t). \tag{2.10.1}$$

Intuitively, this definition of a curve* may be interpreted as follows. Suppose that a point z moves continuously in the plane during the time interval I: $t_1 \leq t \leq t_2$. Then at each instant t of the time interval I, the traveling point occupies a definite position $z = z(t)$ in the plane. Thus we have a continuous mapping C which assigns to each instant t in I, a definite complex number $z = z(t)$ denoting the position of the traveling point at that instant. The mapping C thus gives the motion of the point during the time interval I.

EXAMPLE 2.10.1. Suppose that the position z of a moving point is given by

$$z(t) = \cos 2\pi t + i \sin 2\pi t, \qquad 0 \leq t \leq 1. \tag{2.10.2}$$

Then as t varies from 0 to 1, the moving point travels once around the unit circle in a counterclockwise direction.

Now consider a moving point whose position $z = z(t)$ at each instant t is given by

$$z(t) = \cos 4\pi t + i \sin 4\pi t, \qquad 0 \leq t \leq 1. \tag{2.10.3}$$

Then as t varies from 0 to 1, the point will travel around the unit circle twice in a counterclockwise direction.

Although the locus of the traveling point, namely, the set of points on the unit circle, is the same in (2.10.2) as in (2.10.3), the path is said to be different in each case. For, in (2.10.2) the point traverses the unit circle once, whereas in (2.10.3) the unit circle is traversed twice. If we now let C_1 and C_2 denote, respectively, the mappings of the interval $[0, 1]$ given by (2.10.2) and (2.10.3), then even though the image of the interval $[0, 1]$, namely, the set of points on the unit circle, is the same in both cases, nevertheless the mappings C_1 and C_2 are considered to represent different curves.

Consider, however, the path traced by a moving point during the time $0 \leq t \leq 2$, whose position at each instant t is given by

$$z(t) = \cos 2\pi t + i \sin 2\pi t, \qquad 0 \leq t \leq 2. \tag{2.10.3'}$$

---

* Here and in the sequel the curves under consideration are understood to be continuous, except where the context clearly indicates otherwise.

It is clear that although the motion of the traveling point given in (2.10.3) is different from that in (2.10.3)′, the path traced by the moving point is the same in both cases, namely, in each case the unit circle is traversed twice in the counterclockwise direction. We say that the mappings given by (2.10.3) and (2.10.3)′ represent the same continuous curve.

More generally, a point traveling during the time interval I: $\alpha \leq t \leq \beta$ according to the law $z = C(t)$, and a point traveling during the time interval I': $\alpha' \leq t' \leq \beta'$ according to the law $z = C'(t')$, are said to *describe the same path* if for every t_1 and t_2 in I with $t_1 < t_2$, there correspond points t_1' and t_2' in I' such that (a) $t_1' < t_2'$, (b) $C(t_1) = C'(t_1')$, (c) $C(t_2) = C'(t_2')$ and (d) the correspondence between the set of points t in I and the set of points t' in I' is one-to-one.

Equivalently, if the continuous mappings C and C' map respectively, the closed intervals I: $\alpha \leq t \leq \beta$ and I': $\alpha' \leq t' \leq \beta'$ into the plane, then C and C' are said to *represent the same curve*, if there exists a topological mapping T of I onto I' with $T(\alpha) = \alpha'$ and $T(\beta) = \beta'$ such that C is the product of the mapping T followed by the mapping C', that is, $C = C'T$.

The mappings $\mathscr{R}$ and $\mathscr{I}$ which respectively assign to every point $z = x + iy$ in the plane the real numbers $x = \mathscr{R}(z)$ and $y = \mathscr{I}(z)$ are clearly continuous. Hence, the product mappings $\mathscr{R}C$ and $\mathscr{I}C$ which assign to every point t in I the points $x = \mathscr{R}[C(t)]$ and $y = \mathscr{I}[C(t)]$ are also continuous. The image points of t under these mappings are usually denoted by

$$x = x(t) \quad \text{and} \quad y = y(t). \tag{2.10.4}$$

Definition 2.10.1. Let C be a continuous mapping of the closed interval $I = [t_1, t_2]$ into the plane. Let t_0 be any point in I, and let $z_0 = C(t_0)$ be the image of t_0. Then by a *neighborhood of z_0 along the curve C*, we mean the set of all $z = C(t)$, with t in a neighborhood $N(t_0)$ of t_0 with respect to the interval I. (See Fig. 2.10.1.)

Definition 2.10.2. Let C be a continuous mapping of the closed interval $I = [\alpha, \beta]$ into the plane. Let $\alpha = t_0 < t_1 < t_2 < \cdots < t_n = \beta$ be a sub-

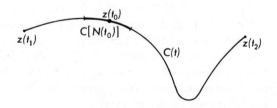

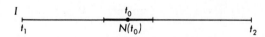

FIG. 2.10.1. Neighborhood Along a Curve.

division of I, and let I_k denote the closed intervals $[t_{k-1}, t_k]$, $k = 1, 2, \cdots, n$. Suppose that C maps each interval I_k onto a line segment. Then the curve respresented by the mapping C is said to be a *polygonal curve* or a *polygonal line*.

In the following theorem we shall prove a characteristic property of open connected sets which is often used to define a domain.

———*THEOREM* 2.10.1.   An open set D is a domain if, and only if, any two points in D can be joined by a polygonal line lying in D.

Proof.   Suppose that any two points in D can be joined by a polygonal line lying in D. Let z_0 be a fixed point in D. Then D is the union of all polygonal lines in D joining z_0 to the points of D. Each such polygonal line is a connected set. (See Exercise 2.10.2.) Since the union of a family of connected sets having a common point z_0 is also connected (see Exercise 2.2.9), it follows that D is connected.

Conversely, suppose that D is a domain and let z_1 be any point in D. We shall show that any other point z in D can be joined to z_1 by a polygonal line in D. For, suppose to the contrary, that there is some point z_2 in D which cannot be joined to z_1 by a polygonal line in D. Let D_1 and D_2 denote, respectively, the set of all points in D which can and which cannot be joined to z_1. (The point z_1 itself will belong to D_1.) It is not difficult to see (see Exercise 2.10.6) that if a point z in D can be joined to z_1 by means of a polygonal line in D, then there exists a neighborhood $N(z)$ of z, contained in D, such that every point of $N(z)$ can be joined to z_1 by a polygonal line in D. In other words, if a point z belongs to D_1, then there exists a neighborhood $N(z)$ of z such that all points in $N(z)$ are in D_1. It follows that D_1 contains no accumulation points of D_2. Similarly, if a point z belongs to D_2, then there is a neighborhood $N(z)$ of z such that all points in $N(z)$ are in D_2. It follows that D_2 contains no accumulation points of D_1. Thus D is separated (in the sense of Definition 2.2.3) into the sets D_1 and D_2. Since D is a connected set, this is not possible. Hence, all points in D can be joined by a polygonal line in D to the point z_1. Since z_1 is an arbitrary point in D, the theorem is established.

The following lemma will be found useful and the proof will be left as an exercise for the reader. (See Exercise 2.10.8.)

LEMMA 2.10.1.   Let C: $z = z(t)$, where t is in the closed interval $I = [\alpha, \beta]$, represent a continuous curve. Let each $z = z(t)$, t in I, be contained in some domain D_t (where the D_t are not necessarily all distinct). Then there exists a finite subfamily $D_{t_j}, j = 1, 2, \cdots, k$ of $\{D_t\}$ where the intersections $D_{t_j} \cap D_{t_{j+1}}$ are not empty, and a subdivision of I given by: $\alpha = t_0' < t_1' < \cdots < t_k' = \beta$ such that if Γ_j denotes the curve given by $z = z(t)$, $t_{j-1}' \leq t \leq t_j'$, then Γ_j is contained in D_{t_j}.

EXERCISES 2.10

1. Let $z_0 = C(t_0)$ be a point on the curve represented by the continuous mapping C, and let $N(z_0)$ be a neighborhood of z_0 in the plane [that is, $N(z_0)$ is the set of all z such that $|z - z_0| < \epsilon$, $\epsilon > 0$]. Show that there exists a neighborhood of z_0 along the curve which is contained in $N(z_0)$.

2. Show that the set of all points z on a continuous curve is connected.

3. Let $\{D_\alpha\}$ be a family of domains having in common at least one point z_0. Show that the union $\bigcup D_\alpha$ is a domain.

4. A set S in the plane is said to be *convex* if given any two points z_1 and z_2 in S, then the line segment joining z_1 to z_2 is also contained in S. Show that the interior of a circle is convex.

5. Let the interior S of a circle be contained in an open set D, and let z_1 and z_2 be any two points in S. Show that a point z_0 in D can be joined to z_1 by means of a polygonal line in D if, and only if, z_0 can also be joined to z_2 by means of a polygonal line in D.

6. Let D be an open set and let z_1 be a fixed point in D.

(a) Let z be a point in D which can be joined to z_1 by a polygonal line in D. Show that there is a neighborhood $N(z)$ of z in D such that every point in $N(z)$ can be joined to z_1 by polygonal line in D.

(b) Show that if z is in D and cannot be joined to z_1 by means of a polygonal line in D, then there is a neighborhood of z contained in D none of whose points can be joined to z_1 by means of a polygonal line in D.

7. Let C be a continuous curve given by $z = z(t)$, $\alpha \leq t \leq \beta$. Show that the set of all points of C is compact.

8. Prove Lemma 2.10.1.

2.11. SETS OF POINTS IN k-DIMENSIONAL EUCLIDEAN SPACE. By a *point* in k-dimensional Euclidean space (denoted by E_k), we mean an ordered k-tuplet of real numbers $(x_1, x_2, \cdots, x_k)$. If S is a set of points in E_k, then by a *neighborhood* of a point P^0: $(x_1^{(0)}, x_2^{(0)}, \cdots, x_k^{(0)})$ with respect to S, we mean the set of all points P: $(x_1, x_2, \cdots, x_k)$ in S such that

$$\sqrt{(x_1 - x_1^{(0)})^2 + (x_2 - x_2^{(0)})^2 + \cdots + (x_k - x_k^{(0)})^2} < \epsilon, \qquad (2.11.1)$$

for some $\epsilon > 0$.

Remark 2.11.1. Observe that for $k = 2$ we have the familiar definition of neighborhoods in the plane. The definitions in the previous sections concerning sets and sequences in the plane such as the definitions of Cauchy sequence, limit of a convergent sequence, compact sets, continuous mappings and so on, are carried over, word for word, to the case of point sets and sequences in E_k.

The only change to be made is that expressions of the type $|z - z_0|$, denoting the distance between the two points z and z_0 in the plane, are to be replaced by the distance given in (2.11.1), between the points P and P^0 in E_k. This also applies to the theorems concerning mappings, point sets, and sequences in the plane proved in the previous sections. However, some of the theorems in Section 2.6, such as those relating to division of one sequence by another, apply only to sequences of complex numbers.

In the next section, we shall be concerned with sets of points in three-dimensional Euclidean space E_3. Then a neighborhood of a point P_0: (x_0, y_0, z_0), with respect to a set S in E_3, is the set of all points P: (x, y, z) in S such that

$$\sqrt{(x - x_0)^2 + (y - y_0)^2 + (z - z_0)^2} < \epsilon, \qquad (2.11.2)$$

for some $\epsilon > 0$. That is, a neighborhood of the point P_0 with respect to S, consists of all points P in S lying within a sphere of center at P_0 and radius ϵ.

EXERCISES 2.11

1. Show that the sequence $\{P^{(n)}\}$ of points in E_k, where $P^{(n)} = (x_1^{(n)}, x_2^{(n)}, \cdots, x_k^{(n)})$, converges to a point $P^{(0)} = (x_1^{(0)}, x_2^{(0)}, \cdots, x_k^{(0)})$ in E_k if and only if

$$\lim_{n \to \infty} x_j^{(n)} = x_j^{(0)}, \qquad j = 1, 2, \cdots, k.$$

2.12. STEREOGRAPHIC PROJECTION. Consider the sphere Σ with center at $(\xi, \eta, \zeta) = (0, 0, 1/2)$, radius $1/2$, and tangent at the point S: $(0, 0, 0)$ to the plane π whose equation is $\zeta = 0$. (See Fig. 2.12.1.) Let N be the point

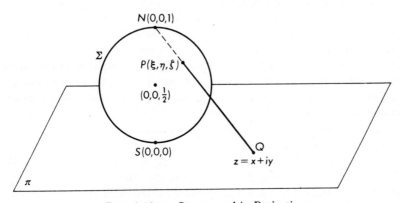

FIG. 2.12.1. Stereographic Projection.

$(0, 0, 1)$ diametrically opposite to the point of tangency S. Let P: (ξ, η, ζ) be any point on the sphere other than N. The line joining N to P will pierce the plane π at the point Q: $[\xi/(1 - \zeta), \eta/(1 - \zeta), 0]$, corresponding to the complex number $z = (\xi + \eta i)/(1 - \zeta)$. [See Exercise 2.12.2(a).] Thus the π plane can also be considered as the z plane with the x, y axes coinciding respectively with the ξ, η axes. We say that the point Q is the *projection* of the point P into the plane π. The point N is called the *center* of projection.

Conversely, any point Q: (x, y) in the plane corresponding to the complex number $z = x + iy$ lies on a line passing through the point N and intersecting the sphere at the point P whose coordinates are given by

$$\left(\frac{x}{x^2 + y^2 + 1}, \frac{y}{x^2 + y^2 + 1}, \frac{x^2 + y^2}{x^2 + y^2 + 1} \right). \qquad (2.12.1)$$

[See Exercise 2.12.2(b).]

Let T be the mapping which assigns to each point P on the punctured sphere Σ' (that is, the set of all points on Σ other than N) the point Q at which the line NP intersects the plane π. Then T maps Σ' one-to-one onto the plane π while the inverse mapping T^{-1} maps the plane π one-to-one onto the punctured sphere Σ'.

Furthermore, it is not difficult to show (see Exercise 2.12.5) that the mappings T and T^{-1} are both continuous. Thus, T is a topological mapping of Σ' onto the z plane. Under this mapping, there corresponds to every point P: (ξ, η, ζ) on the sphere a unique complex number $z = (\xi + \eta i)/(1 - \zeta)$; and vice versa, to every complex number $z = x + iy$ there corresponds the point P given by (2.12.1). Moreover, this correspondence between the points of Σ' and the set of all complex numbers is bicontinuous, that is, nearby points on Σ' will correspond to complex numbers which differ little from each other, and vice versa.

Thus, we may consider the mapping T as setting up a new coordinate system on Σ' whereby to each point P, with Euclidean coordinates (ξ, η, ζ), there is assigned the complex coordinate z given by $z = (\xi + \eta i)/(1 - \zeta)$. Consequently, the set of all complex numbers, instead of being considered as points on a plane, may be considered as points on the punctured sphere Σ'. Thus we have another geometric representation of the complex numbers. In view of this representation, we may define a *spherical neighborhood* of a complex number z_0, represented on Σ' by the point P_0, as being the set of all complex numbers represented by the points of Σ' which lie within a spherical cap of radius ϵ and center at P_0.

As in Definition 2.3.2, we shall say that a sequence of complex numbers $\{z_n\}$ approaches the limit z_0, if, given any spherical neighborhood $N(z_0)$ of z_0, there exists an integer K such that z_n is in $N(z_0)$ when $n > K$. It is not difficult to see (see Exercise 2.12.6) that $z_n \to z_0$ in the above sense if, and only if, $z_n \to z_0$ in the sense of Definition 2.3.2. We say that this system of neighborhoods is equivalent to the system of neighborhoods given in Definition 2.2.1.

It is geometrically evident (see also Exercise 2.12.10) that a sequence of points $\{P_n\}$ on the punctured sphere Σ' converges to the point $N(0, 0, 1)$ if, and only if, $z_n \to \infty$, where z_n are the complex numbers represented by the points P_n. Thus, it is natural to say that the point $N(0, 0, 1)$ has the coordinate $z = \infty$.

It is also geometrically evident (see also Exercise 2.12.9) that for any number $M > 0$, the set of all complex numbers z with $|z| > M$ corresponds to the set of all points on Σ' lying in a neighborhood V of $N(0, 0, 1)$. Consequently, a *neighborhood* of $z = \infty$ consists of all complex numbers z such that $|z| > M$, $M > 0$. Thus, in addition to the ordinary complex numbers, we have by means of the spherical representation, arrived at an additional number $z = \infty$, whose neighborhoods are given by $|z| > M$, $M > 0$. This number cannot be considered a member of the set of all complex numbers as far as the algebraic operations of addition, subtraction, multiplication, and division are concerned; however, it can serve as the limit of a sequence of complex numbers $\{z_n\}$. This happens when $|z_n|$ exceeds, for sufficiently large n, any preassigned positive number.

We shall also discover in later chapters other instances where the adjoining of $z = \infty$ to the system of complex numbers leads to considerable simplification in the statement and proof of theorems. The system of complex numbers augmented with $z = \infty$ is known as the *extended complex plane*. In the spherical representation, every complex number including $z = \infty$ is represented by a point on the sphere. In the planar representation, however, only ordinary (finite) complex numbers are represented by points in the plane. The number $z = \infty$ is represented by an abstract or ideal point outside the plane. A neighborhood of $z = \infty$ consists, along with itself, of the exterior of a circle in the ordinary plane with center at the origin.

As in Definition 2.2.5, any connected set D on the sphere Σ, which is open with respect to Σ, will be called a *domain on the sphere*. The set of complex numbers corresponding to the points of a domain on the sphere will be called a *domain in the extended complex plane*. Such domains are of two types. Those that do not contain the point $z = \infty$ are clearly domains in the sense of Definition 2.2.5. (See Exercise 2.12.12.) Those that do contain the point $z = \infty$, consist of the point $z = \infty$ together with a domain, in the sense of Definition 2.2.5, containing the exterior of some circle $|z| = M$.

EXERCISES 2.12

1. Let Σ be the sphere with center at $(0, 0, 1/2)$ and radius $1/2$. Show that if (ξ, η, ζ) is any point on Σ, then $\xi^2 + \eta^2 = \zeta(1 - \zeta)$.

2. Let $N(0, 0, 1)$ and $P(\xi, \eta, \zeta)$ be points on the sphere Σ with center at $(0, 0, 1/2)$ and radius $1/2$. Let $z = x + iy$ denote the point Q at which the line NP pierces the plane $\pi: \zeta = 0$.

   (a) Show that $z = (\xi + \eta i)/(1 - \zeta)$.

   (b) Show that $\xi = \dfrac{z + \bar{z}}{2(z\bar{z} + 1)}$, $\eta = \dfrac{z - \bar{z}}{2i(z\bar{z} + 1)}$ and $\zeta = \dfrac{z\bar{z}}{z\bar{z} + 1}$.

3. Suppose that a sequence $z_n = x_n + iy_n$ in the plane converges to $z_0 = x_0 + iy_0$. Show that the sequence of points on the punctured sphere Σ'

$$\left(\frac{x_n}{x_n^2 + y_n^2 + 1} , \frac{y_n}{x_n^2 + y_n^2 + 1} , \frac{x_n^2 + y_n^2}{x_n^2 + y_n^2 + 1} \right)$$

converges to

$$\left(\frac{x_0}{x_0^2 + y_0^2 + 1} , \frac{y_0}{x_0^2 + y_0^2 + 1} , \frac{x_0^2 + y_0^2}{x_0^2 + y_0^2 + 1} \right).$$

4. Suppose that a sequence of points (ξ_n, η_n, ζ_n) on the punctured sphere Σ' converges to the point (ξ_0, η_0, ζ_0), $\zeta_0 \neq 1$. Show that the sequence of points $[\xi_n/(1 - \zeta_n), \eta_n/(1 - \zeta_n), 0]$ converges to the point $[\xi_0/(1 - \zeta_0), \eta_0/(1 - \zeta_0), 0]$.

5. Show that the mapping T of the punctured sphere Σ' onto the plane π described in this section, and the inverse mapping T^{-1} are both continuous.

6. Show that a sequence $\{z_n\}$ converges to z_0, when z_n and z_0 are regarded as points on the punctured sphere Σ' if, and only if, $\{z_n\}$ also converges to z_0, when z_n and z_0 are regarded as points in the plane π.

7. Show that if z is the complex number corresponding to the point $P(\xi, \eta, \zeta)$ on the punctured sphere Σ', then $|z| > M$ if, and only if, $(1 - \zeta) < 1/(1 + M^2)$, $M > 0$.

8. Let $P(\xi, \eta, \zeta)$ be a point on the punctured sphere Σ'. Show that the distance of P from $N(0, 0, 1)$ is equal to $\sqrt{1 - \zeta}$.

9. Show that the complex numbers $|z| > M$ correspond to the points $P(\xi, \eta, \zeta)$ on the punctured sphere Σ' lying within a spherical cap whose radius is equal to $1/(\sqrt{M^2 + 1})$, $M > 0$.

10. Let $\{z_n\}$ be a sequence of complex numbers, and let P_n be the points representing z_n on the punctured sphere Σ'. Show that $\lim_{n \to \infty} z_n = \infty$ if, and only if, the sequence of points $\{P_n\}$ converges to the point $N(0, 0, 1)$.

11. Let A be a subset of the punctured sphere Σ'. Show that A is open with respect to the sphere Σ if, and only if, A is open with respect to the punctured sphere Σ'.

12. Show that under the mapping T described in this section, a set A on the punctured sphere Σ' is connected and open with respect to the sphere Σ if, and only if, its image in the plane π is a domain.

2.13. STEREOGRAPHIC PROJECTION FROM THE POINT $S(0, 0, 0)$.

If instead of projecting the points on the sphere Σ from the point $N(0, 0, 1)$ into the plane π: $\zeta = 0$, we project them from the point $S(0, 0, 0)$ into the plane π': $\zeta = 1$, we see that to each point $P(\xi, \eta, \zeta)$ on the punctured sphere Σ'', consisting of all points on the sphere other than $S(0, 0, 0)$, there corresponds the point $(\xi/\zeta, \eta/\zeta, 1)$, which may be represented by the complex number $(\xi + \eta i)/\zeta$. Let T_1 be the mapping which assigns to each point $P(\xi, \eta, \zeta)$ on

Σ'' the complex number $(\xi + \eta i)/\zeta$. As in the previous section, it is easy to see that T_1 is a topological mapping of Σ'' onto the set of all complex numbers.

Let us also consider the mapping T_2 which assigns to each point $P(\xi, \eta, \zeta)$ on Σ'' the point $P'(\xi, -\eta, \zeta)$. Then, clearly, T_2 is a topological mapping of Σ'' onto itself. Let $T_3 = T_1 T_2$ be the mapping of Σ'' onto the set of all complex numbers obtained as follows: To each point $P(\xi, \eta, \zeta)$ on Σ'', we first assign by the mapping T_2 the point $P'(\xi, -\eta, \zeta)$; then we follow by assigning to P', by means of the mapping T_1, the complex number $(\xi - \eta i)/\zeta$. It is easy to establish (see Exercise 2.9.5) that T_3 is a topological mapping of Σ'' onto the set of all complex numbers. This allows us to introduce another coordinate system on Σ'' whereby each point P, whose Euclidean coordinates are given by (ξ, η, ζ), is assigned the coordinate $w = (\xi - \eta i)/\zeta$. The point $S(0, 0, 0)$ has no coordinate while the point $N(0, 0, 1)$ has the coordinate $w = 0$.

As in the previous section, a sequence of points $\{P_n\}$ on Σ'' converges to the point S if, and only if, for any number $K > 0$, $|w_n| > K$ for n sufficiently large. Hence, it is natural to assign to the point $S(0, 0, 0)$ the coordinate $w = \infty$. Thus, under the coordinate system introduced in this section, the roles of the points $N(0, 0, 1)$ and $S(0, 0, 0)$ are interchanged. That is, under the coordinate system given in Section 2.12, the points $S(0,0,0)$ and $N(0,0,1)$ had the respective coordinates $z = 0$ and $z = \infty$ whereas, in this section, the coordinates of $S(0, 0, 0)$ and $N(0, 0, 1)$ are $w = \infty$ and $w = 0$.

Any point $P(\xi, \eta, \zeta)$ on the sphere Σ, other than $N(0, 0, 1)$ and $S(0, 0, 0)$, is contained both in Σ' and Σ'' and thus has the coordinate $z = (\xi + \eta i)/(1 - \zeta)$ as well as $w = (\xi - \eta i)/\zeta$. It is easily seen (Exercise 2.12.1) that $wz = 1$. Hence $w = 1/z$ and $z = 1/w$.

EXERCISES 2.13

1. Show that under the stereographic mappings described in Sections 2.12 and 2.13:
   (a) angles are preserved; that is, the mappings are *isogonal;* and
   (b) circles on the sphere Σ are mapped into circles and straight lines in the extended complex plane.

2. Verify that the complex numbers form a commutative group under addition; and the non zero complex numbers form a commutative group under multiplication.

   Note, further, that by (1.1.6), multiplication of complex numbers is distributive with respect to addition. Thus, the complex numbers form what is known as a *field*. The complex numbers also form a *division algebra* of order two over the field of real numbers.

3

(Single-valued)
Analytic Functions
of a Complex Variable

3.1. FUNCTIONS OF A COMPLEX VARIABLE

Definition 3.1.1.   Let D be an arbitrary nonempty point set of the complex plane. If z is allowed to denote any point of D, then z is called a *complex variable* and D is called the *domain* of variation* or *domain of definition* of z.

Definition 3.1.2.   We say that w is a *complex* or *complex-valued function* of the complex variable z with domain of definition D and range of values R if D and R are two nonempty point sets of the complex plane; if to each point z of D there corresponds at least one point w of R; and if for each point w of R there is at least one point z of D to which w corresponds. The symbolic notation

$$w = f(z) \tag{3.1.1}$$

then indicates that w is a function of z. We call z and w the *independent* and *dependent variable*, respectively. In case no two points of R correspond to the same point of D, $f(z)$ is called *single-valued*.

We would like to remark that in case R consists of just one point, $f(z)$ is called a *constant function*.

Remark 3.1.1.   A complex function $f(z)$ of the complex variable z can be regarded as a sort of machine which when a complex number z is fed into it, delivers at least one complex number $f(z)$. A single-valued function $f(z)$ with domain of definition D and range R is the same thing as a mapping of the set D onto R. (See Section 2.9.)

---

* *Domain of variation* and *domain of definition* are to be distinguished from *domain* which designates an open connected set. (See Definition 2.2.5.)

66

Examples of single-valued functions:

$$w_1 = z^3, \qquad w_2 = \frac{z+1}{z-4}, \qquad w_3 = \frac{z-1}{z^2}, \qquad w_4 = \bar{z}, \qquad w_5 = |z|^2.$$

The functions w_1, w_4, and w_5 are defined for all values of z, whereas w_2 and w_3 are not defined* for $z = 4$ and $z = 0$, respectively. In accordance with Definition 3.1.2, we see that the function $w_1 = z^3$ has for its domain of definition D the entire complex plane, and for its range of values R also the entire complex plane. For the function $w_2 = (z+1)/(z-4)$, D is the entire complex plane except the point $z = 4$, and R is the entire complex plane except the point $w_2 = 1$.

Remark 3.1.2.   A complex function $w = f(z)$ may also be written in the form

$$w = f(z) = u(z) + iv(z), \tag{3.1.2}$$

where $u(z)$ and $v(z)$ are real valued functions of the complex variable z, and are equal, respectively, to the real and imaginary parts of $f(z)$. Letting $z = x + iy$, we see that w, u, and v may also be regarded as functions of a pair of real variables (x, y). For, if x and y are given, then the value of z and consequently also the values of $f(z)$, $u(z)$, and $v(z)$ are determined. Hence we may write

$$w = f(z) = u(x, y) + iv(x, y). \tag{3.1.3}$$

EXAMPLE 3.1.1.   Let us determine $u(x, y)$ and $v(x, y)$ when

$$f(z) = z^2 + 3z + 4.$$

Solution. $u(x, y) + iv(x, y) = f(z) = (x + iy)^2 + 3(x + iy) + 4$. Hence

$$u(x, y) = x^2 - y^2 + 3x + 4, \qquad v(x, y) = 2xy + 3y.$$

3.2.   LIMITS OF FUNCTIONS

Definition 3.2.1.   Let $w = f(z)$ be a single-valued function defined in a domain† D except perhaps at the point z_0 of D. We say that the *limit of the*

---

* Except where the context indicates otherwise, we only consider functions whose domain and range are contained in the finite complex plane; that is, the set of all finite complex numbers; and phrases such as *all z* or the *entire complex plane* refer to the finite complex plane. However, if we regard w_2 and w_3, in the examples above, as functions with values in the extended complex plane (see Section 2.12), then they may also be defined for $z = 4$ and $z = 0$, respectively. At times, we shall explicitly state that the complex numbers under consideration are finite valued.

† The definitions and theorems in Sections 3.2 and 3.3 relating to limits and continuity in domains are essentially the same for sets of complex numbers other than domains.

function $f(z)$ as z approaches z_0 equals w_0, and we write

$$\lim_{z \to z_0} f(z) = w_0 \quad \text{or} \quad f(z) \to w_0 \text{ as } z \to z_0$$

if, for every $\epsilon > 0$, there exists a number $\delta > 0$ such that

$$|f(z) - w_0| < \epsilon \tag{3.2.1}$$

when $0 < |z - z_0| < \delta$.

If no such w_0 exists, we shall say that $\lim_{z \to z_0} f(z)$ *does not exist.*

Remark 3.2.1. *If a limit exists, it is unique.* For suppose that

$$\lim_{z \to z_0} f(z) = w_1 \quad \text{and} \quad \lim_{z \to z_0} f(z) = w_2.$$

Then, given any $\epsilon > 0$, there exist $\delta_1 > 0$, $\delta_2 > 0$ such that

$$|f(z) - w_1| < \frac{\epsilon}{2} \quad \text{when} \quad 0 < |z - z_0| < \delta_1,$$

$$|f(z) - w_2| < \frac{\epsilon}{2} \quad \text{when} \quad 0 < |z - z_0| < \delta_2.$$

Hence, for $\delta = \min(\delta_1, \delta_2)$, we obtain

$$
\begin{aligned}
|w_2 - w_1| &= |[f(z) - w_1] - [f(z) - w_2]| \\
&\leq |f(z) - w_1| + |f(z) - w_2| \\
&< \epsilon \text{ when } 0 < |z - z_0| < \delta.
\end{aligned}
$$

Since ϵ is any arbitrarily small positive number, it follows that $|w_2 - w_1| = 0$, that is, $w_2 = w_1$.

EXAMPLE 3.2.1.   Let us show that

$$\lim_{z \to 2i} \frac{z^2 + 4}{z - 2i} = 4i.$$

Solution.   Observe that the function $f(z) = (z^2 + 4)/(z - 2i)$ is defined everywhere except at $z = 2i$. Definition 3.2.1 does not require that $f(z)$ be defined at $z = 2i$. All that matters is what happens to $f(z)$ when z is sufficiently close to $2i$. Thus, for $z \neq 2i$, we have

$$|f(z) - 4i| = |z - 2i|.$$

If we take $0 < |z - 2i| < \epsilon = \delta$, we obtain

$$|f(z) - 4i| < \epsilon \quad \text{when} \quad 0 < |z - 2i| < \delta.$$

Hence

$$\lim_{z \to 2i} \frac{z^2 + 4}{z - 2i} = 4i.$$

The following theorem will give us a useful criterion for a function to have a limit.

——**THEOREM** 3.2.1.   Let $w = f(z) = u(z) + iv(z)$ be   defined   in   a domain D except possibly at the point z_0 of D. Then

$$\lim_{z \to z_0} f(z) = w_0 \equiv u_0 + iv_0 \tag{3.2.2}$$

if and only if

$$\lim_{z \to z_0} u(z) = u_0, \qquad \lim_{z \to z_0} v(z) = v_0. \tag{3.2.3}$$

Proof.   Suppose that the limit (3.2.2) exists. From Definition 3.2.1 we have

$$|f(z) - w_0| < \epsilon \quad \text{when} \quad 0 < |z - z_0| < \delta.$$

This relation may be written as

$$|(u - u_0) + i(v - v_0)| < \epsilon \quad \text{when} \quad 0 < |z - z_0| < \delta.$$

Using (1.4.2) we obtain

$$|u(z) - u_0| < \epsilon, \qquad |v(z) - v_0| < \epsilon \quad \text{when} \quad 0 < |z - z_0| < \delta.$$

Expressed in the form of limits, these relations are

$$\lim_{z \to z_0} u(z) = u_0, \qquad \lim_{z \to z_0} v(z) = v_0.$$

Now, suppose that the two limits (3.2.3) exist. Then

$$|u(z) - u_0| < \frac{\epsilon}{2} \quad \text{when} \quad 0 < |z - z_0| < \delta_1,$$

$$|v(z) - v_0| < \frac{\epsilon}{2} \quad \text{when} \quad 0 < |z - z_0| < \delta_2.$$

Letting $\delta = \min(\delta_1, \delta_2)$, we have utilizing (1.3.9)

$$|f(z) - w_0| \leq |u(z) - u_0| + |v(z) - v_0| < \epsilon \quad \text{when} \quad 0 < |z - z_0| < \delta.$$

Expressing this result in terms of a limit, we have

$$\lim_{z \to z_0} f(z) = w_0,$$

as the theorem requires.

Remark 3.2.2.   According to the definition of a limit of a real function of two real variables [see W. Kaplan, *Advanced Calculus*, page 76 (Reading: Addison-Wesley, 1957)] condition (3.2.3) can be written as

$$\lim_{\substack{x \to x_0 \\ y \to y_0}} u(x, y) = u_0, \qquad \lim_{\substack{x \to x_0 \\ y \to y_0}} v(x, y) = v_0, \tag{3.2.4}$$

and means that given any $\epsilon > 0$, there exists a number $\delta > 0$ such that

$$| u(x, y) - u_0 | < \epsilon \quad \text{and} \quad | v(x, y) - v_0 | < \epsilon$$

$$\text{when } 0 < \sqrt{(x - x_0)^2 + (y - y_0)^2} < \delta. \tag{3.2.5}$$

Thus, one may use the properties of limits of a real function of two real variables to study the properties of limits of a function of a complex variable.

We shall now establish the following useful

——THEOREM 3.2.2.

$$\lim_{z \to z_0} (\alpha z + \beta) = \alpha z_0 + \beta \qquad (\alpha, \beta \text{ constants}). \tag{3.2.6}$$

In particular

$$\lim_{z \to z_0} \beta = \beta, \tag{3.2.7}$$

$$\lim_{z \to z_0} z = z_0. \tag{3.2.8}$$

Proof.   Suppose first that $\alpha \neq 0$. Then for every $\epsilon > 0$

$$| (\alpha z + \beta) - (\alpha z_0 + \beta) | < \epsilon$$

provided that

$$| z - z_0 | < \frac{\epsilon}{| \alpha |}.$$

Thus, for $\delta = \epsilon / | \alpha |$, we have

$$| (\alpha z + \beta) - (\alpha z_0 + \beta) | < \epsilon \quad \text{when} \quad 0 < | z - z_0 | < \delta,$$

from which (3.2.6) now follows for the case when $\alpha \neq 0$.

If $\alpha = 0$, then $(\alpha z + \beta) - (\alpha z_0 + \beta) = 0$ for every z. Thus, for any $\delta > 0$, we have

$$| (\alpha z + \beta) - (\alpha z_0 + \beta) | < \epsilon \quad \text{when} \quad 0 < | z - z_0 | < \delta,$$

from which (3.2.6) now follows for the case when $\alpha = 0$.

Letting $\alpha = 0$ in (3.2.6), we obtain (3.2.7).

Letting $\alpha = 1$ and $\beta = 0$ in (3.2.6), we obtain (3.2.8).

——**THEOREM** 3.2.3. If $\lim_{z \to z_0} f(z) = w_0$ and $\lim_{z \to z_0} F(z) = W_0$, then

$$\lim_{z \to z_0} [f(z) + F(z)] = w_0 + W_0, \tag{3.2.9}$$

$$\lim_{z \to z_0} [f(z) - F(z)] = w_0 - W_0, \tag{3.2.10}$$

$$\lim_{z \to z_0} [f(z) F(z)] = w_0 W_0, \tag{3.2.11}$$

$$\lim_{z \to z_0} kf(z) = kw_0 \quad (k \text{ constant}), \tag{3.2.12}$$

$$\lim_{z \to z_0} \frac{f(z)}{F(z)} = \frac{w_0}{W_0} \quad (W_0 \neq 0). \tag{3.2.13}$$

Proof. Concerning (3.2.9). Let $\epsilon > 0$ be given. Then for some $\delta_1 > 0$ and $\delta_2 > 0$, we have (see Definition 3.2.1)

$$|f(z) - w_0| < \frac{\epsilon}{2} \quad \text{when} \quad 0 < |z - z_0| < \delta_1,$$

$$|F(z) - W_0| < \frac{\epsilon}{2} \quad \text{when} \quad 0 < |z - z_0| < \delta_2.$$

Letting $\delta = \min(\delta_1, \delta_2)$, we have utilizing (1.3.9)

$$|[f(z) + F(z)] - (w_0 + W_0)| \leq |f(z) - w_0| + |F(z) - W_0| < \epsilon$$

when $0 < |z - z_0| < \delta$, from which (3.2.9) now follows.

Concerning (3.2.11). We observe that

$$f(z) F(z) - w_0 W_0 = [F(z) - W_0][f(z) - w_0]$$
$$+ W_0[f(z) - w_0] + w_0[F(z) - W_0].$$

Now, given any $\epsilon > 0$, there exists a $\delta > 0$ such that when $0 < |z - z_0| < \delta$, we have

$$|F(z) - W_0| < \min\left[1, \frac{\epsilon}{3(|w_0| + 1)}\right] \quad \text{and} \quad |f(z) - w_0| < \frac{\epsilon}{3(|W_0| + 1)}.$$

Hence by Theorems 1.3.4 and 1.3.2 we have

$$|f(z) F(z) - w_0 W_0| \leq |F(z) - W_0||f(z) - w_0| + |W_0||f(z) - w_0|$$
$$+ |w_0||F(z) - W_0| < 1 \cdot \frac{\epsilon}{3(|W_0| + 1)}$$
$$+ |W_0| \frac{\epsilon}{3(|W_0| + 1)} + |w_0| \frac{\epsilon}{3(|w_0| + 1)}$$
$$< \frac{\epsilon}{3} + \frac{\epsilon}{3} + \frac{\epsilon}{3} = \epsilon \quad \text{when} \quad 0 < |z - z_0| < \delta,$$

from which (3.2.11) now follows.

From (3.2.11) and (3.2.7), (3.2.12) now follows.

Write $f(z) - F(z) = f(z) + (-1) F(z)$. Using (3.2.9) and (3.2.12), (3.2.10) now follows.

Concerning (3.2.13). This result may be established by showing that if $\lim_{z \to z_0} F(z) = W_0 \neq 0$, then $\lim_{z \to z_0} 1/F(z) = 1/W_0 \neq 0$ and then applying (3.2.11). Let $\lim_{z \to z_0} F(z) = W_0 \neq 0$. It follows that given an $\epsilon > 0$, there exists a $\delta > 0$ such that if $0 < |z - z_0| < \delta$, then

$$|F(z) - W_0| < \min \left(\frac{|W_0|}{2}, \frac{\epsilon |W_0|^2}{2} \right).$$

Consequently, when $0 < |z - z_0| < \delta$, we have

$$|F(z)| = |W_0 + [F(z) - W_0]| \geqq |W_0| - |F(z) - W_0|$$

$$> |W_0| - \frac{|W_0|}{2} = \frac{|W_0|}{2}.$$

Hence, when $0 < |z - z_0| < \delta$, we see that

$$\left| \frac{1}{F(z)} - \frac{1}{W_0} \right| = \frac{|W_0 - F(z)|}{|F(z)| \, |W_0|} < \frac{|W_0 - F(z)|}{(|W_0|/2) \, |W_0|} < \frac{\epsilon |W_0|^2/2}{|W_0|^2/2} = \epsilon.$$

Utilizing (3.2.11), (3.2.13) may now be established.

Remark 3.2.3. Let the polynomial $P(z)$ be given by

$$P(z) = a_0 + a_1 z + a_2 z^2 + \cdots + a_n z^n.$$

It follows from (3.2.7) and Theorem 3.2.3 that

$$\lim_{z \to z_0} P(z) = P(z_0). \qquad (3.2.14)$$

3.3. CONTINUITY

Definition 3.3.1. The function $w = f(z)$ defined in a domain D is said to be *continuous at the point* z_0 in D if

$$\lim_{z \to z_0} f(z) = f(z_0). \qquad (3.3.1)$$

Observe that this definition essentially asserts three conditions, namely:

$$f(z_0) \text{ is defined,}$$

$$\lim_{z \to z_0} f(z) \text{ exists,} \qquad (3.3.2)$$

$$\lim_{z \to z_0} f(z) = f(z_0).$$

We see that $f(z)$ is continuous at a point z_0 in D if, and only if, for every $\epsilon > 0$, there exists a number $\delta > 0$ such that

$$|f(z) - f(z_0)| < \epsilon \qquad (3.3.3)$$

for all points z interior to D satisfying $|z - z_0| < \delta$. Observe that the number δ depends on ϵ and also, in general, upon z_0.

Definition 3.3.2. A function is said to be *continuous in a domain* D if it is continuous at all points of D.

Observe that if $f(z)$ is a continuous complex-valued function in a domain D^*, then it is, of course, single-valued and forms a continuous mapping of the domain D into the complex plane. (See Remark 3.1.1 and Section 2.9.)

Utilizing Theorem 3.2.3, one may readily establish the following

—**THEOREM** 3.3.1. If the functions $f(z)$ and $F(z)$ are defined in a domain D and are continuous at the point z_0 in D, then

$$f(z) + F(z), \qquad (3.3.4)$$
$$f(z) - F(z), \qquad (3.3.5)$$
$$f(z) F(z), \qquad (3.3.6)$$
$$kf(z) \qquad (k \text{ constant}), \qquad (3.3.7)$$
$$f(z)/F(z) \qquad [F(z_0) \neq 0], \qquad (3.3.8)$$

are also continuous at the point z_0.

Remark 3.3.1. From (3.2.14) it follows that

$$P(z) = a_0 + a_1 z + a_2 z^2 + \cdots + a_n z^n$$

is continuous at any point z_0. Any rational function

$$\frac{P(z)}{Q(z)},$$

where $P(z)$ and $Q(z)$ are polynomials, is continuous at any point z_0 provided that $Q(z_0) \neq 0$.

—**THEOREM** 3.3.2. If $f(z)$ is continuous and has the value w_0 at the point z_0 and if $F(w)$ is continuous at w_0, then $F[f(z)]$ is continuous at z_0.

Proof. Since $F(w)$ is continuous at w_0, for every $\epsilon > 0$, there exists $\epsilon' > 0$ such that

$$|F(w) - F(w_0)| < \epsilon \quad \text{when} \quad |w - w_0| < \epsilon'.$$

* We ordinarily say that functions have properties *on* a set S but *in* a domain D.

Also, since $f(z)$ is continuous at z_0, there exists a $\delta > 0$ such that

$$|f(z) - w_0| < \epsilon' \quad \text{when} \quad |z - z_0| < \delta.$$

Letting $w = f(z)$, we obtain from the above inequalities,

$$|F[f(z)] - F[f(z_0)]| < \epsilon \quad \text{when} \quad |z - z_0| < \delta,$$

from which it follows that $F[f(z)]$ is continuous at z_0.

Thus we see that a continuous function of a continuous function is continuous.

——**THEOREM** 3.3.3. Let $f(z)$ be defined in a domain D and let $f(z)$ be continuous at the point z_0 of D. Then

$$\lim_{n \to \infty} f(z_n) = f(z_0)$$

for every sequence $\{z_n\}$ in D converging to z_0.

Proof. Since $f(z)$ is continuous at z_0, we have from (3.3.3)

$$|f(z) - f(z_0)| < \epsilon \quad \text{when} \quad |z - z_0| < \delta.$$

Since the sequence $\{z_n\}$ converges to z_0, we have from Definition 2.3.2

$$|z_n - z_0| < \delta \quad \text{for} \quad n > N.$$

Hence

$$|f(z_n) - f(z_0)| < \epsilon \quad \text{for} \quad n > N,$$

from which it follows that $f(z_n)$ converges to $f(z_0)$.

Definition 3.3.3. A function $f(z)$ defined in a domain D is said to be *uniformly continuous* in D if for every $\epsilon > 0$, there exists a $\delta = \delta(\epsilon) > 0$ such that for all z_1 and z_2 in D

$$|f(z_1) - f(z_2)| < \epsilon \tag{3.3.9}$$

when $|z_1 - z_2| < \delta$.

——**THEOREM** 3.3.4. Let $f(z)$ be continuous on a compact set R, then $f(z)$ is uniformly continuous on R.

Proof. We shall establish the proof by assuming the contrary to be true and show that this leads to a contradiction. Thus, assume that $f(z)$ is continuous on a compact set R, but fails to be uniformly continuous there. Then there exists an $\epsilon > 0$ such that for each $\delta > 0$, there exist two points z and ζ belonging to R so that

$$|z - \zeta| < \delta \quad \text{and} \quad |f(z) - f(\zeta)| \geq \epsilon.$$

Letting $\delta = 1/2, 1/3, \cdots, 1/n, \cdots$, we get two sequences of points in R: $\{z_n\}$ and $\{\zeta_n\}$ such that

$$|z_n - \zeta_n| < \frac{1}{n} \quad \text{and} \quad |f(z_n) - f(\zeta_n)| \geq \epsilon. \tag{3.3.10}$$

Since the set R is bounded and closed, we see by Theorem 2.5.2 (see also Exercise 2.5.7) that the sequence $\{z_n\}$ has an accumulation point z_0 in R. Therefore, by Exercise 2.3.1 we may pick a subsequence $\{z'_m\}$ which converges to z_0. Let $\{\zeta'_m\}$ be the corresponding subsequence of $\{\zeta_n\}$. Now

$$|z_0 - \zeta'_m| \leq |z_0 - z'_m| + |z'_m - \zeta'_m|. \tag{3.3.11}$$

Since $z'_m \to z_0$, we have $|z_0 - z'_m| \to 0$. Also, from (3.3.10), we have $|z'_m - \zeta'_m| \to 0$. It follows by (3.3.11) that $|z_0 - \zeta'_m| \to 0$ and thus $\zeta'_m \to z_0$. Now

$$|f(z'_m) - f(\zeta'_m)| \leq |f(z'_m) - f(z_0)| + |f(z_0) - f(\zeta'_m)|. \tag{3.3.12}$$

Since $f(z)$ is continuous at z_0, we see by Theorem 3.3.3 that the right-hand members of (3.3.12) both approach zero as $m \to \infty$. Hence

$$|f(z'_m) - f(\zeta'_m)| \to 0 \quad \text{as} \quad m \to \infty,$$

contradicting the statement made in (3.3.10) asserting that

$$|f(z'_m) - f(\zeta'_m)| \geq \epsilon \quad \text{for all } m.$$

Thus $f(z)$ is uniformly continuous on R, and the theorem is established.

We shall illustrate the differences between continuity and uniform continuity of a function $f(z)$ defined on a set R by the following examples.

EXAMPLE 3.3.1.   Let R consist of the set of all points z such that $0 < |z| \leq 1$. Let $f(z) = 1/z$ for each value of z belonging to R. Clearly $f(z)$ is continuous on R; however, we shall now show that $f(z)$ is not uniformly continuous on R. Suppose for definiteness we take $\epsilon = 1/10$ and that a δ, $0 < \delta < 1$, can be found in accordance with Definition 3.3.3. We choose two points of R to be $z_1 = \delta$ and $z_2 = (9/10)\delta$. Thus

$$|z_1 - z_2| = |\delta - \frac{9}{10}\delta| = \frac{\delta}{10} < \delta.$$

For these two points we have

$$|f(z_1) - f(z_2)| = \left|\frac{1}{\delta} - \frac{10}{9\delta}\right| = \frac{1}{9\delta} > \frac{1}{10},$$

since $0 < \delta < 1$, thus contradicting the definition of uniform continuity.

EXAMPLE 3.3.2.   Suppose that the set R is the same as in Example 3.3.1. Let $f(z) = z^2$. We shall verify that $f(z)$ is uniformly continuous on R. For z_1 and z_2 belonging to R, we have

$$| f(z_1) - f(z_2) | = | z_1^2 - z_2^2 | = | z_1 + z_2 | \, | z_1 - z_2 | \leqq 2 \, | z_1 - z_2 |,$$

since $0 < |z| \leqq 1$. If we take $\delta = \epsilon/2$, then for any two points z_1, z_2 of R such that $| z_1 - z_2 | < \delta$, we will always have

$$| f(z_1) - f(z_2) | < \epsilon.$$

Thus $f(z) = z^2$ is uniformly continuous on R.

Definition 3.3.4.   Let $f(z)$ be defined in a domain D except possibly at the point z_0 of D. If, for any positive number N, a positive number δ can be found such that

$$| f(z) | > N \quad \text{when} \quad 0 < | z - z_0 | < \delta, \tag{3.3.13}$$

then $f(z)$ is said to *tend to the limit infinity* as z tends to z_0, and we write

$$\lim_{z \to z_0} f(z) = \infty \text{ or } f(z) \to \infty \text{ as } z \to z_0. \tag{3.3.14}$$

EXAMPLE 3.3.3.

$$\lim_{z \to 1} \frac{1}{z - 1} = \infty.$$

EXERCISES 3.3

In Exercises 1-8 determine the set of values of z where the given function is continuous.

1. $w = z^3 - 2z + 1.$

2. $w = \dfrac{z}{z - 4}.$

3. $w = \dfrac{z + 4i}{z^2 + 1}.$

4. $w = \mathscr{I}(z^2).$

5. $w = \bar{z} + 2i.$

6. $w = \dfrac{z^2 + 2z + 3}{(z - 1)(z^2 + 9)}.$

7. $w = | z + i |.$

8. $w = \mathscr{R}\left(\dfrac{z}{z + 1}\right).$

In Exercises 9-16 decompose the given complex-valued function into its real and imaginary parts expressed as functions of x and y.

9. $w = z^3 - 2z.$

10. $w = yz + iy.$

11. $w = \dfrac{1}{z}$.

12. $w = \dfrac{1}{z+1}$.

13. $w = 2z^2 - z + 1$.

14. $w = \dfrac{z-1}{z+1}$.

15. $w = \dfrac{1}{z^2}$.

16. $w = \dfrac{z}{z^2-1}$.

In Exercises 17-19, find an explicit function $\delta = \delta(\epsilon)$ in conformity with the definition of uniform continuity.

17. $f(z) = z^2 - 1$, $|z| \le 4$.

18. $f(z) = \dfrac{1}{z}$, $|z| \ge 1$.

19. $f(z) = z^3 + 1$, $|z| \le 3$.

20. Consider the function defined by the equations

$$f(z) = \frac{[\mathscr{R}(z^2)]^2}{|z^2|} \quad \text{if} \quad z \neq 0, \quad \text{and} \quad f(0) = 0.$$

Show that $f(z)$ is continuous at $z = 0$.

21. Let the domain D consist of the points interior to the unit circle $|z| = 1$. Prove that $f(z) = 1/(1-z)$ is not uniformly continuous in D.

22. Prove Theorem 3.3.1.

23. Prove that if $f(z)$ is uniformly continuous in a domain D, then $f(z)$ is continuous in D.

24. Prove that if $f(z_n)$ converges to $f(z_0)$ for every sequence $\{z_n\}$ converging to z_0, then $f(z)$ is continuous at z_0.

25. Prove that if $f(z)$ is continuous on a compact set R, then $f(z)$ is bounded on R, that is, there exists a constant M such that $|f(z)| \le M$ for all z in R.

26. Prove that if $g(z)$ is a real-valued continuous function on a compact set R, then there exist points α and β in R such that

$$g(\alpha) \le g(z) \le g(\beta) \qquad \text{for all } z \text{ in } R.$$

In case $g(z)$ is complex-valued, we have $|g(\alpha)| \le |g(z)| \le |g(\beta)|$.

27. (a) Show that if C is a closed and bounded set in the complex plane and ζ_0 is a point not in C, then there exists a point z_1 in C such that

$$|z - \zeta_0| \ge |z_1 - \zeta_0| \qquad \text{for all } z \text{ in } C.$$

(b) Prove the result in part (a) for the case where C is the set of points on a continuous curve $C: z = z(t)$, $\alpha \le t \le \beta$.

(c) Let C be a continuous curve and ζ_0 a point not on C. Show that there exists a number $\rho > 0$ such that $|z - \zeta_0| \ge \rho$ for all z on C.

28. Let S be a connected set and let $w = g(z)$ be a continuous function on S taking on integral values only. Show that $g(z)$ is constant on S.

29. Let Σ be a compact set and let z be any point in the complex plane. Denote by $\rho(z)$ the (minimum) distance from z to Σ. [If z is in Σ, then $\rho(z) = 0$.] Show that $\rho(z)$ is a continuous function of z.

30. Let S and Σ be two disjoint compact sets. Show that there exists a point z_0 in S and a point ζ_0 in Σ such that $| z - \zeta | \geq | z_0 - \zeta_0 |$ for all z in S and ζ in Σ.

31. Let Σ be a compact set and let S be a closed set disjoint from Σ. Show that there exists a point ζ_0 in Σ and a point z_0 in S such that $| z - \zeta | \geq | z_0 - \zeta_0 |$ for all ζ in Σ and all z in S.

32. Let $f(z)$ be defined on a set S and let z_0 be an accumulation point of S. Show that if

$$\lim_{\substack{\eta \to z_0 \\ \zeta \to z_0}} [f(\eta) - f(\zeta)] = 0,$$

then $\lim_{z \to z_0} f(z)$ exists.

33. Let $w = f(z)$ be a continuous one-to-one mapping of a compact set onto its image. Show that the mapping is bicontinuous.

3.4. THE DERIVATIVE OF A FUNCTION

Definition 3.4.1. Let $w = f(z)$ be a single-valued function defined in a domain D and let z_0 be any fixed point in D. Then $w = f(z)$ is said to have a derivative at the point z_0 if the following limit exists; the number $f'(z_0)$ defined by this limit is called the *derivative*:

$$\frac{df(z_0)}{dz} \equiv f'(z_0) \equiv \lim_{z \to z_0} \frac{f(z) - f(z_0)}{z - z_0} . \tag{3.4.1}$$

The above definition asserts that given any $\epsilon > 0$, there exists a number $\delta > 0$, depending upon ϵ and z_0, such that

$$\left| \frac{f(z) - f(z_0)}{z - z_0} - f'(z_0) \right| < \epsilon \tag{3.4.2}$$

when $0 < | z - z_0 | < \delta$.

Definition 3.4.2. A single-valued function is said to be *analytic (or an analytic function) in a domain D* if it has a derivative at every point in D.

Remark 3.4.1. In the sequel, functions are to be considered single-valued except when the contrary is clearly indicated.*

---

* However, for the sake of emphasis, we occasionally shall explicitly state that a given analytic function is single-valued.

A function $f(z)$ is said to be *analytic at a point* z_0 if $f(z)$ is analytic in a domain D containing z_0. A function $f(z)$ is said to be *analytic on a set* S if it is analytic at each point of S. The terms *holomorphic* and *regular* are often used in place of analytic.

——**THEOREM** 3.4.1. If $f(z)$ has a derivative at a point z_0, then $f(z)$ is continuous at z_0.

Proof. Utilizing Theorems 3.2.2 and 3.2.3, we obtain

$$\lim_{z \to z_0} [f(z) - f(z_0)] = \lim_{z \to z_0} (z - z_0) \lim_{z \to z_0} \frac{f(z) - f(z_0)}{z - z_0} = 0 \cdot f'(z_0) = 0.$$

Thus

$$\lim_{z \to z_0} f(z) = \lim_{z \to z_0} \{f(z_0) + [f(z) - f(z_0)]\} = f(z_0) + 0 = f(z_0).$$

Remark 3.4.2. The above result implies (see Exercise 3.5.11) that in the neighborhood of z_0, $f(z)$ is bounded, that is, there exists a neighborhood of z_0 and a constant M such that for z in this neighborhood, we have $|f(z)| \leq M$.

We shall now show that continuity of a function at a point z_0 does not imply that the function has a derivative at z_0. Consider the function

$$f(z) = |z|^2. \tag{3.4.3}$$

Observe that this function is continuous for all values of z, however, as we shall see, it has a derivative only at the origin. Let

$$g(z) = \frac{f(z) - f(z_0)}{z - z_0} = \frac{|z|^2 - |z_0|^2}{z - z_0}, \qquad z \neq z_0.$$

Utilizing (1.3.5) we may write $g(z)$ as

$$g(z) = \frac{z\bar{z} - z_0\bar{z}_0}{z - z_0} = \bar{z} + z_0 \left(\frac{\bar{z} - \bar{z}_0}{z - z_0} \right).$$

Let $z - z_0 = re^{i\theta}$, $r > 0$. Utilizing Theorem 1.6.2 and equation (1.6.1), we may now write $g(z)$ as

$$g(z) = \bar{z} + z_0 \frac{re^{-i\theta}}{re^{i\theta}} = \bar{z} + z_0 e^{-2i\theta} = \bar{z} + z_0(\cos 2\theta - i \sin 2\theta).$$

It is now evident that $g(z)$ does not tend to a unique limit as z approaches z_0. Thus, for instance, if $\theta = 0$, then $g(z)$ approaches the limit $\bar{z}_0 + z_0$, while if $\theta = \pi/4$, $g(z)$ approaches the limit $\bar{z}_0 - iz_0$. This is contrary to the requirement (see Remark 3.2.1) that if the limit of $g(z)$ exists it must be unique. Thus $f'(z_0)$ does not exist when $z_0 \neq 0$.

However, if $z_0 = 0$, then $g(z) = \bar{z}$ which tends to zero as z approaches 0 in any manner. Thus $f'(0)$ exists.

3.5. DIFFERENTIATION FORMULAS. The formal rules for differentiating complex functions are similar to those for real-valued functions of one variable. We shall give these rules in the following

——*THEOREM* 3.5.1.

$$\frac{dc}{dz} = 0 \qquad (c \text{ constant}), \tag{3.5.1}$$

$$\frac{dz}{dz} = 1. \tag{3.5.2}$$

If $f(z)$ and $g(z)$ are analytic functions in a domain D, then $f(z) \pm g(z)$, $f(z)\,g(z)$, $f(z)/g(z)$ $[g(z) \neq 0$ in $D]$ are analytic functions in D and

$$\frac{d}{dz}\,[f(z) \pm g(z)] = \frac{df(z)}{dz} \pm \frac{dg(z)}{dz}, \tag{3.5.3}$$

$$\frac{d}{dz}\,[f(z)\,g(z)] = f(z)\,\frac{dg(z)}{dz} + g(z)\,\frac{df(z)}{dz}, \tag{3.5.4}$$

$$\frac{d}{dz}\left[\frac{f(z)}{g(z)}\right] = \frac{g(z)\,\dfrac{df(z)}{dz} - f(z)\,\dfrac{dg(z)}{dz}}{[g(z)]^2}, \qquad [g(z) \neq 0 \text{ in } D]. \tag{3.5.5}$$

If n is a positive integer, then

$$\frac{dz^n}{dz} = nz^{n-1}. \tag{3.5.6}$$

Proof. The verification of (3.5.1) and (3.5.2) will be left as an exercise for the reader.

Verification of (3.5.3) for the sum. Take any point z_0 belonging to D. Utilizing Theorem 3.2.3 and (3.4.1) we have

$$\lim_{z \to z_0} \left\{ \frac{[f(z) + g(z)] - [f(z_0) + g(z_0)]}{z - z_0} \right\}$$

$$= \lim_{z \to z_0} \frac{f(z) - f(z_0)}{z - z_0} + \lim_{z \to z_0} \frac{g(z) - g(z_0)}{z - z_0}$$

$$= f'(z_0) + g'(z_0),$$

from which (3.5.3) now follows for the case of the sum.

Verification of (3.5.4).

$$\lim_{z \to z_0} \left[\frac{f(z)\,g(z) - f(z_0)\,g(z_0)}{z - z_0} \right]$$

$$= \lim_{z \to z_0} f(z)\,\frac{g(z) - g(z_0)}{z - z_0} + \lim_{z \to z_0} g(z_0)\,\frac{f(z) - f(z_0)}{z - z_0}$$

$$= f(z_0)\,g'(z_0) + g(z_0)\,f'(z_0),$$

from which (3.5.4) now follows.

Verification of (3.5.5). Suppose that $g(z_0) \neq 0$. Since we are assuming that $g'(z_0)$ exists, we know from Theorem 3.4.1 that $g(z)$ is continuous at z_0. It follows that for z sufficiently close to z_0, $g(z) \neq 0$ and $1/g(z)$ is finite. We further have

$$\lim_{z \to z_0} \left\{ \frac{1}{z - z_0} \left[\frac{1}{g(z)} - \frac{1}{g(z_0)} \right] \right\}$$

$$= \lim_{z \to z_0} \left\{ -\frac{1}{g(z_0)} \left[\frac{g(z) - g(z_0)}{z - z_0} \right] \frac{1}{g(z)} \right\} = -\frac{g'(z_0)}{[g(z_0)]^2},$$

from which follows that

$$\left[\frac{1}{g(z)} \right]' = -\frac{g'(z)}{[g(z)]^2} \qquad [g(z) \neq 0].$$

Since $f(z)/g(z) = f(z) \cdot 1/g(z)$, utilizing (3.5.4), (3.5.5) now follows.

Verification of (3.5.6). Observe that $z^n = z \cdot z^{n-1}$. Using mathematical induction and (3.5.4), we see that (3.5.6) now follows.

Note that the proof of Theorem 3.5.1 parallels the proof of the similar theorem for real-valued functions of a real variable.

Remark 3.5.1. Before establishing the next theorem for finding the derivative by the chain rule, we would like to make the following observation. From the definition of a derivative, it follows that a function has a derivative at $z = z_0$ if, and only if, it satisfies an equation of the form

$$f(z) - f(z_0) = (z - z_0) \left[f'(z_0) + \lambda(z) \right] \tag{3.5.7}$$

where $\lambda(z)$ is a null function, that is, it tends to zero as $z \to z_0$.

——**THEOREM** 3.5.2. If $\eta = g(z)$ is an analytic function of z in a domain D with values in a domain R and if $w = f(\eta)$ is an analytic function of η in R, then $w = f[g(z)]$ is an analytic function of z in D, and has a derivative given by the *chain rule*:

$$\frac{dw}{dz} = \frac{dw}{d\eta} \cdot \frac{d\eta}{dz}. \tag{3.5.8}$$

Proof. Let z_0 belong to D. Then $\eta_0 = g(z_0)$ belongs to R. For convenience, we let $\Delta z = z - z_0$, $\Delta g = g(z) - g(z_0)$ and

$$\Delta w = f(\eta) - f(\eta_0) = f[g(z)] - f[g(z_0)].$$

Let an arbitrary increment Δz produce an increment Δg in the function $g(z)$ while Δg in turn produces an increment Δw in the function $f(\eta)$. Since both functions have a derivative, by (3.5.7) we have

$$\Delta g = [g'(z_0) + \lambda_1] \Delta z \quad \text{and} \quad \Delta w = \{ f'[g(z_0)] + \lambda_2 \} \Delta g.$$

As $\Delta z \to 0$, $\lambda_1 \to 0$. Also by Theorem 3.4.1, $\Delta g \to 0$ and consequently $\lambda_2 \to 0$. Eliminating Δg from the above expressions, we find

$$\frac{\Delta w}{\Delta z} = \{f'[g(z_0)] + \lambda_2\}\,[g'(z_0) + \lambda_1].$$

Now utilizing Theorem 3.2.3, we obtain

$$\frac{dw}{dz}\bigg|_{z=z_0} = \lim_{\Delta z \to 0} \frac{\Delta w}{\Delta z} = f'[g(z_0)]\,g'(z_0)$$

for any z_0 belonging to D. Hence for all z in D

$$\frac{dw}{dz} = f'[g(z)]\,g'(z) = \frac{dw}{d\eta} \cdot \frac{d\eta}{dz}.$$

Remark 3.5.2.   From Theorem 3.5.1, we see that a polynomial is analytic for all values of z. A rational function, being a quotient of two polynomials, is also an analytic function in any domain D not containing zeros of the denominator.

EXERCISES 3.5

In Exercises 1-5 find dw/dz by using Theorems 3.5.1 and 3.5.2.

1. $w = 10z^4 + \dfrac{2}{3}z^3 - 8z + \dfrac{11}{2}$.

2. $w = z(z^2 - 1)^2$.

3. $w = (z^2 - 4)/(z^3 + 2z - 5)$.

4. $w = \left(z + \dfrac{1}{z}\right)^2$.

5. $w = \left(\dfrac{1}{3}z^3 - \dfrac{1}{3z^3}\right)^4$.

6. Use Definition 3.4.1 to prove formulas (3.5.1) and (3.5.2).

7. Use (3.5.7) to prove formula (3.5.4).

8. Show that the functions $w_1 = \mathscr{R}(z)$, $w_2 = \mathscr{I}(z)$, $w_3 = |z|$ and $w_4 = \mathrm{Arg}\,z$ do not have a derivative anywhere.

9. By mathematical induction extend the chain rule for differentiating a composite function for the case of n functions: $w = f_1\{f_2[\cdots f_n(z)]\}$.

10. Define $D[f(z)] = f'(z)/f(z)$. Prove by mathematical induction that $D(f_1 \cdot f_2 \cdots f_n) = \sum_{j=1}^{n} D(f_j)$. This is known as logarithmic differentiation.

11. Let $f(z)$ be a function defined in a domain D and let z_0 be a point in D at which $f(z)$ is continuous. Show that there exists a neighborhood of z_0 where $f(z)$ is bounded.

3.6. THE CAUCHY-RIEMANN CONDITIONS.

From (3.1.3) we may write $w = f(z)$ as

$$f(z) = u(x, y) + iv(x, y)$$

where u and v are real-valued functions of x and y. Denote, as usual, the partial derivatives of u and v with respect to x and y by u_x, v_x, u_y, v_y.

——**THEOREM** 3.6.1. A necessary condition for a function $f(z)$ to be analytic in a domain D is that the four partial derivatives u_x, v_x, u_y, v_y exist and satisfy the Cauchy-Riemann conditions

$$u_x = v_y, \qquad u_y = -v_x \tag{3.6.1}$$

at each point of D.

Proof. Let $z_0 = x_0 + iy_0$ be any fixed point in D. Since $f'(z_0)$ exists, the ratio

$$\frac{f(z) - f(z_0)}{z - z_0}$$

must tend to a definite limit as $z \to z_0$ in any manner. We first choose to approach z_0 along a line parallel to the real axis, $y = y_0$. Then $z - z_0 = x - x_0 = \Delta x$. Thus

$$f'(z_0) = \lim_{\Delta x \to 0} \frac{u(x_0 + \Delta x, y_0) - u(x_0, y_0)}{\Delta x} + i \lim_{\Delta x \to 0} \frac{v(x_0 + \Delta x, y_0) - v(x_0, y_0)}{\Delta x}.$$

By Theorem 3.2.1, the partial derivatives u_x and v_x exist at (x_0, y_0) and we have

$$f'(z_0) = u_x(x_0, y_0) + iv_x(x_0, y_0). \tag{3.6.2}$$

Now, we choose to approach z_0 along a line, $x = x_0$, parallel to the imaginary axis. Then $z - z_0 = i(y - y_0) = i\Delta y$. Thus

$$f'(z_0) = \lim_{\Delta y \to 0} \frac{u(x_0, y_0 + \Delta y) - u(x_0, y_0)}{i\Delta y} + \lim_{\Delta y \to 0} \frac{v(x_0, y_0 + \Delta y) - v(x_0, y_0)}{\Delta y}.$$

Hence the partial derivatives u_y and v_y exist at (x_0, y_0) and

$$f'(z_0) = -iu_y(x_0, y_0) + v_y(x_0, y_0). \tag{3.6.3}$$

The right hand members of (3.6.2) and (3.6.3) are equal to the same complex number $f'(z_0)$ hence, on equating the real and imaginary parts, we get

$$u_x(x_0, y_0) = v_y(x_0, y_0), \qquad u_y(x_0, y_0) = -v_x(x_0, y_0).$$

Since z_0 was any point in D, the theorem now follows.

Remark 3.6.1. Observe that the Cauchy-Riemann conditions or *Cauchy-Riemann differential equations* (3.6.1) imply that the real and imaginary parts of an analytic function $f(z) = u + iv$ are not arbitrary; that is, we cannot, in general, specify the functions $u = u(x, y)$ and $v = v(x, y)$ independently and expect that the resulting function $f(z) = u + iv$ will be analytic. In particular, observe that no real-valued function [for which $v(x, y) = 0$] can be analytic in a domain D unless it is a constant in D.

Remark 3.6.2. To show that the conditions (3.6.1) of Theorem 3.6.1 are *not sufficient*, we appeal to the following example.

EXAMPLE 3.6.1. Consider the function defined by the equations

$$f(z) = u(x, y) + iv(x, y) \quad \text{if} \quad z \neq 0, \quad \text{and} \quad f(0) = 0 \qquad (3.6.4)$$

where

$$u(x, y) = \frac{x^3 - y^3}{x^2 + y^2} \quad \text{and} \quad v(x, y) = \frac{x^3 + y^3}{x^2 + y^2}. \qquad (3.6.5)$$

We shall show that the Cauchy-Riemann conditions (3.6.1) are satisfied at the origin, but $f'(0)$ fails to exist at the origin.

From the definition of partial derivative of real-valued functions, we have

$$u_x(0, 0) = \lim_{x \to 0} \frac{u(x, 0) - u(0, 0)}{x} = \lim_{x \to 0} \frac{(x^3/x^2) - 0}{x} = 1,$$

and

$$u_y(0, 0) = \lim_{y \to 0} \frac{u(0, y) - u(0, 0)}{y} = \lim_{y \to 0} \frac{(-y^3/y^2) - 0}{y} = -1.$$

Similarly, we find that

$$v_x(0, 0) = 1 \quad \text{and} \quad v_y(0, 0) = 1.$$

Thus, the Cauchy-Riemann conditions are satisfied at the origin, that is,

$$u_x(0, 0) = 1 = v_y(0, 0) \quad \text{and} \quad u_y(0, 0) = -1 = -v_x(0, 0).$$

Now, we shall show that $f'(z)$ does not exist at the origin. Let z vary along the line $y = x$. Then from (3.6.4) and (3.6.5) we have

$$f(z) = u + iv = 0 + ix.$$

Thus, along the line $y = x$

$$f'(0) = \lim_{z \to 0} \frac{f(z) - f(0)}{z - 0} = \lim_{z \to 0} \frac{ix}{x + ix} = \frac{i}{1 + i} = \frac{1}{2} + \frac{1}{2}i.$$

However, if (x, y) approaches the origin along the x axis, we have by (3.6.2), since $u_x(0, 0) = 1$ and $v_x(0, 0) = 1$,

$$f'(0) = u_x(0, 0) + iv_x(0, 0) = 1 + i.$$

Therefore, $f'(0)$ does not exist.

The following theorem will give us a sufficient condition for $f(z)$ to be analytic.

────**THEOREM** 3.6.2.   A function $f(z) = u(x, y) + iv(x, y)$ is *analytic* in a domain D if the four partial derivatives u_x, v_x, u_y, v_y exist, are continuous, *and satisfy the Cauchy-Riemann conditions* (3.6.1) *at each point of* D.

Proof.   Let z_0 be any fixed point in D. Consider the expressions

$$\Delta u = u(x_0 + \Delta x, y_0 + \Delta y) - u(x_0, y_0),$$

$$\Delta v = v(x_0 + \Delta x, y_0 + \Delta y) - v(x_0, y_0).$$

By the continuity of the partial derivatives of $u(x, y)$ and $v(x, y)$, we have [see W. Kaplan, *Advanced Calculus*, pp. 83-84, (Reading: Addison-Wesley, 1957)]

$$\Delta u = u_x(x_0, y_0)\, \Delta x + u_y(x_0, y_0)\, \Delta y + \epsilon_1\, \Delta x + \epsilon_2\, \Delta y,$$

$$\Delta v = v_x(x_0, y_0)\, \Delta x + v_y(x_0, y_0)\, \Delta y + \epsilon_3\, \Delta x + \epsilon_4\, \Delta y,$$

(3.6.6)

where ϵ_1, ϵ_2, ϵ_3, ϵ_4 all approach zero when $(\Delta x, \Delta y)$ approaches $(0, 0)$.

Let $w = f(z)$ and consider the ratio

$$\frac{\Delta w}{\Delta z} = \frac{\Delta u + i\, \Delta v}{\Delta x + i\, \Delta y}.$$

(3.6.7)

Substituting the values of Δu and Δv of (3.6.6) into (3.6.7) and utilizing equations (3.6.1), we obtain

$$\frac{\Delta w}{\Delta z} = u_x + iv_x + (\epsilon_1 + i\epsilon_3)\frac{\Delta x}{\Delta z} + (\epsilon_2 + i\epsilon_4)\frac{\Delta y}{\Delta z}.$$

(3.6.8)

From (1.4.2) we have

$$\left|\frac{\Delta x}{\Delta z}\right| \leqq 1 \quad \text{and} \quad \left|\frac{\Delta y}{\Delta z}\right| \leqq 1.$$

Thus, as $(\Delta x, \Delta y)$ approach $(0, 0)$, $(\epsilon_1 + i\epsilon_3)\,(\Delta x/\Delta z)$ and $(\epsilon_2 + i\epsilon_4)\,(\Delta y/\Delta z)$ both approach zero. Consequently, letting $\Delta z \to 0$ in (3.6.8), we obtain

$$f'(z_0) = \lim_{\Delta z \to 0} \frac{\Delta w}{\Delta z} = u_x(x_0, y_0) + iv_x(x_0, y_0).$$

Since z_0 was any point in D, the theorem now follows.

Remark 3.6.3.   Observe that the above sufficiency conditions for $f(z)$ to be analytic include the requirement that the partial derivatives u_x, u_y, v_x, v_y be continuous. Conversely, if $f(z)$ is analytic then u_x, u_y, v_x, v_y are continuous. (See Theorem 5.13.1). Now combining Theorems 3.6.1 an 3.6.2, we obtain

——**THEOREM** 3.6.3.   A necessary and sufficient condition for a function $f(z) = u(x, y) + iv(x, y)$ to be *analytic* in a domain D is that the four partial derivatives u_x, u_y, v_x, v_y *exist, are continuous, and satisfy the Cauchy-Riemann conditions*

$$u_x = v_y, \qquad u_y = -v_x \tag{3.6.1}$$

at each point of D.

It follows from Theorem 3.6.1 that if $f(z)$ is analytic,

$$f'(z) = u_x + iv_x = v_y - iu_y. \tag{3.6.9}$$

EXAMPLE 3.6.2.   By using the Cauchy-Riemann conditions, we will show that $f(z) = z^3$ is analytic in the entire complex plane and that $g(z) = |z|^2$ is not analytic in any domain.

Solution. $u + iv = f(z) = (x + iy)^3$,

hence

$$u = x^3 - 3xy^2, \qquad v = 3x^2y - y^3.$$

Thus

$$u_x = 3x^2 - 3y^2 = v_y, \qquad u_y = -6xy = -v_x.$$

Hence $f(z) = z^3$ is analytic everywhere.
    Concerning $g(z) = |z|^2$.

$$u + iv = g(z) = x^2 + y^2,$$

hence

$$u = x^2 + y^2, \qquad v = 0.$$

Consequently

$$u_x = 2x, \qquad v_y = 0, \qquad u_y = 2y, \qquad v_x = 0.$$

Thus the Cauchy-Riemann conditions are not satisfied for $z \neq 0$. Hence $g(z) = |z|^2$ cannot be analytic in any domain.

Definition 3.6.1.   A point z_0 is called an *isolated singular point* or an *isolated singularity* of the function $f(z)$ if $f(z)$ is not analytic at z_0, but is analytic in a deleted neighborhood of z_0. (By a deleted neighborhood of a point z_0 we mean a neighborhood of z_0 with the point z_0 excluded.) Other types of singularities are discussed in Section 7.1.

EXAMPLE 3.6.3. Let us determine the singular points of

$$f(z) = \frac{z^2 + 2z + 5}{(z^2 + 4)(z^2 - 5z + 6)}.$$

Solution. From Theorem 3.5.1 we know that $f(z)$ is analytic except for those values of z for which the denominator becomes equal to zero. Hence, the singularities of $f(z)$ are $z = \pm 2i$, $z = 3$, $z = 2$.

EXERCISES 3.6

In Exercises 1-8 test for analyticity.

1. $w = z^3 + 2i$.

2. $w = (\bar{z} + 3i)^2 + 6$.

3. $w = |z - 1|^2$.

4. $w = \dfrac{z - 1}{z^2 + 4}$.

5. $w = \mathscr{R}\left(\dfrac{z}{z - 1}\right)$.

6. $w = \dfrac{|z|}{|z| + 1}$.

7. $w = \dfrac{z + i}{\bar{z} - i}$.

8. $w = \dfrac{z^2}{z + \bar{z}}$.

9. Show that the function defined by the equations

$$f(z) = \frac{xy^2(x + iy)}{x^2 + y^4} \quad \text{if} \quad z \neq 0, \quad \text{and} \quad f(0) = 0$$

does not have a derivative at $z = 0$.

10. Suppose that u and v are expressed in polar coordinates r, θ and have continuous partial derivatives in a domain D which does not include $z = 0$. Show that a necessary and sufficient condition that $w = f(z) = u + iv$ be analytic is that

$$\frac{\partial u}{\partial r} = \frac{1}{r}\frac{\partial v}{\partial \theta}, \qquad \frac{\partial v}{\partial r} = -\frac{1}{r}\frac{\partial u}{\partial \theta}.$$

Moreover, if $w = f(z)$ is analytic

$$\frac{dw}{dz} = (\cos\theta - i\sin\theta)\frac{\partial w}{\partial r}.$$

11. Use Exercise 10 above to show that the functions

$$w = \sqrt[n]{z} = \sqrt[n]{r}\left[\cos\frac{\theta}{n} + i\sin\frac{\theta}{n}\right], r > 0, \qquad 0 < \theta < 2\pi$$

and

$$w = \frac{x - iy}{x^2 + y^2} = \frac{\cos\theta}{r} - i\frac{\sin\theta}{r}, r > 0, \qquad 0 < \theta < 2\pi$$

are analytic.

12. Suppose that $f(z) = u + iv$ is analytic in a domain D and that u and v have continuous second partial derivatives in D. Show that

(a) $\left[\dfrac{\partial}{\partial x}\,|\,f(z)\,|\,\right]^2 + \left[\dfrac{\partial}{\partial y}\,|\,f(z)\,|\,\right]^2 = |\,f'(z)\,|^2$,

and

(b) $\left(\dfrac{\partial^2}{\partial x^2} + \dfrac{\partial^2}{\partial y^2}\right)|\,f(z)\,|^2 = 4\,|\,f'(z)\,|^2$.

13. Suppose that $f(z)$ is analytic in a domain D and that $f'(z) = 0$ for all z in D. Show that $f(z)$ is a constant in D.

14. Suppose that two analytic functions have the same derivative in a domain D. Show that they differ only by an additive constant.

15. Suppose that $f(z)$ and $\overline{f(z)}$ are analytic functions in a domain D. Show that $f(z)$ is constant in D.

16. Let $f(z)$ be analytic in a domain D.

(a) Show that if $f(z) = u(x, y) + ic$, where c is a real constant, then $f(z)$ is constant in D.

(b) Show that if $f(z) = c + iv(x, y)$, where c is a real constant, then $f(z)$ is constant in D.

17. Suppose that $f(z) = u + iv$ is analytic in a domain D. Show that if $u^2 + v^2$ is constant in D, then $f(z)$ is constant in D.

18. Let $f(z)$ and $g(z)$ be analytic functions in a domain containing the point z_0. Suppose that $f(z_0) = g(z_0) = 0$ and $g'(z_0) \neq 0$. Show that

$$\lim_{z \to z_0} \frac{f(z)}{g(z)} = \frac{f'(z_0)}{g'(z_0)}\,.$$

The above result is known as *L'Hospital's rule*.

19. Show that the functions $u(x, y)$ and $v(x, y)$ given in (3.6.5) are continuous at the origin.

20. Suppose that $f(z)$ is analytic in a domain D. Show that if $g(z) = \overline{f(\bar{z})}$, then $g(z)$ is analytic in $\bar{D}$, the mirror image of D in the real axis.

3.7. THE LAPLACE PARTIAL DIFFERENTIAL EQUATION. We have observed from the Cauchy-Riemann conditions (3.6.1) that we cannot choose two arbitrary differentiable functions $u(x, y)$ and $v(x, y)$ and be assured that the resulting function $f(z) = u + iv$ will be analytic. As soon as the real part u (or the imaginary part v) of an analytic function $f(z)$ is assigned, the imaginary part v (or the real part u) of $f(z)$ is determined within an arbitrary constant by equations (3.6.1):

$$v_x = -u_y, \qquad v_y = u_x.$$

We shall now see that even the function $u(x, y)$ or $v(x, y)$ cannot be chosen arbitrarily. For the present, we shall assume the following result which will be established in Theorem 5.13.1.

If $f(z)$ is analytic in a domain D, then the derivatives of all orders $f'(z)$, $f''(z)$, ... exist in D. Moreover, the partial derivatives of u and v of all orders exist and are continuous functions of x and y for all (x, y) in D.

For the present discussion, we are interested in knowing that the second partial derivatives of u and v with respect to x and y exist and are continuous in a domain D whenever $f(z)$ is analytic in D. Differentiating equations (3.6.1) we obtain

$$v_{xy} = -u_{yy}, \qquad v_{yx} = u_{xx}. \tag{3.7.1}$$

Since $v_{xy} = v_{yx}$, we see that

$$u_{xx} + u_{yy} = 0. \tag{3.7.2}$$

Equation (3.7.2) is called the *Laplace partial differential equation* in two independent variables x and y. It is also known as the *potential equation* and plays an important role in Mathematical Physics and other branches of Analysis. It is also written in the following forms:

$$\nabla^2 u = 0 \qquad \text{or} \qquad \Delta u = 0, \tag{3.7.3}$$

where ∇^2, Δ represents the Laplacian *operator* $\partial^2/\partial x^2 + \partial^2/\partial y^2$.

Definition 3.7.1. A real-valued function $u(x, y)$ is said to be *harmonic* in a domain D if for all x, y in D, all second partial derivatives exist, are continuous, and

$$u_{xx} + u_{yy} = 0.$$

——**THEOREM 3.7.1.** If $f(z) = u(x, y) + iv(x, y)$ is analytic in a domain D, then $u(x, y)$ and $v(x, y)$ are harmonic in D.

Proof. That $u(x, y)$ is harmonic follows from (3.7.2). Since $v(x, y)$ is the real part of the analytic function $-if(z)$, it is also harmonic, and the theorem is established.

Thus we see that neither the real part $u(x, y)$ nor the imaginary part $v(x, y)$ of the analytic function $f(z)$ can be assumed arbitrary; on the contrary, each must satisfy the corresponding Laplace differential equation:

$$u_{xx} + u_{yy} = 0, \qquad v_{xx} + v_{yy} = 0.$$

Definition 3.7.2. If $u(x, y)$ and $v(x, y)$ are harmonic functions in a domain D such that $f(z) = u(x, y) + iv(x, y)$ is analytic in D, then $v(x, y)$ is said to be the *conjugate* of $u(x, y)$.

Remark 3.7.1. Observe that the word *conjugate* used in the above definition is different from that used in defining the *conjugate* of a complex number z, which is denoted by $\bar{z}$. Note also that if $v(x, y)$ is conjugate to $u(x, y)$, then $- u(x, y)$ is conjugate to $v(x, y)$, since $v(x, y)$ and $- u(x, y)$ are respectively the real and imaginary parts of the analytic function $- if(z)$.

EXAMPLE 3.7.1. Let us show that the function

$$u(x, y) = e^x \cos y$$

is harmonic, and then determine its harmonic conjugate $v(x, y)$ and the analytic function $f(z) = u + iv$. (NOTE: Theorem 8.19.1 assures us in advance that these last two functions exist.)

Solution. Observe that

$$u_x = e^x \cos y, \qquad u_{xx} = e^x \cos y, \qquad u_y = - e^x \sin y, \qquad u_{yy} = - e^x \cos y.$$

Hence

$$u_{xx} + u_{yy} = e^x \cos y - e^x \cos y = 0,$$

thus $u(x, y) = e^x \cos y$ is harmonic.

In order to determine its harmonic conjugate v, we utilize equations (3.6.1):

$$u_x = v_y, \qquad u_y = - v_x.$$

We see that

$$v_y = e^x \cos y.$$

Integrating this equation with respect to y, and keeping x constant, we obtain

$$v = e^x \sin y + \lambda(x),$$

where $\lambda(x)$ is an arbitrary function of x such that $\lambda'(x)$ exists. Since $u_y = - v_x$, we see that

$$- e^x \sin y = - e^x \sin y - \lambda'(x).$$

Hence $\lambda'(x) = 0$ and $\lambda(x) = c$, where c is a real constant. Thus $v = e^x \sin y + c$ is the harmonic conjugate of the function $u = e^x \cos y$. The function $f(z) = u + iv$ may now be written as

$$f(z) = e^x \cos y + ie^x \sin y + ic.$$

Using (1.6.1) and defining for the present $e^z = e^{x+iy} \equiv e^x \cdot e^{iy}$, we may write $f(z)$ as

$$f(z) = e^z + ic.$$

3.8. LEVEL CURVES

Definition 3.8.1. Let the function $f(z)$ be defined in a domain D. The set of all points z in D such that $|f(z)| = M$ $(M > 0)$ is known as a *level curve* (or *contour curve*) of the function $f(z)$.

Observe that by giving M different values, we obtain different level curves.

EXAMPLE 3.8.1. Let us find the level curves of $f(z) = z^2 - 1$.

Solution. The level curves of $f(z) = z^2 - 1$ are given by

$$|z^2 - 1| = M$$

or

$$[(x - 1)^2 + y^2][(x + 1)^2 + y^2] = M^2.$$

If we use polar coordinates, the level curves of $f(z)$ are given by

$$(\rho^2 + 1)^2 = 4\rho^2 \cos^2 \theta + M^2.$$

When $M > 1$, we have a system of level curves known as the Ovals of Cassini. When $M = 1$, the level curve is known as the Lemniscate of Bernoulli. When $0 < M < 1$, we have two systems of nonintersecting ovals surrounding the points $z = 1$ and $z = -1$, respectively. (See Fig. 3.8.1.)

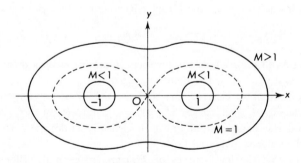

FIG. 3.8.1

A *level curve* of a real function $\lambda(x, y)$ defined in a domain D is given by the locus of a point (x, y) in D such that $\lambda(x, y) = C$ (C constant). We shall now consider the level curves of the real part $u(x, y)$ and the imaginary part $v(x, y)$ of an analytic function $f(z)$ defined in D. That is,

$$u(x, y) = C_1, \qquad v(x, y) = C_2 \tag{3.8.1}$$

where C_1 and C_2 are constants. We shall now show that this system of level curves forms an orthogonal system in D. For definiteness, let us consider two level curves $u(x, y) = c_1$ and $v(x, y) = c_2$. Suppose that they intersect at a point (x_0, y_0) in D. Also, let us assume that $f'(z_0) \neq 0$. This condition implies that $u_x(x_0, y_0)$ and $u_y(x_0, y_0)$ do not vanish simultaneously, say $u_y(x_0, y_0) \neq 0$. By the implicit function theorem, $u(x, y) = c_1$ determines in a neighborhood of x_0 a single-valued differentiable function $y = \phi(x)$ with the values of y lying in a neighborhood of y_0. We have, moreover,

$$\frac{dy}{dx} = -\frac{u_x}{u_y}.$$

Similarly, since $v_x(x_0, y_0) \neq 0$, we get for the curve $v(x, y) = c_2$

$$-\frac{dx}{dy} = \frac{v_y}{v_x}.$$

In order that the curve $v(x, y) = c_2$ be orthogonal to the curve $u(x, y) = c_1$ at (x_0, y_0), the slope of $v(x, y) = c_2$ must be the negative reciprocal of the slope $u(x, y) = c_1$ at (x_0, y_0). Thus, the condition of orthogonality is given by

$$-\frac{u_x(x_0, y_0)}{u_y(x_0, y_0)} = \frac{v_y(x_0, y_0)}{v_x(x_0, y_0)},$$

which can be written as

$$u_y(x_0, y_0)\, v_y(x_0, y_0) + u_x(x_0, y_0)\, v_x(x_0, y_0) = 0. \qquad (3.8.2)$$

Since $f(z)$ is analytic at z_0, the Cauchy-Riemann differential equations (3.6.1)

$$u_x(x_0, y_0) = v_y(x_0, y_0), \qquad v_x(x_0, y_0) = -u_y(x_0, y_0),$$

imply equation (3.8.2). Thus, the level curve $u(x, y) = c_1$ is orthogonal to the level curve $v(x, y) = c_2$ at the point (x_0, y_0) of D.

In applications to electrostatics and the theory of gravitational potential, the two systems of level curves $u(x, y) = C_1$ and $v(x, y) = C_2$ are the lines of force and the equipotential lines; in hydrodynamics they are the stream lines and the velocity potential lines.

Observe that the level curves of $f(z)$ are, in general, different from the level curves of its real and imaginary parts.

EXAMPLE 3.8.2.   Let us sketch the level curves of $u = C_1$ and $v = C_2$ when

$$f(z) = z^2 \qquad z \neq 0,$$

and verify directly the orthogonality of these curves.

Solution.

$$u + iv = f(z) = (x + iy)^2,$$

hence

$$u = x^2 - y^2, \qquad v = 2xy.$$

Thus the level curves

$$x^2 - y^2 = C_1, \qquad 2xy = C_2$$

are rectangular hyperbolas. Their slopes are given respectively by

$$m_1 \equiv \frac{dy}{dx} = \frac{x}{y}, \qquad m_2 \equiv \frac{dy}{dx} = -\frac{y}{x}.$$

At their points of intersection we see that $m_1 m_2 = -1$, hence the family of curves $x^2 - y^2 = C_1$, $2xy = C_2$ form an orthogonal system. A few level curves of $u = C_1$ and $v = C_2$ are illustrated in Fig. 3.8.2.

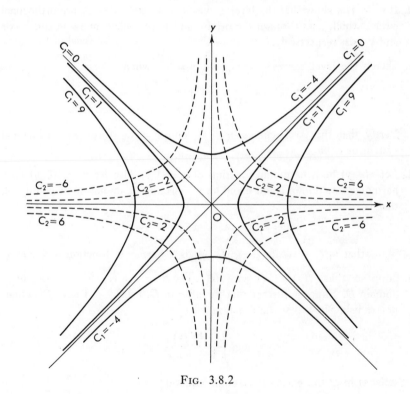

FIG. 3.8.2

EXERCISES 3.8

In Exercises 1-5 show that the given function is harmonic, then determine its harmonic conjugate.

1. $u = \dfrac{x}{x^2 + y^2}$ $\qquad (x^2 + y^2 \neq 0).$

2. $u = \frac{1}{2} \log_e (x^2 + y^2)$ $(x^2 + y^2 \neq 0)$.

3. $u = x^3 - 3xy^2$.

4. $u = \cosh x \cos y$.

5. $u = \tan^{-1}[(y - b)/(x - a)]$ $(a, b \text{ constants}, x \neq a)$.

In Exercises 6-9, the given function satisfies Laplace's equation. Determine the corresponding analytic function $u + iv$.

6. $u = e^x x \cos y - e^x y \sin y$.

7. $u = x^3 - 3xy^2 + 3x^2 - 3y^2 + 1$.

8. $u = (x - 1)^3 - 3xy^2 + 3y^2$.

9. $u = e^{(x^2 - y^2)} \cos 2xy$.

10. If $w = 1/z$, show that the level curves $u = C_1$ and $v = C_2$ are orthogonal circles which pass through the origin, and have their centers on the x axis and y axis, respectively.

11. Sketch the level curves $u = C_1$ and $v = C_2$ when

$$f(z) = \frac{z + 4}{z - 4}.$$

Verify that the level curves $u = C_1$ and $v = C_2$ form an orthogonal system of circles.

12. Let $u(x, y)$ be a harmonic function of x and y. Also let $x = x(\zeta, \eta)$ be a harmonic function of ζ and η and let $y = y(\zeta, \eta)$ be its harmonic conjugate, that is,

$$x_\zeta = y_\eta \quad \text{and} \quad x_\eta = -y_\zeta.$$

Show that $u_1(\zeta, \eta) = u[x(\zeta, \eta), y(\zeta, \eta)]$ is a harmonic function of ζ and η.

13. Suppose that $f(z) = u(x, y) + iv(x, y)$, $z = x + iy$, is analytic in a domain D. Suppose further that for all z in D, $|f(z)| < 1$ and $f'(z)$ does not vanish. Show that the function

$$w = \log_e \left[\frac{|f'(z)|}{1 - |f(z)|^2} \right]$$

satisfies in D the partial differential equation

$$\frac{\partial^2 w}{\partial x^2} + \frac{\partial^2 w}{\partial y^2} = 4e^{2w}.$$

14. Suppose that the function $u(x, y)$ is harmonic in a domain D, and that the partial derivatives of u of all orders exist and are continuous functions of x and y in D. Show that the functions $u_x, u_y, u_{xx}, u_{xy}, u_{yy}, u_{xxx}, \cdots$ are harmonic in D.

15. Let $w = u(x, y) + iv(x, y)$, where u and v have continuous first order partial derivatives with respect to x and y in a domain D. Since $z = x + iy$ and $\bar{z} = x - iy$, we have $x = (1/2)(z + \bar{z})$ and $y = (1/2i)(z - \bar{z})$. Thus w can be written as

$$w = u\left(\frac{z + \bar{z}}{2}, \frac{z - \bar{z}}{2i}\right) + iv\left(\frac{z + \bar{z}}{2}, \frac{z - \bar{z}}{2i}\right),$$

which can be looked upon as a formal identity in two independent variables z and $\bar{z}$. A necessary and sufficient condition that w be independent of $\bar{z}$ is that $\partial w / \partial \bar{z} = 0$. Show that this condition is equivalent to

$$\frac{\partial u}{\partial x} = \frac{\partial v}{\partial y}, \qquad \frac{\partial v}{\partial x} = -\frac{\partial u}{\partial y}$$

which are the Cauchy-Riemann conditions. Show that, if $f(z)$ is analytic and if either $f(\bar{z})$ or $f(|z|)$ is also analytic, then $f(z)$ is constant. Verify that the functions $w = 2ix$, $w = -4y$, $w = |z|^2$ are not analytic.

16. It can be shown that if $u(x, y)$ is harmonic at a point $z_0 = x_0 + iy_0$ (that is, harmonic in a domain D containing z_0), then it has a development in powers of $(x - x_0)$ and $(y - y_0)$ in a neighborhood of z_0. Also, this power series development will remain convergent and will converge to $u(\xi, \eta)$ if x and y are replaced by the complex variables ξ and η provided that $|\xi - x_0|$ and $|\eta - y_0|$ are sufficiently small; in particular, if ξ and η are replaced by $x_0 + (z - z_0)/2$ and $y_0 + (z - z_0)/2i$, for $|z - z_0|$ sufficiently small. It will then follow that in a neighborhood of z_0, the analytic function $f(z) = u(x, y) + iv(x, y)$ associated with $u(x, y)$ is given by

$$f(z) = 2u\left[\frac{z + \bar{z}_0}{2}, \frac{z - \bar{z}_0}{2i}\right] - u(x_0, y_0) + ic, \qquad \text{(a)}$$

where c is a real constant.

In particular, if $u(x, y)$ is harmonic at the origin and $z_0 = 0$, formula (a) becomes

$$f(z) = 2u\left(\frac{z}{2}, \frac{z}{2i}\right) - u(0, 0) + ic. \qquad \text{(b)}$$

Formulas (a) and (b) may be obtained (see hint) by expressing $f(z)$ as a power series and using relations of the form

$$2u(x, y) = f(z) + \overline{f(z)} = f(x + iy) + \overline{f(x + iy)}.$$

Use formula (b) to check Exercises 7 and 8 above.

17. Let $u(x, y)$ be harmonic in a domain D. Show that the Laplace equation in polar coordinates is given in D by

$$\frac{\partial}{\partial r}\left(r\frac{\partial u}{\partial r}\right) + \frac{1}{r}\frac{\partial^2 u}{\partial \theta^2} = 0.$$

4

Elementary Functions

4.1. THE EXPONENTIAL FUNCTION. The exponential function e^x, where x is a real number and e is the base of the natural logarithms, was studied in calculus. We now wish to define e^z when z is a complex number. The function e^z should be so defined as to include, as a special case, the function e^x, and preserve the main properties of e^x, namely, the law of exponents $e^{x_1} e^{x_2} = e^{x_1+x_2}$, the fact that $e^0 = 1$ and $(d/dx)(e^{\alpha x}) = \alpha e^{\alpha x}$, where α is a constant.

Let $z = x + iy$ (x, y real numbers). Then in order that the law of exponents should hold, we require that

$$e^{x+iy} = e^x e^{iy}.$$

In defining $f(y) = e^{iy}$, we require that $f(0) = 1$ and $df/dy = if(y)$. Observe that these two conditions are satisfied by the function $\cos y + i \sin y$, since $\cos 0 + i \sin 0 = 1$ and

$$\frac{d}{dy}(\cos y + i \sin y) = -\sin y + i \cos y = i(\cos y + i \sin y).$$

We consequently make the following

Definition 4.1.1.   If $z = x + iy$, we define $e^z = e^{x+iy}$ to be the complex number

$$e^z = e^x(\cos y + i \sin y). \tag{4.1.1}$$

Observe that when z is real, that is, when $y = 0$, e^z becomes equal to e^x. Also, when $z = 0$, $e^z = 1$. Note that $\arg e^z = y$.

We shall now show that the law of exponents still holds.

——**THEOREM** 4.1.1.   If $z_1 = x_1 + iy_1$ and $z_2 = x_2 + iy_2$ are two complex numbers, then

$$e^{z_1}e^{z_2} = e^{z_1+z_2}. \tag{4.1.2}$$

Proof.

$$e^{z_1}e^{z_2} = e^{x_1}(\cos y_1 + i \sin y_1)\,e^{x_2}(\cos y_2 + i \sin y_2)$$
$$= e^{x_1+x_2}[\cos y_1 \cos y_2 - \sin y_1 \sin y_2$$
$$+ i(\sin y_1 \cos y_2 + \sin y_2 \cos y_1)]$$
$$= e^{x_1+x_2}[\cos (y_1 + y_2) + i \sin (y_1 + y_2)] = e^{z_1+z_2}.$$

If we let $z_1 = z$ and $z_2 = -z$ in (4.1.2), we obtain

$$e^{-z} = \frac{1}{e^z}. \qquad (4.1.3)$$

Further properties of the exponential function e^z will be given in the following

——**THEOREM** 4.1.2.   (a) For all z

$$e^z \neq 0. \qquad (4.1.4)$$

(b) $|e^{iy}| = 1$ and $|e^z| = e^x$ $(z = x + iy)$. \qquad (4.1.5)

(c)   A necessary and sufficient condition that

$$e^z = 1 \qquad (4.1.6)$$

is that $z = 2k\pi i$ (where k is an integer).

(d)   A necessary and sufficient condition that

$$e^{z_1} = e^{z_2} \qquad (4.1.7)$$

is that $z_1 - z_2 = 2k\pi i$ (where k is an integer).

Proof.   Concerning (a). Using (4.1.2) we have

$$e^z \cdot e^{-z} = e^0 = 1.$$

Since the product is never zero, neither factor can be zero. Therefore $e^z \neq 0$.

Concerning (b). From Definitions 4.1.1 and 1.3.2 we have

$$|e^{iy}| = \sqrt{\cos^2 y + \sin^2 y} = 1$$

Also

$$|e^z| = |e^x|\,|e^{iy}| = e^x,$$

since $e^x > 0$.

Concerning (c).   *Necessity.* Suppose that $e^z = 1$. Thus

$$e^x \cos y = 1 \quad \text{and} \quad e^x \sin y = 0.$$

Since $e^x \neq 0$, we see that $\sin y = 0$. Hence $y = n\pi$, where n is an integer.

But $\cos n\pi = (-1)^n$. Since $e^x > 0$, we see that $e^x(-1)^n = 1$ only if $x = 0$ and $n = 2k$, where k is an integer. Thus $z = x + iy = 0 + in\pi = 2k\pi i$.

Sufficiency. Suppose that $z = 2k\pi i$, where k is an integer. Using (4.1.1) we obtain

$$e^z = e^{2k\pi i} = \cos(2k\pi) + i\sin(2k\pi) = 1.$$

Concerning (d). Observe that

$$e^{z_1} = e^{z_2} \quad \text{if, and only if,} \quad e^{z_1 - z_2} = 1.$$

Hence, from (c) we have that

$$z_1 - z_2 = 2k\pi i \qquad \text{(where } k \text{ is an integer).}$$

The theorem is thus established.

Definition 4.1.2. Let $w = f(z)$ be a single-valued function defined in a domain D of the complex plane, and let $\lambda \neq 0$ be a constant. Suppose that for every z in D, $z + \lambda$ is also in D. The function $f(z)$ is said to be *periodic* of period λ in D, if for all z in D

$$f(z + \lambda) = f(z). \tag{4.1.8}$$

From (4.1.2) and (4.1.6) we see that e^z is of period $2\pi i$, since

$$e^{z + 2\pi i} = e^z \cdot e^{2\pi i} = e^z. \tag{4.1.9}$$

——**THEOREM** 4.1.3. The exponential function e^z is analytic for all values of z. Moreover

$$\frac{d}{dz}(e^z) = e^z. \tag{4.1.10}$$

Proof. Let $u + iv = f(z) = e^z$. Since $e^z = e^x \cos y + ie^x \sin y$, we have

$$u = e^x \cos y, \qquad v = e^x \sin y.$$

It is easily seen that

$$u_x = e^x \cos y = v_y, \qquad u_y = -e^x \sin y = -v_x.$$

From Theorem 3.6.3, it now follows that e^z is analytic for all values of z. Using (3.6.9), we have for any complex number z

$$\frac{d}{dz}(e^z) = f'(z) = u_x + iv_x = e^x \cos y + ie^x \sin y = e^z,$$

and the theorem is thus established.

From Theorems 3.5.2 and 4.1.3 we obtain the following

——*THEOREM* 4.1.4.   If w is an analytic function of z, then e^w is an analytic function of z and

$$\frac{d}{dz}(e^w) = e^w \frac{dw}{dz}.$$ (4.1.11)

Let us put for convenience

$$e^z = \exp z.$$ (4.1.12)

EXAMPLE 4.1.1.   Let us show that $\exp \bar{z} = \overline{\exp z}$, and that $\exp \bar{z}$ is not an analytic function of z in any domain D.

Solution. $\exp \bar{z} = e^x e^{-iy} = e^x (\cos y - i \sin y)$.
Also

$$\overline{\exp z} = \overline{e^x(\cos y + i \sin y)} = e^x(\cos y - i \sin y),$$

hence

$$\exp \bar{z} = \overline{\exp z}.$$

Let $u + iv = \exp \bar{z}$. Then

$$u = e^x \cos y \quad \text{and} \quad v = -e^x \sin y.$$

One easily finds that

$$u_x \neq v_y \quad \text{and} \quad u_y \neq -v_x.$$

Since the Cauchy-Riemann differential equations are not satisfied anywhere, $\exp \bar{z}$ is not an analytic function of z in any domain D. (Also see Exercise 3.6.15.)

EXERCISES 4.1

1. Show that a necessary and sufficient condition that $\exp z = -1$ is that $z = (2n + 1)\pi i$ (where n is an integer).

2. Show that $\exp (iz)$ and $\exp (-iz)$ are analytic functions of z.

3. Show that $\exp (nz) = (\exp z)^n$ for all integers n.

4. Show that $|\exp (\lambda iz^2)| = e^{-2\lambda xy}$ for λ real.

5. Show that if $\mathscr{I}(z) > 0$, then $|\exp (iz)| < 1$.

6. Show that the function given by $\mathscr{R}[\exp (1/(z - 1))]$ is a harmonic function of x and y in any domain D not including the point $z = 1$.

4.2. THE TRIGONOMETRIC FUNCTIONS. Since

$$e^{iy} = \cos y + i \sin y \quad \text{and} \quad e^{-iy} = \cos y - i \sin y,$$

subtracting and adding these equations we obtain

$$\sin y = \frac{e^{iy} - e^{-iy}}{2i}, \qquad \cos y = \frac{e^{iy} + e^{-iy}}{2}. \tag{4.2.1}$$

These real trigonometric functions will be extended to the domain of a complex variable by the following

Definition 4.2.1. Given any complex number z, we define

$$\sin z = \frac{e^{iz} - e^{-iz}}{2i}, \qquad \cos z = \frac{e^{iz} + e^{-iz}}{2}. \tag{4.2.2}$$

Taking z to be real, we note that these equations are consistent with equations (4.2.1). Also, note that $\sin z$ and $\cos z$ are both periodic with period 2π.

Using Theorems 4.1.4 and 3.5.1 we have the following

——**THEOREM** 4.2.1. The functions $\sin z$ and $\cos z$ are analytic for all values of z. Moreover

$$\frac{d}{dz}(\sin z) = \cos z, \qquad \frac{d}{dz}(\cos z) = -\sin z. \tag{4.2.3}$$

Definition 4.2.2. A point z_0 for which $f(z_0) = 0$ is called a *zero of the function* $f(z)$.

——**THEOREM** 4.2.2. The zeros of the functions $\sin z$ and $\cos z$ are given respectively by

$$z = n\pi \quad \text{and} \quad z = \frac{\pi}{2} + n\pi, \tag{4.2.4}$$

where $n = 0, \pm 1, \pm 2, \cdots$.

Proof. If $\sin z = 0$, then from (4.2.2) we obtain $\exp(2iz) = 1$. We then have in view of part (c) of Theorem 4.1.2

$$2iz = 2n\pi i \quad \text{or} \quad z = n\pi \quad (n = 0, \pm 1, \pm 2, \cdots).$$

If $\cos z = 0$, then from (4.2.2) we obtain $\exp(2iz) = -1$. Consequently, $z = \pi/2 + n\pi$ $(n = 0, \pm 1, \pm 2, \cdots)$ in virtue of Exercise 4.1.1. The theorem is thus established.

Note that the only zeros of the complex sine and cosine functions are the real numbers that appear already as the zeros of the real sine and cosine functions.

We shall say that a domain D is *symmetric* with respect to the origin, if for every point z in D the point $-z$ is also in D.

Definition 4.2.3. Let $w = f(z)$ be a function defined in a domain D which is symmetric with respect to the origin. If $f(-z) = f(z)$ for all values of z in D, then $f(z)$ is called an *even function*; if $f(-z) = -f(z)$ for all values of z in D, then $f(z)$ is called an *odd function*.

From (4.2.2) we see that sin z and cos z are respectively odd and even functions:

$$\sin(-z) = -\sin z \quad \text{and} \quad \cos(-z) = \cos z. \tag{4.2.5}$$

The other trigonometric functions are given by the following

Definition 4.2.4. Given the complex number z, we define

$$\tan z = \frac{\sin z}{\cos z} \text{ for } z \neq \frac{\pi}{2} + n\pi,$$

$$\cot z = \frac{\cos z}{\sin z} \text{ for } z \neq n\pi,$$

$$\sec z = \frac{1}{\cos z} \text{ for } z \neq \frac{\pi}{2} + n\pi, \tag{4.2.6}$$

$$\csc z = \frac{1}{\sin z} \text{ for } z \neq n\pi,$$

where in all cases $n = 0, \pm 1, \pm 2, \cdots$.

Tan z, cot z have period π, while sec z, csc z have period 2π.

Utilizing Theorems 4.2.1 and 3.5.1, we may readily establish the following

——**THEOREM** 4.2.3. The functions tan z, cot z, sec z, and csc z are analytic functions of z except for those values of z excluded by Definition 4.2.4. Moreover

$$\frac{d}{dz}(\tan z) = \sec^2 z \text{ for } z \neq \frac{\pi}{2} + n\pi,$$

$$\frac{d}{dz}(\cot z) = -\csc^2 z \text{ for } z \neq n\pi,$$

$$\frac{d}{dz}(\sec z) = \sec z \tan z \text{ for } z \neq \frac{\pi}{2} + n\pi, \tag{4.2.7}$$

$$\frac{d}{dz}(\csc z) = -\csc z \cot z \text{ for } z \neq n\pi,$$

where in all cases $n = 0, \pm 1, \pm 2, \cdots$.

——**THEOREM** 4.2.4.   If $z = x + iy$, then

$$\sin z = \sin x \cosh y + i \cos x \sinh y, \qquad (4.2.8)$$

$$\cos z = \cos x \cosh y - i \sin x \sinh y. \qquad (4.2.9)$$

Proof.   Verification of (4.2.8). Using (4.2.2) and (4.1.1), and recalling the definitions that $\sinh y = (e^y - e^{-y})/2$ and $\cosh y = (e^y + e^{-y})/2$, y real, we obtain

$$
\begin{aligned}
2i \sin z &= e^{iz} - e^{-iz} \\
&= e^{-y}(\cos x + i \sin x) - e^y(\cos x - i \sin x) \\
&= i \sin x(e^y + e^{-y}) - \cos x(e^y - e^{-y}) \\
&= 2i \sin x \cosh y - 2 \cos x \sinh y,
\end{aligned}
$$

from which (4.2.8) now follows.

The proof for $\cos z$ is similar to that given for $\sin z$.

——**THEOREM** 4.2.5.   If $z = x + iy$, then

$$\sin iy = i \sinh y, \qquad \cos iy = \cosh y, \qquad (4.2.10)$$

$$\sin \bar{z} = \overline{\sin z}, \qquad \cos \bar{z} = \overline{\cos z}, \qquad (4.2.11)$$

$$|\sin z|^2 = \sin^2 x + \sinh^2 y, \qquad (4.2.12)$$

$$|\cos z|^2 = \cos^2 x + \sinh^2 y. \qquad (4.2.13)$$

Proof.   Verification of (4.2.10). If we substitute $z = 0 + iy$ into (4.2.8) and (4.2.9), we obtain (4.2.10).

Verification of (4.2.11). Replace z by $\bar{z}$ in (4.2.8) and (4.2.9) and recall that $\cosh(-y) = \cosh y$ and $\sinh(-y) = -\sinh y$; we obtain

$$\sin \bar{z} = \sin x \cosh y - i \cos x \sinh y = \overline{\sin z},$$

$$\cos \bar{z} = \cos x \cosh y + i \sin x \sinh y = \overline{\cos z}.$$

Verification of (4.2.12). Utilizing (4.2.8) and Definition 1.3.2, and recalling the identity $\cosh^2 y - \sinh^2 y = 1$, we obtain

$$
\begin{aligned}
|\sin z|^2 &= \sin^2 x \cosh^2 y + \cos^2 x \sinh^2 y \\
&= \sin^2 x(1 + \sinh^2 y) + \cos^2 x \sinh^2 y \\
&= \sin^2 x + \sinh^2 y.
\end{aligned}
$$

Similarly, one verifies (4.2.13), and the theorem is established.

Remark 4.2.1.   From (4.2.12) and (4.2.13) we see that the absolute values of $\sin z$ and $\cos z$ can be made as large as we please; however, when z is real, the absolute values of $\sin z$ and $\cos z$ are never greater than unity.

Remark 4.2.2. Using properties of the exponential function, one may show directly that the standard identities for the trigonometric functions of a real variable x extend to the case of a complex variable z. Thus we have, for example,

$$\sin^2 z + \cos^2 z = 1, \tag{4.2.14}$$

$$\sin(z_1 \pm z_2) = \sin z_1 \cos z_2 \pm \cos z_1 \sin z_2. \tag{4.2.15}$$

$$\cos(z_1 \pm z_2) = \cos z_1 \cos z_2 \mp \sin z_1 \sin z_2, \tag{4.2.16}$$

$$\sin\left(\frac{\pi}{2} - z\right) = \cos z, \tag{4.2.17}$$

$$\sin 2z = 2 \sin z \cos z, \tag{4.2.18}$$

$$\cos 2z = \cos^2 z - \sin^2 z. \tag{4.2.19}$$

EXAMPLE 4.2.1. Let us show that

$$\tan(z_1 + z_2) = \frac{\tan z_1 + \tan z_2}{1 - \tan z_1 \tan z_2}. \tag{4.2.20}$$

Solution. From (4.2.15) and (4.2.16) we have, as in the real case,

$$\tan(z_1 + z_2) = \frac{\sin(z_1 + z_2)}{\cos(z_1 + z_2)}$$

$$= \frac{\sin z_1 \cos z_2 + \cos z_1 \sin z_2}{\cos z_1 \cos z_2 - \sin z_1 \sin z_2}$$

$$= \frac{\tan z_1 + \tan z_2}{1 - \tan z_1 \tan z_2}.$$

EXERCISES 4.2

1. Prove Theorem 4.2.3.

2. Establish identities (4.2.14) to (4.2.19).

3. Prove (4.2.9).

4. Prove that $\exp(iz) = \cos z + i \sin z$ and $\exp(-iz) = \cos z - i \sin z$.

5. Prove that

$$\cos z_2 - \cos z_1 = -2 \sin\left(\frac{z_2 + z_1}{2}\right) \sin\left(\frac{z_2 - z_1}{2}\right).$$

6. Prove that

$$\sin z_2 - \sin z_1 = 2 \cos\left(\frac{z_2 + z_1}{2}\right) \sin\left(\frac{z_2 - z_1}{2}\right).$$

7. Prove that $|\cos z|^2 = \cos^2 x + \sinh^2 y$.

8. Show that the functions $\sin \bar{z}$ and $\cos \bar{z}$ are not analytic functions of z in any domain D.

9. Show that $|\sin z| \leq \cosh y$ and $|\sin z| \geq |\sinh y|$.

10. Show that $|\cos z| \leq \cosh y$ and $|\cos z| \geq |\sinh y|$.

11. Show that if $|z| \leq 1$, then $|\cos z| < 2$ and $|\sin z| < \frac{6}{5}|z|$, $z \neq 0$.

12. Show that if w is an analytic function of z, then $\sin w$ and $\cos w$ are also analytic functions of z, and

$$\frac{d}{dz}(\sin w) = \cos w \frac{dw}{dz}, \qquad \frac{d}{dz}(\cos w) = -\sin w \frac{dw}{dz}.$$

13. Prove results for the functions in Theorem 4.2.3 similar to those given in Exercise 12 above.

14. Find the roots of the equation $\cos z = 2$.

15. Find the roots of the equation $\sin z = \cosh k$, where k is a real constant.

16. Prove that if $\sin z_1 = \sin z_2$, then either

$$z_1 = z_2 + 2n\pi \quad \text{or} \quad z_1 = (2n+1)\pi - z_2, \quad \text{where } n \text{ is an integer.}$$

17. Prove that if $\cos z_1 = \sin z_2$, then either

$$\frac{\pi}{2} - z_1 = z_2 + 2n\pi \text{ or } \frac{\pi}{2} - z_1 = (2n+1)\pi - z_2, \quad \text{where } n \text{ is an integer.}$$

18. Prove that if $\cos z_1 = \sin z_2$, then

$$z_1 = (-1)^{k+1} z_2 + \frac{\pi}{2} + k\pi, \qquad \text{where } k \text{ is an integer.}$$

19. Prove that $\tan z_1 = \tan z_2$ if and only if $z_1 = z_2 + n\pi$, where n is an integer.

20. Prove that

$$\tan z = \frac{\sin 2x + i \sinh 2y}{\cos 2x + \cosh 2y}.$$

21. Show that the equation $\tan z = cz$, where c is real, has no complex roots of the form $z = x + iy$, $x \neq 0$, $y \neq 0$.

22. Show that if $\sin(x + iy) = \csc(u + iv)$, where x, y, u, v are real, then

(a) $\sin x \cosh y = \dfrac{\sin u \cosh v}{\cosh^2 v - \cos^2 u}$, $\cos x \sinh y = -\dfrac{\cos u \sinh v}{\cosh^2 v - \cos^2 u}$;

(b) $\tan x \coth y + \tan u \coth v = 0$;

(c) $e^{iz} = i \tan \dfrac{w}{2} \ (z = x + iy, \ w = u + iv)$;

(d) $\tan x = -\sin u \operatorname{csch} v$;

(e) $\tanh y \cosh v = \cos u$;

(f) $\tanh v \cosh y = \cos x$.

23. Use formula (b) of Exercise 3.8.16 to check Exercises 3.8.6 and 3.8.9.

4.3. THE HYPERBOLIC FUNCTIONS

Definition 4.3.1.   Given any complex number z, we define

$$\sinh z = \frac{e^z - e^{-z}}{2}, \qquad \cosh z = \frac{e^z + e^{-z}}{2}. \qquad (4.3.1)$$

Taking z to be real, we note that these equations are consistent with those for the hyperbolic sine and cosine with real arguments:

$$\sinh x = \frac{e^x - e^{-x}}{2}, \qquad \cosh x = \frac{e^x + e^{-x}}{2}. \qquad (4.3.2)$$

Observe that $\sinh z$ and $\cosh z$ are periodic with period $2\pi i$.

Using Theorems 4.1.3 and 3.5.1, we have the following

——*THEOREM* 4.3.1.   The functions $\sinh z$ and $\cosh z$ are analytic for all values of z. Moreover

$$\frac{d}{dz}(\sinh z) = \cosh z, \qquad \frac{d}{dz}(\cosh z) = \sinh z. \qquad (4.3.3)$$

Utilizing (4.3.1), (4.1.6), and Exercise 4.1.1, we have the following

——*THEOREM* 4.3.2.   The zeros of the functions $\sinh z$ and $\cosh z$ are given respectively by

$$z = n\pi i \quad \text{and} \quad z = \left(n + \frac{1}{2}\right)\pi i \qquad (4.3.4)$$

where $n = 0, \pm 1, \pm 2, \cdots$.

Note that the zeros of $\sinh z$ and $\cosh z$ are pure imaginary numbers. From (4.3.1) and Definition 4.2.3, we see that $\sinh z$ and $\cosh z$ are respectively odd and even functions:

$$\sinh(-z) = -\sinh z \quad \text{and} \quad \cosh(-z) = \cosh z. \qquad (4.3.5)$$

The other hyperbolic functions are given by the following

Definition 4.3.2.   Given the complex number z, we define

$$\tanh z = \frac{\sinh z}{\cosh z} \text{ for } z \neq \left(n + \frac{1}{2}\right)\pi i,$$

$$\coth z = \frac{\cosh z}{\sinh z} \text{ for } z \neq n\pi i,$$

$$\qquad (4.3.6)$$

$$\operatorname{sech} z = \frac{1}{\cosh z} \text{ for } z \neq \left(n + \frac{1}{2}\right)\pi i,$$

$$\operatorname{csch} z = \frac{1}{\sinh z} \text{ for } z \neq n\pi i,$$

where in all cases $n = 0, \pm 1, \pm 2, \cdots$.

Tanh z, coth z have period πi, while sech z, csch z have period $2\pi i$.

Utilizing Theorems 4.3.1 and 3.5.1, we may establish the following

——**THEOREM** 4.3.3.   The functions tanh z, coth z, sech z and csch z are analytic functions of z except for those values of z excluded by Definition 4.3.2. Moreover

$$\frac{d}{dz}(\tanh z) = \operatorname{sech}^2 z \text{ for } z \neq \left(n + \frac{1}{2}\right)\pi i,$$

$$\frac{d}{dz}(\coth \bar{z}) = -\operatorname{csch}^2 z \text{ for } z \neq n\pi i,$$

$$\frac{d}{dz}(\operatorname{sech} z) = -\operatorname{sech} z \tanh z \text{ for } z \neq \left(n + \frac{1}{2}\right)\pi i, \tag{4.3.7}$$

$$\frac{d}{dz}(\operatorname{csch} z) = -\operatorname{csch} z \coth z \text{ for } z \neq n\pi i,$$

where in all cases $n = 0, \pm 1, \pm 2, \cdots$.

Using techniques similar to those employed to establish Theorem 4.2.4, one may establish the following

——**THEOREM** 4.3.4.   If $z = x + iy$, then

$$\sinh z = \cos y \sinh x + i \sin y \cosh x, \tag{4.3.8}$$
$$\cosh z = \cos y \cosh x + i \sin y \sinh x. \tag{4.3.9}$$

By comparing (4.2.2) and (4.3.1), and also utilizing the above theorem, one may readily establish the following

——**THEOREM** 4.3.5.   If $z = x + iy$, then

$$\sinh (iz) = i \sin z, \qquad \sin (iz) = i \sinh z, \tag{4.3.10}$$
$$\cosh (iz) = \cos z, \qquad \cos (iz) = \cosh z, \tag{4.3.11}$$
$$\sinh \bar{z} = \overline{\sinh z}, \qquad \cosh \bar{z} = \overline{\cosh z}, \tag{4.3.12}$$
$$|\sinh z|^2 = \sin^2 y + \sinh^2 x,$$
$$\tag{4.3.13}$$
$$|\cosh z|^2 = \cos^2 y + \sinh^2 x.$$

Remark 4.3.1.   By means of the relations (4.3.10) and (4.3.11), all the properties of hyperbolic functions enumerated in this section may be derived from the corresponding properties of the trigonometric functions; and vice versa.

Also, we may easily verify the following identities:

$$\cosh^2 z - \sinh^2 z = 1, \tag{4.3.14}$$

$$\sinh (z_1 \pm z_2) = \sinh z_1 \cosh z_2 \pm \cosh z_1 \sinh z_2, \tag{4.3.15}$$

$$\cosh (z_1 \pm z_2) = \cosh z_1 \cosh z_2 \pm \sinh z_1 \sinh z_2, \tag{4.3.16}$$

$$\sinh \left(\frac{\pi}{2} i - z\right) = i \cosh z, \tag{4.3.17}$$

$$\sinh 2z = 2 \sinh z \cosh z, \tag{4.3.18}$$

$$\cosh 2z = \cosh^2 z + \sinh^2 z. \tag{4.3.19}$$

EXERCISES 4.3

1. Prove Theorem 4.3.1.   **2.** Prove Theorem 4.3.2.

3. Prove Theorem 4.3.3.   **4.** Prove Theorem 4.3.4.

5. Prove Theorem 4.3.5.   **6.** Verify (4.3.14)-(4.3.19).

7. Prove that if $z = x + iy$, then

$$\tanh z = \frac{\sinh x \cosh x + i \sin y \cos y}{\cos^2 y \cosh^2 x + \sin^2 y \sinh^2 x}.$$

8. Show that if $\tanh (x + iy) = u + iv$, where x, y, u, v are real, then

$$u = \frac{\sinh 2x}{\cosh 2x + \cos 2y}, \qquad v = \frac{\sin 2y}{\cosh 2x + \cos 2y}.$$

9. Find the values of z for which $\sinh z = -i$; $\sinh z = -1$.

10. Show that if w is an analytic function of z, then $\sinh w$ and $\cosh w$ are also analytic functions of z, and

$$\frac{d}{dz} (\sinh w) = \cosh w \frac{dw}{dz}, \qquad \frac{d}{dz} (\cosh w) = \sinh w \frac{dw}{dz}.$$

11. Prove Theorem 4.3.4 by using Theorems 4.3.5 and 4.2.4.

12. Prove Theorem 4.3.2 by using Theorems 4.3.5 and 4.2.2.

4.4. THE LOGARITHMIC FUNCTION. We observed in Theorem 4.1.2 that e^w (where $w = a + bi$, a, b real numbers) is never zero. We now ask whether there exist other values that e^w cannot assume. The following theorem shows that e^w attains all values except the value zero. We shall use the symbol $\text{Log} \, |z|$ to mean the real natural logarithm of the positive number $|z|$, $z = x + iy \neq 0$.

——*THEOREM* 4.4.1. For any complex number $z \neq 0$, there exist complex numbers w such that $e^w = z$. In particular, one such w is the complex number

$$\text{Log} \,|\, z \,| + i \,\text{Arg}\, z, \tag{4.4.1}$$

and any such w is given by

$$\text{Log} \,|\, z \,| + i \,\text{Arg}\, z + 2n\pi i \quad (n \text{ is an integer}). \tag{4.4.2}$$

Proof. Writing $z = x + iy$ in polar form, we have

$$z = |\, z \,|\, e^{i\theta}, \quad (|\, z \,| = r = \sqrt{x^2 + y^2}, \; \theta = \text{Arg}\, z, \; -\pi < \theta \leqq \pi).$$

Now, observe that

$$e^{\text{Log}\,|z|+i\,\text{Arg}\,z} = e^{\text{Log}\,|z|}\, e^{i\,\text{Arg}\,z} = |\, z \,|\, e^{i\theta} = z.$$

Hence, $w = \text{Log} \,|\, z \,| + i \,\text{Arg}\, z$ is a solution of the equation $e^w = z$.

Suppose that w_1 is another solution of $e^w = z$. Then $e^{w_1 - w} = 1$, and from Theorem 4.1.2 we see that

$$w_1 - w = 2n\pi i \quad (n \text{ is an integer}).$$

thus establishing the theorem.

Definition 4.4.1. Let $z \neq 0$ be any complex number. If w is a complex number such that $e^w = z$, then w is called a *logarithm* of z and will be denoted by $w = \log z$.

By Theorem 4.4.1, we have

$$w = \log z = \text{Log} \,|\, z \,| + i \,\text{Arg}\, z + 2n\pi i, \tag{4.4.3}$$
$$(-\pi < \text{Arg}\, z \leqq \pi, \, n \text{ an integer}).$$

In particular, the number w given by (4.4.1) will be called the *principal value of the logarithm* of z, and will be denoted by

$$w = \text{Log}\, z = \text{Log} \,|\, z \,| + i \,\text{Arg}\, z, \quad (-\pi < \text{Arg}\, z \leqq \pi). \tag{4.4.4}$$

Note that $\log z$ is not a single-valued but rather a multiple-valued function of z.

EXAMPLE 4.4.1. Let us show that

(a) $\text{Log}\, i = i \,\dfrac{\pi}{2}$.

(b) $\text{Log}\, (-1 + i) = \frac{1}{2} \text{Log}\, 2 + i \,\frac{3}{4}\pi$.

(c) $\text{Log}\, (-1 - i) = \frac{1}{2} \text{Log}\, 2 - i \,\frac{3}{4}\pi$.

Solution.   (a) $|i| = 1$ and Arg $i = \pi/2$, hence

$$\text{Log } i = \text{Log } 1 + i\frac{\pi}{2} = i\frac{\pi}{2}.$$

(b) $|-1+i| = \sqrt{2}$ and Arg $(-1+i) = \frac{3}{4}\pi$, hence

$$\text{Log }(-1+i) = \text{Log }\sqrt{2} + i\,\tfrac{3}{4}\pi = \tfrac{1}{2}\text{Log } 2 + i\,\tfrac{3}{4}\pi.$$

(c) $|-1-i| = \sqrt{2}$ and Arg $(-1-i) = -\frac{3}{4}\pi$, hence

$$\text{Log }(-1-i) = \text{Log }\sqrt{2} - i\,\tfrac{3}{4}\pi = \tfrac{1}{2}\text{Log } 2 - i\,\tfrac{3}{4}\pi.$$

Remark 4.4.1.   From Example 4.4.1 we see that it is not true, in general, that

$$\text{Log }(z_1 \cdot z_2) = \text{Log } z_1 + \text{Log } z_2,$$

for $(-1-i) = i(-1+i)$ and yet

$$\text{Log }(-1-i) \neq \text{Log } i + \text{Log }(-1+i).$$

However, we have the following

——**THEOREM** 4.4.2.   If the complex numbers z, z_1, z_2 are different from zero, then the principal values of the arguments and logarithms of the product, quotient and powers are given by

$$\text{Arg }(z_1 \cdot z_2) = \text{Arg } z_1 + \text{Arg } z_2 + 2\pi n_1(z_1, z_2), \tag{4.4.5}$$

$$\text{Log }(z_1 \cdot z_2) = \text{Log } z_1 + \text{Log } z_2 + 2\pi i n_1(z_1, z_2), \tag{4.4.6}$$

$$\text{Arg }(z_1/z_2) = \text{Arg } z_1 - \text{Arg } z_2 + 2\pi n_2(z_1, z_2), \tag{4.4.7}$$

$$\text{Log }(z_1/z_2) = \text{Log } z_1 - \text{Log } z_2 + 2\pi i n_2(z_1, z_2), \tag{4.4.8}$$

$$\text{Arg }(z^n) = n\,\text{Arg } z + 2\pi k(z, n), \tag{4.4.9}$$

$$\text{Log } z^n = n\,\text{Log } z + 2\pi i k(z, n), \tag{4.4.10}$$

where n is any integer, and n_1 and n_2 take on values $-1, 0, 1$ as follows:

$$n_1(z_1, z_2) = \begin{cases} -1, \text{ if } \pi < \text{Arg } z_1 + \text{Arg } z_2 \leq 2\pi, \\ 0, \text{ if } -\pi < \text{Arg } z_1 + \text{Arg } z_2 \leq \pi, \\ 1, \text{ if } -2\pi < \text{Arg } z_1 + \text{Arg } z_2 \leq -\pi, \end{cases} \tag{4.4.11}$$

$$n_2(z_1, z_2) = \begin{cases} -1, \text{ if } \pi < \text{Arg } z_1 - \text{Arg } z_2 < 2\pi, \\ 0, \text{ if } -\pi < \text{Arg } z_1 - \text{Arg } z_2 \leq \pi, \\ 1, \text{ if } -2\pi < \text{Arg } z_1 - \text{Arg } z_2 \leq -\pi \end{cases} \tag{4.4.12}$$

and k is the integer given by the bracket function

$$k(z, n) = \left[\frac{1}{2} - \frac{n}{2\pi}\text{Arg } z\right]. \tag{4.4.13}$$

Proof. Verification of (4.4.5). Let $z_1 = |z_1| e^{i\theta_1}$, $z_2 = |z_2| e^{i\theta_2}$, where $\theta_1 = \text{Arg } z_1$, $\theta_2 = \text{Arg } z_2$, $-\pi < \theta_1 \leq \pi$ and $-\pi < \theta_2 \leq \pi$. Note that

$$-2\pi < \theta_1 + \theta_2 \leq 2\pi.$$

Utilizing (1.6.4) we have

$$z_1 \cdot z_2 = |z_1| |z_2| e^{i(\theta_1 + \theta_2)} = |z_1| |z_2| e^{i(\theta_1 + \theta_2 + 2n_1\pi)},$$

where n_1 is an integer such that

$$-\pi < \theta_1 + \theta_2 + 2n_1\pi \leq \pi. \tag{4.4.14}$$

Suppose that

$$\pi < \theta_1 + \theta_2 \leq 2\pi.$$

Then

$$-\pi < \theta_1 + \theta_2 - 2\pi \leq 0,$$

so

$$-\pi < \theta_1 + \theta_2 - 2\pi \leq \pi,$$

and upon comparing this inequality with (4.4.14), we have $n_1(z_1, z_2) = -1$. Suppose that

$$-\pi < \theta_1 + \theta_2 \leq \pi,$$

then clearly $n_1(z_1, z_2) = 0$. Finally, suppose that

$$-2\pi < \theta_1 + \theta_2 \leq -\pi,$$

then

$$0 < \theta_1 + \theta_2 + 2\pi \leq \pi,$$

so

$$-\pi < \theta_1 + \theta_2 + 2\pi \leq \pi,$$

thus $n_1(z_1, z_2) = 1$, and (4.4.5) is established.
  Verification of (4.4.6).

$$\begin{aligned}
\text{Log} (z_1 \cdot z_2) &= \text{Log} |z_1 \cdot z_2| + i \text{Arg} (z_1 \cdot z_2) \\
&= (\text{Log} |z_1| + i \text{Arg } z_1) + (\text{Log} |z_2| + i \text{Arg } z_2) + 2\pi i n_1(z_1, z_2) \\
&= \text{Log } z_1 + \text{Log } z_2 + 2\pi i n_1(z_1, z_2).
\end{aligned}$$

  We shall leave the verification of the remaining formulas as an exercise for the reader.
  Referring to Example 4.4.1 and Remark 4.4.1, let $z_1 = i$, $z_2 = -1 + i$ and $z_3 = (-1 - i) = z_1 \cdot z_2$. Since $\text{Arg } z_1 + \text{Arg } z_2 = \pi/2 + 3\pi/4 = 5\pi/4$,

then $\pi < \text{Arg } z_1 + \text{Arg } z_2 \leqq 2\pi$. Thus, according to the above theorem, we have

$$\text{Log } (z_1 \cdot z_2) = \text{Log } z_1 + \text{Log } z_2 - i2\pi = i\frac{\pi}{2} + \frac{1}{2} \text{Log } 2 + i\frac{3}{4}\pi - i2\pi$$

$$= \frac{1}{2} \text{Log } 2 - i\frac{3}{4}\pi = \text{Log } z_3.$$

Remark 4.4.2. It follows from Theorem 4.4.2 that

$$\log (z_1 \cdot z_2) = \log z_1 + \log z_2, \tag{4.4.15}$$

where the equation has the following meaning: Taking any value for any two of the terms, we can find an appropriate value for the other term such that (4.4.15) holds. In a similar sense, we also have

$$\log \left(\frac{z_1}{z_2}\right) = \log z_1 - \log z_2. \tag{4.4.16}$$

Let us write (4.4.4) as

$$u + iv = \text{Log } z = \text{Log } r + i\theta, \tag{4.4.17}$$

$$(z = x + iy, \, |z| = r = \sqrt{x^2 + y^2}, \, \text{Arg } z = \theta, \, -\pi < \theta \leqq \pi).$$

Thus

$$u = \text{Log } r \quad \text{and} \quad v = \theta.$$

Observe that $\text{Log } r$ is not continuous at the origin. Also, $\text{Arg } z$ is not continuous at the points on the negative half of the real axis; for, if $x < 0$ and $y > 0$, we have

$$\lim_{y \to 0} \text{Arg } (x + iy) = \pi, \qquad \lim_{y \to 0} \text{Arg } (x - iy) = -\pi.$$

However, if we restrict our attention to the domain D consisting of the points of the z plane with the nonpositive half of the real axis removed, then u and v and their partial derivatives with respect to r and θ are continuous functions of r and θ. Moreover, utilizing Exercise 3.6.10, we see that the Cauchy-Riemann differential equations

$$\frac{\partial u}{\partial r} = \frac{1}{r}\frac{\partial v}{\partial \theta}, \qquad \frac{\partial v}{\partial r} = -\frac{1}{r}\frac{\partial u}{\partial \theta}$$

are satisfied when $u = \text{Log } r$ and $v = \theta$. It follows that $\text{Log } z$ is analytic in D.

Also, again utilizing Exercise 3.6.10, we have

$$\frac{d}{dz}(\text{Log } z) = (\cos \theta - i \sin \theta)\frac{\partial}{\partial r}(\text{Log } r + i\theta)$$

$$= \frac{(\cos \theta - i \sin \theta)}{r} = \frac{1}{z}.$$

Thus we have established the following

——**THEOREM** 4.4.3.   The function Log z is single-valued and analytic in the domain D consisting of all points of the complex plane except those lying on the nonpositive real axis. Moreover, for z in D.

$$\frac{d}{dz}(\text{Log } z) = \frac{1}{z}. \qquad (4.4.18)$$

We shall now define what is meant by a complex number raised to a complex power.

Definition 4.4.2.   If $z \neq 0$ and w is any complex number, we define z^w by

$$z^w = e^{w \log z}, \qquad (4.4.19)$$

where log z is given by (4.4.3).

Observe that if w is not a rational real number, then

$$e^{w \log z} = e^{w[\text{Log}|z| + i\text{Arg}z + 2n\pi i]}$$

$n = 0, \pm 1, \pm 2, \cdots$, has an infinite number of values. The *principal value* of z^w will be defined as the value

$$e^{w\text{Log}z},$$

where Log z is given by (4.4.4). *Henceforth, z^w will denote the value $e^{w\text{Log}z}$*, except where the contrary is indicated. Thus z^w becomes a single-valued function.

EXAMPLE 4.4.2.   Let us find the value of the following expressions: (a) $(-i)^i$ and (b) $(-1)^{2i}$.

Solution.

(a) $(-i)^i = e^{i\text{Log}(-i)} = e^{i(-i\pi/2)} = e^{\pi/2}$.

(b) $(-1)^{2i} = e^{2i\text{Log}(-1)} = e^{2i(+i\pi)} = e^{-2\pi}$.

——**THEOREM** 4.4.4.   If $z \neq 0$ and w_1 and w_2 are any complex numbers, then

$$z^{w_1}z^{w_2} = z^{w_1+w_2}. \qquad (4.4.20)$$

Proof.

$$z^{w_1}z^{w_2} = e^{w_1\text{Log}z}\, e^{w_2\text{Log}z} = e^{(w_1+w_2)\text{Log}z} = z^{w_1+w_2}.$$

——**THEOREM** 4.4.5. If $z_1 \neq 0$, $z_2 \neq 0$ and w is any complex number, then

$$(z_1 z_2)^w = z_1^w z_2^w e^{2\pi i w n_1(z_1, z_2)}, \tag{4.4.21}$$

$$\left(\frac{z_1}{z_2}\right)^w = \frac{z_1^w}{z_2^w} e^{2\pi i w n_2(z_1, z_2)}, \tag{4.4.22}$$

where $n_1(z_1, z_2)$ and $n_2(z_1, z_2)$ are the integers defined in Theorem 4.4.2.

Proof. Verification of (4.4.21). Utilizing Theorems 4.1.1 and 4.4.2, we have

$$(z_1 z_2)^w = e^{w \operatorname{Log}(z_1 z_2)} = e^{w[\operatorname{Log} z_1 + \operatorname{Log} z_2 + 2\pi i n_1(z_1, z_2)]}$$

$$= e^{w \operatorname{Log} z_1} e^{w \operatorname{Log} z_2} e^{2\pi i w n_1(z_1, z_2)}$$

$$= z_1^w z_2^w e^{2\pi i w n_1(z_1, z_2)}.$$

Similarly, one verifies (4.4.22), and the theorem is thus established.

Observe that the usual laws of exponents still hold, provided that $-\pi < \operatorname{Arg} z_1 + \operatorname{Arg} z_2 \leq \pi$. However, since $n_1(z_1, z_2)$ and $n_2(z_1, z_2)$ can also take on values ± 1, we see that, in general,

$$(z_1 z_2)^w \neq z_1^w z_2^w \quad \text{and} \quad \left(\frac{z_1}{z_2}\right)^w \neq \frac{z_1^w}{z_2^w}.$$

Let us write z^w as $z^w = e^{w\mu}$ where $\mu = \operatorname{Log} z$. Then, utilizing Theorems 4.1.4, 4.4.3, and 3.5.2, we see that z^w is analytic in the domain D consisting of all the points of the complex plane except the points $z = -|z|$. Moreover, its derivative is given by

$$\frac{d}{dz}(z^w) = \frac{d}{d\mu}(e^{w\mu}) \frac{d\mu}{dz} = w e^{w\mu} \cdot \frac{1}{z} = w z^{w-1}.$$

Thus we have established the following

——**THEOREM** 4.4.6. The function z^w, where w is any fixed complex number, is analytic in the domain D, which consists of all the points of the complex plane except those points lying on the nonpositive real axis. Moreover

$$\frac{d}{dz}(z^w) = w z^{w-1}. \tag{4.4.23}$$

——**THEOREM** 4.4.7. If $z \neq 0$, w, and λ are any complex numbers, then

$$\operatorname{Log}(z^w) = w \operatorname{Log} z + 2\pi i k, \tag{4.4.24}$$

$$(z^w)^\lambda = z^{w\lambda} e^{2\pi i \lambda k}, \tag{4.4.25}$$

where k is the integer given by the bracket function

$$k = \left[\frac{1}{2} - \frac{\mathscr{I}(w)\,\text{Log}\,|\,z\,| + \mathscr{R}(w)\,\text{Arg}\,z}{2\pi}\right]. \qquad (4.4.26)$$

Proof. Verification of (4.4.24). Denote z^w by α, Arg z by θ, and let $w = u + iv$. Then

$$\alpha = z^w = e^{w\text{Log}\,z} = e^{(u+iv)(\text{Log}|z|+i\theta)} = e^{u\text{Log}|z|-v\theta}\,e^{i(v\text{Log}|z|+u\theta)}.$$

Thus

$$|\,\alpha\,| = e^{u\text{Log}|z|-v\theta} \quad \text{and} \quad \text{Arg}\,\alpha = v\,\text{Log}\,|\,z\,| + u\theta + 2\pi k,$$

where k is the integer such that

$$-\pi < v\,\text{Log}\,|\,z\,| + u\theta + 2\pi k \leqq \pi.$$

Upon solving for k we get

$$t < k \leqq t + 1,$$

where

$$t = -\frac{1}{2} - \frac{v\,\text{Log}\,|\,z\,| + u\theta}{2\pi}.$$

Therefore

$$k = [t + 1] = \left[\frac{1}{2} - \frac{v\,\text{Log}\,|\,z\,| + u\theta}{2\pi}\right] = \left[\frac{1}{2} - \frac{\mathscr{I}(w)\,\text{Log}\,|\,z\,| + \mathscr{R}(w)\,\text{Arg}\,z}{2\pi}\right].$$

Now

$$\begin{aligned}
\text{Log}\,z^w = \text{Log}\,\alpha &= \text{Log}\,|\,\alpha\,| + i\,\text{Arg}\,\alpha \\
&= u\,\text{Log}\,|\,z\,| - v\theta + i(v\,\text{Log}\,|\,z\,| + u\theta + 2\pi k) \\
&= (u + iv)(\text{Log}\,|\,z\,| + i\theta) + 2\pi ik = w\,\text{Log}\,z + 2\pi ik.
\end{aligned}$$

The verification of (4.4.25) is left as an exercise for the reader.

EXERCISES 4.4

1. Prove (4.4.7)-(4.4.10).

2. Prove (4.4.22) and (4.4.25).

3. For any complex number $z \neq 0$, show that (a) $\text{Log}\,(e^z) = z + 2\pi ik$, where $k = [\frac{1}{2} - (\mathscr{I}(z))/2\pi]$ and $[\ ]$ denotes the bracket function;
(b) $|\,z^i\,| < e^{\pi}$; \qquad (c) $|\,z^\lambda\,| = |\,e^{\lambda\text{log}z}\,| = |\,z\,|^\lambda$, where λ is real.

4. Find the value of $\text{Log}\,(1 - i)$.

5. Find the values of log 3.

6. Find the value of $(1 + i)^i$.

7. Find the value of Log $[(1 + i)^{1-i}]$.

8. Find the value of $e^{\log(1+i)}$.

9. Find the value of $[(1 + i)^{(1-i)}]^{(1+i)}$.

10. Find the value of $(-1 + i)^i$.

11. Find the value of $[(1 + i)/2]^{-i}$.

12. Show that $(\sqrt{3} + i)^{i/2} = e^{-\pi/12}[\cos (\frac{1}{2} \text{Log } 2) + i \sin (\frac{1}{2} \text{Log } 2)]$.

13. Show that $(d/dz) (\alpha^z) = \alpha^z \text{Log } \alpha$, where α is a complex constant different from zero.

14. Show that $\mathscr{R}[(1 + i)^{\text{Log}(1+i)}] = 2^{(1/4)\text{Log}2} e^{-(\pi^2/16)} \cos (\frac{1}{4} \pi \text{Log } 2)$.

15. Give another proof of Theorem 4.4.3 by utilizing Theorem 4.1.3.

16. Show that for a fixed integer n, and Arg z varying according to the inequality, $-\pi < \text{Arg } z \leq \pi$, k of Theorem 4.4.2 will also vary as follows: $k_{\min} \leq k \leq k_{\max}$, where $k_{\max} = |[n/2]|$ and $k_{\min} = -[|n|/2]$, and $[\ ]$ denotes the bracket function.

17. Find the principal argument of z^5 in terms of the principal argument of z.

18. Show that if θ is any real number such that $z = |z| e^{i\theta}$, then

$$\text{Arg } z = \theta + 2\pi \left[\frac{1}{2} - \frac{\theta}{2\pi}\right],$$

where $[\ ]$ denotes the bracket function.

4.5. MULTIPLE-VALUED FUNCTIONS. A careful reading of the definition of a function given in Section 3.1 shows that we did not exclude the case in which for some values of z in the domain of definition there corresponds more than one value of $w = f(z)$. When this is the case, we say that $w = f(z)$ is a *multiple-valued function*. Although in Definition 3.4.2 the concept of analytic functions was defined only for single-valued functions, the property of analyticity may also be enjoyed by multiple-valued functions of a complex variable in the sense to be explained below. An important class of such multiple-valued functions arises when we consider the inverse of a single-valued analytic function. In this section we shall study several examples of such functions.

EXAMPLE 4.5.1. Let us consider the equation

$$w^2 = z. \tag{4.5.1}$$

Observe that z is a single-valued analytic function of w. However, when we consider the inverse function $w = \sqrt{z}$, we see that for each value of $z \neq 0$ there correspond two values of w.

Let $z = re^{i\theta}$. Using formula (1.7.3) we may write (4.5.1) as

$$w = \sqrt{r}\, e^{i(\theta+2k\pi)/2}, \qquad k = 0, 1. \tag{4.5.2}$$

If we restrict θ to the range $0 \leq \theta < 2\pi$, we obtain two single-valued functions of z, namely,

$$w_1 = \sqrt{r}\, e^{i(\theta/2)} \quad \text{and} \quad w_2 = \sqrt{r}\, e^{i[(\theta/2)+\pi]}, \qquad 0 \leq \theta < 2\pi. \tag{4.5.3}$$

Observe that $w_2 = -w_1$. Note, however, that although w_1 is defined and is single-valued for all values of z, it is not continuous at any point z_0 on the positive real axis. For, as $z \to z_0$ from above, $\theta \to 0$ and $w_1 \to \sqrt{r}$, while as $z \to z_0$ from below, $\theta \to 2\pi$ and $w_1 \to -\sqrt{r}$. In order to make w_1 continuous, we restrict ourselves to the domain D_0: $0 < \theta < 2\pi$, $r > 0$, consisting of the z plane with the nonnegative half of the real axis removed. Then, the values of w are given in D_0 by the two single-valued continuous functions w_1 and $w_2 = -w_1$. To see that w_1 is a continuous function of z in D_0, observe that w_1 is a single-valued continuous function of r and θ, which in turn are single-valued continuous functions of z in D_0. The nonnegative half of the real axis, which is excluded from the domain D_0, is called a *branch cut* for w_1 and w_2. We shall now show that w_1 is also an analytic function of z in D_0.

Since $z = w_1^2$, we have $dz/dw_1 = 2w_1$. Also, since w_1 is a continuous function of z in D_0, we have

$$\lim_{\Delta z \to 0} \Delta w_1 = 0.$$

Therefore

$$\lim_{\Delta z \to 0} \frac{\Delta w_1}{\Delta z} = \lim_{\Delta w_1 \to 0} \frac{\Delta w_1}{\Delta z} = \lim_{\Delta w_1 \to 0} \frac{1}{\Delta z/\Delta w_1}$$

$$= \frac{1}{\lim_{\Delta w_1 \to 0} \Delta z/\Delta w_1} = \frac{1}{dz/dw_1} = \frac{1}{2w_1}.$$

For z in D_0, $w_1 \neq 0$; thus dw_1/dz exists (and is finite) for every point z in D_0. Hence w_1 is a single-valued analytic function of z in D_0. Since $w_2 = -w_1$, w_2 is also a single-valued analytic function of z in D_0.

Each of the functions w_1 and w_2 is called a *branch* in D_0 of the multiple-valued function w. More generally, we may define a branch of a multiple-valued function as follows:

Definition 4.5.1. Given a multiple-valued function $w = f(z)$ defined in a domain D in the complex plane. Let D_0 be a domain contained in D. Then, by a *branch* of w in D_0, we mean a single-valued analytic function $w_1 = g(z)$ defined in D_0, such that for any z in D_0, $g(z)$ is one of the values of $f(z)$.

Returning to Example 4.5.1, instead of taking $0 < \theta < 2\pi$, we could have restricted θ to the values $-\pi < \theta < \pi$. Setting $z = re^{i\theta}$ and denoting by D_π the domain consisting of the z plane with the nonpositive half of the real axis removed, the values of w in D_π would again be given by the branches*

$$W_1 = \sqrt{r}\, e^{i(\theta/2)}, \qquad W_2 = -W_1, \qquad r > 0, \; -\pi < \theta < \pi. \qquad (4.5.4)$$

Let us now examine the behavior of $w = \sqrt{z}$ as z moves along a circle with center at the origin and radius r_0. Let us begin with a fixed point $z_0 = r_0\, e^{i\theta_0}$, $r_0 > 0$. Then as θ increases continuously, starting with the value θ_0, the point $z = r_0\, e^{i\theta}$ will traverse the circle in a counterclockwise direction. Let us take $\mathscr{W} = \sqrt{r_0}\, e^{i(\theta/2)}$. Thus, $\mathscr{W}$ is a single-valued continuous function of θ (not necessarily of z) varying continuously as z varies along the circle, and such that $\mathscr{W}^2 = z$. It is not difficult to show that for each value θ_1 of θ, there is a neighborhood, $N(\theta_1)$, of θ_1 such that the values of $\mathscr{W}$ for θ in $N(\theta_1)$ agree with those given by at least one of the four branches $w_i(z)$ and $W_i(z)$, $i = 1, 2$. We now observe that as θ increases by 2π, the value of $\mathscr{W}$ is multiplied by -1, since

$$\sqrt{r_0}\, e^{i(\theta + 2\pi)/2} = -\sqrt{r_0}\, e^{i(\theta/2)}.$$

Thus, if the value of $\mathscr{W}$ corresponding to the point z_0 is originally given by one of the branches of w in D_α, $\alpha = 0, \pi$, we find, after encircling the origin once and returning to the point z_0, that the value of w assigned to it is now given by the other branch.

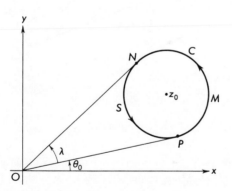

FIG. 4.5.1

The behavior of w that we have just described is equally valid for any circle with center at the origin. Let us now consider a circle C with center at $z_0 \neq 0$ and of radius such that the origin is exterior to this circle. Let $z = re^{i\theta}$ vary around this circle, making a complete revolution. We see geometrically (Fig. 4.5.1) that if z starts at P and traverses C in a counterclockwise direction, then as z describes the arc PMN, $\arg z$ increases from θ_0 to $\theta_0 + \lambda$, that is, by λ. When z traverses the arc NSP, however, $\arg z$ decreases by the same amount. Thus we see that the total change in the $\arg z$ after one complete

* Any ray $\theta = \alpha$ determines a domain D_α, $\alpha < \theta < \alpha + 2\pi$, $r > 0$, in which $w = \sqrt{z}$ has two branches.

revolution is zero. Therefore r and θ, and hence w, have returned to their initial values. Consequently, the branches w_1 and w_2 *interchange* only when z encircles the origin. This property, distinguishing the origin from all other points, is one of the main characteristics of what is known as a *branch point*.

EXAMPLE 4.5.2.   Let us consider the multiple-valued function $w = \sqrt{z^2 - 1}$ defined by the equation

$$w^2 = z^2 - 1. \qquad (4.5.5)$$

Let

$$\begin{cases} z - 1 = \rho_1 e^{i\theta_1}, \\ z + 1 = \rho_2 e^{i\theta_2}. \end{cases} \qquad (4.5.6)$$

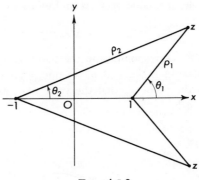

FIG. 4.5.2

(See Fig. 4.5.2.) Then (4.5.5) may be written as

$$w^2 = \rho_1 \rho_2 e^{i(\theta_1 + \theta_2)}.$$

Hence

$$w = \sqrt{\rho_1 \rho_2}\, e^{i[(\theta_1 + \theta_2)/2 + k\pi]} \qquad k = 0, 1. \qquad (4.5.7)$$

By making the restrictions

$$-\pi < \theta_1 \leqq \pi, \qquad 0 \leqq \theta_2 < 2\pi, \qquad (4.5.8)$$

we obtain two single-valued functions of z

$$w_1 = \sqrt{\rho_1 \rho_2}\, e^{i[(\theta_1 + \theta_2)/2]} \quad \text{and} \quad w_2 = -w_1. \qquad (4.5.9)$$

From Fig. 4.5.2 we see that the $\lim (\theta_1 + \theta_2)$ as z approaches any point on the real axis to the right of the point $z = 1$ is zero if approached from above and 2π if approached from below. Thus the two limiting values of $[(\theta_1 + \theta_2)/2]$ differ by π. Hence w_1 (and also w_2) is discontinuous at such a point. Similarly, one finds that w_1 (and also w_2) is discontinuous at points on the real axis to the left of $z = -1$, and continuous at the points of the real axis lying on the segment $-1 < x < 1$. Thus, in order to make w_1 and w_2 continuous, we restrict ourselves to the domain D_1 consisting of all the points of the z plane with the exception of the points $z = x + 0i$, $|x| \geq 1$. As in Example 4.5.1, we can show that w_1 is also analytic in D_1 with $dw_1/dz = z/w_1$. Moreover, for each z in D_1, the value of w_1 is one of the values of the multiple-valued function $w = \sqrt{z^2 - 1}$. Hence by Definition 4.5.1, w_1 (and also w_2) is a branch in D_1 of the multiple-valued function $w = \sqrt{z^2 - 1}$. The half lines $x \geq 1$, $y = 0$ and $x \leq -1$, $y = 0$ are branch cuts for the branches w_1 and w_2.

We could have made the following restrictions on θ_1 and θ_2:

$$-\pi < \theta_1 \leq \pi \quad \text{and} \quad -\pi < \theta_2 \leq \pi. \qquad (4.5.10)$$

Then we would again obtain two single-valued functions of z

$$W_1 = \sqrt{\rho_1 \rho_2}\, e^{i[(\theta_1 + \theta_2)/2]} \quad \text{and} \quad W_2 = -W_1. \qquad (4.5.11)$$

If z_0 is any point on the real axis such that $|z_0| > 1$, then W_1 approaches the same value irrespective of the manner in which z approaches z_0. However, if z_0 is real and $|z_0| < 1$, then W_1 approaches different values according as z approaches z_0 from above or below. In order to make W_1 continuous, we restrict ourselves to a domain D_2 consisting of all the points in the z plane with the exception of the points $z = x + 0i$, $|x| \leq 1$. As above, it can be shown that W_1 and W_2 are branches in D_2 of the multiple-valued function $w = \sqrt{z^2 - 1}$. The branch cut is now the segment $-1 \leq x \leq 1$, $y = 0$.

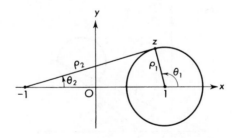

FIG. 4.5.3

Note that each point $z \neq \pm 1$ is in some domain (say D_1 or D_2) in which there are two branches of the function w given by $w^2 = z^2 - 1$. However, this cannot be said for the points $z = 1$ and $z = -1$. To see this, let z vary continuously in a counterclockwise direction along a circle C with center at $z = 1$, radius ρ_1 and having $z = -1$ in its exterior. (See Fig. 4.5.3.) Let the initial point on C be z_0 so that

$$z_0 - 1 = \rho_1 e^{i\lambda_1}$$

and

$$z_0 + 1 = \rho_2^0 e^{i\lambda_2},$$

where λ_1, λ_2 and ρ_2^0 are particular values of θ_1, θ_2 and ρ_2, respectively, and ρ_2 is the distance from the point $z = -1$ to a point on the circle C. Let the value of w at z_0 be given by

$$w_0 = \sqrt{\rho_1\rho_2^0}\, e^{i[(\lambda_1+\lambda_2)/2]}.$$

As z travels in a counterclockwise direction along C, let θ_1 and θ_2 vary continuously, starting from the initial values λ_1 and λ_2. Thus,

$$w = \sqrt{\rho_1\rho_2}\, e^{i[(\theta_1+\theta_2)/2]}$$

will also vary continuously beginning with the initial value w_0. As z completes one revolution arriving at the point z_0, we see from Fig. 4.5.3 that θ_2 returns to its initial value λ_2 while θ_1 assumes the value $\lambda_1 + 2\pi$. Hence w assumes the value

$$\sqrt{\rho_1\rho_2^0}\, e^{i[(\lambda_1+2\pi)+\lambda_2]/2} = e^{i\pi}w_0 = -w_0.$$

Thus w, starting with the initial value w_0 given by one of the branches of the function w for $z = z_0$, and varying continuously as z travels along the circle, arrives at a new value $-w_0$ given for $z = z_0$ by another branch of w. This shows that $z = 1$ cannot be in any domain D where there exists a branch of w. For, if $z = 1$ were in such a domain D, then we could draw the circle C in D, and encircling the point $z = 1$ we should arrive at the same value w_0 of w initially given by our branch. A similar argument applies to the point $z = -1$.

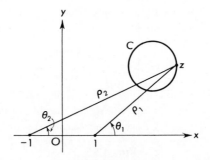

FIG. 4.5.4

Observe, however, [see Fig. (4.5.4)], that if z completes a revolution along a circle C having both $z = 1$ and $z = -1$ exterior to it, then if w starts out with the initial value w_0 for the point z_0 on C, it will return to this same value. This fact is also true when the circle C contains both points $z = 1$ and $z = -1$ in its interior. These exceptional points $z = \pm 1$, are the branch points of the multiple-valued function $w = \sqrt{z^2 - 1}$.

EXAMPLE 4.5.3. $w = \log z$.

From Definition 4.4.1 we have for $z = re^{i\theta}$, $z \neq 0$, that

$$w = \log z = \text{Log} \,|\, z \,| + i \, \text{Arg} \, z + 2n\pi i \qquad (4.5.12)$$
$$(-\pi < \text{Arg} \, z \leq \pi, \, r > 0 \text{ and } n = 0, \pm 1, \pm 2, \cdots).$$

If we set $n = 0$ in (4.5.12), we obtain the single-valued function

$$\text{Log} \, z = \text{Log} \,|\, z \,| + i \, \text{Arg} \, z \qquad (-\pi < \text{Arg} \, z \leq \pi, \, r > 0).$$

However, as we have already observed, (see the discussion preceding Theorem 4.4.3) Log z fails to be continuous for real nonpositive values of z. If we confine ourselves to the domain D_π, consisting of the z plane with the nonpositive half of the real axis removed, then Log z is a single-valued analytic function in D_π. Thus according to Definition 4.5.1, Log $z + 2n\pi i$ is for each value of n a branch in D_π of the multiple-valued function $w = \log z$.

The branch cut consists of the points on the nonpositive half of the real axis. Also, from Exercise 4.5.4 we see that we could have chosen for a branch cut the nonnegative half of the real axis. The values of log z would then be given in the domain D_0, consisting of the z plane with the nonnegative half of the real axis removed, by the branches

$$[\text{Log} \, (-z) + i\pi] + 2n\pi i, \qquad n = 0, \pm 1, \pm 2, \cdots.$$

Thus, any point $z \neq 0$ is in some domain (say D_0 or D_π) where the values of $w = \log z$ are given by the branches of this function. However, this is not true for the point $z = 0$, which is a branch point of the function $w = \log z$.

Now, let C be a circle with center at the origin and arbitrary radius r_0 and let $z = r_0 e^{i\theta}$ with θ increasing continuously from θ_0 to $\theta_0 + 2\pi$. Thus, the point z will traverse continuously the circle C in a counterclockwise direction starting at $z_0 = r_0 e^{i\theta_0}$ and upon completing one revolution will return to its initial position. Let us define

$$\mathscr{W} = \mathscr{W}(z) = \text{Log} \, r_0 + i\theta.$$

Observe that as z traverses the circle C, $\mathscr{W}$ varies continuously with θ. It is not difficult to show (see Exercise 4.5.5) that in the neighborhood of each value θ_1 of θ, $\mathscr{W}$ coincides with at least one of the branches of $w = \log z$. Further observe that although the real part, Log r_0, of $\mathscr{W}$ returns to its initial value as z makes one revolution around C, the imaginary part θ of $\mathscr{W}$ changes by 2π.

However, if $z = re^{i\theta}$ traverses a circle C with center at $z = a \neq 0$ and of sufficiently small radius so that the origin is exterior to C, and if $\mathscr{W}$ is given by

$$\mathscr{W} = \mathscr{W}(z) = \text{Log} \, r + i\theta, \qquad \theta_0 \leq \theta < \theta_0 + 2\pi, \quad r > 0, \qquad (4.5.13)$$

then, as in Example 4.5.1 (see Fig. 4.5.1), upon completing a revolution, r and θ; and hence $\mathscr{W}$, assume their initial values.

Remark 4.5.1.   If in Example 4.5.1 we consider the domain D consisting of the z plane with the point $z = 0$ removed, we see that the multiple-valued function $w = \sqrt{z}$ displays the following behavior:

(1) Given any point z_0 in D and one of the values $w_\alpha(z_0)$ of $w = \sqrt{z}$, then there exists a neighborhood $N(z_0)$ of z_0 contained in D and a branch $G_\alpha(z)$ of the multiple-valued function $w = \sqrt{z}$ defined in $N(z_0)$, such that the value of the branch at $z = z_0$ coincides with the given value $w_\alpha(z_0)$, that is, $w_\alpha(z_0) = G_\alpha(z_0)$.

(2) Given any two branches of the function $w = \sqrt{z}$, we can pass from one branch to the other by continuous variation along some curve.

The same two properties are also true for the multiple-valued function $w = \log z$ (see Example 4.5.3) and $w = \sqrt{z^2 - 1}$ (see Example 4.5.2). In Example 4.5.2, however, the domain D is taken as the z plane with the points $z = \pm 1$ removed. We shall now formulate explicitly the definition of a multiple-valued analytic function in terms of the above two properties.

In Chapter 2 the reader has already encountered the concept of a (continuous) curve or arc. It is defined by a pair of continuous parametric equations $x = x(t)$, $y = y(t)$, $t_1 \leq t \leq t_2$; or simply by $C\colon z = z(t)$, $t_1 \leq t \leq t_2$, with $z(t) = x(t) + iy(t)$. The reader has also encountered the definition of a neighborhood of a point z along a curve, z being a point on the curve. (See Definition 2.10.1.) A function $g(z)$ defined for all z on the curve C is said to be *continuous along* C if $g[z(t)]$ is a continuous function of t for $t_1 \leq t \leq t_2$.

Definition 4.5.2.   Let $f(z)$ be a function (not necessarily single-valued) defined over a domain D, and suppose that $C\colon z = z(t)$, $t_1 \leq t \leq t_2$, is a curve contained in D. Let $g(z)$ be a continuous function defined along the curve C. Suppose that for each point $z_0 = z(t_0)$ on C there exists a neighborhood $N(z_0)$ in D and a neighborhood N of z_0 along the curve C such that (1) N is contained in $N(z_0)$, (2) there exists over $N(z_0)$ a branch $G(z)$ of $f(z)$ and (3) for z in N, $g(z) = G(z)$. Then $g(z)$ will be called a *branch* of $f(z)$ *along* C.

Definition 4.5.3.   Let $f(z)$ be a function (not necessarily single-valued) defined over a domain D and let $G_1(z)$ and $G_2(z)$ be two branches of $f(z)$ defined respectively over two subdomains D_1 and D_2 of D. Let $C\colon z = z(t)$, $t_1 \leq t \leq t_2$, be a curve joining a point $z_1 = z(t_1)$ in D_1 to a point $z_2 = z(t_2)$ in D_2. Suppose that $g(z)$ is a branch of $f(z)$ along C such that $g(z) = G_1(z)$ in some neighborhood N_1 of z_1 along the curve C, and $g(z) = G_2(z)$ in some neighborhood N_2 of z_2 along the curve C. Then the branch $G_2(z)$ is said to be an *analytic continuation* of $G_1(z)$ *along the curve* C.

Definition 4.5.4.   A multiple-valued function $f(z)$ defined over a domain D is said to be an *analytic function in* D, if

(1) for any point z_0 in D and any one of the values $f_\alpha(z_0)$ of $f(z)$ at $z = z_0$, there exists a neighborhood $N(z_0)$ of z_0, and a branch $G_\alpha(z)$ of the multiple-valued function $f(z)$ defined over $N(z_0)$ such that $G_\alpha(z_0) = f_\alpha(z_0)$; and

(2) for any two branches $G_1(z)$ and $G_2(z)$ of $f(z)$, $G_2(z)$ is an analytic continuation of $G_1(z)$ along some curve C in D.

EXAMPLE 4.5.4. The function

$$f_1(z) = \log z = \text{Log } r + i\theta, \qquad 0 < \theta < 6\pi, \qquad z = re^{i\theta},$$

is a multiple-valued analytic function in the domain D of all complex z such that $z \neq 0$. Similarly the function $f_2(z) = \log z = \text{Log } r + i\theta$, $-\infty < \theta < \infty$, is analytic in the same domain D. The function $f_2(z)$ is said to be an *extension* of $f_1(z)$ since every branch of $f_1(z)$ is also a branch of $f_2(z)$. The function $f_2(z)$ has no further extensions in D and is said to be *maximal* in D.

EXERCISES 4.5

1. In Example 4.5.2 show that w_1 and W_1 given in (4.5.9) and (4.5.11), respectively, satisfy the relations $w_1(-z) = w_1(z)$ for $\mathscr{I}(z) \neq 0$, $W_1(z) = w_1(z)$ for $\mathscr{I}(z) > 0$, and $W_1(z) = -w_1(z)$ for $\mathscr{I}(z) < 0$.

2. In Example 4.5.2 show that w_1 given in (4.5.9) is analytic in the domain D_1, consisting of the z plane with the points $x + 0i$, $|x| \geq 1$ removed. Also show that

$$\frac{dw_1}{dz} = \frac{z}{w_1}, \qquad \text{for } z \text{ in } D_1.$$

3. In Example 4.5.2 show that W_1 and W_2 given in (4.5.11) are analytic in the domain D_2, consisting of the z plane with the points $x + 0i$, $|x| \leq 1$ removed. In particular show that

$$\frac{dW_1}{dz} = \frac{z}{W_1}, \qquad \text{for } z \text{ in } D_2.$$

4. In Example 4.5.3 show that $\text{Log}(-z) + i\pi$ is a branch of the function $\log z$ and is analytic in the domain D_0, consisting of the z plane with the nonnegative half of the real axis removed. Also show that for z in the upper half of the z plane

$$\text{Log}(-z) + i\pi = \text{Log } z,$$

whereas for z in the lower half of the z plane

$$\text{Log}(-z) + i\pi = \text{Log } z + 2\pi i.$$

5. Show that in a neighborhood of each point (r, θ), $r > 0$, the function $\mathscr{W} = \text{Log } r + i\theta$ coincides with at least one of the branches $\text{Log } z + 2n\pi i$, $z \neq -|z|$; or $\text{Log}(-z) + \pi i + 2n\pi i$, $z \neq |z|$, of $\log z$, where n is an integer, and $z = re^{i\theta}$.

6. Show that if $z = a + r_0 e^{it}$, $a \neq 0$, $r_0 < |a|$ and $\mathscr{W} = \mathscr{W}(t)$ is a continuous function of t such that for each value of t we have $\mathscr{W}^2 = z$, then $\mathscr{W}(t + 2\pi) = \mathscr{W}(t)$.

7. Show that if $z = r_0 e^{it}$, $r_0 > 0$, $r_0 \neq 1$, and $\mathscr{W}(t)$ is a continuous function of t such that $[\mathscr{W}(t)]^2 = z^2 - 1$, then $\mathscr{W}(t + 2\pi) = \mathscr{W}(t)$.

4.6.   THE INVERSE TRIGONOMETRIC FUNCTIONS: arc sin z,
arc cos z AND arc tan z. The function $w = \text{arc sin } z$ is defined by the equation

$$z = \sin w. \tag{4.6.1}$$

From (4.2.2) we may write (4.6.1) as

$$z = \frac{e^{iw} - e^{-iw}}{2i} = \frac{e^{2iw} - 1}{2ie^{iw}}.$$

Thus

$$e^{2iw} - 2ize^{iw} - 1 = 0.$$

Letting $W = e^{iw}$, we may write the above equation as

$$W^2 - 2izW - 1 = 0. \tag{4.6.2}$$

The roots of this equation are given by

$$W = iz + \sqrt{1 - z^2}, \tag{4.6.3}$$

where $\sqrt{1 - z^2}$ is a two-valued function. Setting

$$\nu = \nu(z) = \sqrt{\rho_1 \rho_2} \, e^{i(\theta_1 + \theta_2)/2},$$

where $\rho_1, \rho_2, \theta_1, \theta_2$ are given by (4.5.6) and (4.5.8) (see Fig. 4.5.2), we have

$$\nu^2 = z^2 - 1 \quad \text{and} \quad (\pm i\nu)^2 = 1 - z^2.$$

The values of the multiple-valued function $\sqrt{1 - z^2}$ are thus given by

$$i\nu(z) \quad \text{and} \quad - i\nu(z).$$

Hence, the values of W in (4.6.3) are given by

$$W_1 = iz + i\nu(z) \quad \text{and} \quad W_2 = iz - i\nu(z), \tag{4.6.4}$$

where ν is single-valued. [See (4.5.8).]

Since the product of the roots of equation (4.6.2) equals the constant term, we have

$$W_1 W_2 = -1 = e^{(2k+1)i\pi}, \qquad k = 0, \pm 1, \pm 2, \cdots.$$

Hence

$$\log W_2 = -\operatorname{Log} W_1 + (2k+1)i\pi$$

and by (4.6.4) we have

$$\log [iz - iv(z)] = -\operatorname{Log} [iz + iv(z)] + (2k+1)i\pi. \qquad (4.6.5)$$

Since $W = e^{iw}$ and $w = \arcsin z$, we see, upon taking logarithms in (4.6.4), that the values of w are given by the following equations

$$w = \arcsin z = -i \log (iz + iv),$$

$$(4.6.6)$$

$$w = \arcsin z = -i \log (iz - iv).$$

Observe that $\log (iz + iv)$ has a meaning, since $iz + i\sqrt{z^2 - 1} \neq 0$ for every z. From (4.6.6) and (4.6.5) we see that the values of w are given by

$$w = \arcsin z = -i \operatorname{Log} (iz + iv) + 2k\pi,$$
$$w = \arcsin z = i \operatorname{Log} (iz + iv) + (2k+1)\pi,$$
$$k = 0, \pm 1, \pm 2, \cdots.$$

The above expressions can be combined into a single equivalent expression

$$w = \arcsin z = k\pi - (-1)^k i \operatorname{Log} (iz + iv), \quad k = 0, \pm 1, \pm 2, \cdots. \qquad (4.6.7)$$

Since [see (4.4.6)]

$$\operatorname{Log} (iz + iv) = \operatorname{Log} i + \operatorname{Log} (z + v) + 2n\pi i$$

$$= \frac{\pi}{2} i + \operatorname{Log} (z + v) + 2n\pi i, \qquad n = 0, \pm 1,$$

and noticing that k is an arbitrary integer, we may write (4.6.7) as

$$w = \arcsin z = k\pi + (-1)^k \left[\frac{\pi}{2} - i \operatorname{Log} (z + v)\right], \qquad (4.6.8)$$

$$k = 0, \pm 1, \pm 2, \cdots.$$

For each value of k, equation (4.6.8) gives $\arcsin z$ as a single-valued function defined for all finite values of z. This function, however, is discontinuous at all real values of z such that $|z| \geq 1$, since $v(z)$ is discontinuous at these points. To express $\arcsin z$ in terms of a single-valued analytic function, we confine ourselves to the domain D_1 in Example 4.5.2, *which consists of the*

finite z plane with the exception of all $z = x + 0i$, $|x| \geq 1$. In this domain,
$z + v$ is analytic. Moreover for z in D_1, $z + v$ cannot take on nonpositive real
values. For, if

$$z + v = -b, \qquad b \text{ real and } b \geq 0,$$

then

$$z^2 - 1 = v^2 = (b + z)^2.$$

Hence

$$z = -\frac{1}{2}\left(b + \frac{1}{b}\right),$$

thus z is real and $z \leq -1$. Therefore, it cannot be in D_1. It follows that for
z in D_1, Log $(z + v)$ and hence the function arc sin z given in (4.6.8), for each k,
is single-valued and analytic.

A similar development for other inverse trigonometric functions may be
given. In addition to the domain D_1 of Example 4.5.2, we shall also refer to the
domain $\mathscr{D}_1$ *consisting of the finite z plane with the exception of all $z = 0 + iy$,*
$|y| \geq 1$. Observe that iz is in D_1 if and only if z is in $\mathscr{D}_1$, and iz is in $\mathscr{D}_1$ if
and only if z is in D_1.

We shall summarize the above results for $w = $ arc sin z in Theorem 4.6.1
below and state corresponding theorems for arc cos z and arc tan z. For convenience we shall restate the definition of $v(z)$ $[v^2(z) = z^2 - 1]$ given earlier.

$$\begin{cases} v(z) = \sqrt{\rho_1\rho_2}\, e^{i[(\theta_1+\theta_2)/2]}, \\ \rho_1 e^{i\theta_1} = z - 1, \qquad -\pi < \theta_1 \leq \pi, \\ \rho_2 e^{i\theta_2} = z + 1, \qquad 0 \leq \theta_2 < 2\pi. \end{cases} \qquad (4.6.9)$$

Remark 4.6.1.   In the ensuing theorems, the domains D_1 and $\mathscr{D}_1$ are those
given in italics in the above paragraphs.

——*THEOREM* 4.6.1.   For all z,

$$\text{arc sin } z = k\pi + (-1)^k \left\{\frac{\pi}{2} - i \text{ Log } [z + v(z)]\right\}, \qquad (4.6.10)$$

$$k = 0, \pm 1, \pm 2, \cdots,$$

where $v(z)$ is given in (4.6.9). Moreover for z in the domain D_1 and k fixed,
arc sin z is single-valued and analytic and has the derivative

$$\frac{d}{dz}(\text{arc sin } z) = \frac{(-1)^{k+1} i}{v(z)}. \qquad (4.6.11)$$

——*THEOREM* 4.6.2.   For all z,

$$\text{arc cos } z = 2k\pi + i(-1)^n \text{ Log } [z + v(z)], \qquad k = 0, \pm 1, \pm 2, \cdots, \quad (4.6.12)$$

$n = 1, 2$ and $v(z)$ is given in (4.6.9). Moreover for z in the domain D_1 and k and n fixed, arc cos z is single-valued and analytic and has the derivative

$$\frac{d}{dz} (\text{arc cos } z) = \frac{(-1)^n i}{v(z)}, \qquad (4.6.13)$$

where n has the same value as in (4.6.12).

——**THEOREM** 4.6.3. For all z except $z = \pm i$,

$$\text{arc tan } z = k\pi + \frac{1}{2i} \text{ Log } \left(\frac{1 + iz}{1 - iz}\right), \qquad k = 0, \pm 1, \pm 2, \cdots. \quad (4.6.14)$$

Moreover for z in the domain $\mathscr{D}_1$ and k fixed, arc tan z is single-valued and analytic and has the derivative

$$\frac{d}{dz} (\text{arc tan } z) = \frac{1}{1 + z^2}. \qquad (4.6.15)$$

To obtain similar results for the inverse hyperbolic functions, we first observe that by using (4.3.10) and (4.3.11) we can deduce the following relations

$$\left\{ \begin{array}{l} \text{arc sinh } z = -i \text{ arc sin } iz, \\ \text{arc cosh } z = -i \text{ arc cos } z, \\ \text{arc tanh } z = -i \text{ arc tan } iz. \end{array} \right. \qquad (4.6.16)$$

Consequently, we can now derive the following three theorems from Theorems 4.6.1-4.6.3.

——**THEOREM** 4.6.4. For all z,

$$\text{arc sinh } z = k\pi i - (-1)^k \left\{ \text{Log } [iz + v(iz)] + i\frac{\pi}{2} \right\}, \qquad (4.6.17)$$

$$k = 0, \pm 1, \pm 2, \cdots,$$

where $v(z)$ is given in (4.6.9). Moreover, for z in the domain $\mathscr{D}_1$ and k fixed, arc sinh z is single-valued and analytic and has the derivative

$$\frac{d}{dz} (\text{arc sinh } z) = \frac{(-1)^{k+1} i}{v(iz)}. \qquad (4.6.18)$$

——**THEOREM** 4.6.5. For all z,

$$\text{arc cosh } z = 2k\pi i + (-1)^n \text{ Log } [z + v(z)], \qquad k = 0, \pm 1, \pm 2, \cdots, \quad (4.6.19)$$

$n = 1, 2$ and $v(z)$ is given in (4.6.9). Moreover for z in the domain D_1 and k and n fixed, arc cosh z is single-valued and analytic and has the derivative

$$\frac{d}{dz} (\text{arc cosh } z) = \frac{(-1)^n}{v(z)}, \qquad (4.6.20)$$

where n has the same value as in (4.6.19).

——*THEOREM* 4.6.6. For all z except $z = \pm 1$,

$$\text{arc tanh } z = k\pi i + \frac{1}{2} \text{Log} \left(\frac{1+z}{1-z}\right), \qquad k = 0, \pm 1, \pm 2, \cdots. \quad (4.6.21)$$

Moreover, for z in the domain D_1 (the C_i described positively) and k fixed, arc tan z is single-valued and analytic and has the derivative

$$\frac{d}{dz} (\text{arc tanh } z) = \frac{1}{1-z^2}. \qquad (4.6.22)$$

EXAMPLE 4.6.1. Let us find the values of arc sin i.

Solution. From (4.6.9) we have

$$\rho_1 e^{i\theta_1} = z - 1 = -1 + i, \qquad \rho_2 e^{i\theta_2} = z + 1 = 1 + i.$$

Thus

$$\rho_1 = \sqrt{2}, \qquad \rho_2 = \sqrt{2}, \qquad \theta_1 = \frac{3}{4}\pi, \qquad \theta_2 = \frac{\pi}{4}.$$

Hence

$$v(i) = \sqrt{\rho_1 \rho_2} \, e^{i[(\theta_1 + \theta_2)/2]} = \sqrt{2} \, e^{i(\pi/2)}.$$

Therefore

$$\text{arc sin } i = k\pi + (-1)^k \left[\frac{\pi}{2} - i \, \text{Log} \, (i + \sqrt{2} \, e^{i(\pi/2)})\right], \qquad k = 0, \pm 1, \pm 2, \cdots.$$

But

$$\text{Log} \, (i + \sqrt{2} \, e^{i(\pi/2)}) = \text{Log} \, [(1 + \sqrt{2}) \, e^{i(\pi/2)}] = \text{Log} \, (1 + \sqrt{2}) + i\frac{\pi}{2}.$$

Hence

$$\text{arc sin } i = k\pi + (-1)^k [\pi - i \, \text{Log} \, (1 + \sqrt{2})], \qquad k = 0, \pm 1, \pm 2, \cdots.$$

4.7. THE ELEMENTARY OPERATIONS AND ELEMENTARY FUNCTIONS. We are now in a position to define what is meant by elementary operations and elementary functions.

Definition 4.7.1. The elementary operations on functions $f(z)$ and $g(z)$ are those that yield any of the following:

$$f(z) \pm g(z), \quad f(z) \cdot g(z), \quad f(z)/g(z), \quad [f(z)]^\alpha, \quad [\alpha]^{f(z)}, \quad \log \, [f(z)],$$

where α is a complex constant.

In this definition, we are implicitly assuming that the indicated operations are defined. For example, we require that $g(z) \neq 0$ for $f(z)/g(z)$, and that $f(z) \neq 0$ for $\log \, [f(z)]$, and so on.

Definition 4.7.2. The elementary functions are those generated by constants and the independent variable by means of a finite number of elementary operations.

Examples of elementary functions:

$$e^{3 \log z}, \qquad \log [1 + \sqrt{1 - z^2 \cos z}],$$

$$(z^2 + 5z + 3) \text{ arc cos } [(\log \tan z) (3 + 4i)^{\sqrt{z}}],$$

$$\sinh^{-1} [z + \sqrt{z^2 - 1}] + \cosh^{-1} [\log \sqrt{z^2 + 1}].$$

EXERCISES 4.7

1. Verify the relations in (4.6.16).

2. Prove Theorem 4.6.2.

3. Prove Theorem 4.6.3.

4. Prove Theorem 4.6.4.

5. Prove Theorem 4.6.5.

6. Prove Theorem 4.6.6.

7. Find the roots of the equations (a) $\sin z = -i$; (b) $\cos z = 2$.

8. Find the values of (a) $\tan^{-1}(1 - 2i)$; (b) $\tan^{-1}(1 - i)$.

9. Find the values of (a) $\sinh^{-1}(-\tfrac{1}{2})$; (b) $\cosh^{-1}(\tfrac{1}{2})$.

10. Show that arc $\cos z = (-1)^{k+1}$ arc $\sin z + (\pi/2) + k\pi, k = 0, \pm 1, \pm 2, \cdots$.

5

Integration

5.1. DEFINITIONS. The reader has already encountered the concept of a continuous curve. (See Section 2.10.) In the sequel we shall utilize almost exclusively a special kind of continuous curve, namely, piecewise regular curves or contours.

Let $z = f(t)$ be a continuous complex-valued function defined on the closed interval $I: \alpha \leq t \leq \beta$. Then, as we have seen in Section 2.10, the function $z = f(t)$ represents a continuous curve described by the point $z = f(t)$ as t increases from α to β. Let us suppose in addition that the derivative $f'(t)$ exists and is continuous on the interval I, and that $f'(t) \neq 0$, except perhaps at the end points $t = \alpha$ and $t = \beta$. We shall then say that the function $z = f(t)$ defined on the interval I represents a *regular curve*.

Let $z = f(t)$ be a continuous complex-valued function defined on the interval $I: \alpha \leq t \leq \beta$. Suppose furthermore that there exists a subdivision of $I: \alpha = t_0 < t_1 < t_2 < \cdots < t_n = \beta$ such that if we restrict the function $z = f(t)$ to any subinterval $I_k: t_{k-1} \leq t \leq t_k$, $k = 1, 2, \cdots, n$, it will represent a regular curve. Then we shall say that the function $z = f(t)$ defined on the interval I represents a *piecewise regular curve* or a *contour*.

It follows that at any point t other than the points $t_0, t_1, \cdots, t_n$ of the subdivision, $f'(t)$ is continuous and is not equal to zero. The points $f(\alpha)$ and $f(\beta)$ are called, respectively, the *initial* and *terminal points* of the contour. Graphically, a contour consists of a finite number of regular curves joined in succession. At the points of junction, there may be vertices, cusps, or corners. (See Fig. 5.1.1.)

A function $z = f(t)$ is said to be *piecewise continuous* on the interval I: $\alpha \leq t \leq \beta$, if $z = f(t)$ is defined and is continuous for all but at most a finite number of points of I, and if at each point of I where the function is not defined or is not continuous, the right-hand and left-hand limits exist. (At α we require only that the right-hand limit exist and at β we require only that the left-hand limit exist.) Observe that a contour has a piecewise continuous derivative.

Remark 5.1.1. If $g(s)$ is a complex-valued function defined on a set S, and if for all points s in S, $|g(s)| < M$ for some constant M, then the function $g(s)$ is said to be *bounded on S*. The statement that $g(s)$ is, except for at most a

130

finite number of points, bounded on S, will be understood to mean that $|g(s)| < M$ for all s in S, except for at most a finite number of points in S where $g(s)$ may be undefined.

Let $z = f(t)$, $\alpha \leq t \leq \beta$, represent a contour C. Writing $z = x + iy$ and $f(t) = f_1(t) + if_2(t)$, we see that the contour C is also given by the two equations

$$x = f_1(t), \qquad y = f_2(t), \qquad \alpha \leq t \leq \beta,$$

where $f_1(t)$ and $f_2(t)$ are continuous real-valued functions. Moreover, $f_1'(t)$ and $f_2'(t)$ are piecewise continuous, and except for at most a finite number of values of t, $\alpha \leq t \leq \beta$, $[f_1'(t)]^2 + [f_2'(t)]^2 \neq 0$. The verification of this is left as an exercise for the reader. (See Exercise 5.1.2.)

We would also like to make the following observation. Since every continuous function on a bounded closed interval I is bounded on I (see Exercise 3.3.25), it follows that the set of all points on a contour C is contained within a sufficiently large square Q with center at the origin. Similarly, we observe that since $f'(t)$ is continuous on each closed interval $I_k : t_{k-1} \leq t \leq t_k$, $k = 1, 2, \cdots, n$ of the subdivision of $I: \alpha \leq t \leq \beta$, we have $|f'(t)| \leq M_k$ for t in I_k. Letting $M = \max (M_1, M_2, \cdots, M_n)$, we see that $|f'(t)| \leq M$ for t in I, $t \neq t_k$, $k = 1, 2, \cdots, n-1$. Thus, except for at most a finite number of points in I, $f(t)$ and $f'(t)$ are both bounded on I.

Two functions $z = f(t)$, $\alpha \leq t \leq \beta$, and $z = g(\tau)$, $\gamma \leq \tau \leq \delta$, will be said to *represent the same contour* if there exists a function $h(t)$, $\alpha \leq t \leq \beta$, such that (1) $h'(t)$ is continuous and positive on $\alpha \leq t \leq \beta$, (2) $h(\alpha) = \gamma$ and $h(\beta) = \delta$ and (3) $g[h(t)] = f(t)$. It follows from (1) that $h(t)$ is continuous and strictly increasing. If we set $\tau = h(t)$, then as t increases from α to β, τ will increase from γ to δ and the point $z = g(\tau) = g[h(t)]$ will trace the same path as the point $z = f(t)$.

A contour C represented by $z = f(t)$ on the interval $I: \alpha \leq t \leq \beta$, is said to be *closed* if $f(\alpha) = f(\beta)$. A contour C is said to be *simple* if for any two points $t_1 \neq t_2$ in I we have $f(t_1) \neq f(t_2)$, except possibly when $t_1 = \alpha$ and $t_2 = \beta$, that is, the contour does not cross itself. A contour which is both simple and closed is called a *simple closed* contour. A circle and a polygon are examples of simple closed contours.

If C is a contour given by $z = f(t)$, $\alpha \leq t \leq \beta$, then by the *inverse* of C we mean the contour $\bar{C}$ given by $z = g(t)$, $\alpha \leq t \leq \beta$, where $g(t) = f(\alpha + \beta - t)$. As t increases from α to β, $\alpha + \beta - t$ decreases from β to α and the moving point $z = g(t)$ describing $\bar{C}$ retraces in the opposite direction the path of the moving point $z = f(t)$ describing C. Since $f(t) = g(\alpha + \beta - t)$, it follows that C is the inverse of $\bar{C}$. The contours C and $\bar{C}$ are thus inverses of each other. Intuitively, C and $\bar{C}$ represent the same curve traced in opposite directions.

We leave it as an exercise for the reader to show that the same contour $\bar{C}$ is obtained no matter what function is used to represent the contour C.

Similarly, the definitions of closed and simple contours do not depend on the function $z = f(t)$ used to represent the contour. Also, in the sequel, definitions and theorems involving contours do not depend on the functions used to represent them, and the verification of this will be left as an exercise for the reader.

If C is a contour given by $z = f(t)$, $\alpha \leqq t \leqq \beta$, then by a *section* of the contour C we mean a contour C^* given by $z = f(t)$, $\alpha_1 \leqq t \leqq \beta_1$, where $\alpha \leqq \alpha_1 < \beta_1 \leqq \beta$.

Remark 5.1.2. The terms *closed, simple, simple closed, inverse* and *section* are defined for continuous curves as they are for contours.

Let C_1 and C_2 be contours given respectively by $z = f(t)$, $\alpha \leqq t \leqq \gamma$, and $z = g(t)$, $\gamma \leqq t \leqq \delta$, and such that $f(\gamma) = g(\gamma)$, that is, the initial point of C_2 coincides with the terminal point of C_1. Then the contour C given by $z = h(t)$, $\alpha \leqq t \leqq \delta$, where

$$h(t) = \begin{cases} f(t), & \text{for} \quad \alpha \leqq t \leqq \gamma \\ g(t), & \text{for} \quad \gamma \leqq t \leqq \delta, \end{cases} \qquad (5.1.1)$$

is called the *sum* of C_1 and C_2 and we write

$$C = C_1 + C_2.$$

In the general case when C_1 and C_2 are given by functions defined respectively by $z = f(t), \alpha \leqq t \leqq \gamma$, and $z = g(t), \lambda \leqq t \leqq \mu$, with $\gamma \neq \lambda$ and $f(\gamma) = g(\lambda)$, we may (see Exercise 5.1.1) find a function representing C_2 which is defined over an interval $\gamma \leqq t \leqq \delta$. Since now the terminal point of C_1 coincides with the initial point of C_2, we may find the sum $C = C_1 + C_2$ as before. (See Fig. 5.1.1.)

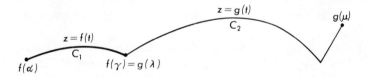

FIG. 5.1.1

Similarly, given any finite number of contours $C_0, C_1, \cdots, C_n$ such that the terminal point of C_{k-1} coincides with the initial point of C_k, $k = 1, 2, \cdots, n$, we can find a contour C such that

$$C = C_0 + C_1 + \cdots + C_n.$$

Intuitively, C is the path traced by describing first the path C_0, then the path C_1, then C_2 and so on. Each C_i, $i = 0, 1, 2, \cdots, n$ is a section of the contour C.

Let $z = f(t)$, $a \leq t \leq b$, represent a contour C. Suppose that $z_0 = f(t_0)$ is a fixed point on C. Let $z_\eta = f(t_0 - \eta)$ and $z_\epsilon = f(t_0 + \epsilon)$, $\eta > 0$ and $\epsilon > 0$ be two other points on C. (In case $t_0 = a$ or b, we consider only one point z_ϵ or z_η.) Let R_η denote the ray issuing from z_η and passing through z_0, and let R_ϵ denote the ray issuing from z_0 and passing through z_ϵ. (See Fig. 5.1.2.)

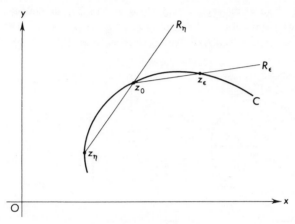

FIG. 5.1.2

Then the angles θ_η and θ_ϵ which the rays R_η and R_ϵ form with the positive x axis are given respectively by $\theta_\eta = \arg(z_0 - z_\eta)$ and $\theta_\epsilon = \arg(z_\epsilon - z_0)$. Equivalently, we have

$$e^{i\theta_\eta} = \frac{z_0 - z_\eta}{|z_0 - z_\eta|} \quad \text{and} \quad e^{i\theta_\epsilon} = \frac{z_\epsilon - z_0}{|z_\epsilon - z_0|}. \tag{5.1.2}$$

If as η and ϵ approach zero, $e^{i\theta_\eta}$ and $e^{i\theta_\epsilon}$ both approach a common limit $e^{i\alpha}$, then both rays R_η and R_ϵ approach coincidence with the ray

$$z = z_0 + e^{i\alpha} s, \quad 0 \leq s < \infty, \tag{5.1.3}$$

issuing from z_0 and forming the angle α with the positive x axis. This ray is called a *tangent* to, or a *tangent ray* of, the contour C at the point z_0.

It is not difficult to show (see Exercise 5.1.5) that if $f'(t_0) \neq 0$, then

$$e^{i\alpha} = \frac{f'(t_0)}{|f'(t_0)|}, \tag{5.1.4}$$

where $e^{i\alpha}$ is given in (5.1.3).

We also leave it as an exercise for the reader to show that a tangent at a given point on C is independent of the function $z = f(t)$ used to represent C.

EXAMPLE 5.1.1. The contour C: $z = z_1 + (z_2 - z_1)\, t$, $0 \leq t \leq 1$, describes a straight line segment with initial point z_1 and terminal point z_2. The inverse contour is given by

$$\bar{C}: \quad z = z_1 + (z_2 - z_1)\,(0 + 1 - t) = z_2 + (z_1 - z_2)\, t, \; 0 \leq t \leq 1.$$

The initial point is now z_2 and the terminal point is z_1.

EXAMPLE 5.1.2. Let z_1 be a point on the circle $|z - z_0| = \rho$. Then the contour C: $z = z_0 + (z_1 - z_0)\, e^{it}$, $0 \leq t \leq 2\pi$, is simple and closed, and each of its points lies on the circle $|z - z_0| = \rho$. We say that C describes the circle once in the *counterclockwise direction*. (See Fig. 5.1.3.)

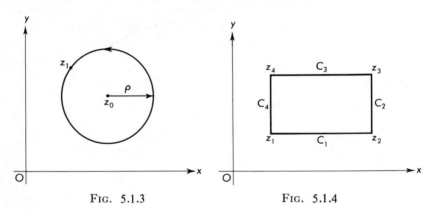

FIG. 5.1.3   FIG. 5.1.4

The inverse contour is given by

$$\bar{C}: \; z = z_0 + (z_1 - z_0)\, e^{i(0 + 2\pi - t)}$$
$$= z_0 + (z_1 - z_0)\, e^{-it}, \qquad 0 \leq t \leq 2\pi.$$

$\bar{C}$ is said to describe the circle once in the *clockwise direction*.

EXAMPLE 5.1.3. Let z_1, z_2, z_3, z_4 be the successive vertices of a rectangle. (See Fig. 5.1.4.) The simple contours

$$
\begin{aligned}
C_1: \quad & z = z_1 + (z_2 - z_1)\, t, & 0 \leq t \leq 1, \\
C_2: \quad & z = z_2 + (z_3 - z_2)\,(t - 1), & 1 \leq t \leq 2, \\
C_3: \quad & z = z_3 + (z_4 - z_3)\,(t - 2), & 2 \leq t \leq 3, \\
C_4: \quad & z = z_4 + (z_1 - z_4)\,(t - 3), & 3 \leq t \leq 4
\end{aligned}
$$

describe the successive sides of the rectangle. The sum $C = C_1 + C_2 + C_3 + C_4$ is a simple closed contour describing the perimeter of the rectangle.

EXAMPLE 5.1.4. Let z_1 and z_2 be two distinct points on the circle $|z| = \rho$. Then $|z_2/z_1| = 1$, and we may write $z_2/z_1 = e^{i\phi}$, $0 < \phi < 2\pi$.

Consider the contours

$$C': \quad z = z_1 e^{it}, \qquad 0 \leq t \leq \phi,$$

$$C'': \quad z = z_1 e^{-it}, \qquad 0 \leq t \leq 2\pi - \phi.$$

Then C' and C'' are simple contours with initial point z_1 and terminal point z_2, whose points lie on the circle $|z| = \rho$. (See Fig. 5.1.5.) C' and C'' describe

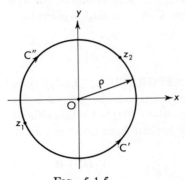

FIG. 5.1.5

the two arcs of the circle $|z| = \rho$ joining the point z_1 to the point z_2.

The inverse contour $\bar{C}''$ of C'', with initial point z_2 and terminal point z_1, is given by

$$\bar{C}'': \quad z = z_1 e^{-i(0 + 2\pi - \phi - t)} = z_1 e^{i(\phi + t)}, \qquad 0 \leq t \leq 2\pi - \phi.$$

Setting $\tau = \phi + t$, $\bar{C}''$ may be written as

$$\bar{C}'': \quad z = z_1 e^{i\tau}, \qquad \phi \leq \tau \leq 2\pi.$$

The sum $C = C' + \bar{C}''$ is then a simple closed contour which is given by

$$C: \quad z = z_1 e^{it}, \qquad 0 \leq t \leq 2\pi.$$

By Example 5.1.2, C describes a circle once in the counterclockwise direction.

EXERCISES 5.1

1. Suppose that a contour C is represented by the function $z = f(t), \lambda \leq t \leq \mu$. Let $\gamma \leq t \leq \delta$ be any other interval. Show that there exists a function $z = g(\tau), \gamma \leq \tau \leq \delta$, also representing the contour C.

2. Let the contour C be represented by the function $f(t) = f_1(t) + i f_2(t)$, $\alpha \leq t \leq \beta$, where $f_1(t)$ and $f_2(t)$ are real-valued functions. Show that $f_1'(t)$ and $f_2'(t)$ are piecewise continuous and that $[f_1'(t)]^2 + [f_2'(t)]^2 \neq 0$ at all except at most a finite number of values of t in the interval $\alpha \leq t \leq \beta$.

3. Let $C: z = f(t), \alpha \leq t \leq \beta$, be a contour and let $t_0, \alpha < t_0 < \beta$, be a value of t such that $f'(t_0)$ is defined. Show that $f'(t)$ is continuous at t_0.

4. Let $C: z = f(t)$, $\alpha \leq t \leq \beta$, be a contour and let $z_0 = f(t_0)$, $\alpha < t_0 < \beta$, be a point on C such that $f'(t_0)$ exists and is not equal to zero. Show that after a suitable translation and rotation of the coordinate axes, the equation of C becomes $Z = F(t) = e^{-i\theta}[f(t) - f(t_0)]$, $\theta = \arg[f'(t_0)/|f'(t_0)|]$, where Z denotes the new coordinate of any point P in the plane, and we have $F(t_0) = 0$ and $F'(t_0) > 0$.

5. Let $C: z = f(t)$, $\alpha \leq t \leq \beta$, be a contour. Show that if $f'(t_0) \neq 0$, $\alpha < t_0 < \beta$, then the tangent to C at $z_0 = f(t_0)$ is given by

$$z = z_0 + \frac{f'(t_0)}{|f'(t_0)|} s, \qquad 0 \leq s < \infty.$$

5.2. CONTOUR INTEGRATION. Let $H(t)$ and $G(t)$ be bounded functions defined and continuous over the interval $\alpha \leq t \leq \beta$, except possibly at a finite number of points where $H(t)$ or $G(t)$ are either undefined or discontinuous. The reader is already familiar from calculus with the existence of the integral

$$\int_\alpha^\beta H(t)\, dt$$

and its basic properties, namely,

$$\int_\alpha^\beta [H(t) \pm G(t)]\, dt = \int_\alpha^\beta H(t)\, dt \pm \int_\alpha^\beta G(t)\, dt, \tag{5.2.1}$$

$$\int_\alpha^\beta kH(t)\, dt = k \int_\alpha^\beta H(t)\, dt \qquad (k \text{ is a constant}), \tag{5.2.2}$$

$$\int_\alpha^\beta H(t)\, dt = - \int_\beta^\alpha H(t)\, dt, \tag{5.2.3}$$

$$\int_\alpha^\gamma H(t)\, dt + \int_\gamma^\beta H(t)\, dt = \int_\alpha^\beta H(t)\, dt, \quad \alpha < \gamma < \beta. \tag{5.2.4}$$

Furthermore, if

$$F(t) = \int_\alpha^t H(\zeta)\, d\zeta,$$

then $F(t)$ is continuous for $\alpha \leq t \leq \beta$ and

$$F'(t) = H(t) \tag{5.2.5}$$

at each point t where $H(t)$ is continuous.

In elementary calculus, the functions $H(t)$ and $G(t)$ were assumed to be real-valued. The integral of a complex-valued function of a real variable is defined to be the integral of the real part of the function plus i times the integral of the imaginary part of the function. That is, if $H(t) = H_1(t) + iH_2(t)$, $\alpha \leq t \leq \beta$, where $H_1(t)$ and $H_2(t)$ are real-valued functions, then

$$\int_\alpha^\beta H(t)\, dt = \int_\alpha^\beta H_1(t)\, dt + i \int_\alpha^\beta H_2(t)\, dt. \tag{5.2.6}$$

For later use, we now introduce the following notation. The expression

$$\int_\alpha^\beta H(t) \sum_{i=1}^n [G_i(t)\, dt] \tag{5.2.7}$$

shall denote the integral

$$\int_\alpha^\beta \left[H(t) \sum_{i=1}^n G_i(t) \right] dt,$$

where $H(t)$ and $G_i(t)$, $i = 1, 2, \cdots, n$ are complex-valued functions on I: $\alpha \leq t \leq \beta$.

Let

$$H(t) = H_1(t) + iH_2(t) \quad \text{and} \quad G(t) = G_1(t) + iG_2(t).$$

Then applying (5.2.1) to (5.2.5) to the real-valued functions H_1, G_1, H_2 and G_2, we see that *properties (5.2.1) to (5.2.5) are also enjoyed by complex-valued functions which are defined, bounded and continuous over the interval* $\alpha \leq t \leq \beta$ *except possibly at a finite number of points where the functions are either undefined or discontinuous.*

Let the contour C be represented by $z = f(t)$ on the interval I: $\alpha \leq t \leq \beta$, and let $G(z)$ be a continuous complex-valued function defined on the contour C. Then $G[f(t)]$ is defined and continuous on the interval I. Now, $dz/dt = f'(t)$ is, except possibly for a finite number of points, also defined, bounded, and continuous on the interval I. It follows that the integral

$$\int_\alpha^\beta G[f(t)] f'(t)\, dt \tag{5.2.8}$$

exists. The value of this integral depends only on the function $G(z)$ and the contour C. That is, if the contour C is also given by $z = g(t)$, $\gamma \leq t \leq \delta$, then we have (see Exercise 5.2.14)

$$\int_\alpha^\beta G[f(t)] f'(t)\, dt = \int_\gamma^\delta G[g(t)] g'(t)\, dt.$$

Therefore, we may denote the integral given in (5.2.8) by

$$\int_C G(z)\, dz,$$

and we have by definition

$$\int_C G(z)\, dz = \int_\alpha^\beta G[f(t)] f'(t)\, dt, \tag{5.2.9}$$

for any function $z = f(t)$, $\alpha \leq t \leq \beta$, representing C.

Remark 5.2.1. The integral $\int_C G(z)\, dz$ may also be defined directly as follows. Suppose that C is a contour given by $z = f(t)$, $\alpha \leq t \leq \beta$. Let $G(z)$ be a continuous complex-valued function defined on C, and let

$$\alpha = t_0 < t_1 < \cdots < t_{n-1} < t_n = \beta$$

be a subdivision of the interval $\alpha \leq t \leq \beta$. For each k, $k = 1, 2, \cdots, n$ choose a point t'_k, $t_{k-1} \leq t'_k \leq t_k$, and let $z_k = f(t_k)$ and $z'_k = f(t'_k)$. (See Fig. 5.2.1.)

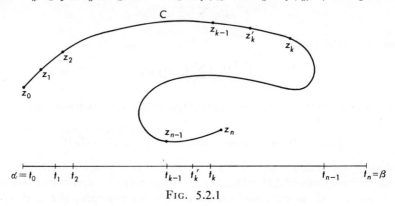

FIG. 5.2.1

Let us form the sum

$$S_n = \sum_{k=1}^{n} G(z'_k)\,(z_k - z_{k-1}). \tag{5.2.10}$$

It can be shown that there exists a number S having the following property: Given any $\epsilon > 0$, there exists a $\delta > 0$ such that

$$|S_n - S| < \epsilon$$

whenever $\max |t_k - t_{k-1}| < \delta$. In other words, by making the subdivision sufficiently fine, the sum S_n in (5.2.10) can be made to differ from S by as little as we please. This number S may be shown to be equal to the integral (5.2.8). Thus, we also have

$$\int_C G(z)\,dz = \lim_{\substack{n \to \infty \\ \max|t_k - t_{k-1}| \to 0}} \sum_{k=1}^{n} G(z'_k)\,(z_k - z_{k-1}). \tag{5.2.11}$$

From the definition of the integral $\int_C G(z)\,dz$ given in (5.2.9) and utilizing (5.2.1) to (5.2.4), we may establish the following

——*THEOREM* 5.2.1. Let $F(z)$ and $G(z)$ be continuous complex-valued functions defined on the contour C. Let $C = C_1 + C_2$ be the sum of the contours C_1 and C_2 and let $\bar{C}$ denote the inverse of C. Then

$$\int_C [F(z) \pm G(z)]\,dz = \int_C F(z)\,dz \pm \int_C G(z)\,dz, \tag{5.2.12}$$

$$\int_C kF(z)\,dz = k \int_C F(z)\,dz \qquad (k \text{ is a constant}), \tag{5.2.13}$$

$$\int_C F(z)\,dz = \int_{C_1} F(z)\,dz + \int_{C_2} F(z)\,dz, \tag{5.2.14}$$

$$\int_C F(z)\,dz = -\int_{\bar{C}} F(z)\,dz. \tag{5.2.15}$$

Proof. The verification of (5.2.12) and (5.2.13) is left to the reader.

Concerning (5.2.14). Let C_1 be given by $z = f(t)$, $\alpha \le t \le \gamma$. Then (see Exercise 5.1.1) we may consider C_2 as given by $z = g(t)$, $\gamma \le t \le \delta$. From (5.1.1), $C = C_1 + C_2$ will then be given by $z = h(t)$, $\alpha \le t \le \delta$, where

$$h(t) = \begin{cases} f(t), & \text{for } \alpha \le t \le \gamma \\ g(t), & \text{for } \gamma \le t \le \delta. \end{cases}$$

It follows that

$$\int_{C_1} F(z)\, dz + \int_{C_2} F(z)\, dz = \int_\alpha^\gamma F[f(t)] f'(t)\, dt + \int_\gamma^\delta F[g(t)]\, g'(t)\, dt$$

$$= \int_\alpha^\gamma F[h(t)]\, h'(t)\, dt + \int_\gamma^\delta F[h(t)]\, h'(t)\, dt = \int_\alpha^\delta F[h(t)]\, h'(t)\, dt$$

$$= \int_C F(z)\, dz.$$

Concerning (5.2.15). Let C be given by $z = h(t)$, $\alpha \le t \le \delta$. Then from Section 5.1, $\bar{C}$ is given by $z = p(\tau)$, $\alpha \le \tau \le \delta$, where $p(\tau) = h(\alpha + \delta - \tau)$. Let $t = \alpha + \delta - \tau$. Then $p(\tau) = h(t)$ and $dp(\tau)/d\tau = -dh(t)/dt$. Hence

$$\int_{\bar{C}} F(z)\, dz = \int_\alpha^\delta F[p(\tau)]\, p'(\tau)\, d\tau = \int_\delta^\alpha F[h(t)]\, h'(t)\, dt$$

$$= -\int_\alpha^\delta F[h(t)]\, h'(t)\, dt = -\int_C F(z)\, dz.$$

Thus the theorem is established.

Remark 5.2.2. In the sequel, we shall use the notation

$$\int_{C_1+C_2} f(z)\, dz$$

even in cases where C_1 and C_2 are disjoint contours and $C_1 + C_2$ is not a contour. The symbol $\int_{C_1+C_2} f(z)\, dz$ will then denote the sum of the integrals

$$\int_{C_1} f(z)\, dz + \int_{C_2} f(z)\, dz.$$

Similarly, by the integral

$$\int_{\sum_{i=1}^n C_i} f(z)\, dz,$$

we shall mean the sum:

$$\sum_{i=1}^n \int_{C_i} f(z)\, dz.$$

We go one step further and assign to the symbol

$$\int_{\sum_{i=1}^{n} m_i C_i} f(z)\, dz$$

the meaning

$$\sum_{i=1}^{n} m_i \int_{C_i} f(z)\, dz.$$

Here the m_i are any integers, positive, negative, or zero.

Two formal sums of contours $\Gamma = \sum_{j=1}^{n} m_j C_j$ and $\Gamma' = \sum_{i=1}^{k} \mu_i C_i'$ will be considered *equivalent* and we write $\Gamma = \Gamma'$, if

$$\int_{\Gamma} f(z)\, dz = \int_{\Gamma'} f(z)\, dz, \qquad (5.2.16)$$

that is,

$$\sum_{j=1}^{n} m_j \int_{C_j} f(z)\, dz = \sum_{i=1}^{k} \mu_i \int_{C_i'} f(z)\, dz \qquad (5.2.17)$$

for all functions $f(z)$ defined and continuous on the contours C_j, C_i', $j = 1, 2, \cdots, n$ and $i = 1, 2, \cdots, k$.

The following operations upon a formal sum

$$\Gamma = \sum_{j=1}^{n} m_j C_j \qquad (5.2.18)$$

lead to an equivalent formal sum:

1. If in (5.2.18) the C_j are themselves expressible as sums of other contours, then these sums may be substituted for the C_j and the resulting expression may then be simplified by the ordinary rules of algebra.*

For example, if $\Gamma = 4C_1 - 3C_2$, $C_1 = \gamma_1 + \gamma_2$ and $C_2 = \gamma_1 - \gamma_2$, then after substitution and simplification, we get $\Gamma = \gamma_1 + 7\gamma_2$. We shall now verify that

$$\int_{4C_1-3C_2} f(z)\, dz = \int_{\gamma_1+7\gamma_2} f(z)\, dz.$$

For

$$\int_{4C_1-3C_2} f(z)\, dz = 4 \int_{C_1} f(z)\, dz - 3 \int_{C_2} f(z)\, dz = 4 \left[\int_{\gamma_1} f(z)\, dz + \int_{\gamma_2} f(z)\, dz \right]$$

$$- 3 \left[\int_{\gamma_1} f(z)\, dz - \int_{\gamma_2} f(z)\, dz \right] = \int_{\gamma_1} f(z)\, dz + 7 \int_{\gamma_2} f(z)\, dz = \int_{\gamma_1+7\gamma_2} f(z)\, dz.$$

* These are the rules applying to the addition and multiplication of scalars and vectors. For example, $m_1 C + m_2 C = (m_1 + m_2) C$, $m_1(m_2 C) = (m_1 m_2) C$, and so on.

2. If one or more of the C_j in the formal sum (5.2.18) is expressible as the inverse of some other contour, say, $C_k = \bar{\gamma}_k$, then we may replace C_k by $-\gamma_k$ and simplify the resulting expression by the ordinary rules of algebra.

For example, if $\Gamma = m_1 C_1 + m_2 C_2$ and $C_1 = \bar{C}_2$, then substituting $-C_2$ for C_1, we obtain upon simplifying $\Gamma = (m_2 - m_1) C_2$. We shall now verify that when $C_1 = \bar{C}_2$

$$\int_{m_1 C_1 + m_2 C_2} f(z)\,dz = \int_{(m_2 - m_1) C_2} f(z)\,dz.$$

For

$$\int_{m_1 C_1 + m_2 C_2} f(z)\,dz = m_1 \int_{C_1} f(z)\,dz + m_2 \int_{C_2} f(z)\,dz$$

$$= m_1 \int_{\bar{C}_2} f(z)\,dz + m_2 \int_{C_2} f(z)\,dz = -m_1 \int_{C_2} f(z)\,dz + m_2 \int_{C_2} f(z)\,dz$$

$$= (m_2 - m_1) \int_{C_2} f(z)\,dz = \int_{(m_2 - m_1) C_2} f(z)\,dz.$$

Expressions such as $\Gamma = \sum_{j=1}^{n} m_j C_j$ arise in a natural manner when we consider an integral over a contour Γ, where part of the path is traced more than once.

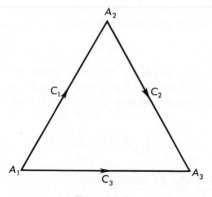

FIG. 5.2.2

For example, if the contour Γ describes the path indicated by the succession of vertices $A_1 A_2 A_3 A_1 A_2 A_3$ in Fig. 5.2.2, then $\int_\Gamma f(z)\,dz$ may be written as $\int_{2C_1 + 2C_2 - C_3} f(z)\,dz$, where the contours C_1, C_2, and C_3 describe respectively the paths $A_1 A_2$, $A_2 A_3$, and $A_1 A_3$.

If C is a contour given by $z = f(t)$, $\alpha \leq t \leq \beta$, and $G(z)$ is a continuous complex-valued function defined on C, then the symbol

$$\int_C G(z) \, |dz|$$

is used to denote the integral

$$\int_{\alpha}^{\beta} G[f(t)] \, |f'(t)| \, dt,$$

and we write

$$\int_{C} G(z) \, |dz| = \int_{\alpha}^{\beta} G[f(t)] \, |f'(t)| \, dt. \qquad (5.2.19)$$

Since (see Exercise 5.2.1)

$$\left| \int_{\alpha}^{\beta} G[f(t)] \, f'(t) \, dt \right| \leq \int_{\alpha}^{\beta} |G[f(t)]| \, |f'(t)| \, dt,$$

it follows that

$$\left| \int_{C} G(z) \, dz \right| \leq \int_{C} |G(z)| \, |dz|. \qquad (5.2.20)$$

We also have (see Exercise 5.2.2)

$$\int_{C} |dz| = L, \qquad (5.2.21)$$

where L is finite and is the length of the contour C.* Thus every contour has finite length.

We shall now obtain a useful upper bound for the complex integral given in (5.2.9).

——**THEOREM** 5.2.2.   Let C be a contour given by $z = f(t)$, $\alpha \leq t \leq \beta$, and let $G(z)$ be a complex-valued function defined and continuous on C. If L is the length of the contour C and $|G(z)| \leq M$ at all points of C, then

$$\left| \int_{C} G(z) \, dz \right| \leq ML. \qquad (5.2.22)$$

Proof.   Utilizing (5.2.20) and (5.2.21) we have

$$\left| \int_{C} G(z) \, dz \right| \leq \int_{C} |G(z)| \, |dz| \leq M \int_{C} |dz| = ML.$$

We shall now develop another expression for the integral

$$\int_{C} F(z) \, dz,$$

* The length L of a contour C: $z(t) = x(t) + iy(t)$, $\alpha \leq t \leq \beta$, is defined by

$$L = \int_{\alpha}^{\beta} \{[x'(t)]^2 + [y'(t)]^2\}^{1/2} dt.$$

where $F(z)$ is a continuous complex-valued function defined on the contour C: $z(t) = x(t) + iy(t)$, $\alpha \leq t \leq \beta$. Since $z'(t)$ is piecewise continuous on the interval I: $\alpha \leq t \leq \beta$ and $z'(t) = x'(t) + iy'(t)$, it follows that $x'(t)$ and $y'(t)$ are also piecewise continuous on I. For brevity we shall write

$$dx \quad \text{for} \quad x'(t)\,dt \qquad \text{and} \qquad dy \quad \text{for} \quad y'(t)\,dt. \tag{5.2.23}$$

Let

$$F(z) = u(z) + iv(z).$$

Since z is determined by the values of x and y, we write

$$u[z(t)] = u[x(t), y(t)] \quad \text{and} \quad v[z(t)] = v[x(t), y(t)].$$

Again, for brevity we shall write

$$u \text{ for } u[x(t), y(t)] \quad \text{and} \quad v \text{ for } v[x(t), y(t)]. \tag{5.2.24}$$

Thus

$$\int_{\alpha}^{\beta} F[z(t)]\,z'(t)\,dt = \int_{\alpha}^{\beta} (u + iv)\,(dx + i\,dy)$$
$$= \int_{\alpha}^{\beta} u\,dx - v\,dy + i \int_{\alpha}^{\beta} u\,dy + v\,dx, \tag{5.2.25}$$

where the meaning of the symbols u, v, dx and dy is given by (5.2.23) and (5.2.24). The usual way of writing (5.2.25) is

$$\int_C F(z)\,dz = \int_C u\,dx - v\,dy + i \int_C u\,dy + v\,dx. \tag{5.2.26}$$

Although the integrands on the right-hand side of the equality sign in (5.2.26) are defined as functions of t, they may equivalently be defined as functions of x and y. (See W. Kaplan, *Advanced Calculus*, pp. 228-229, 506, Reading: Addison-Wesley, 1957).

EXAMPLE 5.2.1.   Let us find the value of the integral $\int_C z^2\,dz$

(a) when C is the contour OB from $z = 0$ to $z = 1 + i$ (see Fig. 5.2.3);

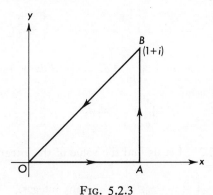

FIG. 5.2.3

(b) when C is the contour OAB;

(c) when C is the simple closed contour $OABO$.

Solution. $F(z) = z^2 = (x + iy)^2 = x^2 - y^2 + 2xyi$, thus

$$u(x, y) = x^2 - y^2 \quad \text{and} \quad v(x, y) = 2xy.$$

The contours OA, AB, and OB are given respectively by

$$OA: \quad x(t) = t, \qquad y(t) = 0, \qquad 0 \leq t \leq 1.$$
$$AB: \quad x(t) = 1, \qquad y(t) = t, \qquad 0 \leq t \leq 1.$$
$$OB: \quad x(t) = t, \qquad y(t) = t, \qquad 0 \leq t \leq 1.$$

On OA, we have $u = t^2$, $v = 0$, $dx = x'(t)\, dt = dt$ and $dy = y'(t)\, dt = 0$. On AB, we have $u = 1 - t^2$, $v = 2t$, $dx = 0$ and $dy = dt$. On OB, we have $u = 0$, $v = 2t^2$, $dx = dt$ and $dy = dt$. Utilizing Theorem 5.2.1 and (5.2.26) we obtain

(a) $\displaystyle \int_{OB} z^2\, dz = \int_0^1 - 2t^2\, dt + i \int_0^1 2t^2\, dt = -\frac{2}{3} + \frac{2}{3} i.$

(b) $\displaystyle \int_{OAB} z^2\, dz = \int_{OA} z^2\, dz + \int_{AB} z^2\, dz = \int_0^1 t^2\, dt + \int_0^1 - 2t\, dt$

$$+ i \int_0^1 (1 - t^2)\, dt = -\frac{2}{3} + \frac{2}{3} i.$$

(c) $\displaystyle \int_{OABO} z^2\, dz = \int_{OAB} z^2\, dz + \int_{BO} z^2\, dz = \int_{OAB} z^2\, dz - \int_{OB} z^2\, dz$

$$= \left(-\frac{2}{3} + \frac{2}{3} i \right) - \left(-\frac{2}{3} + \frac{2}{3} i \right) = 0.$$

Remark 5.2.3.   When the integrands on the right-hand side of (5.2.26) are expressed as functions of x and y, the solutions in (a) and (b) are given by

(a') $\displaystyle \int_{OB} z^2\, dz = \int_0^1 - 2y^2\, dy + i \int_0^1 2x^2\, dx = -\frac{2}{3} + \frac{2}{3} i.$

(b') $\displaystyle \int_{OAB} z^2\, dz = \int_{OA} z^2\, dz + \int_{AB} z^2\, dz = \int_0^1 x^2\, dx + \int_0^1 - 2y\, dy$

$$+ i \int_0^1 (1 - y^2)\, dy = -\frac{2}{3} + \frac{2}{3} i.$$

EXAMPLE 5.2.2.   Let us find the value of the integral

$$\int_C (z - z_0)^n\, dz \qquad (n \text{ any integer}),$$

along the circle C with center at z_0 and radius r described in the counterclock-wise direction.

Solution. The equation of the circle C is given by

$$z = f(t) = z_0 + re^{it}, \qquad 0 \leqq t \leqq 2\pi.$$

Using (5.2.9) with $G(z) = (z - z_0)^n$ and $f'(t) = ire^{it}$, we obtain

$$\int_C (z - z_0)^n \, dz = ir^{n+1} \int_0^{2\pi} e^{i(n+1)t} \, dt$$

$$= ir^{n+1} \int_0^{2\pi} [\cos(n+1)t + i\sin(n+1)t] \, dt.$$

If $n = -1$, then

$$\int_C (z - z_0)^{-1} \, dz = i \int_0^{2\pi} dt = 2\pi i.$$

If $n \neq -1$, then

$$\int_C (z - z_0)^n \, dz = \frac{ir^{n+1}}{n+1} [\sin(n+1)t - i\cos(n+1)t]_0^{2\pi} = 0.$$

Summarizing these results, we have for the circle C described above

$$\int_C (z - z_0)^n \, dz = \begin{cases} 2\pi i, & n = -1 \\ 0, & n \neq -1. \end{cases} \qquad (5.2.27)$$

EXAMPLE 5.2.3. Using Theorem 5.2.2 let us show that

$$\left| \int_i^{2+i} \frac{dz}{z^2} \right| \leqq 2,$$

where the path is the straight line from $z = 0 + i$ to $z = 2 + i$.

Solution. Note that the length L of the curve C is simply 2. (See Fig. 5.2.4.) Also $|z^2| = |z|^2 = x^2 + y^2$. Since along C, $y = 1$, we see that $x^2 + y^2 \geqq 1$. Thus $|G(z)| = 1/|z|^2 \leqq 1$, for every point on C. Hence, by Theorem 5.2.2 we have

$$\left| \int_i^{2+i} \frac{dz}{z^2} \right| \leqq 2.$$

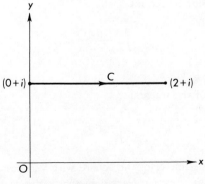

FIG. 5.2.4

EXERCISES 5.2

1. Let $f(t)$ be a complex-valued function which is bounded and continuous on $\alpha \leq t \leq \beta$ except for at most a finite number of points. Show that

$$\left| \int_\alpha^\beta f(t)\, dt \right| \leq \int_\alpha^\beta |f(t)|\, dt.$$

2. Let C be a contour given by $z = f(t)$, $\alpha \leq t \leq \beta$. Show that the length L of C is finite and is given by

$$L = \int_\alpha^\beta |f'(t)|\, dt.$$

3. Evaluate the following integrals:

(a) $\int_1^i (z - 1)\, dz$ on a straight line from 1 to i,

(b) $\int_0^{1+i} (z - 1)\, dz$ on the parabola $y = x^2$,

(c) $\int_1^{1+2i} x\, dz$ on the straight line from 1 to $1 + 2i$,

(d) $\int_C x\, dz$ on the circle $|z| = 1$ described in the counterclockwise direction,

(e) $\int_0^{1+i} (x + y - ix^2)\, dz$ on the path along the lines $x = 0$ and $y = 1$,

(f) $\int_{-i}^i (x^2 + iy^2)\, dz$ on the right half of the unit circle $|z| = 1$ described in the counterclockwise direction.

4. Utilizing equation (5.2.9) show that

(a) $\int_C dz = z_2 - z_1$, where z_1 and z_2 are respectively the initial and terminal points of the contour C,

(b) $\int_C z\, dz = \frac{1}{2}(z_2^2 - z_1^2)$ for every contour C with initial point z_1 and terminal point z_2,

(c) $\int_C z\, dz = 0$ on a closed contour C.

5. Compute the value of the integral

$$\int_C \frac{dz}{z^2 - 1},$$

where C is the circle $|z| = 2$.

6. Find the value of the integral

$$\int_C e^z\, dz,$$

where C is the perimeter of the square with vertices at the points $z = 0$, $z = 1$, $z = 1 + i$, $z = i$ traversed in that order.

7. Find the value of the integral

$$\int_C (z^2 + 1) \, dz,$$

where C is the perimeter of the square as given in Exercise 6 above.

8. Find the value of the integral

$$\int_C \sin z \, dz,$$

where C is the polygonal line connecting, in the given order, the points $z = \frac{1}{2}\pi$, $z = \frac{1}{2}\pi + i$, $z = -\frac{1}{2}\pi + i$, $z = -\frac{1}{2}\pi$.

9. (a) Find the value of the integral

$$\int_C \frac{dz}{z},$$

where C is the circle $|z| = r$ described in the counterclockwise direction.

(b) Show that

$$\int_C \frac{dz}{z^2} = 0,$$

for every closed contour C not passing through the origin.

10. Using Theorem 5.2.2, show that

$$\left| \int_C (x^2 + iy^2) \, dz \right| \leq \pi,$$

where C is a semicircle with $z = \pm i$ as ends of a diameter.

11. Show that

$$\int_C \frac{dz}{(z - z_0)^{n+1}} = 0 \qquad n = \pm 1, \pm 2, \cdots,$$

where C is a closed contour and z_0 is any point not on C.

12. Find the value of the integral

$$\int_C |z - 1| \, |dz|,$$

where C is the circle $|z| = 1$ described in the counterclockwise direction.

13. Find the value of the integral

$$\int_{-i}^{i} |z| \, dz$$

(a) on the straight line from $-i$ to i,

(b) on the right half of the unit circle $|z| = 1$ described in the counter-clockwise direction.

14. Let the same contour C be represented by the functions $z = f(t)$ and $z = g(t)$ defined respectively over the intervals $\alpha \leq t \leq \beta$ and $\gamma \leq t \leq \delta$. Suppose that $G(z)$ is continuous on C. Show that

$$\int_\alpha^\beta G[f(t)] f'(t)\, dt = \int_\gamma^\delta G[g(t)] g'(t)\, dt.$$

5.3. VARIATION OF THE LOGARITHM ALONG A CONTOUR.

Suppose that we are given a contour $C: z = z(t)$, $\alpha \leq t \leq \beta$, and a function $G(z)$ analytic and nonvanishing on C. Suppose further that we have a complex-valued function $\phi(t)$ continuous on the interval $\alpha \leq t \leq \beta$, such that

$$e^{\phi(t)} = G[z(t)]. \tag{5.3.1}$$

That is, for each t on the interval $\alpha \leq t \leq \beta$, $\phi(t)$ is one of the values of $\log\{G[z(t)]\}$. Then the value of $\phi(\beta) - \phi(\alpha)$ is called the *variation of* $\log[G(z)]$ *along* C and is denoted by

$$\Delta_C \log G(z).$$

In other words, if $\log G(z)$ is allowed to vary continuously as the point $z = z(t)$ traverses the contour C, then $\Delta_C \log G(z)$ is the net change in the value of $\log G(z)$. It is not difficult to show (see Exercise 5.3.1) that $\Delta_C \log G(z)$ depends only on $G(z)$ and C and is independent of $\phi(t)$. That is, if $\psi(t)$, $\alpha \leq t \leq \beta$, is another continuous function such that

$$e^{\psi(t)} = G[z(t)],$$

then

$$\psi(\beta) - \psi(\alpha) = \phi(\beta) - \phi(\alpha).$$

The following lemma will be utilized in the proof of Rouché's Theorem 7.4.3.

LEMMA 5.3.1. Given a closed contour $C: z = z(t)$, $\alpha \leq t \leq \beta$, and an analytic function $h(z)$ such that $|h(z)| < 1$ for all z on C, then

$$\Delta_C \log[1 + h(z)] = 0. \tag{5.3.2}$$

Proof. Since for z on C we have $|h(z)| < 1$, it follows (see Exercise 1.4.10) that the value of $1 + h(z)$ lies in the half plane $\mathscr{R}(z) > 0$. We know (see Example 4.5.3) that there exists a branch of $\log[1 + h(z)]$ in $\mathscr{R}(z) > 0$, namely,

$$\mathrm{Log}[1 + h(z)] = \mathrm{Log}|1 + h(z)| + i\,\mathrm{Arg}[1 + h(z)],$$
$$-\pi < \mathrm{Arg}[1 + h(z)] < \pi.$$

Let $\phi(t) = \text{Log}\,\{1 + h[z(t)]\}$, $\alpha \leq t \leq \beta$. Then $\phi(t)$ is continuous and $e^{\phi(t)} = 1 + h[z(t)]$. Since the contour C is closed, $z(\beta) = z(\alpha)$ and we see that

$$\phi(\beta) - \phi(\alpha) = \text{Log}\,\{1 + h[z(\beta)]\} - \text{Log}\,\{1 + h[z(\alpha)]\} = 0.$$

Consequently $\Delta_C \log [1 + h(z)] = 0$, and the lemma is established.

To show the existence of a complex-valued function $\phi(t)$ as given in (5.3.1), we consider the indefinite integral

$$\phi(T) = \int_\alpha^T \frac{G'[z(t)]\,z'(t)}{G[z(t)]}\,dt + k, \qquad \alpha \leq T \leq \beta, \tag{5.3.3}$$

where k is a constant such that

$$e^k = G[z(\alpha)]. \tag{5.3.4}$$

Since $G(z) \neq 0$ for z on C, $G'[z(t)]/G[z(t)]$ is continuous for $\alpha \leq t \leq \beta$. Also $z'(t)$ is bounded and continuous except for at most a finite number of points. Consequently $\phi(T)$ is continuous for $\alpha \leq T \leq \beta$, and at each point of continuity of $z'(T)$ we have from (5.2.5)

$$\phi'(T) = \frac{G'[z(T)]\,z'(T)}{G[z(T)]}. \tag{5.3.5}$$

To show that $e^{\phi(T)} = G[z(T)]$, we shall prove that the function

$$H(T) = G[z(T)]\,e^{-\phi(T)} \tag{5.3.6}$$

is equal to 1, $\alpha \leq T \leq \beta$.

To this end, we note first of all that $H(T)$ is continuous. Furthermore, using (5.3.5), we find that $H'(T) = 0$, except for at most a finite number of points where $z'(T)$ fails to exist. We know that any function $H(T)$ satisfying these conditions must be equal to a constant, say, $H(T) = c$. We shall next show that $c = 1$.

From (5.3.3) we see that $\phi(\alpha) = k$. By (5.3.4) we then have

$$e^{\phi(\alpha)} = e^k = G[z(\alpha)].$$

It now follows from (5.3.6) that $H(\alpha) = 1$. Thus $c = 1$. Consequently $H(T) = 1$ and $e^{\phi(T)} = G[z(T)]$, $\alpha \leq T \leq \beta$.

From (5.3.3) we further obtain

$$\phi(\beta) - \phi(\alpha) = \int_\alpha^\beta \frac{G'[z(t)]\,z'(t)}{G[z(t)]}\,dt, \tag{5.3.7}$$

or

$$\Delta_C \log G(z) = \int_C \frac{G'(z)}{G(z)}\,dz. \tag{5.3.8}$$

In the special case when $C: z = z(t)$, $\alpha \leqq t \leqq \beta$, is a closed contour, we have $z(\alpha) = z(\beta)$, and consequently

$$e^{\phi(\alpha)} = G[z(\alpha)] = G[z(\beta)] = e^{\phi(\beta)}.$$

It follows from (4.1.7) that $\phi(\beta) - \phi(\alpha) = 2n\pi i$, where n is an integer. Hence, for any closed contour C, we have in virtue of (5.3.7) and (5.3.8)

$$\frac{1}{2\pi i} \varDelta_C \log G(z) = \frac{1}{2\pi i} \int_C \frac{G'(z)}{G(z)} \, dz = n, \tag{5.3.9}$$

where n is an integer.

EXERCISES 5.3

1. Show that if the complex-valued functions $\phi(t)$ and $\psi(t)$ are continuous on the interval $\alpha \leqq t \leqq \beta$ and $e^{\phi(t)} = e^{\psi(t)}$, then

$$\phi(\beta) - \phi(\alpha) = \psi(\beta) - \psi(\alpha).$$

2. Given a contour $C: z = z(t)$, $\alpha \leqq t \leqq \beta$. Let the functions $f(z)$ and $g(z)$ be analytic and nonvanishing on C. Show that

$$\varDelta_C \log [f(z) \, g(z)] = \varDelta_C \log f(z) + \varDelta_C \log g(z).$$

5.4. THE WINDING NUMBER. A very important special case of (5.3.8) is obtained when we set $G(z) = z - \zeta$, where ζ is a point not on C. Then $G(z)$ does not vanish on the contour C, and we have from (5.3.8)

$$\frac{1}{2\pi i} \varDelta_C \log (z - \zeta) = \frac{1}{2\pi i} \int_C \frac{dz}{z - \zeta}. \tag{5.4.1}$$

The value of the expression in (5.4.1) depends on C and ζ and we shall denote it by

$$\nu(C, \zeta) = \frac{1}{2\pi i} \int_C \frac{dz}{z - \zeta}. \tag{5.4.2}$$

When C is a closed contour, then by (5.3.9), $\nu(C, \zeta)$ is an integer and is called the *winding number of C with respect to ζ*.

Remark 5.4.1. If a contour C is the sum of the contours C_1 and C_2, then by (5.2.14) we have

$$\frac{1}{2\pi i} \int_C \frac{dz}{z - \zeta} = \frac{1}{2\pi i} \int_{C_1} \frac{dz}{z - \zeta} + \frac{1}{2\pi i} \int_{C_2} \frac{dz}{z - \zeta}.$$

Hence

$$\nu(C, \zeta) = \nu(C_1, \zeta) + \nu(C_2, \zeta) \quad \text{for} \quad C = C_1 + C_2. \tag{5.4.3}$$

Also, since by (5.2.15)

$$\frac{1}{2\pi i}\int_{\bar{C}}\frac{dz}{z-\zeta}=-\frac{1}{2\pi i}\int_{C}\frac{dz}{z-\zeta},$$

we have

$$\nu(\bar{C},\zeta)=-\nu(C,\zeta),\qquad(5.4.4)$$

where $\bar{C}$ is the inverse of C.

If $C=\sum_{j=1}^{n}m_{j}C_{j}$ denote a formal sum, where the C_{j} are (possibly disjoint) contours and the m_{j} are integers, then we assign to the symbol $\nu(C,\zeta)$ the value

$$\frac{1}{2\pi i}\int_{\sum\limits_{j=1}^{n}m_{j}C_{j}}\frac{dz}{z-\zeta}=\sum_{j=1}^{n}m_{j}\frac{1}{2\pi i}\int_{C_{j}}\frac{dz}{z-\zeta}\qquad(5.4.5)$$

in accordance with Remark 5.2.2, and we have

$$\nu(C,\zeta)=\sum_{j=1}^{n}m_{j}\nu(C_{j},\zeta).\qquad(5.4.6)$$

——**THEOREM** 5.4.1.   Let C be a contour. Then $\nu(C,\zeta)$ is a continuous function of ζ for ζ not on C.

Proof.   For ζ_{0} and ζ not on C, utilizing (5.4.2), (5.2.12), and (5.2.20) we obtain

$$|\,\nu(C,\zeta)-\nu(C,\zeta_{0})\,|=\frac{1}{2\pi}\left|\int_{C}\frac{(\zeta-\zeta_{0})\,dz}{(z-\zeta)\,(z-\zeta_{0})}\right|$$

$$\leqq\frac{|\,\zeta-\zeta_{0}\,|}{2\pi}\int_{C}\frac{|\,dz\,|}{|\,z-\zeta\,|\,|\,z-\zeta_{0}\,|}.$$

Since ζ_{0} is not on C, there exists a constant $\rho>0$ such that $|\,z-\zeta_{0}\,|\geqq\rho$ for all z on C. [See Exercise 3.3.27.(c).] Also when $|\,\zeta-\zeta_{0}\,|\leqq\rho/2$, we have by (1.3.11) for all z on C

$$|\,z-\zeta\,|=|\,(z-\zeta_{0})-(\zeta-\zeta_{0})\,|\geqq|\,z-\zeta_{0}\,|-|\,\zeta-\zeta_{0}\,|\geqq\frac{\rho}{2}.$$

It follows from these inequalities that for $|\,\zeta-\zeta_{0}\,|\leqq\rho/2$

$$|\,\nu(C,\zeta)-\nu(C,\zeta_{0})\,|\leqq\frac{|\,\zeta-\zeta_{0}\,|\,L}{\pi\rho^{2}},$$

where L is the length of the contour C. Hence

$$\lim_{\zeta\to\zeta_{0}}\nu(C,\zeta)=\nu(C,\zeta_{0}),$$

and the theorem is established.

——*THEOREM* 5.4.2. Let C be a closed contour and let S be a connected set having no points in common with C. Then $\nu(C, \zeta)$ is constant for all ζ in S.

Proof. By Theorem 5.4.1, $\nu(C, \zeta)$ is a continuous function of ζ. Since S is a connected set and $\nu(C, \zeta)$ takes on integral values only, it must be constant on S. (See Exercise 3.3.28.)

In the sequel, we shall make use of the following

LEMMA 5.4.1. Let C be a closed contour and let S be a connected set having no points in common with C. If S contains a sequence of points $\{\zeta_n\}$ such that $\zeta_n \to \infty$ as $n \to \infty$, then $\nu(C, \zeta) = 0$ for all ζ in S.

Proof. By Theorem 5.4.2, $\nu(C, \zeta)$ is constant on S. Since $\zeta_n \to \infty$, we have (see Exercise 5.4.1) $\nu(C, \zeta_n) \to 0$. It follows that $\nu(C, \zeta) = 0$ for all ζ in S.

EXERCISES 5.4

1. Let C be a contour, and let $\{\zeta_n\}$ be a sequence of points such that $\zeta_n \to \infty$ as $n \to \infty$. Show that $\lim\limits_{n \to \infty} \nu(C, \zeta_n) = 0$.

5.5. SIMPLE CLOSED CONTOURS. A continuous curve $C\colon z = z(t)$, $\alpha \le t \le \beta$, is said to be *simple closed* if $z(\alpha) = z(\beta)$ and it does not intersect itself. We shall now state without proof the following important

——*THEOREM* 5.5.1 (*Jordan curve theorem*). Let C be a simple closed curve. Then C divides the plane into two disjoint domains D_1 and D_2. Furthermore, C is the boundary of D_1 as well as the boundary of D_2.

In other words, the points not on C form two disjoint domains. Every point of C is an accumulation point of D_1 as well as of D_2. Finally, D_1 and D_2 have no boundary points other than the points of C.

It can be further shown (see Exercise 5.5.2) that one of the two domains is bounded and the other is unbounded. The bounded domain is called the *interior* of C and the unbounded domain is called the *exterior* of C. A point is said to be interior or exterior to C according as it is contained in the bounded or unbounded domain, respectively. (See Fig. 5.5.1, with D_1 bounded, D_2 unbounded.)

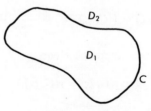

FIG. 5.5.1

——*THEOREM* 5.5.2.   Let C be a simple closed contour. Then $\nu(C, \zeta) = 0$ for all ζ exterior to C.

Proof.   Let D_2 denote the exterior of C. Since D_2 is unbounded, it contains a sequence of points $\{\zeta_n\}$ such that $\zeta_n \to \infty$ as $n \to \infty$. Since D_2 is also connected it follows from Lemma 5.4.1 that $\nu(C, \zeta) = 0$ for all ζ in D_2.

EXERCISES 5.5

1. Let C be a simple closed curve and let D_1 and D_2 be the two domains into which C divides the plane. Let S be a connected set having no points in common with C. Show that S is contained either entirely in D_1 or entirely in D_2.

2. Let C be a simple closed curve and let D_1 and D_2 be the two domains into which C divides the plane. Show that one of the domains D_1, D_2 is bounded and the other is unbounded.

3. Suppose that $C = C_1 + C_2$ is a simple closed contour and let ζ be any point in the exterior of C. Show that $\nu(C_1, \zeta) = \nu(\bar{C}_2, \zeta)$ where $\bar{C}_2$ is the inverse of C_2.

4. Show that the winding number of a contour with respect to a point in the plane is invariant under translation and rotation of the coordinate axes.

5.6.   THE POSITIVE DIRECTION ALONG A SIMPLE CLOSED CONTOUR.   Let $C: z = re^{it}$, $0 \leq t \leq 2\pi$, describe a circle. With $\zeta = 0$ in (5.4.2) and using (5.2.27), we obtain

$$\nu(C, 0) = \frac{1}{2\pi i} \int_C \frac{dz}{z} = 1.$$

Since the interior of C is a connected set, we have by Theorem 5.4.2 that $\nu(C, \zeta) = 1$ for all ζ interior to C.

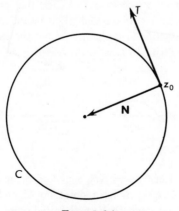

FIG. 5.6.1

As t increases from $t = 0$ to $t = 2\pi$, the point $z = re^{it}$ describes the circle C in the counterclockwise direction. A traveler whose position at each instant t is given by $z = re^{it}$, and who is facing in the direction of the motion, traverses the circle in such a way that the interior of C is always to his left.

More precisely, at each point $z_0 = z(t_0)$ on C, one may draw a directed segment N with initial point at z_0, perpendicular to the tangent T and contained in the interior of C. (See Fig. 5.6.1.) Such a directed segment is called the inner normal to C at z_0. The traveler, facing in the direction of the tangent T, will find the inner normal N pointing to his left.

This, in turn, means that the inner normal N is oriented relative to the tangent T in the same way as the positive y axis is oriented relative to the positive x axis. We may also express this as follows: If the coordinate axes are rotated and translated until the new origin $Z = 0$ coincides with $z = z_0$ and the positive direction of the new X axis lies along the tangent T, then the inner normal N will lie along the positive Y axis. We shall say for brevity that the ordered pair (T, N) is positively oriented.

We shall now extend the above observations to the case in which C is any simple closed contour. Before doing so, we shall make the following two definitions.

Definition 5.6.1. Let A and B denote two mutually perpendicular vectors issuing from a point z_0. If by a rotation and translation of the xy axes we may obtain a new coordinate system with the origin at z_0 and the positive x and y axes directed respectively along A and B, then we shall say that the ordered pair of vectors (A, B) is *positively oriented*.

Figures 5.6.2 and 5.6.3 illustrate respectively positively and nonpositively (or negatively) oriented ordered pairs of vectors, (A, B).

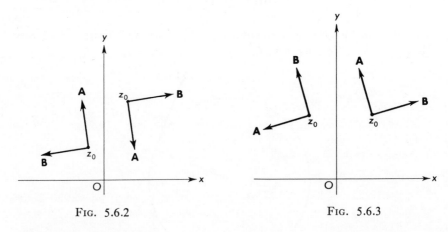

FIG. 5.6.2   FIG. 5.6.3

Definition 5.6.2. Let $C: z = f(t)$, $\alpha \le t \le \beta$, be a simple closed contour and let $z_0 = f(t_0)$, $\alpha < t_0 < \beta$, be a point on C such that $f'(t_0)$ is defined, and $f'(t_0) \ne 0$. A directed segment N, with initial point at z_0 and perpendicular to the tangent T at z_0, is called an *inner normal* to C at the point z_0 if, except for the point z_0, it lies in the interior of C.

Observe that the above definition does not assert the existence of such an inner normal. The existence will be asserted in the second of the following two theorems, the proofs of which we shall omit.

————**THEOREM** 5.6.1.   Let C be a simple closed contour. Then $\nu(C, \zeta) = \pm 1$ for all ζ interior to C.

Observe that since the interior of C is a connected set, it follows from Theorem 5.4.2 that $\nu(C, \zeta)$ is constant in the interior of C. Theorem 5.6.1 thus asserts that either $\nu(C, \zeta) = 1$ for all ζ interior to C or else $\nu(C, \zeta) = -1$ for all ζ interior to C.

————**THEOREM** 5.6.2.   Let $C: z = f(t)$, $\alpha \leq t \leq \beta$, be a simple closed contour and let $z_0 = f(t_0)$, $\alpha < t_0 < \beta$, be a point on C such that $f'(t_0)$ exists and is not equal to zero. Then there exists an inner normal N to C at $z = z_0$. Moreover, if T denotes the tangent to C at z_0, then the pair (T, N) is positively oriented if, and only if, $\nu(C, \zeta) = 1$ for all ζ interior to C.

As a result of Theorem 5.6.1, we can formulate the following

Definition 5.6.3.   Let C be a simple closed contour. If $\nu(C, \zeta) = 1$ for all ζ interior to C, we say that the contour C is described in the *positive direction*. If $\nu(C, \zeta) = -1$ for all ζ interior to C, we say that the contour C is described in the *negative direction*. In the latter case, the inverse contour $\bar{C}$ is described in the positive direction.

Let $G(z)$ be a continuous complex-valued function defined on the simple closed contour C described in the positive direction. Then by the *integral of $G(z)$ in the positive direction along C*, we mean

$$\int_C G(z)\, dz.$$

Remark 5.6.1.   From Theorem 5.6.2 it follows that as one describes a simple closed contour C in the positive direction and facing in the direction of the motion, then, except for at most a finite number of points on C, the interior of C is always to one's left. It is this criterion that is most often used in practice for determining the positive direction along a contour.

5.7. SIMPLY CONNECTED DOMAINS.   An important role in the theory of analytic functions is played by the concept of a *simply connected* domain. Intuitively, this means a domain without "holes." For example, the interior of a circle and the set consisting of all points z such that $\mathscr{R}(z) > 0$ are each simply connected domains. The annulus D consisting of all z such that $r < |z| < R$ (see Fig. 5.7.1) is not a simply connected domain. Before pro-

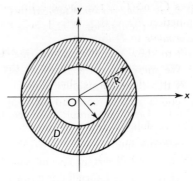

Fig. 5.7.1

ceeding with the formal definition of a simply connected domain, we shall define the auxiliary notion of the continuous deformation of one curve into another.

Let C: $z = f(s)$ and Γ: $z = \phi(s)$, $\alpha \leq s \leq \beta$, be two continuous curves having the same initial point $z_1 = f(\alpha) = \phi(\alpha)$ and the same terminal point $z_2 = f(\beta) = \phi(\beta)$. Then, it is intuitively clear what is meant by gradually deforming the curve C until it is brought into coincidence with Γ, while keeping the initial and terminal points fixed. The process can be considered to take place during a certain time interval, say, from $t = 0$ to $t = 1$. During each instance t, the curve C occupies a certain position and as t varies, C is continuously altered until in the end, when $t = 1$, C occupies the position Γ.

In other words, at each instant t, $0 \leq t \leq 1$, the curve C occupies a position given by

$$C_t: \quad z = f_t(s), \qquad \alpha \leq s \leq \beta, \tag{5.7.1}$$

with $f_t(\alpha) = z_1$, $f_t(\beta) = z_2$, $0 \leq t \leq 1$, z_1 and z_2 fixed. The initial position C_0 is identical with C and the final position C_1 is identical with Γ. As t increases from $t = 0$ to $t = 1$, the function $f_t(s)$ changes "continuously" from $f_0(s) = f(s)$ to $f_1(s) = \phi(s)$. Let s' be any fixed s, then $f_t(s')$, $0 \leq t \leq 1$, gives the position corresponding to s' at each instant t. As t increases from 0 to 1, $f_t(s')$ describes a continuous path beginning at the point $f_0(s') = f(s')$ on C and ending at the point $f_1(s') = \phi(s')$ on Γ. Thus, each point $f(s')$ on C travels along a continuous path until it is brought into coincidence with the corresponding point $\phi(s')$ on Γ.

The function $f_t(s)$ in (5.7.1), which depends upon t and s, may be written as $F(t, s)$. We are now ready to make the following

Definition 5.7.1. Let C: $z = f(s)$ and Γ: $z = \phi(s)$, $\alpha \leq s \leq \beta$, be two continuous curves with the same initial point z_1 and the same terminal point z_2. We say that C can be *deformed continuously* into Γ if there exists a function $F(t, s)$ defined and continuous on the plane interval, $0 \leq t \leq 1$, $\alpha \leq s \leq \beta$, such that $F(t, \alpha) = z_1$, $F(t, \beta) = z_2$ for all $0 \leq t \leq 1$ and $F(0, s) = f(s)$, $F(1, s) = \phi(s)$ for all $\alpha \leq s \leq \beta$.

If the two curves C and Γ in the above definition lie in a domain D and the values of the function $F(t, s)$ $0 \leq t \leq 1$, $\alpha \leq s \leq \beta$, also lie in D, then we say that C is *deformable* in D into Γ.

It is not difficult to show that if C is deformable into Γ, then Γ is also deformable into C. We merely use the function $G(t, s) = F(1 - t, s)$. The reader may also verify that the deformability of one curve into another does not depend upon the functions used to represent these curves.

Definition 5.7.2.   A domain D is said to be *simply connected* if, given any two continuous curves C and Γ in D having the same initial and terminal points, C is deformable in D into Γ.

An alternative definition of a simply connected domain is given by

Definition 5.7.3.   Let D be a domain and let D_Σ be the set corresponding to D on the sphere. (See Section 2.12.) Let D'_Σ be the set of all points on the sphere not contained in D_Σ. Then the domain D is said to be simply connected if D'_Σ is connected.

Definitions 5.7.2 and 5.7.3 are equivalent. We shall not prove this here.*

Definition 5.7.2 is intrinsic in the sense that it does not involve any point sets lying outside the domain D under consideration. Definition 5.7.3 is often more convenient for application, since it allows us to recognize more readily whether or not a domain is simply connected.

EXAMPLE 5.7.1.   Let the domain D be the interior of a simple closed curve C with the interior of a small circle Γ removed. Then D is not simply connected, for the complement of D on the sphere Σ, consisting of the exterior of C together with the point $z = \infty$ and the interior of Γ, is not a connected set. (See Fig. 5.7.2.)

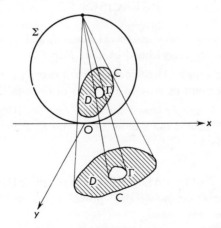

FIG. 5.7.2

* See L. Ahlfors, *Complex Analysis*, p. 220, New York: McGraw-Hill, 1953.

EXAMPLE 5.7.2. Let D be the domain consisting of the finite complex plane with the point $z = 0$ removed. Then D is not simply connected. For, when represented on a sphere, the complement of D consists of the points N and S (see Fig. 2.12.1) corresponding to $z = 0$ and $z = \infty$, which do not form a connected set.

EXAMPLE 5.7.3. Let D consist of the interior of the circle $|z| = 1$ with the segment $0 \leq x < 1$, $y = 0$, removed. Then D is a simply connected domain, for its complement on the sphere, consisting of the point $z = \infty$ together with all the points $|z| \geq 1$ and the segment $0 \leq x < 1$, $y = 0$, is a connected set.

EXAMPLE 5.7.4. Let D be the domain consisting of all finite z such that $|z| > 1$. Then D is not simply connected, for the complement of D on the sphere, consisting of the point $z = \infty$ together with the domain representing the set of points $|z| \leq 1$, is not a connected set.

EXAMPLE 5.7.5. Let D be the domain consisting of the finite plane with the nonpositive half of the x axis removed. Then D is simply connected, for the complement of D on the sphere, consisting of the point $z = \infty$ together with the image of the nonpositive half of the real axis, is a connected set.

EXAMPLE 5.7.6. Let the domains D_1 and D_2 be respectively the interior and the exterior of a simple closed curve. Let D_∞ be D_2 with the point at infinity adjoined. Then considering the complements of the sets D_1, D_2 and D_∞ on the sphere, we see that D_1 and D_∞ are simply connected and that D_2 is not simply connected.

EXERCISES 5.7

1. Show that if D is a simply connected domain, and z is a point not in D, then $\nu(\Gamma, z) = 0$ for every closed contour Γ in D.

2. Let C and C_1 be simple closed contours such that C_1 is in the interior of C. Show that every point exterior to C is also exterior to C_1.

3. Let C_1 and C_2 be simple closed contours, each one lying in the exterior of the other. Let I_1 denote the interior of C_1 and E_2 the exterior of C_2. Show that I_1 is contained in E_2.

5.8. CAUCHY'S INTEGRAL THEOREM FOR THE INTERIOR OF A CIRCLE.

In this section we shall prove* a special, "local," case of the Cauchy integral theorem, namely,

---

* In this section as well as in the next one, we follow the presentation given by L. Ahlfors, *Complex Analysis*, pp. 89–92. New York: McGraw-Hill, 1953.

——**THEOREM** 5.8.1 (*Cauchy-Goursat*).   Let $f(z)$ be analytic in the interior D of a circle and let Γ_1 and Γ_2 be two contours in D with the same initial and the same terminal points. Then

$$\int_{\Gamma_1} f(z)\, dz = \int_{\Gamma_2} f(z)\, dz. \tag{5.8.1}$$

Remark 5.8.1.   The statement that

$$\int_{\Gamma_1} f(z)\, dz = \int_{\Gamma_2} f(z)\, dz$$

for any two contours Γ_1 and Γ_2 in a domain D with the same initial and the same terminal points, is equivalent to the statement that

$$\int_{\Gamma} f(z)\, dz = 0,$$

for any closed contour Γ in D. For, we may write $\Gamma = \Gamma_1 + \bar{\Gamma}_2$, where Γ_1 and Γ_2 have the same initial and terminal points, and $\bar{\Gamma}_2$ is the inverse of Γ_2. (See Fig. 5.8.1.) Then by (5.2.14) and (5.2.15) we obtain

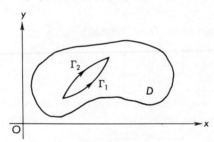

FIG. 5.8.1

$$\int_{\Gamma} f(z)\, dz = \int_{\Gamma_1 + \bar{\Gamma}_2} f(z)\, dz = \int_{\Gamma_1} f(z)\, dz - \int_{\Gamma_2} f(z)\, dz.$$

Consequently, if

$$\int_{\Gamma_1} f(z)\, dz = \int_{\Gamma_2} f(z)\, dz, \quad \text{then} \quad \int_{\Gamma} f(z)\, dz = 0, \quad \text{and conversely.}$$

Theorem 5.8.1 may now be restated in the following equivalent form.

——**THEOREM** 5.8.2 (*Cauchy-Goursat*).   Let $f(z)$ be analytic in the interior D of a circle and let Γ be any closed contour in D. Then

$$\int_{\Gamma} f(z)\, dz = 0.$$

Remark 5.8.2.   It will follow from Theorem 5.8.2 that if $f(z)$ is analytic in the entire finite complex plane, then

$$\int_\Gamma f(z)\, dz = 0$$

for every closed contour Γ. For, since Γ is a bounded set, it is contained in the interior D of a circle with center at the origin and of sufficiently large radius. Now $f(z)$ is analytic in D, and consequently

$$\int_\Gamma f(z)\, dz = 0.$$

Before proving Theorem 5.8.1, we shall establish a number of lemmas.

LEMMA 5.8.1.   Suppose that $F(z)$ is analytic in a domain D and $f(z) = F'(z)$ in D. Let Γ be a contour in D with initial point z_1 and terminal point z_2. Then

$$\int_\Gamma f(z)\, dz = F(z_2) - F(z_1). \tag{5.8.2}$$

Proof.   Let Γ be given by $z = z(t)$, $\alpha \le t \le \beta$. Then by (5.2.9)

$$\int_\Gamma f(z)\, dz = \int_\alpha^\beta f[z(t)]\, z'(t)\, dt.$$

Since the integrand on the right is, except for at most a finite number of points, bounded and continuous on the interval $\alpha \le t \le \beta$ and equal to the derivative of $F[z(t)]$, we have (see Exercise 5.8.2)

$$\int_\alpha^\beta f[z(t)]\, z'(t)\, dt = F[z(\beta)] - F[z(\alpha)].$$

Hence

$$\int_\Gamma f(z)\, dz = F(z_2) - F(z_1).$$

LEMMA 5.8.2.   Suppose that $F(z)$ is analytic in a domain D and $f(z) = F'(z)$ in D. Let Γ_1 and Γ_2 be two contours in D with the same initial and the same terminal point. Then

$$\int_{\Gamma_1} f(z)\, dz = \int_{\Gamma_2} f(z)\, dz. \tag{5.8.3}$$

Proof.   Let z_1 be the common initial point and z_2 the common terminal point of Γ_1 and Γ_2. The result now follows from (5.8.2).

LEMMA 5.8.3 (*Goursat's lemma*). Let $f(z)$ be analytic in the interior and on the perimeter of a rectangle R. Then

$$\int_C f(z)\,dz = 0, \qquad (5.8.4)$$

where C is a contour describing the perimeter of the rectangle R.

Proof. Let us subdivide the rectangle R into four congruent rectangles R_i $(i = 1, \cdots, 4)$ as shown in Fig. 5.8.2. Furthermore, let C and C_i $(i = 1, \cdots, 4)$

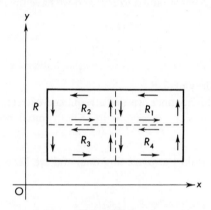

FIG. 5.8.2

denote respectively the contours describing the perimeters of R and R_i in the positive direction. Then we may write each C_i as a sum

$$C_i = \sum_{j=1}^{4} C_{ij},$$

where each C_{ij} is a contour describing a side of the rectangle R_i.

We have by Remark 5.2.2

$$\int_{\sum_{i=1}^{4} C_i} f(z)\,dz = \int_{\sum_{i,j=1}^{4} C_{ij}} f(z)\,dz. \qquad (5.8.5)$$

Each of the sides of the rectangles R_i lying interior to R forms the boundary of two neighboring rectangles and is represented by two of the C_{ij}, one of which is the inverse of the other. Thus (see Remark 5.2.2) the C_{ij} corresponding to the sides lying within R may be omitted from the sum $\sum_{i,j=1}^{4} C_{ij}$ in (5.8.5). The remaining terms in the sum $\sum_{i,j=1}^{4} C_{ij}$ clearly add up to C, and we obtain from (5.8.5)

$$\sum_{i=1}^{4} \int_{C_i} f(z)\,dz = \int_C f(z)\,dz. \qquad (5.8.6)$$

Let R_k be chosen so that

$$\left| \int_{C_k} f(z)\, dz \right| \geq \left| \int_{C_i} f(z)\, dz \right|, \qquad i = 1, 2, 3, 4.$$

Denoting the rectangle R_k by $R^{(1)}$, its boundary by $C^{(1)}$, and the respective values of $\left| \int_C f(z)\, dz \right|$ and $\left| \int_{C^{(1)}} f(z)\, dz \right|$ by J and J_1, we see from (1.3.10) and (5.8.6) that $J \leq 4J_1$.

Subdividing the rectangle $R^{(1)}$ as we did for R and proceeding as above, we obtain a rectangle $R^{(2)}$ contained in $R^{(1)}$ and we have the inequality $J_1 \leq 4J_2$, where

$$J_2 = \left| \int_{C^{(2)}} f(z)\, dz \right|$$

and $C^{(2)}$ is the boundary of $R^{(2)}$.

Continuing in this manner we get a sequence of rectangles

$$R \supset R^{(1)} \supset R^{(2)} \supset \cdots, \tag{5.8.7}$$

each one contained within the preceding one, and we have $J_n \leq 4J_{n+1}$, where

$$J_n = \left| \int_{C^{(n)}} f(z)\, dz \right|$$

and $C^{(n)}$ is the boundary of $R^{(n)}$, $n = 1, 2, \cdots$. It follows that

$$J \leq 4^n J_n, \qquad n = 1, 2, \cdots. \tag{5.8.8}$$

Let $L, L_1, L_2, \cdots$ denote respectively the length of the perimeters of R, $R^{(1)}$, $R^{(2)}$, $\cdots$. We find that

$$L_1 = \tfrac{1}{2}L, \qquad L_2 = \tfrac{1}{2}L_1, \cdots.$$

Hence

$$L_n = (\tfrac{1}{2})^n L, \qquad n = 1, 2, \cdots. \tag{5.8.9}$$

Since (5.8.7) is a sequence of closed rectangles, there exists by Theorem 2.4.3 a point z_0 common to all the rectangles. In particular, z_0 is in R, and hence by the hypothesis $f(z)$ has a derivative at z_0. It follows that

$$f(z) = f(z_0) + f'(z_0)(z - z_0) + \lambda(z)(z - z_0), \tag{5.8.10}$$

where

$$\lambda(z) = \begin{cases} \dfrac{f(z) - f(z_0)}{z - z_0} - f'(z_0), & \text{if } z \neq z_0, \\[2mm] 0, & \text{if } z = z_0. \end{cases} \tag{5.8.11}$$

Consequently

$$\int_{C^{(n)}} f(z)\, dz = \int_{C^{(n)}} [f(z_0) + f'(z_0)\,(z - z_0)]\, dz + \int_{C^{(n)}} \lambda(z)\,(z - z_0)\, dz.$$
$$(5.8.12)$$

The first integrand on the right-hand side is the derivative with respect to z of the analytic function

$$F(z) = f(z_0)\, z + \frac{f'(z_0)}{2}\,(z - z_0)^2.$$

It follows from Lemma 5.8.2 and Remark 5.8.1 that the first integral on the right-hand side of (5.8.12) is equal to zero, and consequently by (5.2.22) we have

$$J_n = \left| \int_{C^{(n)}} f(z)\, dz \right| = \left| \int_{C^{(n)}} \lambda(z)\,(z - z_0)\, dz \right|$$
$$\leq L_n \max_{z \text{ on } C^{(n)}} | \lambda(z)\,(z - z_0) | \leq L_n \max_{z \text{ on } C^{(n)}} | z - z_0 |\, \epsilon_n,$$
$$(5.8.13)$$

where

$$\epsilon_n = \max_{z \text{ on } C^{(n)}} | \lambda(z) |.$$

Now, $| \lambda(z) | \to 0$ as $| z - z_0 | \to 0.$* Consequently, $\epsilon_n \to 0$ as $n \to \infty$. Also, since z and z_0 are both contained in $R^{(n)}$, we have (see Exercise 5.8.1)

$$| z - z_0 | \leq \frac{L_n}{\sqrt{2}}, \qquad n = 1, 2, \cdots. \qquad (5.8.14)$$

It follows from (5.8.13) and (5.8.14) that

$$J_n \leq \frac{L_n^2}{\sqrt{2}}\, \epsilon_n. \qquad (5.8.15)$$

Utilizing (5.8.8), (5.8.9), and (5.8.15) we get

$$0 \leq J \leq \frac{4^n L_n^2}{\sqrt{2}}\, \epsilon_n = \frac{L^2}{\sqrt{2}}\, \epsilon_n. \qquad (5.8.16)$$

Since ϵ_n can be made as small as we please, it follows that

$$J = \left| \int_C f(z)\, dz \right| = 0,$$

and the lemma is established.

* The conditions $| z - z_0 | \to 0$, $| z | \to 0$ are, respectively, equivalent to the conditions $z \to z_0$, $z \to 0$.

LEMMA 5.8.4.   Let $f(z)$ be analytic in the interior D of a circle and let z_0 be the center of the circle D. Let $F(z)$ be defined by

$$F(z) = \int_{z_0}^{z} f(\zeta)\,d\zeta, \tag{5.8.17}$$

where the path of integration is any contour in D with initial point z_0 and terminal point z which is the sum of one horizontal and one vertical segment. Then $F(z)$ is single-valued and analytic in D and we have

$$f(z) = F'(z). \tag{5.8.18}$$

Proof.   To show that $F(z)$ is single-valued in D, let Γ_1 and Γ_2 be two contours joining z_0 to z and each consisting of one horizontal and one vertical segment. (See Fig. 5.8.3.) Then by Lemma 5.8.3 we have

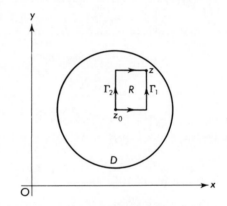

FIG.   5.8.3

$$\int_{\Gamma_1} f(\zeta)\,d\zeta - \int_{\Gamma_2} f(\zeta)\,d\zeta = \int_{\Gamma_1 + \Gamma_2} f(\zeta)\,d\zeta = 0.$$

Hence

$$\int_{\Gamma_1} f(\zeta)\,d\zeta = \int_{\Gamma_2} f(\zeta)\,d\zeta.$$

Thus $F(z)$, defined at each point z in D as the common value of the two contour integrals, is consequently single-valued.

To show that $F(z)$ is analytic in D and that $f(z) = F'(z)$, we shall prove that

$$f(z) = F_x = -iF_y. \tag{5.8.19}$$

Let z and $z + h$, $h \neq 0$, h real, be two points in D. Let Γ_2 be a contour joining z_0 to z and consisting of a vertical segment followed by a horizontal segment. Let γ: $\zeta = z + ht$, $0 \leq t \leq 1$, be a horizontal segment with initial point at z and terminal point at $z + h$. (See Fig. 5.8.4.) Then in view of (5.8.17), we have

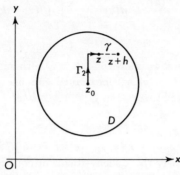

FIG. 5.8.4

$$\frac{F(z+h) - F(z)}{h} = \frac{1}{h}\left[\int_{\Gamma_2+\gamma} f(\zeta)\,d\zeta - \int_{\Gamma_2} f(\zeta)\,d\zeta\right] = \frac{1}{h}\int_\gamma f(\zeta)\,d\zeta$$

$$= \frac{1}{h}\int_0^1 f(z+ht)\,h\,dt = \int_0^1 f(z+ht)\,dt.$$

Also

$$\left|\frac{F(z+h) - F(z)}{h} - f(z)\right| = \left|\int_0^1 f(z+ht)\,dt - \int_0^1 f(z)\,dt\right|$$

$$= \left|\int_0^1 [f(z+ht) - f(z)]\,dt\right| \leq 1 \cdot \max_{0 \leq t \leq 1}|f(z+ht) - f(z)|.$$

Since $f(z)$ is continuous, it follows that

$$\lim_{h\to 0}\left|\frac{F(z+h) - F(z)}{h} - f(z)\right| = 0.$$

Hence $F_x(z) = f(z)$.

To show that $f(z) = -iF_y(z)$, let z and $z + ik$, $k \neq 0$, k real, be any two points in D. Let Γ_1 be as in Fig. 5.8.5 and let $\gamma'\colon \zeta = z + ikt$, $0 \leq t \leq 1$,

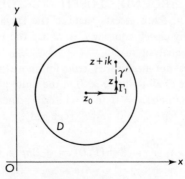

FIG. 5.8.5

be a vertical segment with initial point z and terminal point $z + ik$. Then

$$\left| \frac{F(z + ik) - F(z)}{k} - if(z) \right| = \left| i \int_0^1 [f(z + ikt) - f(z)] \, dt \right|$$

$$\leq 1 \cdot \max_{0 \leq t \leq 1} | f(z + ikt) - f(z) |.$$

Hence

$$\lim_{k \to 0} \frac{F(z + ik) - F(z)}{k} = if(z),$$

that is, $f(z) = -iF_y(z)$.

Letting $F(z) = u(x, y) + iv(x, y)$, we see from (5.8.19) that u_x, u_y, v_x, v_y are continuous and satisfy the Cauchy-Riemann equations (3.6.1), and consequently $F(z)$ is analytic in D. It also follows from (5.8.19) that $f(z) = u_x + iv_x$ and by (3.6.9) we have $f(z) = F'(z)$. Thus the lemma is established.

The proof of Theorem 5.8.1 now follows from Lemma 5.8.4 and Lemma 5.8.2.

EXERCISES 5.8

1. Show that if P is the perimeter of a rectangle R, then for any two points z_1 and z_2 in R we have

$$| z_1 - z_2 | \leq \frac{P}{\sqrt{2}}.$$

2. Let $F(z)$ be analytic in a domain D. Let $\Gamma: z = z(t)$, $\alpha \leq t \leq \beta$, be a contour in D. Show that

$$\int_\alpha^\beta \frac{d\{F[z(t)]\}}{dt} \, dt = F[z(\beta)] - F[z(\alpha)].$$

5.9. INTEGRALS AROUND CLOSED CONTOURS IN A GENERAL DOMAIN. Theorem 5.8.2 asserts that, in the special case where D is the interior of a circle, any closed contour Γ in D has the property: $\int_\Gamma f(z) \, dz = 0$ for all functions $f(z)$ analytic in D.

However, this is not necessarily true for more general domains D. For example, if D consists of all points $z \neq 0$ in the finite plane, and if Γ is a simple closed contour containing $z = 0$ in its interior, then using Theorem 5.6.1 and equation (5.4.2), with $\zeta = 0$ and C replaced by Γ, we have

$$\int_\Gamma \frac{dz}{z} = 2\pi i \nu(\Gamma, 0) = \pm 2\pi i \neq 0,$$

although the function $f(z) = 1/z$ is analytic in D.

We can, however, state the following theorem which is a special case of Theorem 5.9.2 below.

——THEOREM 5.9.1. Let D be any open set and let Γ be a closed contour in D such that $\nu(\Gamma, \zeta) = 0$ for all ζ not in D. Then

$$\int_\Gamma f(z) \, dz = 0 \qquad (5.9.1)$$

for all functions $f(z)$ analytic in D.

Theorem 5.9.1 asserts that if (5.9.1) holds for functions of the type

$$f(z) = \frac{1}{z - \zeta}, \qquad \zeta \text{ not in } D,$$

then (5.9.1) holds for all* functions $f(z)$ analytic in D.

Recalling the meaning of

$$\int_{\sum_{i=1}^n m_i C_i} f(z) \, dz \quad \text{and} \quad \nu\left(\sum_{i=1}^n m_i C_i, \zeta\right)$$

given in Remarks 5.2.2 and 5.4.1, we shall state Theorem 5.9.1 in the following more general form which will be utilized later on.

——THEOREM 5.9.2 (Ahlfors).

Let D be any open set and let $\Gamma = \sum_{i=1}^n m_i \Gamma_i$ be a formal sum of closed contours Γ_i in D such that $\nu(\Gamma, \zeta) = 0$ for all ζ not in D. Then

$$\int_\Gamma f(z) \, dz = 0 \qquad (5.9.2)$$

for all functions $f(z)$ analytic in D.

Before proceeding with the proof of Theorem 5.9.2, we shall establish the following two lemmas.

---

* The reason why the functions $1/(z - \zeta)$ play such a decisive role is as follows: If Γ is a closed contour in D and S is the set of all points lying on Γ, then S is a closed and bounded set. By Runge's Theorem (see Saks and Zygmund, *Analytic Functions*, p. 176, Warsaw: 1952) there exists for every function $f(z)$ analytic in D, a sequence $\phi_n(z)$ of rational functions analytic in D and converging uniformly on S to $f(z)$. Each $\phi_n(z)$ is the sum of a polynomial $P_n(z)$ plus constant multiples of terms of the type $1/(z - \zeta)^k$ for ζ not in D. By Lemma 5.8.1 we have for $k > 1$

$$\int_\Gamma \frac{dz}{(z - \zeta)^k} = 0. \qquad \text{Also,} \qquad \int_\Gamma P_n(z) \, dz = 0.$$

Now, if Γ has the property that $\int_\Gamma dz/(z - \zeta) = 0$ for ζ not in D, then $\int_\Gamma \phi_n(z) \, dz = 0$ for all n, and consequently $\int_\Gamma f(z) \, dz = \lim_{n \to \infty} \int_\Gamma \phi_n(z) \, dz = 0$.

This applies also to the case when Γ is a formal sum of closed contours.

LEMMA 5.9.1. Let D be any open set and let

$$\gamma = \sum_{i=1}^{m} m_i \gamma_i \tag{5.9.3}$$

be a formal sum of closed polygonal contours γ_i in D with sides parallel to the coordinate axes and such that $\nu(\gamma, \zeta) = 0$ for all ζ not in D. Then

$$\int_{\gamma} f(z)\, dz = 0 \tag{5.9.4}$$

for all functions $f(z)$ analytic in D.

Proof. The plan of the proof is (1) to express γ as a formal sum: $\gamma = \sum_{k=1}^{r} \lambda_k C_k$, where $\lambda_k \neq 0$ are integers and each C_k is a simple closed contour describing in the positive direction the perimeter of a rectangle, (2) to show that each rectangle whose contour C_i appears in the sum lies in D, and (3) to obtain from Lemma 5.8.3 that

$$\int_{C_k} f(z)\, dz = 0$$

for each C_k, and consequently

$$\int_{\gamma} f(z)\, dz = \int_{\sum_{k=1}^{m} \lambda_k C_k} f(z)\, dz = \sum_{k=1}^{m} \lambda_k \int_{C_k} f(z)\, dz = 0.$$

We now proceed to carry out step (1) of our plan.

As we have seen in Section 5.1, each polygonal contour γ_k in the formal sum (5.9.3) forms a bounded set. It follows that there exists a square Q bounded by the lines $x = \pm M$, $y = \pm M$, where M is a positive integer, containing all the γ_k in its interior.

We now subdivide the plane into a network of rectangles by (a) drawing the lines $x = n$, $y = n$, $n = \pm M$, $\pm (M + 1)$, $\pm (M + 2)$, $\cdots$, and (b) extending indefinitely the sides of the polygonal contours γ_i. (See Fig. 5.9.1 for the case where $\gamma = m_1 \gamma_1 + m_2 \gamma_2$.) Observe that by extending the sides of the γ_i we are assured that no one of the polygonal contours γ_i has points in common with the interior of any rectangle of the constructed net. We further note that a side of any rectangle in the net is also a side of a contiguous rectangle.

Let now a_j denote the center of each rectangle R_j of the net, and let us write the formal sum

$$\gamma_0 = \sum \lambda_j C_j, \tag{5.9.5}$$

where $\lambda_j = \nu(\gamma, a_j)$ is the winding number of the formal sum γ about the point a_j, and C_j is the contour describing the perimeter of R_j in the positive direction. Since any point a_s exterior to the square Q lies on a straight line which does not intersect Q, it follows from Lemma 5.4.1 that $\nu(\gamma, a_s) = 0$. Thus $\lambda_j = 0$, except for a finite number of the a_j, and the sum (5.9.5) has only a finite number of terms. We write

$$\gamma_0 = \sum_{j=1}^{r} \lambda_j C_j, \qquad (5.9.6)$$

where $\lambda_j = \nu(\gamma, a_j) \neq 0$, $j = 1, 2, \cdots, r$.

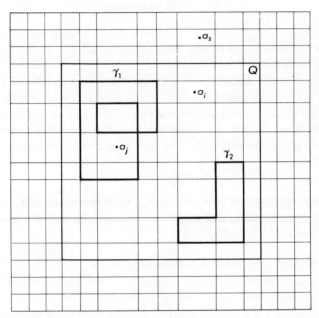

FIG. 5.9.1

As will be explained later (see Remark 5.9.1 at the end of the proof of this lemma), we are led from the consideration of special cases to the conjecture that γ_0 as given in (5.9.6) and γ as given in (5.9.3) are equal. By this we mean that if the C_j in (5.9.6) and the γ_i in (5.9.3) are expressed as sums of the $S_{p,q}$, where each $S_{p,q}$ is a contour describing a common side of two rectangles R_p and R_q of the net, then upon performing the simplifications considered in Remark 5.2.2, γ and γ_0 will become identical. It will then follow that

$$\int_{\gamma_0} f(z)\, dz = \int_{\gamma} f(z)\, dz.$$

First of all, we observe that since a_k is in the interior of C_k, and C_k is described in the positive direction, we have in accordance with Definition 5.6.3, $\nu(C_k, a_k) = 1$. Moreover, if $k \neq j$, then a_k lies on a straight line which does not intersect C_j. Consequently, by Lemma 5.4.1, $\nu(C_j, a_k) = 0$ for $j \neq k$. It follows from (5.9.6) that

$$\nu(\gamma_0, a_k) = \sum_{j=1}^{r} \lambda_j \nu(C_j, a_k) = \begin{cases} \lambda_k, \, k = 1, 2, \cdots, r, \\ 0, \text{ otherwise.} \end{cases} \quad (5.9.7)$$

From the definition of the λ_j, we also have

$$\nu(\gamma, a_k) = \begin{cases} \lambda_k, \, k = 1, 2, \cdots, r, \\ 0, \text{ otherwise.} \end{cases} \quad (5.9.8)$$

It follows that $\nu(\gamma, a_j) = \nu(\gamma_0, a_j)$ for the center a_j of each rectangle R_j in the net. This fact strengthens further our conjecture that $\gamma = \gamma_0$. We proceed now to give the full proof of this assertion.

Suppose to the contrary that $\gamma \neq \gamma_0$. Then when expressed in terms of the $S_{p,q}$, $\gamma - \gamma_0$ will contain at least one term $kS_{m,n}$ with $k \neq 0$. Note that $S_{m,n}$ represents a common side of the two neighboring rectangles R_m and R_n of the net. Thus $S_{m,n}$ forms a part of the positively described perimeter, say C_m, of one of the rectangles R_m. We now form the formal sum

$$\gamma' = \gamma - \gamma_0 - kC_m, \quad (5.9.9)$$

which when expressed in terms of the $S_{p,q}$ no longer contains $S_{m,n}$. Then, for the respective centers a_m and a_n of the rectangles R_m and R_n, we have from (5.9.9), (5.4.6), (5.9.8) and (5.9.7)

$$\nu(\gamma', a_m) = \nu(\gamma, a_m) - \nu(\gamma_0, a_m) - k\nu(C_m, a_m) = \lambda_m - \lambda_m - k = -k, \quad (5.9.10)$$

and

$$\nu(\gamma', a_n) = \nu(\gamma, a_n) - \nu(\gamma_0, a_n) - k\nu(C_m, a_n) = \lambda_n - \lambda_n - 0 = 0. \quad (5.9.11)$$

We shall now show that the results given in (5.9.10) and (5.9.11) lead to a contradiction, for a_m and a_n may be joined by a segment L which, except for its intersection with $S_{m,n}$, lies in the union of the interiors of R_m and R_n. Since γ' does not contain the side $S_{m,n}$, the segment L is a connected set that has no points in common with γ'. But γ' is a sum of closed contours, and consequently, by Theorem 5.4.2, $\nu(\gamma', \zeta)$ is constant for ζ on L. Hence $\nu(\gamma', a_n) = \nu(\gamma', a_m)$, contradicting the results given in (5.9.10) and (5.9.11).

We have thus completed the first step in the outline of our proof by showing that

$$\gamma = \sum_{j=1}^{r} \lambda_j C_j, \qquad \lambda_j = \nu(\gamma, a_j) \neq 0, j = 1, 2, \cdots, r. \quad (5.9.12)$$

We now proceed to show that each perimeter C_j in (5.9.12), together with its interior, is contained in D.

Suppose that there were a rectangle R_j whose perimeter C_j is represented in (5.9.12) and that there were a point ζ in R_j that is not contained in D. Then, from the hypothesis on γ, we would have $\nu(\gamma, \zeta) = 0$. We may join ζ to the center a_j of R_j by a line segment L', lying, except perhaps for the end point ζ, in the interior of C_j. Consequently L' is a connected set having no points in common with γ, and it follows from Theorem 5.4.2 that we would also have $\nu(\gamma, a_j) = 0$. But this would contradict the fact that $\nu(\gamma, a_j) = \lambda_j \nu(C_j, a_j) = \lambda_j \neq 0$. Thus every C_j occurring in (5.9.12) lies, together with its interior, in D.

Now for the final step in our proof: It follows from Lemma 5.8.3 that for any analytic function $f(z)$ in D, we have

$$\int_{C_j} f(z)\, dz = 0.$$

Hence

$$\int_{\gamma} f(z)\, dz = \int_{\sum_{j=1}^{r} \lambda_j C_j} f(z)\, dz = \sum_{j=1}^{r} \lambda_j \int_{C_j} f(z)\, dz = 0,$$

and our lemma is established.

Remark 5.9.1. We can understand the reason for forming the sum (5.9.5) as a possible expression for γ by considering some special cases. For example, if γ is a simple closed contour given by the sequence of vertices $A_1 A_2 A_3 A_4 A_5 A_6 A_1$ in Fig. 5.9.2, then it is intuitively evident that the inner sides

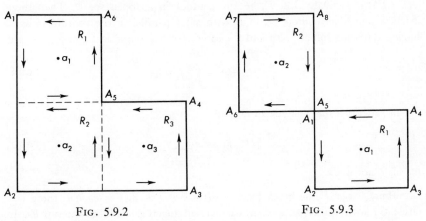

FIG. 5.9.2   FIG. 5.9.3

of the rectangles R_j $(j = 1, 2, 3)$ cancel each other, and we have $\gamma = C_1 + C_2 + C_3$. Since γ is described in the positive direction, we have $\nu(\gamma, a_j) = 1, j = 1, 2, 3$, and consequently

$$\gamma = \sum_{j=1}^{3} \nu(\gamma, a_j)\, C_j.$$

However, if in Fig. 5.9.2, γ denotes the contour $A_6A_5A_4A_3A_2A_1A_6$, then $\gamma = -C_1 - C_2 - C_3$. Since γ is now described in the negative direction, we have $\nu(\gamma, a_j) = -1$, $i = 1, 2, 3$, and we have again

$$\gamma = \sum_{j=1}^{3} \nu(\gamma, a_j)\, C_j.$$

Another illustration is obtained from Fig. 5.9.3. Here γ denotes the contour given by the sequence of vertices $A_1A_2A_3A_4A_5A_6A_7A_8A_1$, $A_5 = A_1$, and we have $\gamma = C_1 - C_2$. If we write $\gamma = \gamma' + \gamma''$, where γ' and γ'' are the simple closed contours $A_1A_2A_3A_4A_1$ and $A_5A_6A_7A_8A_5$, it is easily seen that

$$\nu(\gamma', a_j) = \begin{cases} 1, j = 1, \\ 0, j = 2, \end{cases} \quad \text{and} \quad \nu(\gamma'', a_j) = \begin{cases} 0, j = 1, \\ -1, j = 2. \end{cases}$$

Hence

$$\nu(\gamma, a_j) = \nu(\gamma', a_j) + \nu(\gamma'', a_j) = \begin{cases} 1, j = 1, \\ -1, j = 2. \end{cases}$$

Thus again, we have that

$$\gamma = \sum_{j=1}^{2} \nu(\gamma, a_j)\, C_j.$$

We shall now establish the following

LEMMA 5.9.2. Let Γ_0 be any contour in an open set D. Then there exists a polygonal contour γ_0 in D with sides parallel to the coordinate axes, having the same initial point and the same terminal point as Γ_0, and such that

$$\int_{\Gamma_0} f(z)\, dz = \int_{\gamma_0} f(z)\, dz \tag{5.9.13}$$

for all functions $f(z)$ analytic in D, and

$$\nu(\Gamma_0, \zeta) = \nu(\gamma_0, \zeta) \tag{5.9.14}$$

for all ζ not in D.

Proof. Let Γ_0 be given by $z = z(t)$, $\alpha \leq t \leq \beta$. For each t, there is a circle C_t with center at $z = z(t)$ contained together with its interior D_t in the open set D. (See Fig. 5.9.4.) By Lemma 2.10.1 there exists a subfamily $C_1, C_2, \cdots, C_k$ of the family of circles $\{C_t\}$ and a subdivision:

$$\alpha = t_0 < t_1 < t_2 < \cdots < t_k = \beta$$

of the interval $\alpha \leq t \leq \beta$ such that for each $j = 1, 2, \cdots, k$, the contour Γ_j' given by $z = z(t)$, $t_{j-1} \leq t \leq t_j$, is contained in the interior D_j of the circle C_j.

Clearly, the contour Γ_0 may be expressed as the sum

$$\Gamma_0 = \Gamma_1' + \Gamma_2' + \cdots + \Gamma_k'.$$

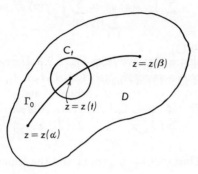

FIG 5.9.4

Furthermore, within each circle C_j we can draw a polygonal contour γ_j' with the same initial and terminal points as Γ_j', and with sides parallel to the coordinate axes (see Fig. 5.9.5, for the case when $j = 1, 2, 3$). By Theorem 5.8.1 we then have

$$\int_{\Gamma_j'} f(z)\, dz = \int_{\gamma_j'} f(z)\, dz$$

for all analytic functions $f(z)$ in D.

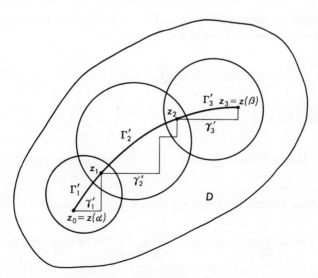

FIG. 5.9.5

Let $\gamma_0 = \gamma_1' + \gamma_2' + \cdots + \gamma_k'$. Then γ_0 is a contour with the same initial point and the same terminal point as Γ_0, and we have

$$\int_{\Gamma_0} f(z)\, dz = \sum_{j=1}^{k} \int_{\Gamma_j'} f(z)\, dz = \sum_{j=1}^{k} \int_{\gamma_j'} f(z)\, dz = \int_{\gamma_0} f(z)\, dz,$$

thus establishing (5.9.13).

Let ζ be any point not in D. Then $f(z) = 1/(z - \zeta)$ is analytic in D and hence by (5.4.2) and (5.9.13) we have

$$\nu(\Gamma_0, \zeta) = \frac{1}{2\pi i} \int_{\Gamma_0} \frac{dz}{z - \zeta} = \frac{1}{2\pi i} \int_{\gamma_0} \frac{dz}{z - \zeta} = \nu(\gamma_0, \zeta),$$

for all ζ not in D. Thus (5.9.14) is proved and the lemma is established.

Proof of Theorem 5.9.2. Let

$$\Gamma = \sum_{i=1}^{n} m_i \Gamma_i$$

be a formal sum of closed contours Γ_i such that $\nu(\Gamma, \zeta) = 0$ for all ζ not in D. By Lemma 5.9.2 there exists for each Γ_i a closed polygonal contour γ_i with sides parallel to the coordinate axes such that

$$\int_{\Gamma_i} f(z)\, dz = \int_{\gamma_i} f(z)\, dz$$

for all analytic functions $f(z)$ in D, and $\nu(\Gamma_i, \zeta) = \nu(\gamma_i, \zeta)$ for all ζ not in D. Let now γ denote the formal sum

$$\gamma = \sum_{i=1}^{n} m_i \gamma_i.$$

We then have for all ζ not in D

$$0 = \nu(\Gamma, \zeta) = \sum_{i=1}^{n} m_i \nu(\Gamma_i, \zeta) = \sum_{i=1}^{n} m_i \nu(\gamma_i, \zeta) = \nu(\gamma, \zeta).$$

It follows from Lemma 5.9.1 that for all functions $f(z)$ analytic in D, we have

$$0 = \int_{\gamma} f(z)\, dz = \sum_{i=1}^{n} m_i \int_{\gamma_i} f(z)\, dz = \sum_{i=1}^{n} m_i \int_{\Gamma_i} f(z)\, dz = \int_{\Gamma} f(z)\, dz.$$

Thus Theorem 5.9.2 is established.

5.10. THE CAUCHY INTEGRAL THEOREMS. We shall now apply Theorem 5.9.1 to establish

————**THEOREM** 5.10.1 (*Cauchy integral theorem for a simply connected domain*). Let $f(z)$ be analytic in a simply connected domain D and let Γ be any closed contour in D. Then

$$\int_\Gamma f(z)\, dz = 0. \qquad (5.10.1)$$

Proof. If D consists of the entire finite complex plane, then (5.10.1) follows from Remark 5.8.2.

Suppose now that D does not consist of the entire finite complex plane. Since D is simply connected, it follows (see Exercise 5.7.1) that $\nu(\Gamma, \zeta) = 0$ for all ζ not in D. Hence by Theorem 5.9.1

$$\int_\Gamma f(z)\, dz = 0$$

for all functions $f(z)$ analytic in D.

Another corollary of Theorem 5.9.1 is

————**THEOREM** 5.10.2 (*Cauchy integral theorem for a simple closed contour*). Let Γ be a simple closed contour and let $f(z)$ be analytic in an open set D containing Γ and its interior. Then

$$\int_\Gamma f(z)\, dz = 0$$

Proof. If D is the entire finite complex plane, then the theorem follows from Remark 5.8.2.

If D is not the entire finite complex plane, then any point ζ not in D must by the assumption of the theorem be exterior to Γ. Hence by Theorem 5.5.2 we have $\nu(\Gamma, \zeta) = 0$ for ζ not in D. It now follows from Theorem 5.9.1 that

$$\int_\Gamma f(z)\, dz = 0$$

for all functions $f(z)$ analytic in D.

We shall now utilize Theorem 5.9.2 to establish a generalization of Theorem 5.10.2.

————**THEOREM** 5.10.3. Let $C, C_1, C_2, \cdots, C_n$, be simple closed contours each described in the positive direction and such that each C_j is interior to C and exterior to C_k for all $j \neq k$, $j, k = 1, 2, \cdots, n$. Let $f(z)$ be analytic on each of the contours C, C_j $(j = 1, 2, \cdots, n)$ and at each point interior *to* C and exterior to all the C_j. Then

$$\int_C f(z)\,dz = \int_{C_1} f(z)\,dz + \int_{C_2} f(z)\,dz + \cdots + \int_{C_n} f(z)\,dz. \qquad (5.10.3)$$

Proof. Let Γ denote the formal sum: $\Gamma = C - C_1 - C_2 - \cdots - C_n$, let R denote the set consisting of the contours C, C_j, $j = 1, 2, \cdots, n$ and the points lying interior to C and exterior to each C_j, and let D be any open

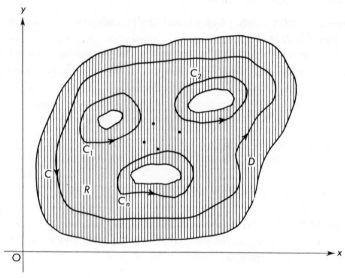

Fig. 5.10.1

set containing R such that $f(z)$ is analytic in D. (See Fig. 5.10.1.)

If D is the entire finite complex plane, then (5.10.3) holds, since each of the integrals occurring in (5.10.3) is zero by Remark 5.8.2.

Suppose that D is not the entire finite complex plane. (See Fig. 5.10.1. D is denoted by the hatched area.) Then for any point ζ not in D we have two cases.

CASE 1. ζ is exterior to C. It follows (see Exercise 5.7.2) that ζ is exterior to all the C_j, and we have in virtue of (5.4.6) and Theorem 5.5.2

$$\nu(\Gamma, \zeta) = \nu\left(C - \sum_{j=1}^{n} C_j, \zeta\right) = \nu(C, \zeta) - \sum_{j=1}^{n} \nu(C_j, \zeta) = 0.$$

CASE 2.   The point ζ is interior to one of the C_j say, C_k. Then ζ is exterior to each of the $C_j, j \neq k$ (see Exercise 5.7.3) and we have

$$\nu(C_j, \zeta) = \begin{cases} 1, & j = k, \\ 0, & j \neq k. \end{cases}$$

Also, since ζ is interior to C, $\nu(C, \zeta) = 1$. Hence

$$\nu(\Gamma, \zeta) = \nu(C, \zeta) - \nu(C_k, \zeta) - \sum_{j \neq k}^{n} \nu(C_j, \zeta) = 1 - 1 - 0 = 0.$$

By Theorem 5.9.2 we then have

$$\int_{\Gamma} f(z)\, dz = 0,$$

from which (5.10.3) now follows.

Remark 5.10.1. The hypothesis in Theorem 5.10.3 may be relaxed somewhat. Let D denote the domain consisting of all points interior to C and exterior to all the C_j, $j = 1, 2, \cdots, n$ and let R denote the union of D, C and all the C_j. Then in order for (5.10.3) to hold, it is only necessary that $f(z)$ should be continuous in R and analytic in D. The proof is based on the fact that the contours C and C_j may be approximated, as closely as we please, by contours C' and C_j' lying in D. We shall not go into the details here.

Remark 5.10.2. When a domain D in the finite complex plane has n "holes", we say that it is n-tuply connected. More precisely, a domain D in the finite plane is said to be *n-tuply connected* if it can be obtained from a simply connected domain D_0 by removing n disjoint connected compact sets. Denoting these sets by E_i, $i = 1, 2, \cdots, n$, it may be shown* that we can construct n simple closed polygonal contours C_i, $i = 1, 2, \cdots, n$ such that E_i is in the interior of C_i and C_j is exterior to C_k for $j \neq k$, $j, k = 1, 2, \cdots, n$. (See Fig. 5.10.2 for the case when $i = 1, 2, 3$.)

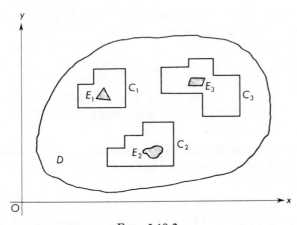

FIG. 5.10.2

Let C be any closed contour in the n-tuply connected domain D and form the formal sum $\Gamma = C - \sum_{i=1}^{n} \lambda_i C_i$, where $\lambda_i = \nu(C, \zeta)$ for ζ in E_i. It is not

---

* See S. Saks and A. Zygmund, *Analytic Functions*, p. 209. Warsaw: 1952.

difficult to see that $\nu(\Gamma, \zeta) = 0$ for all ζ not in D, and we obtain from Theorem 5.9.2 for all functions $f(z)$ analytic in D

$$\int_C f(z)\, dz = \sum_{i=1}^n \lambda_i \int_{C_i} f(z)\, dz. \tag{5.10.4}$$

EXAMPLE 5.10.1.   Let us show that

$$\int_\Gamma \frac{(\sinh 2z + \cos z/2)^2\, dz}{(z + 3i)\,(z^2 + 16)} = 0,$$

where the simple closed contour Γ is the circle $|z| = 2$.

Solution.   Observe that the singular points of

$$f(z) = (\sinh 2z + \cos z/2)^2/(z + 3i)\,(z^2 + 16)$$

are at $z = -3i$, $z = \pm 4i$ and these points are not contained within or on Γ. Thus $f(z)$ is analytic within and on Γ. The result now follows from Theorem 5.10.2.

EXAMPLE 5.10.2.   Let us show that

$$\int_B \frac{(\cosh 2z + \sin z/2)^2\, dz}{z^4(z^2 + 16)} = 0,$$

where the boundary B consists of the circle $|z| = 3$ described in the positive direction (counterclockwise), together with the circle $|z| = 1$ described in the clockwise direction.

Solution.   Observe that the singular points of

$$f(z) = \frac{(\cosh 2z + \sin z/2)^2}{z^4(z^2 + 16)}$$

are at $z = 0$ and $z = \pm 4i$. Thus $f(z)$ is analytic at all points within the annulus $R: 1 < |z| < 3$ and on its boundary B. (See Fig. 5.10.3.) From Theorem 5.10.3 the result now follows.

5.11.   **INDEFINITE INTEGRALS.**   From Theorem 5.10.1, we see that if $\alpha = z_0$ and $\beta = z$ are respectively a fixed and a variable point in a simply connected domain D, and $f(z)$ is an analytic function in D, then the integral

$$\int_{z_0}^z f(\zeta)\, d\zeta$$

taken along a contour joining z_0 to z and lying entirely in D, is independent of the path. Thus, this integral is a (single-valued) function of the upper limit z. Let us write

$$F_0(z) = \int_{z_0}^{z} f(\zeta)\, d\zeta. \qquad (5.11.1)$$

We shall now establish

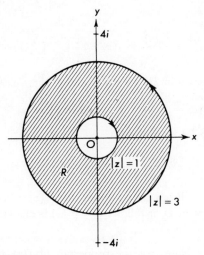

FIG. 5.10.3

——*THEOREM* 5.11.1.   Let $f(z)$ be analytic in a simply connected domain D. Then $F_0(z)$ given by (5.11.1) is analytic in D and has a derivative given by

$$F_0'(z) = f(z). \qquad (5.11.2)$$

Proof.   Let z be any fixed point in D, and let C be a circle with center at z lying, together with its interior, in D. Let $z + \eta$ be any point interior to C. Then z can be joined to $z + \eta$ by a straight line segment. (See Fig. 5.11.1.)

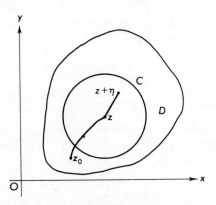

FIG. 5.11.1

Since $\int_{z_0}^{z} f(\zeta)\, d\zeta$ is independent of the path, we may take the integral $\int_{z_0}^{z+\eta} f(\zeta)\, d\zeta$ along the path from z_0 to z and then along the straight line from z to $z + \eta$. Utilizing (5.11.1) and Theorem 5.2.1, we obtain

$$F_0(z + \eta) - F_0(z) = \int_{z_0}^{z+\eta} f(\zeta)\, d\zeta - \int_{z_0}^{z} f(\zeta)\, d\zeta = \int_{z}^{z+\eta} f(\zeta)\, d\zeta.$$

Also

$$\frac{F_0(z + \eta) - F_0(z)}{\eta} - f(z) = \frac{1}{\eta} \int_{z}^{z+\eta} [f(\zeta) - f(z)]\, d\zeta.$$

Since $f(z)$ is continuous in D, for every $\epsilon > 0$, there exist a $\delta > 0$ such that

$$|f(\zeta) - f(z)| < \epsilon \qquad \text{when } |\zeta - z| < \delta.$$

Utilizing Theorem 5.2.2 we obtain

$$\left| \frac{F_0(\zeta + \eta) - F_0(z)}{\eta} - f(z) \right| < \epsilon,$$

provided that $|\eta| < \delta$. From (3.4.2) we see that $F_0'(z)$ exists and is equal to $f(z)$. Since z was any point in D, it follows that $F_0(z)$ is analytic at all points in the simply connected domain D.

Remark 5.11.1. Note that the properties of $f(z)$ needed in the above proof are that $f(z)$ is continuous and that the integral $\int_{z_0}^{z} f(\zeta)\, d\zeta$ is independent of the path.

Any function $F(z)$ such that $F'(z) = f(z)$ is called an *indefinite integral* of $f(z)$. By Lemma 5.8.1 we see that if $F(z)$ is an indefinite integral of $f(z)$, then

$$\int_{z_0}^{z} f(\zeta)\, d\zeta = F(z) - F(z_0), \tag{5.11.3}$$

and consequently $F(z)$ differs from $F_0(z)$ of (5.11.1) by at most a constant.

EXAMPLE 5.11.1. Given the function $f(z) = z^n$, n a positive integer. Let us find the value of the integral

$$\int_{z_0}^{z_1} f(z)\, dz$$

for any contour joining the points z_0 and z_1.

Solution. An indefinite integral of the analytic function $f(z) = z^n$ is given by the analytic function $F(z) = z^{n+1}/(n + 1)$. Thus, for any contour joining z_0 and z_1, we have by (5.11.3)

$$\int_{z_0}^{z_1} z^n\, dz = \frac{z_1^{n+1}}{n + 1} - \frac{z_0^{n+1}}{n + 1}.$$

EXAMPLE 5.11.2. Let us find the value of the integral

$$\int_{-ki}^{ki} \frac{dz}{z} \qquad (k \text{ a positive number}),$$

for any contour joining $-ki$ and ki lying in the simply connected domain D consisting of the complex plane with the nonpositive half of the real axis removed.

Solution. An indefinite integral of the analytic function $f(z) = 1/z$ in D is given (see Theorem 4.4.3) by the analytic function $F(z) = \text{Log } z$ in D. Thus we have by (5.11.3) and (4.4.4)

$$\int_{-ki}^{ki} \frac{dz}{z} = \text{Log } ki - \text{Log } (-ki) = \left(\text{Log } k + \frac{\pi}{2}i\right) - \left(\text{Log } k - \frac{\pi}{2}i\right) = \pi i.$$

5.12. THE CAUCHY INTEGRAL FORMULA. By means of the Cauchy integral formula, equation (5.12.1) below, we can express the value of an analytic function $f(z)$ at any point interior to a simple closed contour C as a contour integral around C.

——**THEOREM** 5.12.1. Let $f(z)$ be analytic within and on a simple closed contour C. If z_0 is any point interior to C, then

$$f(z_0) = \frac{1}{2\pi i} \int_C \frac{f(z)\,dz}{z - z_0}, \qquad (5.12.1)$$

where the integral along C is taken in the positive direction.

Proof. Observe that the function $\phi(z) = f(z)/(z - z_0)$ is analytic at all interior points of C except at $z = z_0$. Describe about $z = z_0$ a small circle Γ of radius r lying entirely within C. (See Fig. 5.12.1.)

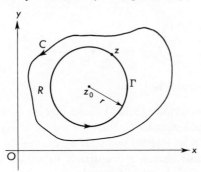

Fig. 5.12.1

In the region R bounded by C and Γ, the function $\phi(z)$ is analytic. Applying Theorem 5.10.3 we have

$$\int_C \phi(z)\,dz = \int_\Gamma \phi(z)\,dz,$$

where the integrals along C and Γ are taken in the positive direction.

Since $f(z)$ is analytic at z_0, utilizing (5.8.10) we have

$$\int_\Gamma \phi(z)\, dz = \int_\Gamma \frac{f(z)\, dz}{z - z_0} = \int_\Gamma \frac{[f(z_0) + f'(z_0)(z - z_0) + \lambda(z)(z - z_0)]\, dz}{z - z_0}$$

where $\lambda(z)$ is given by (5.8.11). Thus

$$\int_\Gamma \phi(z)\, dz = f(z_0) \int_\Gamma \frac{dz}{z - z_0} + f'(z_0) \int_\Gamma dz + \int_\Gamma \lambda\, dz. \qquad (5.12.2)$$

For z on Γ, we have $z - z_0 = re^{i\theta}$. From (5.2.27) we see that

$$\int_\Gamma \frac{dz}{z - z_0} = 2\pi i \quad \text{and} \quad \int_\Gamma dz = 0. \qquad (5.12.3)$$

Also from (5.2.22) we have

$$\left| \int_\Gamma \lambda\, dz \right| < \epsilon \cdot 2\pi r, \qquad (5.12.4)$$

where $\epsilon = \max_{z \text{ on } \Gamma} |\lambda(z)|$. Utilizing (5.12.2), (5.12.3) and (5.12.4) we obtain

$$\left| \int_C \phi(z)\, dz - 2\pi i f(z_0) \right| = \left| \int_\Gamma \lambda\, dz \right| < 2\pi r\epsilon. \qquad (5.12.5)$$

From (5.8.11) we see that ϵ ($= \max_{z \text{ on } \Gamma} |\lambda(z)|$) and hence also $2\pi r\epsilon$ can be made as small as we please if $r = |z - z_0|$ is made sufficiently small. Since the left-hand side of (5.12.5) is independent of r, it must be equal to zero. Hence

$$2\pi i f(z_0) = \int_C \phi(z)\, dz.$$

Thus

$$f(z_0) = \frac{1}{2\pi i} \int_C \frac{f(z)\, dz}{z - z_0} \, ,$$

and the theorem is established.

Cauchy's integral formula (5.12.1) shows that if a function is analytic within and on a simple closed contour C, then the values of $f(z)$ along C completely determine its values at all interior points. If we change the values of the function along C, then we must change appropriately its values in the interior of C if we wish to retain the analyticity of $f(z)$; however, this may not be possible.

Note that the Cauchy integral formula will fail to give $f(z_0)$ if z_0 is taken exterior to the simple closed contour C and $f(z_0) \neq 0$; for then $f(z)/(z - z_0)$ is analytic within and on C, and by Theorem 5.10.2 we have

$$\int_C \frac{f(z)\, dz}{z - z_0} = 0.$$

Remark 5.12.1. Let $f(t)$ be a continuous (complex-valued) function defined on the closed interval $a \leq t \leq b$. Let us divide the interval $[a, b]$ into n equal parts $\Delta t = (b - a)/n$. The *average* or *arithmetic mean* of the n values

$$f(a + \Delta t), f(a + 2\Delta t), \cdots, f(a + n\Delta t)$$

is given by

$$\frac{1}{n}\sum_{k=1}^{n} f(a + k\Delta t) = \frac{1}{b - a}\sum_{k=1}^{n} f(a + k\Delta t)\, \Delta t. \qquad (5.12.6)$$

Now

$$\lim_{n\to\infty}\left[\frac{1}{b-a}\sum_{k=1}^{n} f(a + k\Delta t)\, \Delta t\right] = \frac{1}{b-a}\int_{a}^{b} f(t)\, dt. \qquad (5.12.7)$$

Thus the right-hand member of (5.12.7) can be thought of as the average or arithmetic mean of the continuous function $f(t)$ over the interval $a \leq t \leq b$.

In Theorem 5.12.1, if we take the simple closed contour C to be a circle with center at z_0 and radius r, that is,

$$z = z_0 + re^{i\theta}, \qquad 0 \leq \theta \leq 2\pi,$$

then (5.12.1) can be written as

$$f(z_0) = \frac{1}{2\pi}\int_{0}^{2\pi} f(z_0 + re^{i\theta})\, d\theta. \qquad (5.12.8)$$

Thus the value of an analytic function at the center of a circle equals the arithmetic mean (or average) of the values on the circumference.

EXAMPLE 5.12.1.   Let us find the value of the integral

$$\int_{C} \frac{[\cos^3(3z) + \cosh^4(4z)]^3\, dz}{z},$$

where C is any simple closed contour having $z_0 = 0$ in its interior, and the integral along C is taken in the positive direction.

Solution.   Observe that $f(z) = [\cos^3(3z) + \cosh^4(4z)]^3$ is analytic within and on C. Also $f(z_0) = f(0) = [\cos^3(0) + \cosh^4(0)]^3 = (2)^3 = 8$. Hence by (5.12.1) with $z_0 = 0$, the value of the above integral equals $16\pi i$.

EXAMPLE 5.12.2.   Let us find the value of the integral

$$\int_{C} \frac{(9z^2 - iz + 4)\, dz}{z(z^2 + 1)}$$

where C is the circle $|z| = 2$ and the integral along C is taken in the positive direction.

Solution. Decomposing the integrand into partial fractions, we have

$$\frac{9z^2 - iz + 4}{z(z^2 + 1)} = \frac{A}{z} + \frac{B}{z + i} + \frac{C}{z - i}, \qquad (5.12.9)$$

where A, B and C are constants. To find A, multiply (5.12.9) by z and let $z = 0$. We obtain $A = 4$. To find B, multiply (5.12.9) by $z + i$ and let $z = -i$. We obtain $B = 3$. Similarly, we find $C = 2$. Hence

$$\int_C \frac{(9z^2 - iz + 4)\,dz}{z(z^2 + 1)} = \int_C \frac{4dz}{z} + \int_C \frac{3dz}{z + i} + \int_C \frac{2dz}{z - i}.$$

If we apply (5.12.1) to each of the right-hand members of the above expression, we find

$$\int_C \frac{(9z^2 - iz + 4)\,dz}{z(z^2 + 1)} = 4(2\pi i) + 3(2\pi i) + 2(2\pi i) = 18\pi i.$$

5.13. DERIVATIVES OF ANALYTIC FUNCTIONS. A consequence of Theorem 5.12.1 is that the derivative of an analytic function is again an analytic function. For, suppose that $z_0 + h$ is a point interior to the simple closed contour C, then utilizing (5.12.1) and Theorem 5.2.1 we have

$$\frac{f(z_0 + h) - f(z_0)}{h} = \frac{1}{2\pi i} \int_C \frac{1}{h} \left[\frac{1}{z - z_0 - h} - \frac{1}{z - z_0} \right] f(z)\,dz$$

$$= \frac{1}{2\pi i} \int_C \frac{f(z)\,dz}{(z - z_0 - h)(z - z_0)}.$$

Observe that

$$\frac{1}{(z - z_0 - h)(z - z_0)} = \frac{1}{(z - z_0)^2} + \frac{h}{(z - z_0)^2 (z - z_0 - h)}.$$

Hence

$$\frac{f(z_0 + h) - f(z_0)}{h} = \frac{1}{2\pi i} \int_C \frac{f(z)\,dz}{(z - z_0)^2} + \frac{h}{2\pi i} \int_C \frac{f(z)\,dz}{(z - z_0)^2 (z - z_0 - h)}.$$

$$(5.13.1)$$

We shall now show that

$$\left| \frac{h}{2\pi i} \int_C \frac{f(z)\,dz}{(z - z_0)^2 (z - z_0 - h)} \right| \to 0 \qquad \text{as } |h| \to 0. \qquad (5.13.2)$$

Since $f(z)$ is continuous on C, it is bounded on C so that $|f(z)| \leq M$ on C for some constant M. Let L denote the length of C and let r be the smallest distance from z_0 to C. Note that $r > 0$. Suppose that h is chosen so that $|h| \leq (1/2)r$. We then have for z on C, $|z - z_0| \geq r$ and

$$|z - z_0 - h| \geq |z - z_0| - |h| \geq r - \frac{r}{2} = \frac{r}{2}.$$

Now, using Theorem 5.2.2 we obtain

$$\left| \frac{h}{2\pi i} \int_C \frac{f(z)\, dz}{(z - z_0)^2 (z - z_0 - h)} \right| \leq \left(\frac{ML}{\pi r^3} \right) |h|,$$

from which (5.13.2) now follows.

From (5.13.1) and (5.13.2) we see that

$$f'(z_0) = \lim_{h \to 0} \frac{f(z_0 + h) - f(z_0)}{h} = \frac{1}{2\pi i} \int_C \frac{f(z)\, dz}{(z - z_0)^2}. \qquad (5.13.3)$$

This formula expresses the value of the derivative of a function at a point as an integral taken along a contour enclosing the point. It can be obtained by differentiating equation (5.12.1) under the integral sign with respect to z_0.

Similarly, from (5.13.3) we obtain

$$f''(z_0) = \frac{2!}{2\pi i} \int_C \frac{f(z)\, dz}{(z - z_0)^3}. \qquad (5.13.4)$$

By mathematical induction it can be shown (see Exercise 5.17.6) that

$$f^{(n)}(z_0) = \frac{n!}{2\pi i} \int_C \frac{f(z)\, dz}{(z - z_0)^{n+1}} \qquad (n = 0, 1, 2, 3, \cdots) \qquad (5.13.5)$$

for any z_0 interior to the simple closed contour C. [By $f^{(0)}(z_0)$ we mean $f(z_0)$.]

An immediate consequence of formula (5.13.5) is the following important

——**THEOREM** 5.13.1. Let $f(z)$ be analytic in a domain D. Then all the derivatives of $f(z)$ exist and are analytic functions in D.

Proof. Let z_0 be any point in D, and let C be a circle with center at z_0 contained together with its interior in D. Then for $n = 0, 1, 2, \cdots$, we have from (5.13.5)

$$f^{(n)}(z) = \frac{n!}{2\pi i} \int_C \frac{f(\zeta)\, d\zeta}{(\zeta - z)^{n+1}}$$

for all z interior to C. Thus $f(z)$ has derivatives of all orders in a neighborhood of z_0. Since z_0 was any point in D, the theorem is established.

Remark 5.13.1. When $f(z) = u(x, y) + iv(x, y)$ is analytic in a domain D, we have from (3.6.9)

$$f'(z) = \frac{\partial f(z)}{\partial x} = u_x + iv_x, \qquad (5.13.6)$$

and

$$if'(z) = \frac{\partial f(z)}{\partial y} = u_y + iv_y. \qquad (5.13.7)$$

By mathematical induction (see Exercise 5.17.7) we obtain

$$i^k f^{(n)}(z) = \frac{\partial^n f(z)}{\partial x^r \, \partial y^k} = \frac{\partial^n u(x, y)}{\partial x^r \, \partial y^k} + i \frac{\partial^n v(x, y)}{\partial x^r \, \partial y^k}, \quad r, k = 0, 1, 2, \cdots, n \quad (5.13.8)$$

and $r + k = n$.

Since for all n, $f^{(n)}(z)$ exists and is continuous in D, it follows that the partial derivatives of $u(x, y)$ and $v(x, y)$ of all orders exist and are continuous in D.

It should be observed that the above result is not necessarily true for functions of real variables. For example, $f(x) = x^{3/2}$ has a first derivative at $x = 0$, but fails to have a second derivative at $x = 0$.

EXAMPLE 5.13.1.   Let us find the value of the integral

$$\int_C \frac{(e^z + z \sinh z) \, dz}{(z - \pi i)^3},$$

where C is any simple closed contour having $z_0 = \pi i$ in its interior, and the integral along C is taken in the positive direction.

Solution.   Observe that $f(z) = e^z + z \sinh z$ is analytic within and on C. From (5.13.5) we have

$$\int_C \frac{(e^z + z \sinh z) \, dz}{(z - \pi i)^3} = \frac{2\pi i}{2!} f''(\pi i).$$

Since $f''(z) = e^z + 2 \cosh z + z \sinh z$, we find $f''(\pi i) = -3$. Hence, the value of the above integral is equal to $-3\pi i$.

5.14.   MORERA'S THEOREM.   We shall now establish a theorem, due to Morera, which is a converse of the Cauchy Integral Theorem 5.10.1.

——**THEOREM** 5.14.1.   If $f(z)$ is continuous in a domain D and if

$$\int_\Gamma f(z) \, dz = 0 \qquad\qquad (5.14.1)$$

for every closed contour Γ in D, then $f(z)$ is analytic in D.

Proof.   By hypothesis $f(z)$ is continuous and

$$F(z) = \int_{z_0}^z f(\zeta) \, d\zeta$$

is independent of the path. Hence by Remark 5.11.1, following the proof of Theorem 5.11.1, $F(z)$ is analytic and $F'(z) = f(z)$ for z in D. It follows by Theorem 5.13.1 that $f(z)$, being the derivative of an analytic function, is also analytic for z in D; thus the theorem is established.

Remark 5.14.1. The hypothesis in Morera's Theorem may be relaxed. We need only require that each point z_0 in D be the center of a circle C, lying together with its interior in D, such that (5.14.1) holds for every closed contour Γ in C. For, it will then follow that $f(z)$ is analytic within each such circle C, and consequently $f(z)$ is analytic in D. Moreover, we see from Lemma 5.8.4 that we need only require that (5.14.1) be true for the case where Γ is the perimeter of a rectangle.

5.15. CAUCHY'S INEQUALITY FOR $f^{(n)}(z_0)$

——*THEOREM* 5.15.1. Let $f(z)$ be analytic within and on a circle C with center at z_0 and radius r. Let M be the maximum value of $|f(z)|$ on C, then

$$|f^{(n)}(z_0)| \leqq \frac{Mn!}{r^n} \qquad (n = 0, 1, 2, \cdots). \qquad (5.15.1)$$

Proof. Since the equation of the circle C is given by $|z - z_0| = r$, utilizing (5.13.5) and Theorem 5.2.2 we find

$$|f^{(n)}(z_0)| = \left| \frac{n!}{2\pi i} \int_C \frac{f(z)\,dz}{(z - z_0)^{n+1}} \right| \leqq \frac{n!}{2\pi} \cdot \frac{M}{r^{n+1}} \cdot 2\pi r = \frac{Mn!}{r^n},$$

thus establishing the theorem.

5.16. LIOUVILLE'S THEOREM. We shall now establish an important theorem which is due to Liouville.

——*THEOREM* 5.16.1. If $f(z)$ is analytic and bounded for all values of z in the complex plane, then $f(z)$ is a constant.

Proof. Since $f(z)$ is bounded, there exists a constant M such that $|f(z)| \leqq M$ for all values of z. Then, with $n = 1$ in (5.15.1), we have for any point z_0

$$|f'(z_0)| \leqq \frac{M}{r}, \qquad (5.16.1)$$

where r is an arbitrary positive number. By choosing r sufficiently large, we can make the right-hand side of (5.16.1) as small as we please. Hence $f'(z_0) = 0$. Since z_0 was any point, it follows that $f'(z) = 0$ for all values of z. From Exercise 3.6.13 we conclude that $f(z)$ is a constant, thus establishing the theorem.

Remark 5.16.1. A function $f(z)$ which is analytic for all finite values of z is called an *entire function* or an *integral function*. Examples of nonconstant entire functions are polynomials in z of degree $n \geqq 1$, e^z, $\sin z$, $\cos z$, $\sinh z$ and $\cosh z$. It follows from Theorem 5.16.1 that these functions are not bounded.

As an application of Liouville's Theorem we shall establish the following

——THEOREM 5.16.2 (*Fundamental theorem of algebra*). If $f(z)$ is a polynomial of degree n, $n \geq 1$, with real or complex coefficients, then the equation $f(z) = 0$ has at least one root.

Proof. Let

$$f(z) = a_0 + a_1 z + a_2 z^2 + \cdots + a_n z^n \qquad (a_n \neq 0).$$

Suppose that no value of z exists for which $f(z) = 0$. We shall show that this leads to a contradiction. Let us write $f(z)$ as

$$f(z) = z^n \left(\frac{a_0}{z^n} + \frac{a_1}{z^{n-1}} + \cdots + \frac{a_{n-1}}{z} + a_n \right).$$

For $|z|$ sufficiently large

$$\left| \frac{a_0}{z^n} + \frac{a_1}{z^{n-1}} + \cdots + \frac{a_{n-1}}{z} \right| < \frac{|a_n|}{2},$$

and consequently

$$\left| \frac{a_0}{z^n} + \frac{a_1}{z^{n-1}} + \cdots + \frac{a_{n-1}}{z} + a_n \right| > \frac{|a_n|}{2}.$$

Therefore, for $|z|$ sufficiently large

$$|f(z)| > \frac{|a_n| \, |z|^n}{2}, \tag{5.16.2}$$

and thus $|f(z)|$ can be made as large as we please.

Since $f(z) \neq 0$ for any value of z, the function

$$g(z) = \frac{1}{f(z)}$$

is everywhere analytic. Moreover, for r sufficiently large we have in view of (5.16.2) that for $|z| > r$

$$|g(z)| < M \qquad (M \text{ a constant}).$$

Since $g(z)$ is continuous on the compact set $|z| \leq r$, it follows (see Exercise 3.3.25) that $g(z)$ is bounded there. Thus $g(z)$ is an analytic function which is bounded throughout the finite complex plane, and by Theorem 5.16.1, $g(z)$ is a constant. Hence $f(z)$, the reciprocal of $g(z)$, must also be a constant. This contradicts (5.16.2). Consequently there exists a z such that $f(z) = 0$, and the theorem is thus established.

5.17. THE EXISTENCE OF A BRANCH OF THE LOGARITHM. We shall now establish the following useful

——*THEOREM* 5.17.1.   Let $f(z)$ be analytic in a simply connected domain D with $f(z) \neq 0$ for all z in D. Then there exists in D a single-valued and analytic function $\phi(z)$ such that $e^{\phi(z)} = f(z)$ for all z in D.

Proof.   Let

$$\phi(z) = \int_{z_0}^{z} \frac{f'(\zeta)\, d\zeta}{f(\zeta)} + k, \tag{5.17.1}$$

where z_0 is any fixed point in D and k is a constant such that $e^k = f(z_0)$. Restricting the path of integration to lie in D, we see from Theorem 5.11.1 that $\phi(z)$ is analytic in D and

$$\phi'(z) = \frac{f'(z)}{f(z)}. \tag{5.17.2}$$

Let us now proceed essentially as in Section 5.3. Let us consider the function

$$\psi(z) = e^{-\phi(z)} f(z).$$

Differentiating $\psi(z)$ and utilizing (5.17.2), we find that $\psi'(z) = 0$. Consequently

$$e^{-\phi(z)} f(z) = M \qquad (M \text{ constant}). \tag{5.17.3}$$

Setting $z = z_0$ in (5.17.3), noticing from (5.17.1) that $\phi(z_0) = k$ and recalling that $e^k = f(z_0)$, we find

$$M = e^{-\phi(z_0)} f(z_0) = e^{-k} f(z_0) = \frac{f(z_0)}{f(z_0)} = 1.$$

Thus (5.17.3) may be written as $e^{\phi(z)} = f(z)$, and the theorem is established.

Remark 5.17.1.   As a special case of Theorem 5.17.1, let D be a simply connected domain not containing the origin $z = 0$. Then taking $f(z) = z$, we see that there exists in D an analytic function $\phi(z)$ such that $e^{\phi(z)} = z$. If $\psi(z)$ is any other such function, then as in Section 5.3 (see Exercise 5.3.1) we have for all z in D

$$\psi(z) - \phi(z) = 2k\pi i \tag{5.17.4}$$

where k is a fixed integer.

In particular, D may be the simply connected domain obtained by removing from the finite complex plane a ray issuing from $z = 0$. The results of Chapter 4 concerning the existence of branches of the logarithm are now obtained as a special case of Theorem 5.17.1.

Observe that Theorem 5.17.1 depends only on the theorems and definitions of this chapter, and none of these, including even those of Sections 5.3 and 5.4, depend on any previous acquaintance with the function $\log z$.

EXERCISES 5.17

1. If the simple closed contour C is the circle $|z| = 1$ described in a positive (or negative) direction, prove that the value of each of the following integrals is zero:

(a) $\displaystyle \int_C \frac{z^3\,dz}{z+3}$,

(b) $\displaystyle \int_C \frac{(z + \sinh 2z)^2\,dz}{\cos z}$,

(c) $\displaystyle \int_C \frac{(e^{2z} + 3 \tanh z)\,dz}{z^2 + 4}$,

(d) $\displaystyle \int_C \frac{3 \sin^2 z\,dz}{z^2 - 7z + 7}$,

(e) $\displaystyle \int_C \frac{(1 + \tan^2 z)\,dz}{\cosh^2 z}$,

(f) $\displaystyle \int_C \frac{(z^2 + 3z + 4)\,dz}{z^4 - 7z^3 + 11z^2 - 28z + 28}$.

2. Prove

$$\int_0^z e^{az}\,dz = \frac{1}{a}(e^{az} - 1), \quad \text{and} \quad \int_0^z \sin az\,dz = -\frac{1}{a}(\cos az - 1).$$

3. Use formula (5.11.3) to evaluate each of the following integrals:

(a) $\displaystyle \int_0^{i/2} \sin 2z\,dz$,

(b) $\displaystyle \int_{1-i}^{1+i} (z^2 + 1)\,dz$,

(c) $\displaystyle \int_{\pi-i/3}^{\pi+i/3} \cosh 3z\,dz$,

(d) $\displaystyle \int_{-2i}^{2i} (z - 1)^2\,dz$,

(e) $\displaystyle \int_{-i}^{i} e^{3z}\,dz$,

(f) $\displaystyle \int_{-(\pi/6)i}^{(\pi/6)i} \cos 6z\,dz$.

4. Use Theorem 5.12.1 to evaluate the following integrals. In each case the simple closed contour C is described in the positive direction.

(a) $\displaystyle \int_C \frac{(e^z - 1)\,dz}{z}$, on the circle $|z| = 1$,

(b) $\displaystyle \int_C \frac{(\sinh^2 z + \cos z)\,dz}{z - \pi i}$, on the circle $|z| = 4$,

(c) $\displaystyle \int_C \frac{(z^4 + 3z^2 - 4)\,dz}{z - 2i}$, on the circle $|z| = 3$,

(d) $\displaystyle \int_C \left(\frac{3}{z+1} - \frac{4}{z-1}\right) dz$, on the circle $|z| = 2$,

(e) $\displaystyle \int_C \frac{dz}{z^2 - 1}$, on the circle $|z| = 2$,

(f) $\displaystyle \int_C \frac{dz}{z^4 - 1}$, on the circle $|z| = 2$,

(g) $\int_C \dfrac{(3z^2 + 4z - 1)\, dz}{(z^2 + 4)\,(z^2 + 1)}$, on the circle $|z| = 3$,

(h) $\int_C \dfrac{(\sin z + \cosh^2 z + \sinh 2z)\, dz}{z - (\pi/2)\, i}$, on the circle $|z| = 3$.

5. Use formula (5.13.5) to evaluate each of the following integrals. For the simple closed contour C take the boundary of a square whose sides lie along the lines $x = \pm 4$ and $y = \pm 4$, described in a positive direction.

(a) $\int_C \dfrac{e^z\, dz}{z^6}$,

(b) $\int_C \dfrac{e^{2z}\, dz}{(z - \pi i)^6}$,

(c) $\int_C \dfrac{\sinh 2z\, dz}{[z - (\pi/2)]^4}$,

(d) $\int_C \dfrac{[\cos z + \sin (z/2)]\, dz}{(z + \pi i)^4}$,

(e) $\int_C \dfrac{e^z \cosh z\, dz}{(z - \pi)^3}$,

(f) $\int_C \dfrac{(z^6 + 4z^4 - 2z^2 + 1)\, dz}{(z - 2i)^6}$.

6. Prove formula (5.13.5) by mathematical induction.

7. Show that if $f(z) = u(x, y) + iv(x, y)$ is analytic in a domain D, then

$$i^k f^{(n)}(z) = \frac{\partial^n f(z)}{\partial x^r\, \partial y^k} = \frac{\partial^n u(x, y)}{\partial x^r\, \partial y^k} + i\, \frac{\partial^n v(x, y)}{\partial x^r\, \partial y^k} ,$$

$r, k = 0, 1, 2, \cdots, n;$ $r + k = n$, z in D.

8. Let $f(z)$ and $g(z)$ be analytic in a simply connected domain D. Show that

$$\int_\alpha^\beta f(z)\, g'(z)\, dz = f(\beta)\, g(\beta) - f(\alpha)\, g(\alpha) - \int_\alpha^\beta g(z)\, f'(z)\, dz,$$

where the path of integration is a contour from $z = \alpha$ to $z = \beta$ lying in D. The above formula gives us the rule for *integration by parts*.

9. Let C be a simple closed contour containing the origin. Use formula (5.13.5) to prove that

$$\frac{\alpha^n}{n!} = \frac{1}{2\pi i} \int_C \frac{e^{\alpha z}}{z^{n+1}}\, dz.$$

10. Let C, C_j, $j = 1, 2, \cdots, n$, and $f(z)$ be as in Theorem 5.10.3. Show that for any point z_0 interior to C and exterior to each C_j, $j = 1, 2, \cdots, n$, we have

$$f^{(k)}(z_0) = \frac{k!}{2\pi i} \int_C \frac{f(z)\, dz}{(z - z_0)^{k+1}} - \sum_{j=1}^n \frac{k!}{2\pi i} \int_{C_j} \frac{f(z)\, dz}{(z - z_0)^{k+1}} \quad (k = 0, 1, 2, \cdots).$$

11. Let $f(z)$ be analytic within and on the circle Γ: $z = Re^{i\theta}$. If $z_0 = r_0 e^{i\theta_0}$ is a point interior to Γ, prove that

$$f(z_0) = \frac{1}{2\pi} \int_0^{2\pi} \frac{R^2 - r_0^2}{R^2 + r_0^2 - 2Rr_0 \cos(\theta - \theta_0)}\, f(Re^{i\theta})\, d\theta.$$

This equation is known as *Poisson's integral formula*.

12. Suppose that $f(z)$ is analytic. Show that

(a) $\nabla^2[\text{Log} \,|\, f(z) \,|] = 0$ if $f(z) \neq 0$;   (b) $\nabla^2 |\, f(z) \,| > 0$ if $f(z)f'(z) \neq 0$.

13. Let $\phi(z)$ be a complex-valued function defined and continuous on a contour C. Show that

$$f(z) = \frac{1}{2\pi i} \int_C \frac{\phi(\zeta) \, d\zeta}{\zeta - z}$$

is analytic in every domain D containing no points of C, and its derivative there is given by the formula

$$f'(z) = \frac{1}{2\pi i} \int_C \frac{\phi(\zeta) \, d\zeta}{(\zeta - z)^2}.$$

14. Let $\lambda(z) = 1/z$ and let C be the unit circle. The function

$$f(z) = \frac{1}{2\pi i} \int_C \frac{\lambda(\zeta) \, d\zeta}{\zeta - z}$$

is analytic interior to C. (See Exercise 13 above.) Show that the function $g(z)$ defined on $|\, z \,| \leq 1$ by

$$g(z) = \begin{cases} f(z), & |\, z \,| < 1, \\ \lambda(z), & |\, z \,| = 1, \end{cases}$$

is discontinuous at all points z on C.

15. Let $f(t)$ and $g(t)$ be continuous on the interval $0 \leq t \leq 1$ and suppose that $f(t) \geq 0$ while $g(t)$ is complex-valued. Show that

$$\int_0^1 g(t) f(t) \, dt = \lambda g(t_0) \int_0^1 f(t) \, dt$$

where $0 \leq t_0 \leq 1$ and $|\, \lambda \,| \leq 1$.

16. Suppose that $f(z)$ is analytic in a simply connected domain D, and that $f(z) \neq 0$ for all z in D. Show that for any integer $k \neq 0$, there exists in D an analytic function $\mu(z)$ such that

$$[\mu(z)]^k = f(z) \text{ for all } z \text{ in } D.$$

17. Suppose that $\lambda(z)$ is analytic in a neighborhood of z_0 and that $\lambda(z_0) \neq 0$. Show that for any integer $k \neq 0$, there exists a neighborhood $N(z_0)$ of z_0 and an analytic function $\mu(z)$ in $N(z_0)$ such that

$$[\mu(z)]^k = \lambda(z) \text{ for all } z \text{ in } N(z_0).$$

18. Let D_1 be the domain obtained from the complex plane by removing all points z on the real axis such that $|\, z \,| \geq 1$. Show that there exists an analytic function $\nu(z)$ such that $[\nu(z)]^2 = z^2 - 1$ for all z in D_1. (cf. Example 4.5.2.)

19. Let D_2 be the domain obtained from the complex plane by removing all points z on the real axis such that $|z| \leq 1$. Show that there exists an analytic function $\mu(z)$ such that $[\mu(z)]^2 = z^2 - 1$ for all z in D_2. (cf. Example 4.5.2.)

20. Let $f(z)$ and $g(z)$ be continuous complex-valued functions which are different from zero at each point in a domain D. Suppose that for some integer $k \neq 0$ we have $[f(z)]^k = [g(z)]^k$ for all z in D. Show that there exists an integer m such that for all z in D

$$f(z) = e^{(2\pi i m)/k} g(z).$$

21. Suppose that $f(z)$ is analytic in a domain D, and let z_0 be a point in D. Let $\{z_n\}$ and $\{\zeta_n\}$ be two sequences of points in D such that $z_n \neq \zeta_n$ for all n, and such that $\lim_{n\to\infty} z_n = z_0$ and $\lim_{n\to\infty} \zeta_n = z_0$. Show that

$$\lim_{n\to\infty} \frac{f(\zeta_n) - f(z_n)}{\zeta_n - z_n} = f'(z_0).$$

22. Verify the following integrations. In each case determine the conditions on the integrand and on the path of integration for which the integration is valid. (In each case C depends upon α.)

(a) $\displaystyle\int_\alpha^z \zeta^n \, d\zeta = \frac{z^{n+1}}{n+1} + C, \qquad (n \neq -1),$

(b) $\displaystyle\int_\alpha^z \frac{d\zeta}{\zeta} = \text{Log } z + C,$

(c) $\displaystyle\int_\alpha^z e^\zeta \, d\zeta = e^z + C,$

(d) $\displaystyle\int_\alpha^z a^\zeta \, d\zeta = \frac{a^z}{\text{Log } a} + C \qquad (a \text{ is a complex constant, } a \neq 0),$

(e) $\displaystyle\int_\alpha^z \sin \zeta \, d\zeta = -\cos z + C$

(f) $\displaystyle\int_\alpha^z \cos \zeta \, d\zeta = \sin z + C,$

(g) $\displaystyle\int_\alpha^z \tan \zeta \, d\zeta = -\text{Log } \cos z + C,$

(h) $\displaystyle\int_\alpha^z \frac{d\zeta}{\sqrt{1 - \zeta^2}} = \arcsin z + C,^*$

(i) $\displaystyle\int_\alpha^z \frac{d\zeta}{\sqrt{\zeta^2 - 1}} = i \arccos z + C,$

(j) $\displaystyle\int_\alpha^z \frac{d\zeta}{\zeta^2 + 1} = \arctan z + C,$

* To insure that the integrals in parts (h) to (m) are single-valued, fix the value of k in each of the Theorems 4.6.1 to 4.6.6 and n in Theorems 4.6.2, 4.6.5.

(k) $\displaystyle\int_\alpha^z \frac{d\zeta}{\sqrt{\zeta^2 + 1}} = \sinh^{-1} z + C,$

(l) $\displaystyle\int_\alpha^z \frac{d\zeta}{\sqrt{\zeta^2 - 1}} = \cosh^{-1} z + C,$

(m) $\displaystyle\int_\alpha^z \frac{d\zeta}{1 - \zeta^2} = \tanh^{-1} z + C.$

23. Extend Theorem 5.11.1 to the case where the domain D is not simply connected.

6

Power Series

6.1. DEFINITION OF POWER SERIES. An infinite series of the form

$$\sum_{n=0}^{\infty} c_n(z - z_0)^n = c_0 + c_1(z - z_0) + \cdots + c_n(z - z_0)^n + \cdots, \qquad (6.1.1)$$

where z is a complex variable and $z_0, c_0, c_1, \cdots$, are fixed complex numbers, is called a *power series* in powers of $(z - z_0)$. The numbers c_n, $n = 0, 1, \cdots$, are called the *coefficients* of the power series.

6.2. PROPERTIES OF POWER SERIES. The following theorem will show that the set of all z for which the power series (6.1.1) converges is either the entire complex plane, the interior of a circle (including possibly some points on the boundary) with center at z_0, or the single point z_0.

THEOREM 6.2.1. Every power series $\sum_{n=0}^{\infty} c_n(z - z_0)^n$ has a "radius of convergence" R such that when $0 < R < \infty$ the series converges absolutely for $|z - z_0| < R$ and diverges for $|z - z_0| > R$. When $R = 0$, the series converges only for $z = z_0$. When $R = \infty$, the series converges for all z. The number R is given by

$$R = \frac{1}{\varlimsup_{n\to\infty} \sqrt[n]{|c_n|}}. \qquad (6.2.1)$$

Proof. If we let $\alpha_n = c_n(z - z_0)^n$, we then have

$$\varlimsup_{n\to\infty} \sqrt[n]{|\alpha_n|} = \varlimsup_{n\to\infty} \sqrt[n]{|c_n|}\,|z - z_0| = \frac{|z - z_0|}{R}.$$

From Theorem 2.8.1 we see that the power series converges absolutely when

$$\frac{|z - z_0|}{R} < 1, \quad \text{that is, when} \quad |z - z_0| < R,$$

and diverges when

$$\frac{|z - z_0|}{R} > 1, \quad \text{that is, when} \quad |z - z_0| > R.$$

When $R = 0$, the series will converge only for $z = z_0$. When $R = \infty$, the series converges for all values of z. The theorem is thus established.

When $0 < R < \infty$, the circle $|z - z_0| = R$ is termed the *circle of convergence*. The above theorem asserts that every power series $\sum_{n=0}^{\infty} c_n(z - z_0)^n$ converges absolutely at every point in the interior of its circle of convergence and diverges at every point exterior to its circle of convergence. On the circle of convergence, it may converge at some points and diverge at others, as seen by the following examples. In each of these examples the radius of convergence is equal to one.

EXAMPLE 6.2.1. The series $\sum_{n=0}^{\infty} z^n$ does not converge for any point on the circle of convergence.

EXAMPLE 6.2.2. The series $\sum_{n=1}^{\infty} z^n/n^2$ converges at every point on the circle of convergence.

EXAMPLE 6.2.3. The series $\sum_{n=1}^{\infty} z^n/n$ converges for $z = -1$ and diverges for $z = 1$.

For brevity, we speak of the circle of convergence of a power series, even when the series converges for all values of z. In this case, the *circle of convergence* encompasses the entire finite plane of complex numbers.

Remark 6.2.1. From Theorem 2.7.7 we see that if

$$\lim_{n \to \infty} \left| \frac{c_{n+1}}{c_n} \right|$$

exists, then the power series (6.1.1) will converge when

$$|z - z_0| \lim_{n \to \infty} \left| \frac{c_{n+1}}{c_n} \right| < 1,$$

and will diverge when

$$|z - z_0| \lim_{n \to \infty} \left| \frac{c_{n+1}}{c_n} \right| > 1.$$

Letting

$$R = \lim_{n \to \infty} \left| \frac{c_n}{c_{n+1}} \right|, \tag{6.2.2}$$

we see that the power series $\sum_{n=0}^{\infty} c_n(z - z_0)^n$ converges when $|z - z_0| < R$ and diverges when $|z - z_0| > R$. Hence, the radius of convergence is given by (6.2.2) when the limit on the right-hand side exists.

If $\lim_{n \to \infty} \sqrt[n]{|c_n|}$ exists, then it is equal to $\overline{\lim_{n \to \infty}} \sqrt[n]{|c_n|}$ (see Exercise 2.8.5).

Thus, the radius of convergence is also given by

$$R = \frac{1}{\lim\limits_{n \to \infty} \sqrt[n]{|c_n|}} \tag{6.2.3}$$

when the limit on the right-hand side exists.

Remark 6.2.2. Suppose that the series $\sum_{n=0}^{\infty} c_n(z - z_0)^n$ converges to $F(z)$ for each point z in a set S. We then say that the series represents the function $F(z)$ in S, and we write $F(z) = \sum_{n=0}^{\infty} c_n(z - z_0)^n$ for z in S.

6.3. UNIFORM CONVERGENCE. We shall find the concept of uniform convergence of a power series very useful in the sequel. We can always write (6.1.1) in its circle of convergence as

$$\sum_{n=0}^{\infty} c_n(z - z_0)^n = \sum_{n=0}^{N-1} c_n(z - z_0)^n + R_N(z) \tag{6.3.1}$$

where

$$R_N(z) = \sum_{n=N}^{\infty} c_n(z - z_0)^n. \tag{6.3.2}$$

For a fixed N, $R_N(z)$ is a function of z in the interior D of its circle of convergence. Observe that as $N \to \infty$, $R_N(z) \to 0$ at each point z in D. That is, for every $\epsilon > 0$, there exists a positive integer $M(\epsilon, z)$ such that

$$|R_N(z)| < \epsilon \qquad \text{for } N \geq M(\epsilon, z).$$

The symbol $M(\epsilon, z)$ means that the number M depends not only upon ϵ but also upon the point z of D.

Definition 6.3.1. The power series (6.1.1) is said to *converge uniformly* in a point set S if, for each $\epsilon > 0$ there exists a positive integer $M(\epsilon)$ such that for all points z in S

$$|R_N(z)| < \epsilon \tag{6.3.3}$$

for $N \geq M(\epsilon)$.

The notation $M(\epsilon)$ indicates that $M(\epsilon)$ depends only on ϵ and does not vary with z in S.

We shall now establish the following important

THEOREM 6.3.1. Let the power series $\sum_{n=0}^{\infty} c_n(z - z_0)^n$ have a nonzero radius of convergence R. Then for any circle Γ about z_0 and radius $r < R$, the power series $\sum_{n=0}^{\infty} c_n(z - z_0)^n$ converges uniformly within and on Γ.

Proof. Draw the circles Γ and Γ_1 with centers at z_0 and radii equal to r and R_1, respectively, and such that $r < R_1 < R$. (See Fig. 6.3.1.) Since

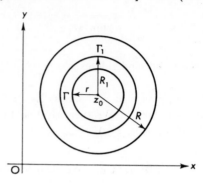

FIG. 6.3.1.

$r < R_1$, $r = \lambda R_1$ where $0 < \lambda < 1$. If $|z - z_0| \leq r$, then $|c_n(z - z_0)^n| \leq |c_n| r^n = |c_n| \lambda^n R_1^n$. Since by hypotheses, the series $\sum_{n=0}^{\infty} c_n(z - z_0)^n$ converges for $|z - z_0| = R_1$, it follows from Theorem 2.7.4 that $|c_n| R_1^n < 1$ for $n \geq M_1$, where M_1 is a sufficiently large fixed number. Also, since $0 < \lambda < 1$, we have for any $\epsilon > 0$, $\lambda^n < \epsilon(1 - \lambda)$ when $n \geq M_2(\epsilon)$, where $M_2(\epsilon)$ is a sufficiently large fixed number. Choose $M(\epsilon) = \max [M_1, M_2(\epsilon)]$. We then have for $N \geq M(\epsilon)$ and $|z - z_0| \leq r$

$$|R_N| = \left| \sum_{n=N}^{\infty} c_n(z - z_0)^n \right| \leq \sum_{n=N}^{\infty} |c_n(z - z_0)^n| \leq \sum_{n=N}^{\infty} |c_n| \lambda^n R_1^n < \sum_{n=N}^{\infty} \lambda^n$$

$$= \lambda^N[1 + \lambda + \lambda^2 + \cdots] = \frac{\lambda^N}{1 - \lambda} < \frac{\epsilon(1 - \lambda)}{(1 - \lambda)} = \epsilon.$$

Thus, in accordance with Definition 6.3.1, the theorem is established.

EXAMPLE 6.3.1. Let us show that the series $\sum_{n=1}^{\infty} nz^n$ converges uniformly within and on a circle $|z| = .999$.

Solution. From (6.2.2) the radius of convergence R of $\sum_{n=1}^{\infty} nz^n$ is given by

$$R = \lim_{n \to \infty} \left| \frac{c_n}{c_{n+1}} \right| = \lim_{n \to \infty} \left| \frac{n}{n + 1} \right| = 1.$$

Hence by Theorem 6.3.1 the series $\sum_{n=1}^{\infty} nz^n$ converges uniformly within and on the circle $|z| = .999$.

——**THEOREM** 6.3.2. Let the power series $\sum_{n=0}^{\infty} c_n(z - z_0)^n$ have a nonzero radius of convergence R. Then for any circle Γ with center at z_0 and radius $r < R$, the power series $\sum_{n=0}^{\infty} c_n(z - z_0)^n$ represents a continuous function of z in the closed region bounded by the circle Γ.

Proof. Without loss of generality we may take $z_0 = 0$. Let us write (6.3.1) with $z_0 = 0$ as

$$F(z) = S_N(z) + R_N(z) \tag{6.3.4}$$

where

$$F(z) = \sum_{n=0}^{\infty} c_n z^n, \qquad S_N(z) = \sum_{n=0}^{N-1} c_n z^n, \qquad R_N(z) = \sum_{n=N}^{\infty} c_n z^n. \tag{6.3.5}$$

Let $\mathscr{S}$ denote the closed region bounded by the circle Γ and let z_1 be a point in $\mathscr{S}$. We would like to show that given any $\epsilon > 0$, there exists a $\delta > 0$ such that

$$|F(z) - F(z_1)| < \epsilon \tag{6.3.6}$$

for all points z in $\mathscr{S}$ satisfying $|z - z_1| < \delta$.

Since by Theorem 6.3.1 the series $\sum_{n=0}^{\infty} c_n z^n$ converges uniformly in $\mathscr{S}$, we can choose an N such that

$$|F(z) - S_N(z)| < \frac{\epsilon}{3} \tag{6.3.7}$$

for all z in $\mathscr{S}$. Since $S_N(z)$ is a polynomial in z, it is a continuous function of z. Having chosen N as above, there exists a $\delta > 0$ such that

$$|S_N(z) - S_N(z_1)| < \frac{\epsilon}{3} \tag{6.3.8}$$

when $|z - z_1| < \delta$. Hence, for z in $\mathscr{S}$ and $|z - z_1| < \delta$, we have in virtue of (6.3.7) and (6.3.8)

$$|F(z) - F(z_1)| \leq |F(z) - S_N(z)| + |S_N(z) - S_N(z_1)|$$

$$+ |S_N(z_1) - F(z_1)| < \frac{\epsilon}{3} + \frac{\epsilon}{3} + \frac{\epsilon}{3} = \epsilon,$$

thus establishing the theorem.

Since any point interior to the circle of convergence $C: |z - z_0| = R$, $R \neq 0$, is also interior to some circle Γ contained entirely within C, utilizing the above theorem we have

——**THEOREM** 6.3.3. A power series represents a continuous function at every point interior to its circle of convergence.

EXERCISES 6.3

1. Determine the radius of convergence of the following series:

(a) $\displaystyle\sum_{n=1}^{\infty} \frac{z^n}{n^4}$,

(b) $\displaystyle\sum_{n=1}^{\infty} \frac{z^n}{n(n+1)}$,

(c) $\displaystyle\sum_{n=1}^{\infty} 4^n(z-2)^n,$

(d) $\displaystyle\sum_{n=1}^{\infty} n^3 z^n,$

(e) $\displaystyle\sum_{n=1}^{\infty} \frac{z^n}{n^n},$

(f) $\displaystyle\sum_{n=1}^{\infty} \left(1 - \frac{1}{n}\right)^{n^2} z^n,$

(g) $\displaystyle\sum_{n=1}^{\infty} \frac{n!\, z^n}{n^n},$

(h) $\displaystyle\sum_{n=1}^{\infty} \left(\frac{n}{n+1}\right)^{n^2} z^n,$

(i) $\displaystyle\sum_{n=1}^{\infty} \frac{(\log n^n)}{n!}\, z^n,$

(j) $\displaystyle\sum_{n=1}^{\infty} \left(\frac{n^2-1}{n^2+3n+2}\right) z^n.$

2. For what disks $|z| \leq r$ do the series in Exercise 1 converge uniformly?

3. Show that the two series

(a) $\displaystyle\sum_{n=1}^{\infty} \left[\frac{1 \cdot 3 \cdot 5 \cdots (2n-1)}{2 \cdot 4 \cdot 6 \cdots 2n}\right] \frac{(1-z)^n}{n},$

(b) $\displaystyle\sum_{n=1}^{\infty} \left[\frac{1 \cdot 3 \cdot 5 \cdots (2n-1)}{2 \cdot 4 \cdot 6 \cdots 2n}\right] \frac{(z-1)^n}{n}$

have the same circle of convergence.

4. Show that the two series

(a) $\displaystyle\sum_{n=0}^{\infty} c_n z^n,$

(b) $\displaystyle\sum_{n=0}^{\infty} \frac{c_n z^{n+1}}{n+1}$

have the same circle of convergence.

5. Show that the radius of convergence of the following series is unity:

$$\sum_{n=1}^{\infty} \left[\frac{\alpha(\alpha-1)(\alpha-2)\cdots(\alpha-n+1)}{n!}\right] z^n,$$

where α is a complex number different from a nonnegative integer.

6. *Abel's Test.* Suppose that the coefficients $c_0, c_1, \cdots$ form a decreasing sequence of positive numbers such that $\lim_{n\to\infty} c_n = 0$. Show that the series $\sum_{n=0}^{\infty} c_n z^n$ converges at all points of the unit circle except possibly at $z = 1$.

7. Show that if the power series $\sum_{n=0}^{\infty} c_n(z-z_0)^n$ converges at $z = z_1$ and diverges at $z = z_2$, then it converges absolutely for all z such that $|z-z_0| < |z_1-z_0|$ and diverges for all z such that $|z-z_0| > |z_2-z_0|$, and its radius of convergence R satisfies the inequality

$$|z_1 - z_0| \leq R \leq |z_2 - z_0|.$$

8. Show that a power series converges uniformly and absolutely on any compact set S contained in the interior of its circle of convergence C.

9. Show that a power series converges absolutely and uniformly on any contour γ lying in the interior of the circle of convergence of the power series.

6.4. TAYLOR'S SERIES.   We are now going to expand an analytic function $f(z)$ in a power series.

——**THEOREM** 6.4.1.   Let $f(z)$ be analytic in the interior of a circle C with center at z_0 and radius R. Then at each point z interior to C

$$f(z) = \sum_{n=0}^{\infty} \frac{f^{(n)}(z_0)}{n!} (z - z_0)^n. \qquad (6.4.1)$$

That is, the infinite series converges and has $f(z)$ as its sum-function. Moreover, the above series converges uniformly within and on any circle Γ with center at z_0 and radius $r < R$.

Proof.   Let Γ and Γ_1 be circles concentric with C with radii r and r_1, respectively, and such that $r < r_1 < R$. (See Fig. 6.4.1.) Let z be any point

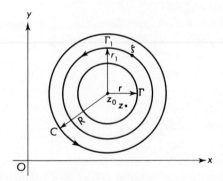

Fig. 6.4.1

within or on Γ and let ζ be any point on Γ_1. Then

$$|\zeta - z| = |(\zeta - z_0) - (z - z_0)| \geqq |\zeta - z_0| - |z - z_0| \geqq r_1 - r. \quad (6.4.2)$$

Using (5.12.1) we have

$$f(z) = \frac{1}{2\pi i} \int_{\Gamma_1} \frac{f(\zeta)\, d\zeta}{\zeta - z}. \qquad (6.4.3)$$

Observe that for any complex number $\beta \neq 1$, we have

$$\frac{1}{1-\beta} = 1 + \beta + \beta^2 + \cdots + \beta^{n-1} + \frac{\beta^n}{1-\beta}. \qquad (6.4.4)$$

Let us write $1/(\zeta - z)$ as

$$\frac{1}{\zeta - z} = \frac{1}{(\zeta - z_0) - (z - z_0)} = \frac{1}{(\zeta - z_0)\left[1 - \left(\dfrac{z - z_0}{\zeta - z_0}\right)\right]}$$

$$= \frac{1}{(\zeta - z_0)}\left[1 + \left(\frac{z - z_0}{\zeta - z_0}\right) + \left(\frac{z - z_0}{\zeta - z_0}\right)^2 + \cdots + \left(\frac{z - z_0}{\zeta - z_0}\right)^{n-1} + \frac{\left(\dfrac{z - z_0}{\zeta - z_0}\right)^n}{1 - \left(\dfrac{z - z_0}{\zeta - z_0}\right)}\right].$$

Thus

$$\frac{1}{\zeta - z} = \frac{1}{(\zeta - z_0)} + \frac{(z - z_0)}{(\zeta - z_0)^2} + \frac{(z - z_0)^2}{(\zeta - z_0)^3} + \cdots$$

$$+ \frac{(z - z_0)^{n-1}}{(\zeta - z_0)^n} + \frac{(z - z_0)^n}{(\zeta - z)(\zeta - z_0)^n}. \qquad (6.4.5)$$

From (5.13.5)

$$\frac{f^{(n)}(z_0)}{n!} = \frac{1}{2\pi i}\int_{\Gamma_1}\frac{f(\zeta)\,d\zeta}{(\zeta - z_0)^{n+1}}, \qquad n = 0, 1, 2, \cdots. \qquad (6.4.6)$$

Multiplying both sides of (6.4.5) by $(1/2\pi i)f(\zeta)$ and then integrating over Γ_1,*
we obtain by (6.4.3) and (6.4.6)

$$f(z) = f(z_0) + \frac{f'(z_0)}{1!}(z - z_0) + \frac{f''(z_0)}{2!}(z - z_0)^2 + \cdots$$

$$+ \frac{f^{(n-1)}(z_0)}{(n - 1)!}(z - z_0)^{n-1} + R_n, \qquad (6.4.7)$$

where

$$R_n = \frac{(z - z_0)^n}{2\pi i}\int_{\Gamma_1}\frac{f(\zeta)\,d\zeta}{(\zeta - z)(\zeta - z_0)^n}. \qquad (6.4.8)$$

We shall now show that $|R_n| \to 0$ as $n \to \infty$.

Let K be the maximum value of $|f(\zeta)|$ on Γ_1. (Such a K exists by Exercise 3.3.26.) Since $|\zeta - z_0| = r_1$ and $|\zeta - z| \geqq r_1 - r$ for all z within or on Γ and all ζ on Γ_1, we have utilizing (5.2.22)

$$|R_n| \leqq \frac{|z - z_0|^n}{2\pi}\int_{\Gamma_1}\frac{|f(\zeta)|\,|d\zeta|}{|\zeta - z|\,|\zeta - z_0|^n}$$

$$\leqq \frac{2\pi K r_1 r^n}{2\pi(r_1 - r)\,r_1^n} = \frac{K}{1 - (r/r_1)}\left(\frac{r}{r_1}\right)^n. \qquad (6.4.9)$$

Since $0 < r < r_1$, $r = \lambda r_1$, where $0 < \lambda < 1$. Hence from (6.4.9) we obtain

$$|R_n(z)| < \left(\frac{K}{1 - \lambda}\right)\lambda^n \qquad (6.4.10)$$

* Unless the contrary is indicated, integration is performed in the positive direction.

for all z within or on Γ. The right-hand side of the above inequality is independent of z and tends to zero as $n \to \infty$. Thus the series (6.4.7) converges uniformly to $f(z)$ for z within and on the circle Γ. Now, given any point z interior to the circle C, we can take r so that $|z - z_0| < r < R$, then z will be interior to a circle Γ: $|\zeta - z_0| = r < R$. Consequently, (6.4.1) is valid for all z interior to C. Thus the theorem is established.

The power series (6.4.1) is called the *Taylor series*. The circle of convergence of this series is at least as large as the largest circle with center at z_0 in which $f(z)$ remains analytic. Thus when it is known that $f(z)$ is analytic in the interior of a circle C, no test is required for the convergence of the Taylor series within C.

In Section 6.6 we shall prove the converse of the above theorem, namely, that every power series represents an analytic function in the interior of its circle of convergence. We may now say that *$f(z)$ is analytic at a point z_0 if and only if it can be expanded in a convergent power series about that point.* When we say that a function can be expanded in a convergent power series about a point, we mean that the convergence takes place in a neighborhood of the point.

In particular when $z_0 = 0$, the Taylor series reduces to one that is known as the *Maclaurin series*:

$$f(z) = \sum_{n=0}^{\infty} \frac{f^{(n)}(0)}{n!} z^n. \tag{6.4.11}$$

EXAMPLE 6.4.1. Let us show that

$$\frac{1}{z^2} = \frac{1}{4} \sum_{n=0}^{\infty} (-1)^n (n+1) \left(\frac{z-2}{2}\right)^n, \qquad |z-2| < 2.$$

Solution. Let $f(z) = 1/z^2$. Then

$$f^{(n)}(z) = \frac{(-1)^n (n+1)!}{z^{n+2}}, \qquad n = 0, 1, 2, \cdots.$$

Thus

$$f^{(n)}(2) = \frac{(-1)^n (n+1)!}{2^{n+2}}, \qquad n = 0, 1, 2, \cdots.$$

Since $f(z)$ is analytic for all values of z such that $|z - 2| < 2$, we have

$$\frac{1}{z^2} = \sum_{n=0}^{\infty} \frac{(-1)^n (n+1)!}{2^{n+2} n!} (z-2)^n$$

$$= \frac{1}{4} \sum_{n=0}^{\infty} (-1)^n (n+1) \left(\frac{z-2}{2}\right)^n, \qquad |z-2| < 2.$$

Remark 6.4.1.   Let $C: |z - z_0| = R$ be the largest circle with center at z_0 in which the function $f(z)$ is defined and is analytic. Then Theorem 6.4.1 assures us that the Taylor series converges to $f(z)$ at each point z interior to the circle C, that is, whenever $|z - z_0| < R$. One should not conclude from this that R is necessarily the radius of convergence of the Taylor series, for it is possible that the radius of convergence can be larger than R. If this is so, then $f(z)$, defined within C, can be extended to a larger domain and still remain analytic.

EXAMPLE 6.4.2.   Let us expand in a Taylor series the function

$$f(z) = \text{Log } z = \text{Log } |z| + i \text{ Arg } z, \quad -\pi < \text{Arg } z \leq \pi,$$

about the point $z_0 = -1 + i$.

Solution.   Since $f(z)$ is not analytic on the nonpositive half of the real axis (see Remark 4.4.2), it follows that the largest circle C with center at $z_0 = -1 + i$ within which $f(z)$ is defined and analytic has radius $R = 1$. However, as we shall see, the radius of convergence R' of the Taylor series is greater than 1. Note that

$$f(-1 + i) = \text{Log } (-1 + i) = \tfrac{1}{2} \text{Log } 2 + \tfrac{3}{4} \pi i,$$

and

$$f^{(n)}(z) = \frac{(-1)^{n-1} (n-1)!}{z^n}, \qquad n = 1, 2, \cdots.$$

Thus

$$f^{(n)}(-1 + i) = \frac{(-1)^{n-1} (n-1)!}{(-1 + i)^n} = (-1)^{n-1} (n-1)! \left[-\left(\frac{1+i}{2} \right) \right]^n$$

$$= -(n-1)! \left(\frac{1+i}{2} \right)^n.$$

Hence, from formula (6.4.1) we obtain

$$\text{Log } z = \frac{1}{2} \text{Log } 2 + \frac{3}{4} \pi i - \sum_{n=1}^{\infty} \left(\frac{1+i}{2} \right)^n \frac{[z - (-1 + i)]^n}{n}. \qquad (6.4.12)$$

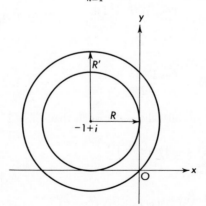

FIG. 6.4.2

From (6.2.2) the radius of convergence R' of the series is given by

$$R' = \lim_{n \to \infty} \left| \frac{c_n}{c_{n+1}} \right| = \lim_{n \to \infty} \left| \left(1 + \frac{1}{n} \right) \left(\frac{2}{1 + i} \right) \right| = \frac{2}{|1 + i|} = \sqrt{2}.$$

Note that by means of the power series (6.4.12), $f_0(z) \equiv \text{Log } z$, $|z - (-1 + i)| < 1$, can be extended to be analytic in the larger circle, with center at $z_0 = -1 + i$ and radius $R' = \sqrt{2}$. (See Fig. 6.4.2.) However, the values of $f_0(z)$ lying in this larger circle below the x axis do not agree with the values of the original function $f(z) = \text{Log } z$.

EXERCISES 6.4

1. Obtain the Maclaurin series expansion of the following functions and determine in each case the circle of convergence:

(a) e^z,

(b) $\sin z$,

(c) $\cos z$,

(d) $\sinh z$,

(e) $\cosh z$,

(f) $1/(1 + z)$,

(g) $z/(1 - z)$,

(h) $\text{Log }(1 + z)$,

(i) $\tan z$ (write the first four nonzero terms).

2. Expand in a Taylor series about the point indicated; determine the radius of convergence R' of the series and the radius R of the largest circle within which the series converges to the given function:

(a) $\dfrac{1}{z}$ about $z = 1$,

(b) $\sqrt[3]{z} = \sqrt[3]{r}\, e^{i(\theta/3)}$, $-\pi < \theta < \pi$, about $z = 1 + i$,

(c) $\sinh z$ about $z = \pi i$,

(d) e^{z-1} about $z = 2$,

(e) $\dfrac{1}{z - 4}$ about $z = 3$,

(f) $\dfrac{2z}{z - 2}$ about $z = 1$,

(g) $f(z) = \displaystyle\int_C \frac{d\zeta}{\zeta - z}$, $|z| \neq 1$, about $z = 0$, where the integral along the circle $C: |\zeta| = 1$ is taken counterclockwise.

3. Let $f(z)$ be analytic in the interior of a circle C with center at z_0. Suppose that $f^{(n)}(z_0) = 0$, $n = 0, 1, 2, \cdots$. Show that $f(z)$ vanishes identically at all points interior to C.

4. Show that for all points z interior to the circle $|z| = 1$,

$$|\text{Log }(1 + z)| \leq -\text{Log }(1 - |z|).$$

5. Show that if the values of an analytic function $f(z)$ are known along an arbitrarily small arc ending at z_0, then its values are completely determined in the entire circle of convergence of the power series of $f(z)$ about z_0.

6.5. LAURENT'S SERIES. The following theorem, which gives us a generalization of the Taylor series, is due to Laurent.

——**THEOREM** 6.5.1. Let S be the region bounded by the concentric circles C_1 and C_2 with center at z_0 and radii r_1 and r_2 respectively, $r_1 < r_2$. Let $f(z)$ be analytic within S and on C_1 and C_2. Then at each point z in the interior of S, $f(z)$ can be represented by a convergent series of positive and negative powers of $(z - z_0)$,

$$f(z) = \sum_{n=0}^{\infty} a_n(z - z_0)^n + \sum_{n=1}^{\infty} b_n(z - z_0)^{-n}, \qquad (6.5.1)$$

where

$$a_n = \frac{1}{2\pi i} \int_{C_2} \frac{f(\zeta)\, d\zeta}{(\zeta - z_0)^{n+1}}, \qquad n = 0, 1, 2, \cdots, \qquad (6.5.2)$$

$$b_n = \frac{1}{2\pi i} \int_{C_1} \frac{f(\zeta)\, d\zeta}{(\zeta - z_0)^{-n+1}}, \qquad n = 1, 2, \cdots, \qquad (6.5.3)$$

the integral along C_1 and C_2 being taken in the positive direction.

Proof. Let ζ denote a point on either C_1: $|\zeta - z_0| = r_1$ or on C_2: $|\zeta - z_0| = r_2$. Let z be any point in the interior of S: $|z - z_0| = r$,

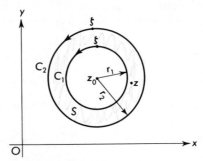

FIG. 6.5.1

$r_1 < r < r_2$ (see Fig. 6.5.1). From Theorem 5.10.3 (see also Exercise 5.17.10) we obtain

$$f(z) = \frac{1}{2\pi i} \int_{C_2} \frac{f(\zeta)\, d\zeta}{\zeta - z} - \frac{1}{2\pi i} \int_{C_1} \frac{f(\zeta)\, d\zeta}{\zeta - z}. \qquad (6.5.4)$$

Proceeding as in connection with the Taylor series, the value of the first integral in (6.5.4) is given by

$$\frac{1}{2\pi i} \int_{C_2} \frac{f(\zeta)\, d\zeta}{\zeta - z} = \sum_{n=0}^{\infty} a_n(z - z_0)^n, \qquad (6.5.5)$$

where the a_n are given by (6.5.2).

Concerning the second integral in (6.5.4), let us write

$$-\frac{1}{\zeta - z} = \frac{1}{(z - z_0) - (\zeta - z_0)} = \frac{1}{(z - z_0)\left[1 - \left(\dfrac{\zeta - z_0}{z - z_0}\right)\right]}$$

$$= \frac{1}{(z - z_0)} + \frac{(\zeta - z_0)}{(z - z_0)^2} + \cdots + \frac{(\zeta - z_0)^{n-1}}{(z - z_0)^n} + \frac{(\zeta - z_0)^n}{(z - z_0)^n (z - \zeta)}.$$

Multiplying the above expression by $(1/2\pi i)f(\zeta)$, and integrating over C_1, we obtain

$$-\frac{1}{2\pi i} \int_{C_1} \frac{f(\zeta)\, d\zeta}{\zeta - z} = \frac{b_1}{(z - z_0)} + \frac{b_2}{(z - z_0)^2} + \cdots + \frac{b_n}{(z - z_0)^n} + T_n, \quad (6.5.6)$$

where the b_n are numbers given by (6.5.3) and

$$T_n = \frac{1}{2\pi i (z - z_0)^n} \int_{C_1} \frac{(\zeta - z_0)^n f(\zeta)\, d\zeta}{(z - \zeta)}. \qquad (6.5.7)$$

Let K be the maximum value of $|f(\zeta)|$ on C_1. For ζ on C_1 we have

$$|z - \zeta| = |(z - z_0) - (\zeta - z_0)| \geqq |z - z_0| - |\zeta - z_0| = r - r_1.$$

Thus

$$|T_n| \leqq \frac{1}{2\pi r^n} \cdot \frac{K r_1^n \, 2\pi r_1}{(r - r_1)} = \frac{K}{\dfrac{r}{r_1} - 1}\left(\frac{r_1}{r}\right)^n.$$

Since $r_1 < r$, $|T_n| \to 0$ as $n \to \infty$. Hence

$$-\frac{1}{2\pi i} \int_{C_1} \frac{f(\zeta)\, d\zeta}{(\zeta - z)} = \sum_{n=1}^{\infty} b_n (z - z_0)^{-n}. \qquad (6.5.8)$$

From (6.5.4), (6.5.5) and (6.5.8), the theorem now follows.

Remark 6.5.1. The series given in (6.5.1) is called the *Laurent series* expansion of $f(z)$ in the annular region S. Observe that the integrands in (6.5.2) and (6.5.3) are analytic functions of ζ in the region S. It follows from Theorem 5.10.3 that any simple closed contour C lying in S and containing z_0 in its interior may be used as the path of integration in place of the circular paths C_1 and C_2. Hence the Laurent series expansion of $f(z)$ can also be written as

$$f(z) = \sum_{n=-\infty}^{\infty} \alpha_n (z - z_0)^n, \qquad r_1 < |z - z_0| < r_2, \qquad (6.5.9)$$

where

$$\alpha_n = \frac{1}{2\pi i} \int_C \frac{f(\zeta)\, d\zeta}{(\zeta - z_0)^{n+1}}, \qquad n = 0, \pm 1, \pm 2, \cdots, \qquad (6.5.10)$$

and the integral along C is taken in the positive direction.

It can be shown that the Laurent series (6.5.1) is uniformly and absolutely convergent in the closed annulus $R_1 \leq |z - z_0| \leq R_2$, provided that $r_1 < R_1 < R_2 < r_2$. (See Exercise 6.8.19.)

Remark 6.5.2.   If $f(z)$ is analytic within and on C_2, then since $-n+1 \leq 0$ for $n = 1, 2, \cdots$, we see that the integrands of (6.5.3) are analytic functions of ζ within and on C_1. Hence, by Theorem 5.10.2

$$b_n = \frac{1}{2\pi i} \int_{C_1} \frac{f(\zeta)\, d\zeta}{(\zeta - z_0)^{-n+1}} = 0, \qquad n = 1, 2, \cdots,$$

and the Laurent series becomes a Taylor series.

Remark 6.5.3.   Theorem 6.5.1 reveals that under certain conditions an analytic function can be expanded in a series as in (6.5.1). At times this theorem does not provide the simplest method for calculating the coefficients a_n and b_n.

In Section 6.6, we shall show that the Laurent expansion as well as the Taylor expansion of a given function about a point are unique in a neighborhood of the point. Taking these results for granted we shall be able to compute the coefficients a_n and b_n of some functions by easier methods. If the series (6.5.9) converges to $f(z)$ in the region $r_1 < |z - z_0| < r_2$, where $r_1 = 0$ or $r_2 = \infty$, the coefficients α_n will still be given by (6.5.10). (See opening remarks of Section 7.2.)

EXAMPLE 6.5.1.   Let us find the Laurent series expansion, in powers of z, for the function $f(z) = 1/(z - 1)(z - 3)$.

Solution.   Observe that $f(z)$ is analytic for all values of z such that $1 < |z| < 3$. We may find the α_n's of (6.5.10) by using the following device. We write $f(z)$ as a sum of two geometric series, one series converging for $|z| > 1$ and the other for $|z| < 3$. Decomposing $f(z)$ into partial fractions, we find

$$\frac{1}{(z - 1)(z - 3)} = -\frac{1}{2(z - 1)} + \frac{1}{2(z - 3)} = -\frac{1}{2z(1 - 1/z)} - \frac{1}{6(1 - z/3)}.$$

We know that the series

$$\frac{1}{1 - \alpha} = 1 + \alpha + \alpha^2 + \cdots = \sum_{n=0}^{\infty} \alpha^n$$

converges for $|\alpha| < 1$. Since $|1/z| < 1$ when $|z| > 1$ and $|z/3| < 1$ when $|z| < 3$, the series

$$\frac{1}{1 - 1/z} = \sum_{n=0}^{\infty} \frac{1}{z^n}$$

converges for $|z| > 1$ and the series

$$\frac{1}{1 - z/3} = \sum_{n=0}^{\infty} \frac{z^n}{3^n}$$

converges for $|z| < 3$. Consequently

$$\frac{1}{(z - 1)(z - 3)} = -\frac{1}{2} \sum_{n=1}^{\infty} \frac{1}{z^n} - \frac{1}{2} \sum_{n=0}^{\infty} \frac{z^n}{3^{n+1}} \qquad (6.5.11)$$

converges for $1 < |z| < 3$.

Let us check (6.5.11) by using (6.5.10) to find the α_n's. Now

$$f(\zeta) = \frac{1}{(\zeta - 1)(\zeta - 3)}.$$

Taking $z_0 = 0$, we may write (6.5.10) as

$$\alpha_n = \frac{1}{2\pi i} \int_C \frac{d\zeta}{(\zeta - 1)(\zeta - 3) \zeta^{n+1}},$$

where C is a simple closed contour enclosing the origin and lying between the circles $|z| = 1$ and $|z| = 3$. Let $n \geq 0$. Decomposing

$$\frac{1}{(\zeta - 1)(\zeta - 3) \zeta^{n+1}}$$

into partial fractions, we obtain

$$\frac{1}{(\zeta - 1)(\zeta - 3) \zeta^{n+1}} = \frac{A_1}{\zeta - 1} + \frac{A_2}{\zeta - 3} + \frac{B_1}{\zeta} + \frac{B_2}{\zeta^2} + \frac{B_3}{\zeta^3} + \cdots + \frac{B_{n+1}}{\zeta^{n+1}},$$
$$(6.5.12)$$

where A_1, A_2 and B_i ($i = 1, 2, \cdots, n + 1$) are constants. From Theorem 5.10.2

$$\int_C \frac{A_2 d\zeta}{\zeta - 3} = 0,$$

and from (5.13.5) we see that

$$\int_C \frac{B_2 d\zeta}{\zeta^2} = \int_C \frac{B_3 d\zeta}{\zeta^3} = \cdots = \int_C \frac{B_{n+1} d\zeta}{\zeta^{n+1}} = 0.$$

Hence

$$\alpha_n = \frac{1}{2\pi i} \int_C \frac{A_1 d\zeta}{\zeta - 1} + \frac{1}{2\pi i} \int_C \frac{B_1 d\zeta}{\zeta}.$$

In virtue of Theorem 5.12.1, we obtain

$$\alpha_n = A_1 + B_1.$$

To find A_1, we multiply (6.5.12) by $\zeta - 1$ and let $\zeta = 1$. We obtain $A_1 = -1/2$. To find B_1, we first find A_2. Multiplying (6.5.12) by $\zeta - 3$ and letting $\zeta = 3$, $A_2 = 1/(2 \cdot 3^{n+1})$. Now multiplying (6.5.12) by ζ and letting $\zeta \to \infty$, we obtain

$$0 = A_1 + A_2 + B_1.$$

Thus

$$B_1 = -A_1 - A_2 = \frac{1}{2} - \frac{1}{2 \cdot 3^{n+1}}.$$

Hence for $n \geq 0$, we have

$$\alpha_n = A_1 + B_1 = -\frac{1}{2} + \frac{1}{2} - \frac{1}{2 \cdot 3^{n+1}} = -\frac{1}{2 \cdot 3^{n+1}}.$$

When $n < 0$, let $-n = q$ and we have

$$\alpha_n = \frac{1}{2\pi i} \int_C \frac{d\zeta}{(\zeta - 1)(\zeta - 3)\zeta^{n+1}} = \frac{1}{2\pi i} \int_C \frac{\left(\dfrac{\zeta^{q-1}}{\zeta - 3}\right) d\zeta}{\zeta - 1}.$$

Since $g(\zeta) = \zeta^{q-1}/(\zeta - 3)$ is analytic within and on C, by Theorem 5.12.1 with $z_0 = 1$, we obtain $\alpha_n = g(1)$ and so

$$\alpha_n = -\frac{1}{2}, \qquad n < 0.$$

Thus we have checked the coefficients in (6.5.11).

EXAMPLE 6.5.2.   Let us show that the Laurent series expansion, in powers of $z + 1$, which represents the function

$$f(z) = \frac{z^2 + 1}{z(z^2 - 3z + 2)},$$

in the region $|z + 1| > 3$, is given by

$$\frac{1}{2} \sum_{n=0}^{\infty} (1 - 2^{n+2} + 5 \cdot 3^n)(z + 1)^{-(n+1)}.$$

Solution.   Let $t = z + 1$. Then

$$f(z) = f(t - 1) = (t^2 - 2t + 2)/(t - 1)(t - 2)(t - 3).$$

Decomposing $f(t - 1)$ into partial fractions, we obtain

$$\frac{t^2 - 2t + 2}{(t - 1)(t - 2)(t - 3)} = \frac{1}{2(t - 1)} - \frac{2}{(t - 2)} + \frac{5}{2(t - 3)}.$$

For $|t| = |z + 1| > 3$, we have

$$\frac{t^2 - 2t + 2}{(t-1)(t-2)(t-3)} = \frac{1}{2t(1-1/t)} - \frac{2}{t(1-2/t)} + \frac{5}{2t(1-3/t)}$$

$$= \frac{1}{2t} \sum_{n=0}^{\infty} \frac{1}{t^n} - \frac{2}{t} \sum_{n=0}^{\infty} \frac{2^n}{t^n} + \frac{5}{2t} \sum_{n=0}^{\infty} \frac{3^n}{t^n}.$$

Hence

$$f(z) = \frac{1}{2} \sum_{n=0}^{\infty} (1 - 2^{n+2} + 5 \cdot 3^n)(z+1)^{-(n+1)}, \qquad |z+1| > 3.$$

EXAMPLE 6.5.3. Let us show that the Laurent series expansion, in powers of z, which represents the function

$$f(z) = \sinh\left(z + \frac{1}{z}\right),$$

in the region $|z| > 0$, is given by

$$\alpha_0 + \sum_{n=1}^{\infty} \alpha_n \left(z^n + \frac{1}{z^n}\right),$$

where

$$\alpha_n = \frac{1}{2\pi} \int_0^{2\pi} \cos n\theta \, \sinh(2\cos\theta) \, d\theta.$$

Solution. Observe that $\sinh(z + 1/z)$ is analytic for all finite $z \neq 0$. With $z_0 = 0$, we may write (6.5.9) as

$$\sinh\left(z + \frac{1}{z}\right) = \sum_{n=-\infty}^{\infty} \alpha_n z^n,$$

where

$$\alpha_n = \frac{1}{2\pi i} \int_C \frac{\sinh(\zeta + 1/\zeta) \, d\zeta}{\zeta^{n+1}}, \qquad n = 0, \pm 1, \pm 2, \cdots,$$

and for the contour C enclosing the origin we shall take the circle $|\zeta| = 1$. Then $\zeta = e^{i\theta}$ on C; and for any integer n

$$\alpha_n = \frac{1}{2\pi i} \int_0^{2\pi} \frac{\sinh(e^{i\theta} + e^{-i\theta}) \, ie^{i\theta} \, d\theta}{e^{ni\theta + i\theta}}$$

$$= \frac{1}{2\pi} \int_0^{2\pi} \sinh(2\cos\theta)[\cos n\theta - i\sin n\theta] \, d\theta$$

$$= \frac{1}{2\pi} \int_0^{2\pi} \cos n\theta \, \sinh(2\cos\theta) \, d\theta - \frac{i}{2\pi} \int_0^{2\pi} \sin n\theta \, \sinh(2\cos\theta) \, d\theta.$$

Observe that

$$\int_0^{2\pi} \sin n\theta \sinh (2 \cos \theta) \, d\theta = 0, \qquad n = 0, \pm 1, \pm 2, \cdots,$$

for, if we let $\theta = 2\pi - \lambda$, then

$$\int_0^{2\pi} \sin n\theta \sinh (2 \cos \theta) \, d\theta = - \int_0^{2\pi} \sin n\lambda \sinh (2 \cos \lambda) \, d\lambda.$$

Now replacing λ by θ in the right-hand member of the above expression, we obtain

$$\int_0^{2\pi} \sin n\theta \sinh (2 \cos \theta) \, d\theta = 0.$$

Thus we have

$$\alpha_n = \frac{1}{2\pi} \int_0^{2\pi} \cos n\theta \sinh (2 \cos \theta) \, d\theta.$$

Since the above expression remains unchanged when $-n$ is substituted for n, it follows that $\alpha_{-n} = \alpha_n$, $n = 1, 2, \cdots$. Hence

$$\sinh \left(z + \frac{1}{z} \right) = \sum_{n=-\infty}^{\infty} \alpha_n z^n = \sum_{n=1}^{\infty} \alpha_{-n} z^{-n} + \alpha_0 + \sum_{n=1}^{\infty} \alpha_n z^n$$

$$= \alpha_0 + \sum_{n=1}^{\infty} \alpha_n \left(z^n + \frac{1}{z^n} \right).$$

EXERCISES 6.5

1. Find the Taylor or the Laurent series expansions (in powers of z) which represent the following functions in the indicated regions:

(a) $\dfrac{1}{z^2(z - 1)(z + 2)}$,

    (1) $0 < |z| < 1$,   (2) $1 < |z| < 2$,   (3) $|z| > 2$;

(b) $\dfrac{1}{(z^2 + 1)(z + 2)}$,

    (1) $|z| < 1$,   (2) $1 < |z| < 2$,   (3) $|z| > 2$;

(c) $\dfrac{z^2 - 1}{(z + 2)(z + 3)}$,

    (1) $|z| < 2$,   (2) $2 < |z| < 3$,   (3) $|z| > 3$;

(d) $\dfrac{1}{(z - \lambda)^k}$,

(1) $|z| < |\lambda|, k = 1, 2, \cdots,$ (2) $|z| > |\lambda|, k = 1, 2, \cdots.$

2. Show that the Laurent series expansion, in powers of z, which represents the function

$$f(z) = e^{(u/2)(z-1/z)},$$

in the region $|z| > 0$, is given by

$$\sum_{n=-\infty}^{\infty} J_n(u)\, z^n,$$

where

$$J_n(u) = (-1)^n J_{-n}(u) = \frac{1}{2\pi}\int_0^{2\pi} \cos(n\theta - u\sin\theta)\, d\theta.$$

The $J_n(u)$ are known as the *Bessel functions of the first kind.*

3. Show that the Laurent series expansion, in powers of z, which represents the function

$$f(z) = \sin\left[u\left(z + \frac{1}{z}\right)\right],$$

in the region $|z| > 0$, is given by

$$\alpha_0 + \sum_{n=1}^{\infty} \alpha_n\left(z^n + \frac{1}{z^n}\right),$$

where

$$\alpha_n = \frac{1}{2\pi}\int_0^{2\pi} \cos n\theta \, \sin(2u\cos\theta)\, d\theta.$$

4. Show that the Laurent series expansion, in powers of z, which represents the function

$$f(z) = \frac{1}{z - h},$$

in the region $|z| > |h|$, is given by

$$\sum_{n=0}^{\infty} \frac{h^n}{z^{n+1}}.$$

Substituting $z = e^{i\theta}$ in the foregoing expansion, deduce the following expansions for h real and $0 < |h| < 1$:

$$\sum_{n=0}^{\infty} h^n \cos[(n+1)\,\theta] = \frac{\cos\theta - h}{1 - 2h\cos\theta + h^2},$$

$$\sum_{n=0}^{\infty} h^n \sin[(n+1)\,\theta] = \frac{\sin\theta}{1 - 2h\cos\theta + h^2}.$$

6.6. INTEGRATION AND DIFFERENTIATION OF POWER SERIES.

From Theorem 6.3.3 we know that a power series $\sum_{n=0}^{\infty} c_n(z - z_0)^n$ represents a continuous function $F(z)$ interior to its circle of convergence C:

$$|z - z_0| = R \neq 0.$$

We shall now show that interior to its circle of convergence, a power series may be integrated or differentiated term by term, and it represents an analytic function. In the ensuing discussion, we shall deal with power series that have a nonzero radius of convergence. We shall now establish the following important

——*THEOREM* 6.6.1. Let Γ be a contour interior to the circle of convergence C: $|z - z_0| = R$ of a power series. Let $h(z)$ be a continuous function defined on Γ. The series formed by multiplying each term of the power series by $h(z)$ can be integrated term by term over Γ. That is, if

$$F(z) = \sum_{n=0}^{\infty} c_n(z - z_0)^n, \qquad |z - z_0| < R,$$

then

$$\int_\Gamma F(z)\, h(z)\, dz = \sum_{n=0}^{\infty} c_n \int_\Gamma (z - z_0)^n\, h(z)\, dz. \qquad (6.6.1)$$

Proof. Since $F(z)$ is a continuous function of z for $|z - z_0| < R$ and $h(z)$ is continuous on Γ, we see that $F(z)\, h(z)$ and $\sum_{n=0}^{N-1} c_n(z - z_0)^n\, h(z)$ are continuous functions on Γ. Thus their integrals over Γ exist. But

$$F(z)\, h(z) = \sum_{n=0}^{N-1} c_n(z - z_0)^n\, h(z) + R_N(z)\, h(z),$$

and consequently the integral of $R_N(z)\, h(z)$ also exists along Γ. Hence, we have

$$\int_\Gamma F(z)\, h(z)\, dz = \sum_{n=0}^{N-1} c_n \int_\Gamma (z - z_0)^n\, h(z)\, dz + \int_\Gamma R_N(z)\, h(z)\, dz. \quad (6.6.2)$$

Utilizing Theorem 6.3.1 (see also Exercise 6.3.9) we see that given any $\epsilon > 0$, there exists a positive integer $M(\epsilon)$ such that for all points z on Γ

$$|R_N(z)| < \epsilon \qquad \text{for } N \geq M(\epsilon).$$

Denote by L the length of the contour Γ and let $|h(z)| \leq K$ for all points z on Γ. (Such a constant K exists by Exercise 3.3.25.) Then

$$\left| \int_\Gamma R_N(z)\, h(z)\, dz \right| \leq \int_\Gamma |R_N(z)|\, |h(z)|\, |dz| < KL\epsilon$$

for $N \geq M(\epsilon)$. Hence

$$\left| \int_\Gamma R_N(z)\, h(z)\, dz \right| \to 0 \qquad \text{as } N \to \infty.$$

Letting $N \to \infty$, equation (6.6.2) becomes

$$\int_\Gamma F(z)\, h(z)\, dz = \lim_{N \to \infty} \sum_{n=0}^{N-1} c_n \int_\Gamma (z - z_0)^n\, h(z)\, dz = \sum_{n=0}^{\infty} c_n \int_\Gamma (z - z_0)^n\, h(z)\, dz,$$

and the theorem is established.

If $|\zeta - z_0| < R$, z_0 and ζ are the initial and terminal points of Γ, and $h(z) = 1$ for all z on Γ, then by Lemma 5.8.1, equation (6.6.1) becomes

$$\int_{z_0}^{\zeta} F(z)\, dz = \sum_{n=0}^{\infty} c_n \int_{z_0}^{\zeta} (z - z_0)^n\, dz = \sum_{n=0}^{\infty} \frac{c_n(\zeta - z_0)^{n+1}}{n + 1}. \qquad (6.6.3)$$

If $|\zeta - z_0| < R$ and $|\alpha - z_0| < R$, with α kept fixed, the expression

$$\int_\alpha^\zeta F(z)\, dz$$

becomes an indefinite integral of $F(z)$. We then have

$$\int_\alpha^\zeta F(z)\, dz = \int_\alpha^{z_0} F(z)\, dz + \int_{z_0}^\zeta F(z)\, dz = \sum_{n=0}^{\infty} \frac{c_n(\zeta - z_0)^{n+1}}{n + 1} + M, \qquad (6.6.4)$$

where M is a constant.

——*THEOREM* 6.6.2. A power series represents an analytic function at every point interior to its circle of convergence.

Proof. Let C denote the circle of convergence of the power series $\sum_{n=0}^{\infty} c_n(z - z_0)^n = F(z)$. By Theorem 6.3.3, $F(z)$ is continuous at every point interior to C. Let Γ be any closed contour interior to C. Since the initial and terminal points on Γ coincide, for each integer n, the right-hand member of (6.6.3) is equal to zero. Consequently

$$\int_\Gamma F(z)\, dz = 0$$

for every closed contour Γ interior to C. Hence by Morera's theorem, $F(z)$ is analytic at every point interior to C.

——*THEOREM* 6.6.3.   A power series can be differentiated term by term at every point z interior to its circle of convergence $C: |z - z_0| = R$. That is, if

$$F(z) = \sum_{n=0}^{\infty} c_n(z - z_0)^n, \qquad |z - z_0| < R,$$

then

$$F'(z) = \sum_{n=1}^{\infty} n c_n(z - z_0)^{n-1}, \qquad |z - z_0| < R. \qquad (6.6.5)$$

Proof.   Let ζ be any point interior to the circle of convergence C of the power series. Let Γ be a circle with center at ζ and contained in the interior of C. Since by Theorem 6.6.2 $F(z)$ is analytic within and on Γ, we have from (5.13.3)

$$F'(\zeta) = \frac{1}{2\pi i} \int_{\Gamma} \frac{F(z)\,dz}{(z - \zeta)^2} = \int_{\Gamma} F(z)\,h(z)\,dz,$$

where

$$h(z) = \frac{1}{2\pi i(z - \zeta)^2}.$$

Using (6.6.1) and again (5.13.3), we find

$$F'(\zeta) = \int_{\Gamma} F(z)\,h(z)\,dz = \sum_{n=0}^{\infty} c_n \frac{1}{2\pi i} \int_{\Gamma} \frac{(z - z_0)^n\,dz}{(z - \zeta)^2}$$

$$= \sum_{n=1}^{\infty} n c_n(\zeta - z_0)^{n-1}, \qquad |\zeta - z_0| < R.$$

Since ζ is any point interior to the circle of convergence, we have

$$F'(z) = \sum_{n=1}^{\infty} n c_n(z - z_0)^{n-1}, \qquad |z - z_0| < R,$$

and the theorem is established.

By repeated application of the above process to (6.6.5), we obtain

$$F^{(k)}(z) = \sum_{n=k}^{\infty} \frac{n!}{(n - k)!} c_n(z - z_0)^{n-k}, \qquad k = 0, 1, 2, \cdots, |z - z_0| < R. \quad (6.6.6)$$

Note that the original series and the series in (6.6.6), $k = 1, 2, \cdots$, have the same radius of convergence.

We are now in a position to show that the representation of an analytic function by means of a power series about a given point is unique.

——**THEOREM** 6.6.4. If a power series $\sum_{n=0}^{\infty} c_n(z - z_0)^n$ converges to a function $f(z)$ at all points interior to a circle $| z - z_0 | = R$, that series is the Taylor series expansion of $f(z)$ in powers of $(z - z_0)$.

Proof. Since $f(z) = \sum_{n=0}^{\infty} c_n(z - z_0)^n$, $| z - z_0 | < R$, we have from (6.6.6)

$$f^{(n)}(z) = n!c_n + (n + 1) n(n - 1) \cdots 2c_{n+1}(z - z_0)$$
$$+ (n + 2) (n + 1) n \cdots 3c_{n+2}(z - z_0)^2 + \cdots, n = 0, 1, 2, \cdots,$$
$$| z - z_0 | < R.$$

Setting $z = z_0$ in the above expression we find

$$f^{(n)}(z_0) = n!c_n, \qquad n = 0, 1, 2, \cdots. \tag{6.6.7}$$

Therefore

$$f(z) = \sum_{n=0}^{\infty} c_n(z - z_0)^n = \sum_{n=0}^{\infty} f^{(n)}(z_0) \frac{(z - z_0)^n}{n!}, \qquad | z - z_0 | < R.$$

Thus, the given series is the Taylor series expansion of $f(z)$ in powers of $(z - z_0)$.

——**THEOREM** 6.6.5. If in an annular region S with center z_0 a given function $f(z)$ permits an expansion of the form

$$f(z) = \sum_{n=-\infty}^{\infty} c_n(z - z_0)^n, \tag{6.6.8}$$

then the coefficients of this expansion are given by the formula

$$c_n = \frac{1}{2\pi i} \int_\Gamma \frac{f(\zeta) \, d\zeta}{(\zeta - z_0)^{n+1}}, \qquad n = 0, \pm 1, \pm 2, \cdots, \tag{6.6.9}$$

where Γ is a simple closed contour lying in S and containing z_0 in its interior and the integral along Γ is taken in the positive direction. That is, the expansion is the Laurent series of $f(z)$ in powers of $(z - z_0)$ for the region S.

Proof. Let the region S be bounded by two concentric circles C_1 and C_2 having center at z_0 and radii r_1 and r_2 respectively, $r_1 < r_2$. Let Γ be a simple closed contour which we shall take to be a circle with center at z_0 and radius $r, r_1 < r < r_2$. Then Γ lies in the interior of S. Denote by ζ the variable along Γ. By hypothesis the given series converges along Γ, and we have

$$f(\zeta) = \sum_{k=-\infty}^{\infty} c_k(\zeta - z_0)^k.$$

Multiplying this expression by $(\zeta - z_0)^{-n-1}$, $n = 0, \pm 1, \pm 2, \cdots$, we obtain upon integration [see Exercise 6.8.19(b)]

$$\int_\Gamma \frac{f(\zeta)}{(\zeta - z_0)^{n+1}}\, d\zeta = \sum_{k=-\infty}^{n-1} c_k \int_\Gamma (\zeta - z_0)^{k-n-1}\, d\zeta + c_n \int_\Gamma \frac{d\zeta}{\zeta - z_0}$$

$$+ \sum_{k=n+1}^{\infty} c_k \int_\Gamma (\zeta - z_0)^{k-n-1}\, d\zeta. \qquad (6.6.10)$$

By Example 5.2.2 we have

$$\int_\Gamma (\zeta - z_0)^k\, d\zeta = \begin{cases} 2\pi i, & k = -1, \\ 0, & k \neq -1. \end{cases}$$

Thus, all terms in the right-hand side of (6.6.10) vanish except one, namely,

$$c_n \int_\Gamma \frac{d\zeta}{\zeta - z_0} = 2\pi i c_n.$$

Hence

$$\int_\Gamma \frac{f(\zeta)\, d\zeta}{(\zeta - z_0)^{n+1}} = 2\pi i c_n.$$

Consequently

$$c_n = \frac{1}{2\pi i} \int_\Gamma \frac{f(\zeta)\, d\zeta}{(\zeta - z_0)^{n+1}}, \qquad n = 0, \pm 1, \pm 2, \cdots,$$

and the theorem is established.

Note that Theorem 6.6.5 is also valid when the region S is of the form $r_1 < |z - z_0| < r_2$, where $r_1 = 0$ or $r_2 = \infty$. An immediate consequence of Theorem 6.6.4 is

——THEOREM 6.6.6.   If two power series

$$\sum_{n=0}^{\infty} a_n(z - z_0)^n \quad \text{and} \quad \sum_{n=0}^{\infty} b_n(z - z_0)^n,$$

both converge to the same function $f(z)$ in some neighborhood $N: |z - z_0| < R$ of z_0, then the series are identical. That is,

$$a_n = b_n, \qquad n = 0, 1, 2, \cdots.$$

Proof.   By hypothesis we have

$$f(z) = \sum_{n=0}^{\infty} a_n(z - z_0)^n = \sum_{n=0}^{\infty} b_n(z - z_0)^n, \qquad |z - z_0| < R.$$

From (6.6.7) we obtain

$$a_n = b_n = \frac{f^{(n)}(z_0)}{n!}, \qquad n = 0, 1, 2, \cdots.$$

Thus the coefficients are equal for every value of n.

Remark 6.6.1.   From the above theorem we see that if a power series $\sum_{n=0}^{\infty} c_n(z - z_0)^n$ converges to zero at every point in some neighborhood of the point z_0, then $c_n = 0$, $n = 0, 1, 2, \cdots$.

6.7.   THE ALGEBRA OF POWER SERIES. By utilizing Theorems 2.7.2 and 2.7.8, one may establish the following

——**THEOREM** 6.7.1.   If two power series

$$f(z) = \sum_{n=0}^{\infty} a_n(z - z_0)^n, \qquad g(z) = \sum_{n=0}^{\infty} b_n(z - z_0)^n$$

have nonzero convergence radii r and R, $r \leqq R$, then

$$f(z) \pm g(z) = \sum_{n=0}^{\infty} (a_n \pm b_n)(z - z_0)^n, \qquad |z - z_0| < r, \qquad (6.7.1)$$

$$f(z)\,g(z) = \sum_{n=0}^{\infty} c_n(z - z_0)^n, \qquad |z - z_0| < r, \qquad (6.7.2)$$

where

$$c_n = \sum_{k=0}^{n} a_k b_{n-k} \qquad (n = 0, 1, 2, \cdots).$$

We shall now establish the following

——**THEOREM** 6.7.2.   If two power series

$$f(z) = \sum_{n=0}^{\infty} a_n(z - z_0)^n, \qquad g(z) = \sum_{n=0}^{\infty} b_n(z - z_0)^n \qquad (6.7.4)$$

have nonzero radii of convergence r and R, respectively, and if $g(z_0) \neq 0$, then there exists a power series $\sum_{n=0}^{\infty} c_n(z - z_0)^n$ and a number $\sigma > 0$ such that

$$\frac{f(z)}{g(z)} = \sum_{n=0}^{\infty} c_n(z - z_0)^n, \qquad |z - z_0| < \sigma. \qquad (6.7.5)$$

The coefficients c_n satisfy the equations

$$a_n = c_0 b_n + c_1 b_{n-1} + c_2 b_{n-2} + \cdots + c_{n-1} b_1 + c_n b_0. \qquad (6.7.6)$$

Proof. Since $g(z)$ is continuous at $z = z_0$ and $g(z_0) \neq 0$, we see that $g(z) \neq 0$ in a neighborhood of z_0. It follows from Theorem 3.5.1 that

$$h(z) = \frac{f(z)}{g(z)}$$

is analytic in a neighborhood $|z - z_0| < \sigma$ of z_0. Hence

$$h(z) = \sum_{n=0}^{\infty} c_n (z - z_0)^n, \qquad |z - z_0| < \sigma.$$

Since $f(z) = h(z)\, g(z)$, we have

$$\sum_{n=0}^{\infty} a_n (z - z_0)^n = \sum_{n=0}^{\infty} c_n (z - z_0)^n \sum_{n=0}^{\infty} b_n (z - z_0)^n.$$

Since by Theorem 6.6.4 the coefficients of the expansion of $f(z)$ in powers of $(z - z_0)$ are unique, we obtain from Theorem 6.7.1

$$a_n = \sum_{k=0}^{n} c_k b_{n-k} \qquad (n = 0, 1, 2, \cdots),$$

thus establishing the theorem.

Let ρ be the minimum distance between z_0 and the zeros of $g(z)$. If $g(z)$ has no zeros, let $\rho = \infty$. Note that in (6.7.5) we may take $\sigma = \min\,(\rho, r, R)$. Letting τ be the radius of convergence of the power series in (6.7.5), we have $\tau \geqq \min\,(\rho, r, R)$.

Remark 6.7.1.   Since $g(z_0) \neq 0$, it follows that $b_0 \neq 0$ in (6.7.4). Thus, from (6.7.6) we obtain

$$c_n = \frac{a_n - c_0 b_n - c_1 b_{n-1} - \cdots - c_{n-1} b_1}{b_0}. \qquad (6.7.7)$$

This equation enables us to compute c_n when $c_0, c_1, \cdots, c_{n-1}$ have already been computed.

At times all that is necessary in a given problem is to find the first few terms of the series (6.7.5). Instead of using (6.7.7) to compute the first few c_n's, it is easier at times to compute them by dividing $g(z)$ into $f(z)$ as in the case of division of two polynomials.*

---

* For justification of this process see L. Ahlfors, *Complex Analysis*, p. 145. New York: McGraw-Hill, 1953.

From the above results, we see that power series can be added, subtracted, multiplied, and divided giving series which correspond, respectively, to the sum, difference, product, and quotient of the sum-functions of the original series.

EXAMPLE 6.7.1.   Given the series expansion

$$\sin z = \sum_{n=1}^{\infty} (-1)^{n+1} \frac{z^{2n-1}}{(2n-1)!}, \qquad |z| < \infty,$$

let us find the first three nonzero terms of the Laurent series expansion of $\csc z$ about the point $z = 0$.

Solution.   From Theorem 4.2.2, $\sin z = 0$ only for $z = n\pi$, $n = 0, \pm 1, \pm 2, \cdots$. Hence $\csc z = 1/\sin z$ is analytic in the region $0 < |z| < \pi$.

$$\csc z = \frac{1}{\sin z} = \frac{1}{z}\left[\frac{1}{1 - \frac{z^2}{3!} + \frac{z^4}{5!} - \frac{z^6}{7!} + \cdots}\right] = \frac{1}{z}\frac{1}{g(z)},$$

where

$$g(z) = 1 - \frac{z^2}{3!} + \frac{z^4}{5!} - \frac{z^6}{7!} + \cdots. \qquad (6.7.8)$$

Method 1.   Apply (6.7.7) to find the coefficients c_n in the series expansion of

$$\frac{f(z)}{g(z)} = \frac{1}{g(z)} = \sum_{n=0}^{\infty} c_n z^n.$$

Note from (6.7.8) that $b_0 = 1$, $b_1 = 0$, $b_2 = -1/3!$, $b_3 = 0$, $b_4 = 1/5!$, $b_5 = 0$, $b_6 = -1/7!$, $\cdots$. Also, since $f(z) = 1$, we have $a_0 = 1$, $a_1 = a_2 = a_3 = \cdots = 0$. We find:

$$n = 0, \qquad c_0 = \frac{a_0}{b_0} = 1.$$

$$n = 1, \qquad c_1 = \frac{a_1 - c_0 b_1}{b_0} = 0.$$

$$n = 2, \qquad c_2 = \frac{a_2 - c_0 b_2 - c_1 b_1}{b_0} = \frac{1}{6}.$$

$$n = 3, \qquad c_3 = \frac{a_3 - c_0 b_3 - c_1 b_2 - c_2 b_1}{b_0} = 0.$$

$$n = 4, \qquad c_4 = \frac{a_4 - c_0 b_4 - c_1 b_3 - c_2 b_2 - c_3 b_1}{b_0} = \frac{7}{360}.$$

Thus

$$\frac{1}{g(z)} = 1 + \frac{1}{6} z^2 + \frac{7}{360} z^4 + \cdots.$$

Hence

$$\csc z = \frac{1}{z} \cdot \frac{1}{g(z)} = \frac{1}{z} + \frac{1}{6} z + \frac{7}{360} z^3 + \cdots, \qquad 0 < |z| < \pi.$$

Method 2. By long division we have

$$\csc z = \frac{1}{\sin z} = \frac{1}{z - \dfrac{z^3}{3!} + \dfrac{z^5}{5!} - \dfrac{z^7}{7!} + \cdots} = \frac{1}{z} + \frac{1}{3!} z + \left(\frac{1}{3!3!} - \frac{1}{5!}\right) z^3 + \cdots$$

$$= \frac{1}{z} + \frac{1}{6} z + \frac{7}{360} z^3 + \cdots, \qquad 0 < |z| < \pi.$$

6.8. SEQUENCES AND SERIES OF FUNCTIONS. If the functions $f_1(z), f_2(z), \cdots, f_n(z), \cdots$ are all defined on a set R, they form a *sequence of functions in R*. Remarks similar to those given in Chapter 2 hold for infinite series whose terms are functions. For example, the symbol

$$f_1(z) + f_2(z) + \cdots + f_n(z) + \cdots, \tag{6.8.1}$$

denotes an *infinite series of complex functions*. An equivalent symbol is

$$\sum_{n=1}^{\infty} f_n(z). \tag{6.8.2}$$

The series will also at times be denoted by $S(z)$, that is, $S(z) \equiv \sum_{n=1}^{\infty} f_n(z)$. The nth partial sum of the series is again a function of z and is denoted by

$$S_n(z) = f_1(z) + f_2(z) + \cdots + f_n(z). \tag{6.8.3}$$

The series $\sum_{n=1}^{\infty} f_n(z)$ may be defined as the pair of sequences

$$\{f_n(z)\} \text{ and } \{S_n(z)\}.$$

Convergence of the series is by definition equivalent to convergence of the sequence of partial sums; if $S_n(z)$ converges to $f(z)$ for a set of values of z, then we write

$$\sum_{n=1}^{\infty} f_n(z) = f(z) \tag{6.8.4}$$

for this set of values of z.

Let the functions $f_n(z)$, $n = 1, 2, \cdots$ be defined in a domain D and let R be a set of points contained in D. Paralleling Definition 6.3.1, we shall say that the series $\sum_{n=1}^{\infty} f_n(z)$ *converges uniformly in R to a function* $f(z)$ if, for each $\epsilon > 0$, there exists a positive integer $M(\epsilon)$, depending only on ϵ, such that for all points z in R

$$\left| \sum_{\mu=1}^{n} f_\mu(z) - f(z) \right| < \epsilon \tag{6.8.5}$$

for $n \geqq M(\epsilon)$.

Definition 6.8.1. The series $S(z) \equiv \sum_{n=1}^{\infty} f_n(z)$ is said to *converge almost uniformly* within a domain D, if for every z_0 in D there exists a neighborhood $N(z_0)$ of z_0 contained in D such that $S(z)$ converges uniformly in $N(z_0)$.

Remark 6.8.1. Using the Heine-Borel Theorem 2.5.1, one may show that $S(z)$ is almost uniformly convergent within D if, and only if, $S(z)$ converges uniformly in every closed and bounded set contained in D. (See Exercise 6.8.22.) We shall need the following two lemmas. (See also Definition 6.8.2.)

LEMMA 6.8.1. Let $\{f_n(z)\}$ be a sequence of functions defined and continuous in a domain D and converging almost uniformly to $f(z)$ in D. Then $f(z)$ is continuous in D.

Proof. Let z_0 be any point in D. By Definition 6.8.2, $f_n(z)$ converges uniformly to $f(z)$ in the interior of a circle C contained in D and containing z_0. Consequently, $f(z)$ is continuous in the interior of C (see Exercise 6.8.21) and, in particular, $f(z)$ is continuous at z_0. Since z_0 is any point in D, it follows that $f(z)$ is continuous in D.

LEMMA 6.8.2. Let $f(\zeta)$ be a continuous function defined on a contour C, and let

$$g(z) = \int_C \frac{f(\zeta)\, d\zeta}{\zeta - z}.$$

Then $g(z)$ is analytic at all points z not lying on C.

To establish this result we need only to verify that

$$\lim_{h \to 0} \frac{g(z+h) - g(z)}{h}$$

exists for z not on C, and for this result, use the method given in Section 5.13.

We shall now establish the following theorem due to Weierstrass.

——**THEOREM** 6.8.1. Suppose that the functions $f_n(z)$ $(n = 1, 2, \cdots)$ are analytic in a domain D, and suppose that the series $\sum_{n=1}^{\infty} f_n(z)$ converges almost uniformly in D to the function $f(z)$. Then

$f(z)$ is analytic in D;   (6.8.6)

the series $\displaystyle\sum_{n=1}^{\infty} f_n'(z)$ is almost uniformly convergent within D; (6.8.7)

$f'(z) = \displaystyle\sum_{n=1}^{\infty} f_n'(z)$ in D.   (6.8.8)

Proof. Put $g_n(z) = \sum_{\mu=1}^{n} f_\mu(z)$. Clearly $g_n(z)$ is analytic within D. Let C and C_1 be two concentric circles interior to D with centers at z_0 and radii r

and r_1 respectively, $r > r_1$, as shown in Fig. 6.8.1. Since $g_n(z)$ converges almost uniformly in D to $f(z)$, it follows by Remark 6.8.1 that for an arbitrary $\epsilon > 0$, there exists an integer $N(\epsilon)$ such that for $n \geq N(\epsilon)$

$$| f(\zeta) - g_n(\zeta) | \leq \epsilon, \tag{6.8.9}$$

for all ζ on the boundary of C.

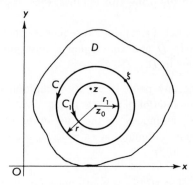

FIG. 6.8.1

Let z be a point interior to C_1. Utilizing Cauchy's formula (5.12.1) we have

$$g_n(z) = \frac{1}{2\pi i} \int_C \frac{g_n(\zeta)\, d\zeta}{\zeta - z}. \tag{6.8.10}$$

Put

$$h(z) = \frac{1}{2\pi i} \int_C \frac{f(\zeta)\, d\zeta}{\zeta - z}. \tag{6.8.11}$$

The existence of this integral for z interior to C is assured by the continuity of $f(\zeta)$. (See Lemma 6.8.1.) By Lemma 6.8.2, $h(z)$ is analytic for z interior to C. For z interior to C_1 we have $| \zeta - z | > r - r_1$. Now using (6.8.11), (6.8.10) and (6.8.9), we obtain for $n \geq N(\epsilon)$

$$| h(z) - g_n(z) | \leq \frac{1}{2\pi} \int_C \frac{| f(\zeta) - g_n(\zeta) |}{| \zeta - z |} | d\zeta |$$

$$< \frac{\epsilon}{2\pi(r - r_1)} \int_C | d\zeta | = \frac{r\epsilon}{(r - r_1)}. \tag{6.8.12}$$

Now $r\epsilon/(r - r_1) \to 0$ as $\epsilon \to 0$. Hence

$$f(z) = \sum_{\mu=1}^{\infty} f_\mu(z) = \lim_{n \to \infty} g_n(z) = h(z). \tag{6.8.13}$$

Thus, $f(z)$ is analytic in a neighborhood of z_0. Since z_0 is any point in D, it follows that $f(z)$ is analytic in D.

Since $g_n(z)$ and $f(z)$ are both analytic in D, using formula (5.13.3) we obtain

$$g'_n(z) = \frac{1}{2\pi i} \int_C \frac{g_n(\zeta)\, d\zeta}{(\zeta - z)^2} \qquad (6.8.14)$$

and

$$f'(z) = \frac{1}{2\pi i} \int_C \frac{f(\zeta)\, d\zeta}{(\zeta - z)^2}. \qquad (6.8.15)$$

Then for all ζ on the boundary of C and for all z interior to C_1, we obtain from (6.8.15), (6.8.14) and (6.8.9) that for $n \geqq N(\epsilon)$

$$|f'(z) - g'_n(z)| \leqq \frac{1}{2\pi} \int_C \frac{|f(\zeta) - g_n(\zeta)|\,|\,d\zeta\,|}{|\,\zeta - z\,|^2}$$

$$< \frac{\epsilon}{2\pi(r - r_1)^2} \int_C |\,d\zeta\,| = \frac{\epsilon r}{(r - r_1)^2}. \qquad (6.8.16)$$

Since ϵ may be taken as small as we please, $\epsilon r/(r - r_1)^2$ can also be made arbitrarily small and consequently

$$\lim_{n \to \infty} g'_n(z) = f'(z)$$

uniformly in the interior of the circle C with center at z_0. Since z_0 is any point in D, $g'_n(z)$ converges to $f'(z)$ almost uniformly within D, in accordance with Definition 6.8.1. This completes the proof of the theorem.

Remark 6.8.2.   Note that Theorem 6.8.2 is a generalization of Theorems 6.6.2 and 6.6.3.

The following definition corresponds to a similar one relating to a series of functions. A sequence of functions $\{f_n(z)\}$ defined on a set R is said to *converge uniformly to a function* $f(z)$ on R if, for every $\epsilon > 0$, there exists a positive integer $N(\epsilon)$, depending only on ϵ, such that for all points z in R

$$|f_n(z) - f(z)| < \epsilon \qquad (6.8.17)$$

for $n \geqq N(\epsilon)$.

Definition 6.8.2.   A sequence of functions $\{f_n(z)\}$ is said to *converge almost uniformly* within a domain D to a function $f(z)$ if for every z_0 in D, there exists a neighborhood $N(z_0)$ of z_0 contained in D such that the sequence $\{f_n(z)\}$ converges uniformly to $f(z)$ in $N(z_0)$.

Since the terms of a sequence $\{f_n(z)\}$ can be interpreted as partial sums of the series:

$$f_1 + (f_2 - f_1) + (f_3 - f_2) + \cdots + (f_n - f_{n-1}) + \cdots,$$

using Theorem 6.8.1, we have the following

——**THEOREM** 6.8.2. If a sequence $\{f_n(z)\}$ of analytic functions defined in a domain D converges almost uniformly within D to a function $f(z)$, then

$f(z)$ is analytic in D; (6.8.18)

the sequence $\{f_n'(z)\}$ converges almost uniformly within D; (6.8.19)

$$\lim_{n\to\infty} f_n'(z) = f'(z) \text{ in } D. \tag{6.8.20}$$

EXERCISES 6.8

1. Find the Laurent series expansions which represent the following functions in the indicated regions:

(a) $\dfrac{1}{z^4(1-z)}$,   (1) $0 < |z| < 1$,   (2) $|z| > 1$;

(b) $\dfrac{\cosh z}{z^4}$, $|z| > 0$;   (c) $e^{(1-z)^{-1}}$, $|z-1| > 0$;

(d) $\sqrt{\dfrac{\beta z}{(z-\alpha)(\beta-z)}}$, $|\alpha| < |z| < |\beta|$.

2. Obtain the first four nonzero terms of the Laurent series expansions of the following functions in the indicated regions:

(a) $\dfrac{e^z}{z^4(1-z^2)}$, $0 < |z| < 1$;

(b) $\sec z$, $\dfrac{\pi}{2} < |z| < \dfrac{3}{2}\pi$;

(c) $\cot z$, $0 < |z| < \pi$.

3. Obtain the first four nonzero terms of the Maclaurin series expansion of

(a) $e^{2z} \sin 3z$;   (b) $\dfrac{\cosh 2z}{e^z}$.

4. Show that if we define Arc tan z as the value obtained by setting $k = 0$ in (4.6.14) of Theorem 4.6.3, then for $|z| < 1$ we have

(a) Arc tan $z = \displaystyle\sum_{n=1}^{\infty} \dfrac{(-1)^{n-1}}{2n-1} z^{2n-1}$,

(b) $(\text{Arc tan } z)^2 = \displaystyle\sum_{n=1}^{\infty} \dfrac{(-1)^{n-1}}{n} J_{2n-1} z^{2n}$,

where $J_{2n-1} = 1 + \dfrac{1}{3} + \dfrac{1}{5} + \cdots + \dfrac{1}{2n-1}$.

5. If $|z| < 1$, show that

$$[\text{Log } (z + 1)]^2 = 2 \sum_{n=1}^{\infty} \frac{(-1)^{n-1}}{n+1} H_n z^{n+1},$$

where

$$H_n = 1 + \frac{1}{2} + \frac{1}{3} + \cdots + \frac{1}{n}.$$

6. Show that if $z \neq 0$, then

$$e^{[z+(a^3/2z^2)]} = \sum_{n=-\infty}^{\infty} \alpha_n z^n,$$

where

$$\alpha_n = \frac{e^{-(1/2)a}}{2\pi a^n} \int_0^{2\pi} e^{a(\cos\theta + \cos^2\theta)} \cos [a \sin \theta(1 - \cos \theta) - n\theta] \, d\theta.$$

7. Show that the Laurent series expansion of $z \coth z$ about the origin is of the form $\sum_{n=0}^{\infty} c_n z^{2n}$.

8. Show that the Laurent series expansion of $z \cot z$ about the origin is given by $\sum_{n=0}^{\infty} (-1)^n c_n z^{2n}$, where the c_n are as in Exercise 7 above.

9. (a) Show that the Laurent series expansion of $f(z) = 1/(e^z - 1)$ about the origin is of the form

$$\sum_{n=0}^{\infty} \frac{B_n}{n!} z^{n-1}.$$

The numbers B_n are called *Bernouilli's numbers*. Show that

$$B_0 = 1, \; B_1 = -\frac{1}{2}, \; B_2 = \frac{1}{6}, \; B_3 = 0, \; B_4 = -\frac{1}{30}, \; B_6 = \frac{1}{42}, \; B_8 = -\frac{1}{30},$$

and $B_{10} = \frac{5}{66}$. Write the above expression as

$$\frac{z}{e^z - 1} + \frac{z}{2} = 1 + \sum_{n=2}^{\infty} \frac{B_n}{n!} z^n.$$

Utilize (4.3.6) and (4.3.1) to deduce that

(b) $$\frac{z}{2} \coth \frac{z}{2} = \frac{z}{e^z - 1} + \frac{z}{2}.$$

Observe that $(z/2) \coth (z/2)$ is an even function. From this fact, show that

(c) $B_3 = B_5 = B_7 = \cdots = B_{2k+1} = 0, \qquad k = 1, 2, 3, \cdots.$

Now show that

(d) $$z \coth z = \sum_{n=0}^{\infty} \frac{B_{2n}}{(2n)!} (2z)^{2n}.$$

10. Show that*

$$z \cot z = \sum_{n=0}^{\infty} (-1)^n \frac{B_{2n}}{(2n)!} (2z)^{2n}.$$

11. Show that

$$\tan z = \sum_{n=1}^{\infty} (-1)^{n-1} \frac{B_{2n}}{(2n)!} (2^{2n} - 1) 2^{2n} z^{2n-1}.$$

12. Show that

$$\frac{z}{\sin z} = \sum_{n=0}^{\infty} (-1)^{n-1} \frac{B_{2n}}{(2n)!} 2(2^{2n-1} - 1) z^{2n}.$$

13. Show that

$$\csc z = \sum_{n=0}^{\infty} (-1)^{n-1} \frac{B_{2n}}{(2n)!} 2(2^{2n-1} - 1) z^{2n-1}.$$

14. Show that

$$\text{Log} \sin z = \text{Log } z + \sum_{n=1}^{\infty} (-1)^n \frac{B_{2n}}{2n(2n)!} (2z)^{2n}.$$

15. Show that

$$\text{Log} \cos z = - \sum_{n=1}^{\infty} (-1)^{n-1} \frac{B_{2n}}{2n(2n)!} (2^{2n} - 1) 2^{2n} z^{2n}.$$

16. Show that

$$\text{Log} \tan z = \text{Log } z + \sum_{n=1}^{\infty} (-1)^{n-1} \frac{B_{2n}}{n(2n)!} (2^{2n-1} - 1) 2^{2n} z^{2n}.$$

17. Show that

$$\text{Log} \sinh z = \text{Log } z + \sum_{n=1}^{\infty} \frac{B_{2n}}{2n(2n)!} (2z)^{2n}.$$

18. (a) Show that the Laurent series expansion of sech z about the origin is of the form

$$\sum_{n=0}^{\infty} \frac{E_n}{n!} z^n.$$

The numbers E_n are called *Euler's numbers*. Show that

$$E_0 = 1, \quad E_2 = -1, \quad E_4 = 5, \quad E_6 = -61 \quad \text{and} \quad E_8 = 1385.$$

---

* In Exercises 10 to 17, the representations hold in a neighborhood of the origin, except possibly at $z = 0$.

Observe that sech z is an even function. Using this fact show that

(b) $E_1 = E_3 = E_5 = \cdots = E_{2k-1} = 0, \qquad k = 1, 2, \cdots$.

Consequently

(c) $$\operatorname{sech} z = \sum_{n=0}^{\infty} \frac{E_{2n}}{(2n)!} z^{2n}.$$

(d) Show that

$$\sec z = \sum_{n=0}^{\infty} (-1)^n \frac{E_{2n}}{(2n)!} z^{2n}.$$

19. Let

$$\sum_{n=-\infty}^{\infty} a_n (z - z_0)^n = \sum_{n=0}^{\infty} a_n (z - z_0)^n + \sum_{n=-1}^{-\infty} a_n (z - z_0)^n$$

converge to the function $f(z)$ in the annular region S:

$$r_1 < |z - z_0| < r_2.$$

(a) Show that $\sum_{n=-\infty}^{\infty} a_n (z - z_0)^n$ converges absolutely and uniformly to $f(z)$ in every annular region

$$S': R_1 < |z - z_0| < R_2, \qquad r_1 < R_1 \le |z - z_0| \le R_2 < r_2,$$

contained in S.

(b) Show that if Γ is a contour in the interior of S and $h(z)$ is a continuous function on Γ, then

$$\int_\Gamma f(z) h(z) \, dz = \sum_{n=-\infty}^{\infty} a_n \int_\Gamma (z - z_0)^n h(z) \, dz,$$

and in particular

$$\int_\Gamma f(z) \, dz = \int_\Gamma \left[\sum_{n=-\infty}^{\infty} a_n (z - z_0)^n \right] dz = \sum_{n=-\infty}^{\infty} \int_\Gamma a_n (z - z_0)^n \, dz.$$

20. Suppose that the series $\sum_{k=0}^{\infty} a_k z^k$ has a radius of convergence $\rho > 0$. Prove that the average of $f_n(z) = (1/z^n) \sum_{k=0}^{\infty} a_k z^k$ over the circle $|z| = r$, $r < \rho$, is a_n, $n = 0, 1, 2, \cdots$.

21. Show that the limit of a uniformly convergent sequence of continuous functions is continuous.

22. Show that a sequence of functions $\{f_n(z)\}$ converges almost uniformly within a domain D if, and only if, it converges uniformly in every closed bounded set contained in D.

7

The Calculus of Residues

7.1. SINGULARITIES AND ZEROS. A point z_0 is called a *singular point* or a *singularity* of the function $f(z)$, if $f(z)$ is not analytic at z_0, but every neighborhood of z_0 contains at least one point at which $f(z)$ is analytic. Recall (see Definition 3.6.1) that z_0 is an isolated singular point of $f(z)$, if $f(z)$ is not analytic at z_0, but is analytic in a deleted neighborhood of z_0.

EXAMPLE 7.1.1. The function $f(z) = 1/(z - 1)$ is analytic except at the point $z = 1$. Thus $z = 1$ is an isolated singular point of $f(z)$.

EXAMPLE 7.1.2. The function $f(z) = 1/[\sin(1/z)]$ has an infinite number of isolated singular points given by (4.2.4), namely, $z = 1/k\pi$, $k = \pm 1, \pm 2, \pm 3, \cdots$. The point $z = 0$ is a singular point of $f(z)$ but is not an isolated singular point, since every neighborhood of $z = 0$ contains an infinite number of other singular points of the function.

Suppose that z_0 is an isolated singular point of a function $f(z)$. In this case the Laurent expansion of $f(z)$ converges for $0 < |z - z_0| < r$, where r is the distance from z_0 to the nearest singular point of $f(z)$ other than z_0 itself. (If z_0 is the only singularity, then $r = \infty$.) Utilizing (6.5.1) we may write $f(z)$ as

$$f(z) = \sum_{n=1}^{\infty} b_n(z - z_0)^{-n} + \sum_{n=0}^{\infty} a_n(z - z_0)^n, \quad 0 < |z - z_0| < r, \qquad (7.1.1)$$

where the coefficients a_n and b_n are given in (6.5.2) and (6.5.3). The series in negative powers of $(z - z_0)$ in (7.1.1) is called the *principal part* of $f(z)$ at the isolated singular point z_0. It is the part that will show the character of the singularity of $f(z)$ at z_0.

We shall now distinguish between three types of isolated singular points.

CASE 1. Suppose that $b_n = 0$, $n = 1, 2, \cdots$, in (7.1.1). We may then write (7.1.1) as

$$f(z) = \sum_{n=0}^{\infty} a_n(z - z_0)^n, \quad z \neq z_0. \qquad (7.1.2)$$

230

If we define (or possibly redefine) $f(z)$ at z_0 to be equal to $a_0 = \lim_{z \to z_0} f(z)$, then $f(z)$ becomes analytic at $z = z_0$. A singularity of this type is said to be a *removable singularity*, and ordinarily is considered removed.

EXAMPLE 7.1.3. Suppose that

$$f(z) = \sum_{n=0}^{\infty} \frac{z^n}{n!}, \qquad z \neq 0,$$

$$f(0) = 2, \qquad z = 0.$$

We can make $f(z)$ analytic at $z = 0$ by redefining $f(0)$:

$$f(0) = \lim_{z \to 0} \sum_{n=0}^{\infty} \frac{z^n}{n!} = 1.$$

CASE 2. Suppose that all but a finite number of the b_n vanish in (7.1.1). In this case z_0 is said to be a *pole* of $f(z)$. Moreover, if b_m, $m \geq 1$, is the last nonzero coefficient in (7.1.1), that is, $b_n = 0$ for $n > m$, then

$$f(z) = \frac{b_m}{(z - z_0)^m} + \frac{b_{m-1}}{(z - z_0)^{m-1}} + \cdots + \frac{b_2}{(z - z_0)^2}$$

$$+ \frac{b_1}{z - z_0} + \sum_{n=0}^{\infty} a_n (z - z_0)^n, \qquad (7.1.3)$$

and $z = z_0$ is said to be a *pole of order* (or *multiplicity*) m of $f(z)$. In particular, when $m = 1$, $z = z_0$ is said to be a *simple pole* of $f(z)$. Observe that z_0 is an isolated singularity.

EXAMPLE 7.1.4. The function

$$f(z) = \frac{\sinh z}{z^6} = \frac{1}{z^5} + \frac{1}{3!} \cdot \frac{1}{z^3} + \frac{1}{5!} \cdot \frac{1}{z} + \frac{1}{7!} z + \cdots, \qquad |z| > 0,$$

has a pole of order 5 at $z = 0$.

CASE 3. Suppose that an infinite number of the b_n do not vanish in (7.1.1). In this case $z = z_0$ is said to be an *essential singular point* of $f(z)$ or an *essential singularity* of $f(z)$. The term essential singularity is also used to denote any nonisolated singular point.

EXAMPLE 7.1.5. The function

$$f(z) = e^{1/z^2} = 1 + \frac{1}{z^2} + \frac{1}{2!} \cdot \frac{1}{z^4} + \frac{1}{3!} \cdot \frac{1}{z^6} + \cdots + \frac{1}{n!} \cdot \frac{1}{z^{2n}} + \cdots, \qquad |z| > 0,$$

has an isolated essential singularity at $z = 0$.

Suppose that a function $f(z)$ has a pole of order m at $z = z_0$, that is, $b_m \neq 0$ and $b_n = 0$ for $n > m$ in (7.1.3). Let

$$\lambda(z) = (z - z_0)^m f(z), \qquad z \neq z_0. \tag{7.1.4}$$

Multiplying both members of (7.1.3) by $(z - z_0)^m$, we obtain

$$\lambda(z) = b_m + b_{m-1}(z - z_0) + \cdots + b_1(z - z_0)^{m-1}$$

$$+ \sum_{n=0}^{\infty} a_n(z - z_0)^{n+m}, \qquad z \neq z_0. \tag{7.1.5}$$

Thus $\lambda(z)$ has a removable singularity at $z = z_0$. Also

$$\lim_{z \to z_0} \lambda(z) = \lim_{z \to z_0} (z - z_0)^m f(z) = b_m \neq 0. \tag{7.1.6}$$

Conversely, we shall now show that if $\lambda(z) = (z - z_0)^m f(z)$ has a removable singularity at $z = z_0$, and $\lim_{z \to z_0} \lambda(z) = c_0 \neq 0$, then $f(z)$ has a pole of order m at $z = z_0$. Since $\lambda(z)$ has a removable singularity at $z = z_0$, it can be expanded in a Laurent expansion about $z = z_0$ with the coefficients of $(z - z_0)^n$, $n < 0$, all vanishing. Thus we have

$$(z - z_0)^m f(z) = \lambda(z) = \sum_{n=0}^{\infty} c_n(z - z_0)^n. \tag{7.1.7}$$

Dividing both sides of (7.1.7) by $(z - z_0)^m$, and denoting c_n by b_{m-n} for $n < m$, and c_n by a_{n-m} for $n \geq m$, we obtain

$$f(z) = \frac{\lambda(z)}{(z - z_0)^m} = \frac{b_m}{(z - z_0)^m} + \frac{b_{m-1}}{(z - z_0)^{m-1}} + \cdots + \frac{b_1}{(z - z_0)}$$

$$+ \sum_{n=0}^{\infty} a_n(z - z_0)^n. \tag{7.1.8}$$

Since $b_m = c_0 = \lim_{z \to z_0} \lambda(z) \neq 0$, we see that $f(z)$ has a pole of order m at $z = z_0$.

Let us summarize the above results by the following

——**THEOREM** 7.1.1.   Suppose that the function $f(z)$ is analytic in a neighborhood of a point $z = z_0$ except possibly at z_0. Then $f(z)$ has a pole of order m, where m is a positive integer, if, and only if, the function

$$\lambda(z) = (z - z_0)^m f(z) \tag{7.1.4}$$

has a removable singularity at $z = z_0$ and

$$\lim_{z \to z_0} \lambda(z) \neq 0. \tag{7.1.6}$$

Observe in the above theorem that the condition $\lim_{z \to z_0} \lambda(z)$ exists and is different from zero is equivalent to the condition that m is the *least* positive integer such that $(z - z_0)^m f(z)$ has a removable singularity at $z = z_0$.

EXAMPLE 7.1.6. The function

$$f(z) = \frac{z^2 + 5}{(z + 2i)(z - 1)^3}$$

has a simple pole at $z = -2i$ and a pole of order three at $z = 1$. For, the functions

$$\lambda_1(z) \equiv (z + 2i) f(z) = \frac{z^2 + 5}{(z - 1)^3}, \qquad z \neq -2i,$$

$$\lambda_2(z) \equiv (z - 1)^3 f(z) = \frac{z^2 + 5}{z + 2i}, \qquad z \neq 1$$

have removable singularities at $z = -2i$ and $z = 1$, respectively. Moreover,

$$\lim_{z \to -2i} \lambda_1(z) = \frac{1}{(-2i - 1)^3} \neq 0, \qquad \lim_{z \to 1} \lambda_2(z) = \frac{6}{(1 + 2i)} \neq 0.$$

If $f(z)$ is analytic in a domain D, then by Theorem 6.4.1, its Taylor series expansion about any point z_0 in D is given by

$$f(z) = \sum_{n=0}^{\infty} a_n(z - z_0)^n, \qquad a_n = \frac{f^{(n)}(z_0)}{n!}, \qquad n = 0, 1, 2, \cdots. \qquad (7.1.9)$$

If $a_0 = a_1 = \cdots = a_{m-1} = 0$ and $a_m \neq 0$, then (7.1.9) becomes

$$f(z) = a_m(z - z_0)^m + a_{m+1}(z - z_0)^{m+1} + \cdots = \sum_{n=m}^{\infty} a_n(z - z_0)^n. \qquad (7.1.10)$$

In this case $f(z)$ is said to have a *zero of order* (or *multiplicity*) m at $z = z_0$. A zero of order one is also called a *simple zero*. Note that we speak of poles or zeros of order m only when m is a positive integer.

Remark 7.1.1. It follows from (7.1.10) that z_0 is a zero of order m of a function $f(z)$ if, and only if,

$$f(z) = (z - z_0)^m \lambda(z), \qquad (7.1.11)$$

where $\lambda(z)$ is analytic at z_0 and $\lambda(z_0) \neq 0$.

Also it follows immediately from Theorem 7.1.1 (see also Exercise 7.1.1) that $z = z_0$ is a pole of order m of a function $f(z)$ if, and only if,

$$f(z) = \frac{1}{(z - z_0)^m} \lambda(z), \qquad (7.1.12)$$

where $\lambda(z)$ is analytic at z_0 and $\lambda(z_0) \neq 0$.

We shall now establish the following

——THEOREM 7.1.2. Suppose that the function $f(z)$ is analytic in a neighborhood of a point $z = z_0$ and that the coefficients of the Taylor expansion of $f(z)$ about $z = z_0$ do not all vanish. If $z = z_0$ is a zero of $f(z)$, then there exists a neighborhood of the point $z = z_0$ which contains no other zero of $f(z)$. That is, this zero is isolated.

Proof. Let z_0 be a zero of order m, then by Remark 7.1.1 we have

$$f(z) = (z - z_0)^m \lambda(z),$$

where $\lambda(z)$ is analytic, and therefore continuous in a neighborhood of z_0, and $\lambda(z_0) \neq 0$. Let $|\lambda(z_0)| = 2k$, $k > 0$. Then there exists a neighborhood $|z - z_0| < \delta$ of z_0 in which

$$|\lambda(z) - \lambda(z_0)| < k.$$

Hence

$$|\lambda(z)| = |\lambda(z_0) - [\lambda(z_0) - \lambda(z)]| \geq |\lambda(z_0)| - |\lambda(z) - \lambda(z_0)| > 2k - k = k$$

when $|z - z_0| < \delta$. Thus, $\lambda(z)$ does not vanish in the neighborhood $|z - z_0| < \delta$. Since $(z - z_0)^m \neq 0$ for $z \neq z_0$, we see that $f(z) \neq 0$ for $0 < |z - z_0| < \delta$, thus establishing the theorem.

Remark 7.1.2. If $z = z_0$ is a pole of order m of the function $f(z)$, then $|f(z)| \to \infty$ as $z \to z_0$. For, by (7.1.12) we have

$$f(z) = (z - z_0)^{-m} \lambda(z),$$

where $\lambda(z_0) \neq 0$ and $\lambda(z)$ is analytic, and hence continuous at z_0. Therefore, we can find a neighborhood $N: |z - z_0| < \delta$ of the pole such that $|\lambda(z)| > \frac{1}{2}|\lambda(z_0)|$ for z in N. Thus for z in N, we have

$$|f(z)| = |z - z_0|^{-m} |\lambda(z)| > \frac{1}{2}|\lambda(z_0)| |z - z_0|^{-m}.$$

Hence

$$|f(z)| \to \infty \quad \text{as} \quad z \to z_0.$$

The following important theorem is due to Picard and we state it without proof.

——THEOREM 7.1.3. In every neighborhood of an isolated essential singularity an analytic function takes on every value, with one possible exception, an infinite number of times.

EXAMPLE 7.1.7. The function $f(z) = e^{1/z}$ has an isolated essential singularity at $z = 0$. Let us show that there are an infinite number of z's in every neighborhood of $z = 0$ which satisfy

$$e^{1/z} = i.$$

Solution. Utilizing part (d) of Theorem 4.1.2, we have

$$e^{1/z} = i = e^{i\pi/2}$$

when

$$\frac{1}{z} = i\frac{\pi}{2} + 2k\pi i, \qquad k = 0, \pm 1, \pm 2, \cdots.$$

Thus

$$e^{1/z} = i$$

will be satisfied by an infinite sequence z_k approaching $z = 0$, namely,

$$z_k = \frac{2}{(1 + 4k)\,\pi i}, \qquad k = 0, \pm 1, \pm 2, \cdots.$$

Here, the exceptional value stated in Picard's theorem is zero, since for $z \neq 0$, $e^{1/z} \neq 0$ by (4.1.4).

EXERCISES 7.1

1. Prove that a point z_0 is a pole of order m of a function $f(z)$ if, and only if,

$$f(z) = \frac{1}{(z - z_0)^m}\,\lambda(z),$$

where $\lambda(z)$ is analytic at z_0 and $\lambda(z_0) \neq 0$.

2. Prove that a point z_0 is a pole of order m of a function $f(z)$ if, and only if, z_0 is a zero of order m of $1/f(z)$.

3. Suppose that $f(z)$ is not identically equal to a constant. Show that if $f(z)$ is analytic at z_0 and $f(z_0) = \alpha$, then there exists a neighborhood $N(z_0)$ of z_0 such that if z is in $N(z_0)$ and $z \neq z_0$, then $f(z) \neq \alpha$.

4. Let $f(z) = e^{1/z}$. Show that there are an infinite number of z's in every neighborhood of $z = 0$ which satisfy $e^{1/z} = -1$.

5. Let N and N_0 be deleted neighborhoods of z_0, with $N_0 \subset N$. Let $f(z)$ be analytic in N. Establish the following results.

(a) If $f(z)$ has a removable singularity at z_0, then $f(z)$ is bounded in N_0.

(b) If $f(z)$ has a pole of order m at z_0, then $(z - z_0)^m f(z)$ is bounded but $(z - z_0)^{m-1} f(z)$ is unbounded in N_0.

6. *Casorati-Weierstrass Theorem.* If $f(z)$ has an isolated essential singularity at z_0, then in any neighborhood of z_0 it must come arbitrarily close to any specified number.

7. Let N and N_0 be deleted neighborhoods of z_0, with $N_0 \subset N$. Let $f(z)$ be analytic in N (but not at z_0). Establish the following results.

(a) If $f(z)$ is bounded in N, then z_0 is a removable singularity of $f(z)$.

(b) If for a positive integer m, $(z - z_0)^m f(z)$ is bounded but $(z - z_0)^{m-1} f(z)$ is unbounded in N, then $f(z)$ has a pole of order m at $z = z_0$.

(c) If $(z - z_0)^m f(z)$ is unbounded in N_0 for every integer m, then $z = z_0$ is an essential singularity of $f(z)$.

(d) If $f(z)$ is unbounded in N_0, then z_0 is a nonremovable singularity.

8. Let $f(z)$ be analytic except for nonessential singularities in a bounded and closed set S. Suppose that $f(z)$ is not identically zero in S.

(a) Show that $f(z)$ has only a finite number of singularities in S.

(b) Show that $f(z)$ has at most a finite number of zeros in S.

9. Let $f(z)$ be analytic except for nonessential singularities in the region S consisting of a simple closed contour C and its interior. Suppose that $f(z)$ is not identically zero in S. Show that $f(z)$ has at most a finite number of zeros and poles in S.

10. Suppose that except for poles, $f(z)$ is analytic at each point of a closed unbounded set R. Suppose furthermore that there exist constants $M > 0$, $k > 0$ and p real such that for z in R and $|z| > M$, we have $|f(z)| \leq k|z|^p$. Show that $f(z)$ has only a finite number of poles in R.

11. Suppose that $f(z)$ is analytic in a domain D and that it has zeros of order m_k at the points $z = z_k$, $k = 1, 2, \cdots, n$. Show that there exists a function $g(z)$ analytic in D such that

$$f(z) = (z - z_1)^{m_1} (z - z_2)^{m_2} \cdots (z - z_n)^{m_n} g(z).$$

7.2. RESIDUES. Suppose that z_0 is an isolated singular point of an analytic function $f(z)$. Let R be the distance from z_0 to the nearest singular point of $f(z)$ other than z_0 itself. Let r_1 and r_2 be arbitrary positive numbers such that $0 < r_1 < r_2 < R$. Let S be the annulus bounded by the concentric circles C_1 and C_2 with center at z_0 and radii r_1 and r_2, respectively. Since $f(z)$ is analytic in S and on C_1 and C_2, we have by Theorem 6.5.1 and Remark 6.5.1 for z in S

$$f(z) = \sum_{n=0}^{\infty} a_n(z - z_0)^n + \sum_{n=1}^{\infty} b_n(z - z_0)^{-n}, \qquad (7.2.1)$$

where

$$a_n = \frac{1}{2\pi i} \int_C \frac{f(\zeta)\, d\zeta}{(\zeta - z_0)^{n+1}}, \qquad n = 0, 1, 2, \cdots, \qquad (7.2.2)$$

$$b_n = \frac{1}{2\pi i} \int_C \frac{f(\zeta)\, d\zeta}{(\zeta - z_0)^{-n+1}}, \qquad n = 1, 2, \cdots, \qquad (7.2.3)$$

and C is taken to be a circle with center at z_0 and radius r such that $r_1 < r < r_2$, and the integrals along C are taken in the positive direction. However, since

r_1 and r_2 may be taken arbitrarily close to 0 and R, respectively, we see that (7.2.1) holds for all z such that $0 < |z - z_0| < R$; and the path of integration C in (7.2.2) and (7.2.3) may be any circle with center at z_0 and radius r, $0 < r < R$.

The coefficient

$$b_1 = \frac{1}{2\pi i} \int_C f(\zeta) \, d\zeta \qquad (7.2.4)$$

of (7.2.3) is called the *residue* of $f(z)$ at $z = z_0$, and will be denoted by Res (z_0) or Res $[f(z), z_0]$.

Remark 7.2.1. If a function has a finite number of singular points, then these singular points are isolated. For, each of the singular points is contained in some neighborhood which does not contain the other singular points.

——**THEOREM** 7.2.1 (*Cauchy's residue theorem*). Let C be a simple closed contour, and let $f(z)$ be analytic on C and in the interior of C except at a finite number of singular points $z_1, z_2, \cdots, z_k$ contained in the interior of C. Then

$$\int_C f(z) \, dz = 2\pi i \sum_{n=1}^{k} \text{Res} \, [f(z), z_n], \qquad (7.2.5)$$

where the integral along C is taken in the positive direction.

Proof. Let $C_1, \cdots, C_k$ be k circles having centers at $z_1, \cdots, z_k$ and such that they all lie interior to C and exterior to each other as shown in Fig. 7.2.1. By Theorem 5.10.3, we have

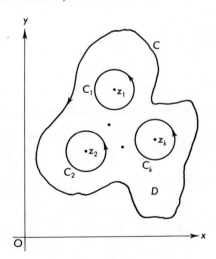

Fig. 7.2.1

$$\int_C f(z) \, dz = \sum_{n=1}^{k} \int_{C_n} f(z) \, dz,$$

where the integrals along C and C_n, $n = 1, \cdots, k$ are taken in the positive direction.

Now, using (7.2.4) we obtain

$$\int_C f(z)\, dz = \sum_{n=1}^{k} \int_{C_n} f(z)\, dz = 2\pi i \sum_{n=1}^{k} \text{Res}\, [f(z), z_n],$$

thus establishing the theorem.

At times, it is easier to find the residue of a function at a given point by using methods other than that given by formula (7.2.4).

EXAMPLE 7.2.1. Let us evaluate

$$\int_C \frac{\sinh z}{z^6}\, dz,$$

where C is the circle $|z| = 1$ described in the positive direction.

Solution. The function $f(z) = \sinh z/z^6$ has a singular point at $z = 0$ interior to C. From Example 7.1.4 we see that $b_1 = \text{Res}\, [f(z), 0] = 1/5!$. Hence, from (7.2.5) we obtain

$$\int_C \frac{\sinh z}{z^6}\, dz = \frac{\pi i}{60}.$$

EXAMPLE 7.2.2. Let us evaluate

$$\int_C \frac{(1 - z^4)\, e^{2z}}{z^5}\, dz,$$

where C is the circle $|z| = 1$ described in the positive direction.

Solution. The function $f(z) = (1 - z^4)e^{2z}/z^5$ has a singular point at $z = 0$ interior to C. To find the residue of $f(z)$ at $z = 0$, we proceed as follows:

$$\frac{(1 - z^4)\, e^{2z}}{z^5} = \frac{e^{2z}}{z^5} - \frac{e^{2z}}{z} = \frac{1}{z^5}\left(1 + 2z + 2z^2 + \frac{4}{3} z^3 + \frac{2}{3} z^4 + \frac{4}{15} z^5 + \cdots\right)$$

$$-\frac{1}{z}(1 + 2z + 2z^2 + \cdots) = \frac{1}{z^5} + \frac{2}{z^4} + \frac{2}{z^3} + \frac{4}{3z^2} - \frac{1}{3z} - \frac{26}{15} - \cdots,\ |z| > 0.$$

Hence, $b_1 = \text{Res}\, [f(z), 0] = -1/3$. Consequently

$$\int_C \frac{(1 - z^4)e^{2z}}{z^5}\, dz = -\frac{2}{3}\pi i.$$

We shall now establish the following useful

——**THEOREM** 7.2.2.   Suppose that $f(z)$ is analytic in a neighborhood of $z = z_0$ except at z_0, where it has a pole of order m. Then

$$\text{Res}\,[\,f(z),\,z_0\,] = \frac{1}{(m-1)!}\,\lim_{z \to z_0}\frac{d^{m-1}}{dz^{m-1}}\,[(z - z_0)^m f(z)]. \qquad (7.2.6)$$

In particular, if $f(z)$ has a simple pole at $z = z_0$, then

$$\text{Res}\,[\,f(z),\,z_0\,] = \lim_{z \to z_0}(z - z_0)\,f(z). \qquad (7.2.7)$$

Proof.   Differentiate $\lambda(z)$ in (7.1.5) $(m-1)$ times with respect to z and take the limit as $z \to z_0$. In view of (7.1.3) and (7.1.4) we obtain

$$\lim_{z \to z_0}\frac{d^{m-1}}{dz^{m-1}}\,[(z - z_0)^m f(z)] = (m-1)!\,b_1 = (m-1)!\,\text{Res}\,[\,f(z),\,z_0\,],$$

thus establishing (7.2.6). When $m = 1$ in (7.2.6), we get (7.2.7).

EXAMPLE 7.2.3.   Let us evaluate the integral

$$\int_C \frac{z^2 - z + 1}{(z - 1)\,(z - 4)\,(z + 3)}\,dz,$$

where C is the circle $|z| = 5$ described in the positive direction.

Solution.   The function $f(z) = (z^2 - z + 1)/(z - 1)\,(z - 4)\,(z + 3)$ has simple poles at $z = 1$, $z = 4$, and $z = -3$ in the interior of C. Utilizing (7.2.7) we find

$$\text{Res}\,(1) = \lim_{z \to 1}(z - 1)\,f(z) = \lim_{z \to 1}\frac{z^2 - z + 1}{(z - 4)\,(z + 3)} = -\frac{1}{12},$$

$$\text{Res}\,(4) = \lim_{z \to 4}(z - 4)\,f(z) = \lim_{z \to 4}\frac{z^2 - z + 1}{(z - 1)\,(z + 3)} = \frac{13}{21},$$

$$\text{Res}\,(-3) = \lim_{z \to -3}(z + 3)\,f(z) = \lim_{z \to -3}\frac{z^2 - z + 1}{(z - 1)\,(z - 4)} = \frac{13}{28}.$$

Hence, $\text{Res}\,(1) + \text{Res}\,(4) + \text{Res}\,(-3) = 1$, and by Theorem 7.2.1 the value of the above integral is equal to $2\pi i$.

EXAMPLE 7.2.4.   Let us find the residues of

$$f(z) = \frac{e^z}{z^2(z - \pi i)^4}.$$

Solution. The above function has a pole of order 2 at $z = 0$ and a pole of order 4 at $z = \pi i$. Utilizing (7.2.6) we find

$$\text{Res}\,(0) = \frac{1}{1!} \lim_{z \to 0} \frac{d}{dz} \left[z^2 f(z) \right] = \lim_{z \to 0} \frac{d}{dz} \left[\frac{e^z}{(z - \pi i)^4} \right]$$

$$= \lim_{z \to 0} \left[\frac{e^z(z - \pi i - 4)}{(z - \pi i)^5} \right] = \frac{\pi - 4i}{\pi^5},$$

$$\text{Res}\,(\pi i) = \frac{1}{3!} \lim_{z \to \pi i} \frac{d^3}{dz^3} \left[(z - \pi i)^4 f(z) \right] = \frac{1}{6} \lim_{z \to \pi i} \frac{d^3}{dz^3} \left[\frac{e^z}{z^2} \right]$$

$$= \frac{1}{6} \lim_{z \to \pi i} \left[\frac{e^z(z^3 - 6z^2 + 18z - 24)}{z^5} \right] = \frac{1}{6\pi^5} (\pi^3 + 6\pi^2 i - 18\pi - 24i).$$

——THEOREM 7.2.3.   Let $f(z) = p(z)/q(z)$, where the functions $p(z)$ and $q(z)$ are both analytic at $z = z_0$ and $p(z_0) \neq 0$. Then $f(z)$ has a pole of order m at $z = z_0$ if, and only if, z_0 is a zero of order m of $q(z)$.

In particular, when $q(z)$ has a simple zero at $z = z_0$, then $f(z)$ has a simple pole at $z = z_0$ and

$$\text{Res}\,[f(z), z_0] = p(z_0)/q'(z_0). \tag{7.2.8}$$

Proof.   Suppose that z_0 is a zero of order m of $q(z)$. Then by Remark 7.1.1 we have

$$q(z) = (z - z_0)^m \lambda(z),$$

where $\lambda(z)$ is analytic at z_0 and $\lambda(z_0) \neq 0$. Therefore

$$f(z) = \frac{p(z)}{q(z)} = \frac{p(z)}{(z - z_0)^m \lambda(z)}.$$

Hence

$$(z - z_0)^m f(z) = \phi(z),$$

where $\phi(z) = p(z)/\lambda(z)$ is analytic in a neighborhood of z_0, since $\lambda(z_0) \neq 0$. Moreover

$$\lim_{z \to z_0} (z - z_0)^m f(z) = \lim_{z \to z_0} \frac{p(z)}{\lambda(z)} = \frac{p(z_0)}{\lambda(z_0)} \neq 0.$$

Hence, by Theorem 7.1.1 $f(z)$ has a pole of order m at $z = z_0$.

Conversely, if $f(z) = p(z)/q(z)$ has a pole of order m at $z = z_0$, then by Remark 7.1.1 we have

$$\frac{p(z)}{q(z)} = \frac{\lambda(z)}{(z - z_0)^m},$$

where $\lambda(z)$ is analytic at $z = z_0$ and $\lambda(z_0) \neq 0$. Hence

$$q(z) = (z - z_0)^m \mu(z),$$

where $\mu(z) = p(z)/\lambda(z)$ is analytic at z_0 and $\mu(z_0) = p(z_0)/\lambda(z_0) \neq 0$. Thus, by Remark 7.1.1, $q(z)$ has a zero of order m at $z = z_0$.

Concerning (7.2.8). Since $q(z)$ has a simple zero at $z = z_0$, we have in virtue of (7.1.10) with $m = 1$ and $a_n = \dfrac{q^{(n)}(z_0)}{n!}$, $\quad n = 1, 2, \cdots$,

$$q(z) = q'(z_0)(z - z_0) + \frac{q''(z_0)}{2!}(z - z_0)^2 + \cdots,$$

where $q'(z_0) \neq 0$. Hence

$$\lim_{z \to z_0} \frac{q(z)}{(z - z_0)} = q'(z_0).$$

By (7.2.7) we have

$$\text{Res}\,[f(z), z_0] = \lim_{z \to z_0} (z - z_0)f(z) = \lim_{z \to z_0} \frac{(z - z_0)p(z)}{q(z)}$$

$$= \frac{p(z_0)}{\displaystyle\lim_{z \to z_0} \frac{q(z)}{(z - z_0)}} = \frac{p(z_0)}{q'(z_0)},$$

and the theorem is established.

EXAMPLE 7.2.5.   Let us find the residues of

$$f(z) = \tanh z.$$

Solution.   We have $f(z) = p(z)/q(z)$, where $p(z) = \sinh z$ and $q(z) = \cosh z$. From Theorem 4.3.2, the zeros of $q(z)$ are given by $z_n = (n + \frac{1}{2})\pi i$, $n = 0$, $\pm 1, \pm 2, \cdots$, and $q'(z_n) = p(z_n) \neq 0$. Consequently, the z_n are simple zeros of $q(z)$. From (7.2.8) we see that the residue at each pole is the same, namely,

$$\text{Res}\,[f(z), z_n] = \frac{p(z_n)}{q'(z_n)} = \frac{\sinh (z_n)}{\sinh (z_n)} = 1, \qquad n = 0, \pm 1, \pm 2, \cdots.$$

EXAMPLE 7.2.6.   Let us evaluate

$$\int_C \frac{e^{2z}}{\cosh \pi z}\, dz,$$

where C is the circle $|z| = 1$ described in the positive direction.

Solution.   Let $f(z) = e^{2z}/\cosh \pi z = p(z)/q(z)$. Using the method in Example 7.2.5 above, we see that the singular points of $f(z)$ contained in the interior of the circle $|z| = 1$ are given by $z_1 = i/2$ and $z_2 = -i/2$. Utilizing (7.2.5), (7.2.8), (4.3.5), (4.3.10) and (4.2.2) we get

$$\int_C \frac{e^{2z}}{\cosh \pi z}\, dz = 2\pi i \left\{ \text{Res}\left[f(z), \frac{i}{2}\right] + \text{Res}\left[f(z), -\frac{i}{2}\right] \right\}$$

$$= 2\pi i \left[\frac{p(z_1)}{q'(z_1)} + \frac{p(z_2)}{q'(z_2)} \right] = 2\pi i \left[\frac{e^i}{\pi i} - \frac{e^{-i}}{\pi i} \right] = 4i \sin 1.$$

EXERCISES 7.2

1. Show that all the singular points in the finite z plane of each of the following functions are poles. Determine the order of each pole and the value of the residue of the function at each pole.

(a) $\dfrac{z^2 + 4z + 1}{z^4 - 3z^2 - 4}$,

(b) $\dfrac{z^3 - 4}{z^4 + 2z^2 + 1}$,

(c) $\coth z$,

(d) $\dfrac{z - 1}{\sin z}$,

(e) $\tan z$,

(f) $\dfrac{e^{az}}{\cosh \pi z}$,

(g) $\dfrac{e^{iz}}{z^4 + 2z^2 + 1}$,

(h) $\dfrac{z^2 - 4}{z^5 - z^3}$,

(i) $\cot z$,

(j) $\dfrac{1}{\sinh z}$,

(k) $\dfrac{1}{z^2 \sin z}$,

(l) $\dfrac{z^6}{z^4 + 1}$,

(m) $\dfrac{e^{aiz}}{z^2 + (a^2 + b^2) z + a^2 b^2}$, $a \neq b$.

2. Evaluate each of the following integrals, each integral being taken in the positive direction along the given circle.

(a) $\displaystyle\int_C \cot z \, dz$ along the circles: (1) $|z| = 4$;   (2) $|z - 1| = 2$.

(b) $\displaystyle\int_C \tanh z \, dz$ along the circles: (1) $|z| = 3$;   (2) $|z - 1| = 2$.

(c) $\displaystyle\int_C \dfrac{dz}{\sinh z}$ along the circles: (1) $|z| = 2$;   (2) $|z - 1| = 3$.

(d) $\displaystyle\int_C \dfrac{dz}{z^2 \sin z}$ along the circle: $|z| = 1$.

(e) $\displaystyle\int_C \dfrac{dz}{z \cos z}$ along the circle: $|z| = 1$.

(f) $\displaystyle\int_C \dfrac{(e^{2iz} - 5z) \, dz}{z + 2i}$ along the circles: (1) $|z + 1| = 3$; (2) $|z - \dfrac{1}{2} i| = 1$.

(g) $\displaystyle\int_C \dfrac{e^{iz} \, dz}{z^4 + 2z^2 + 1}$ along the circle: $|z| = 2$.

(h) $\displaystyle\int_C \dfrac{e^{z^2}}{z^4} \, dz$ along the circle: $|z| = 1$.

(i) $\int_C \dfrac{z\,dz}{(z^2+1)(z^2+2z+2)}$ along the circles: (1) $|z| = \dfrac{3}{2}$;

(2) $|z+i| = 3/2$;   (3) $|z-i| = 3/2$;

(4) $|z+1| = 1.1$;   (5) $|z-1| = 1.9$.

3. Let $f(z)$ be analytic within and on a simple closed contour C, and such that $f(z) \neq 0$ on C. Let $f(z)$ have a simple zero at $z = \alpha$ interior to C and $f(z) \neq 0$ at all other points in the interior of C. Show that the root α is given by

$$\alpha = \frac{1}{2\pi i}\int_C \frac{zf'(\alpha)}{f(z)}\,dz.$$

7.3. SINGULARITIES AT INFINITY. Let the function $f(z)$ be analytic for all values of z such that $|z| > R$, $0 \leq R < \infty$. Then the function $F(w) \equiv f(1/w)$ is analytic for all values of w such that $0 < |w| < 1/R$. Let the Laurent series expansion of $F(w)$ about $w = 0$ be given by

$$f\left(\frac{1}{w}\right) = F(w) = \sum_{n=1}^{\infty} b_n w^{-n} + \sum_{n=0}^{\infty} a_n w^n, \qquad 0 < |w| < \frac{1}{R}. \quad (7.3.1)$$

Then the following cases may occur.

CASE 1. An infinite number of the b_n in (7.3.1) do not vanish. Then $F(w)$ has an essential singularity at $w = 0$. In this case we say that $f(z)$ has an *essential singularity* at $z = \infty$ and we have

$$f(z) = \sum_{n=1}^{\infty} b_n z^n + \sum_{n=0}^{\infty} a_n z^{-n}, \qquad |z| > R. \quad (7.3.2)$$

CASE 2. All but a finite number of the b_n in (7.3.1) vanish. Then we may write (7.3.1) as

$$f\left(\frac{1}{w}\right) = F(w) = \sum_{n=0}^{\infty} a_n w^n + \frac{b_1}{w} + \frac{b_2}{w^2} + \cdots + \frac{b_m}{w^m}, \quad b_m \neq 0, 0 < |w| < \frac{1}{R}.$$

Hence

$$f(z) = \sum_{n=0}^{\infty} a_n z^{-n} + b_1 z + b_2 z^2 + \cdots + b_m z^m, \qquad b_m \neq 0, \quad |z| > R. \quad (7.3.3)$$

Now, $F(w)$ has a pole of order m at $w = 0$ with principal part

$$\frac{b_1}{w} + \frac{b_2}{w^2} + \cdots + \frac{b_m}{w^m}.$$

In this case we say that $f(z)$ has a *pole of order m* at $z = \infty$ with *principal part*

$$b_1 z + b_2 z^2 + \cdots + b_m z^m. \tag{7.3.4}$$

CASE 3. All the b_n in (7.3.1) are equal to zero. Then we may write (7.3.1) as

$$f\left(\frac{1}{w}\right) = F(w) = \sum_{n=0}^{\infty} a_n w^n, \qquad 0 < |w| < \frac{1}{R}.$$

Hence

$$f(z) = \sum_{n=0}^{\infty} a_n z^{-n}, \qquad |z| > R. \tag{7.3.5}$$

Also

$$\lim_{w \to 0} F(w) = a_0,$$

and consequently

$$\lim_{z \to \infty} f(z) = a_0. \tag{7.3.6}$$

$F(w)$ has a removable singularity at $w = 0$, and if we define $F(0)$ to be equal to a_0, then $F(w)$ becomes analytic at $w = 0$. In this case we say that $f(z)$ has a *removable singularity* at $z = \infty$, and if we define $f(\infty)$ to be equal to a_0, we say that $f(z)$ is *analytic* at $z = \infty$.

Remark 7.3.1. Some light may be shed on the definition of singularity at $z = \infty$ if we refer back to Section 2.13. There we constructed two systems of complex coordinates on the sphere. Each point $P(z, w)$ on the sphere, other than N and S, was assigned two complex coordinates z and w, related by the equality $z = 1/w$. On the other hand, the points N and S were assigned only one finite coordinate, namely $N: w = 0$, $S: z = 0$.

A function $f(z)$ defined in a domain D of the complex plane may be regarded as a function defined in the corresponding domain D' on the sphere. This function, which assigns to each point $P(z, w)$ in D' the value $f(z)$, may be denoted by $G(P)$ and we see that

$$G(P) = f(z) = f\left(\frac{1}{w}\right).$$

Again, letting $F(w) = f(1/w)$, we see that $f(z) = F(1/z)$. Thus, $f(z)$ and $F(w)$ are interchangeable. Furthermore, it is evident from the above relations that at points other than N and S, $f(z)$ is analytic in z if, and only if, $F(w)$ is analytic in w. It follows that when we regard a function of a complex variable as a function on the sphere, there is no reason for favoring one coordinate system over the other.

When discussing the behavior of a function in the neighborhood of $z = \infty$, that is, the behavior of a function on the sphere in the neighborhood of the point N ($w = 0$, $z = \infty$), it is natural to use the w coordinate system, since the point N has no finite z coordinate. We then represent the function originally given as $f(z)$ by $F(w) = f(1/w)$. On the other hand, when discussing the behavior of a function in a neighborhood of the point S ($z = 0$, $w = \infty$), we use the z coordinate system.

It is just as natural to speak of a function $f(z) = F(w)$, defined in a neighborhood of N ($w = 0$, $z = \infty$), as being singular or analytic at N ($w = 0$, $z = \infty$), as it is to speak of a function $F(w) = f(z)$, defined in a neighborhood of S ($z = 0$, $w = \infty$), as being singular or analytic at S ($z = 0$, $w = \infty$).

We shall now establish the following two lemmas.

LEMMA 7.3.1. Let $f(z)$ be analytic in the domain $|z| > R$, $R \geq 0$, and let $f(z)$ have a pole of order m at $z = \infty$ with principal part equal to $\sum_{j=1}^{m} b_j z^j$. Then there exists a constant $R_0 > 0$ such that

$$f_1(z) = f(z) - \sum_{j=1}^{m} b_j z^j \tag{7.3.7}$$

is bounded in the region $|z| \geq R_0$.

Proof. From Case 2 above, we have

$$F_1(w) = f_1\left(\frac{1}{w}\right) = f\left(\frac{1}{w}\right) - \left[\frac{b_1}{w} + \frac{b_2}{w^2} + \cdots + \frac{b_m}{w^m}\right] = \sum_{n=0}^{\infty} a_n w^n,$$

$$0 < |w| < \frac{1}{R},$$

and by Case 3 above, defining $F_1(0) = a_0$, $F_1(w)$ becomes analytic in the region $|w| < 1/R$. Taking $R_0 > R$ so that $1/R_0 < 1/R$, we see that $F_1(w)$ is analytic, and therefore continuous, in the bounded closed set $|w| \leq 1/R_0$. By Exercise 3.3.25, there exists a constant K such that

$$|F_1(w)| = \left|f\left(\frac{1}{w}\right) - \frac{b_1}{w} - \frac{b_2}{w^2} - \cdots - \frac{b_m}{w^m}\right| \leq K \text{ for } |w| \leq \frac{1}{R_0}.$$

Hence

$$|f_1(z)| = |f(z) - \sum_{j=1}^{m} b_j z^j| \leq K \text{ for } |z| \geq R_0,$$

thus establishing the lemma.

LEMMA 7.3.2. Suppose that $f(z)$ is analytic everywhere in the finite complex plane except for poles $z_1, z_2, \cdots, z_k$. Let $P(z, z_r)$ be the principal part of $f(z)$ at $z = z_r$, $r = 1, 2, \cdots, k$. Then there exists a function $\phi(z)$ analytic in the entire finite complex plane such that

$$f(z) = \sum_{r=1}^{k} P(z, z_r) + \phi(z). \tag{7.3.8}$$

Moreover, $\phi(z)$ has the same principal part at $z = \infty$ as $f(z)$.

Proof. Consider the function

$$g(z) = \sum_{r=1}^{k} P(z, z_r),$$

where

$$P(z, z_r) = \sum_{j=1}^{m_r} \frac{b_{jr}}{(z - z_r)^j}.$$

Clearly, $g(z)$ is analytic in the entire finite complex plane except at the points $z_1, z_2, \cdots, z_k$ where it has poles. Moreover, since for $s \neq r$, $P(z, z_s)$ is analytic at $z = z_r$, the principal part of $g(z)$ at $z = z_r$ is $P(z, z_r)$. Hence, $g(z)$ has the same poles and principal parts at $z_1, z_2, \cdots, z_k$ as $f(z)$ and is analytic everywhere else.

Now, consider the function

$$\phi(z) = f(z) - g(z), \qquad z \neq z_r, \qquad r = 1, 2, \cdots.$$

This function is analytic in the entire finite complex plane except for possible poles at the points $z_1, z_2, \cdots, z_k$. However, the principal part of each pole of $\phi(z)$ is zero. Hence, $\phi(z)$ has removable singularities at $z_1, z_2, \cdots, z_k$ and may be considered as analytic. Moreover, since $g(z)$ approaches zero as $z \to \infty$, $g(z)$ has a removable singularity at $z = \infty$ [see Exercise 7.3.3(a)]. Hence, $\phi(z)$ has the same principal part at $z = \infty$ as $f(z)$. Writing $f(z) = g(z) + \phi(z)$, we see that the lemma is established.

We shall now establish the following

——**THEOREM** 7.3.1. A function $f(z)$ is a rational function if, and only if, it has no essential singularities either in the finite complex plane or at infinity.

Proof. Suppose that $f(z)$ is a rational function, then $f(z) = p(z)/q(z)$, where $p(z)$ and $q(z)$ are relatively prime polynomials.* If $z = z_0$ is not a zero of $q(z)$, then $f(z)$ is analytic at $z = z_0$. If $z = z_0$ is a zero of $q(z)$, then (see Theorem 7.2.3) $f(z)$ has a pole at $z = z_0$. Thus at all points in the finite complex plane, $f(z)$ is either analytic or has a pole.

To examine the behavior of $f(z)$ at $z = \infty$, we consider the behavior of $f(1/w)$ at $w = 0$. Let

$$p(z) = \sum_{i=0}^{m} a_i z^i \quad \text{and} \quad q(z) = \sum_{j=0}^{n} b_j z^j, \qquad a_m \neq 0, \quad b_n \neq 0.$$

---

* Two polynomials $p(z)$ and $q(z)$ are said to be *relatively prime* if the only common divisors of $p(z)$ and $q(z)$ are constants.

Then

$$f\left(\frac{1}{w}\right) = \frac{p(1/w)}{q(1/w)} = w^{n-m}H(w),$$

where

$$H(w) = \frac{a_0 w^m + a_1 w^{m-1} + \cdots + a_m}{b_0 w^n + b_1 w^{n-1} + \cdots + b_n}.$$

Note that $H(w)$ is analytic at $w = 0$. Thus we see that $w = 0$ is not an essential singularity of $f(1/w)$. Therefore, $z = \infty$ is not an essential singularity of $f(z)$.

Conversely, suppose that $f(z)$ has no essential singularity. Hence $z = \infty$ is at most a pole. Thus we can draw a circle C with center at the origin and sufficiently large radius R so that there are no finite singularities outside the circle C. Also, since $f(z)$ has no essential singularities in the finite plane and since poles are isolated singularities, it can be shown (see Exercise 7.1.9 and the Bolzano-Weierstrass Theorem 2.5.2) that there can only be a finite number of singularities in the interior and on the boundary of C. Let $z_1, z_2, \cdots, z_k$ be these singular points, and let $P(z, z_r)$ denote the principal part of $f(z)$ at $z = z_r$, $r = 1, 2, \cdots, k$. Then by Lemma 7.3.2

$$\phi(z) \equiv f(z) - \sum_{r=1}^{k} P(z, z_r) \tag{7.3.9}$$

is analytic for all finite z, and the principal part of $\phi(z)$ at $z = \infty$ is the same as that of $f(z)$. Denote this principal part by $B_1 z + \cdots + B_m z^m$. Then by Lemma 7.3.1 there exists a constant $R_0 > 0$ such that the function

$$F(z) \equiv \phi(z) - \sum_{j=1}^{m} B_j z^j$$

is bounded for $|z| \geq R_0$. Also $F(z)$ is analytic for all finite z, and hence is bounded in any closed bounded set. Thus it is bounded for $|z| \leq R_0$. Combining the facts that it is bounded for $|z| \geq R_0$ and $|z| \leq R_0$, and using Liouville's Theorem 5.16.1, we see that $F(z)$ is a constant, say K. Thus

$$\phi(z) - \sum_{j=1}^{m} B_j z^j = K. \tag{7.3.10}$$

Utilizing (7.3.9) and (7.3.10), we then have

$$\begin{cases} f(z) = K + \sum_{r=1}^{k} P(z, z_r) + B_1 z + \cdots + B_m z^m, \\ \text{where} \\ P(z, z_r) = \sum_{j=1}^{m_r} \frac{b_{jr}}{(z - z_r)^j}. \end{cases} \tag{7.3.11}$$

Thus the theorem is established.

Remark 7.3.2.   From Theorem 7.3.1 we see that a rational function possesses a decomposition into *partial fractions*. For, if a function is rational, then by the above theorem it has no essential singularities, and hence it is given by the expression (7.3.11).

EXERCISES 7.3

1. Let $f(z)$ be analytic at $z = \infty$, and in the exterior of a circle $|z| = \rho_1$. Show that for $|z| > \rho_1$, we have

$$f(z) = a_0 + \frac{a_1}{z} + \frac{a_2}{z^2} + \cdots.$$

Also show that this series converges uniformly and absolutely on and in the exterior of every circle $|z| = \rho$ for $\rho > \rho_1$.

2. Show that if the series $\sum_{n=0}^{\infty} a_n/z^n$ converges uniformly on a contour Γ to the function $f(z)$, then

$$\int_{\Gamma} f(z)\, dz = \sum_{n=0}^{\infty} \int_{\Gamma} \frac{a_n}{z^n}\, dz.$$

3. Let M and M_0 be deleted neighborhoods of $z = \infty$, with $M_0 \subset M$. Let $F(z)$ be analytic in M. Establish the following results.

   (a) If $F(z)$ is bounded in M, then $z = \infty$ is a removable singularity of $F(z)$.

   (b) If $(1/z)^m F(z)$ is bounded but $(1/z)^{m-1} F(z)$ is not bounded in M, m a positive integer, then $F(z)$ has a pole of order m at $z = \infty$.

   (c) If $(1/z)^m F(z)$ is unbounded in M_0 for every integer m, then $F(z)$ has an essential singularity at $z = \infty$.

4. Suppose that $F(z)$ is analytic in a neighborhood of $z = \infty$ except at $z = \infty$ and $\lim_{z \to \infty} F(z) = Q$. Show that if we define $F(\infty) = Q$, then $F(z)$ is analytic at $z = \infty$.

5. Suppose that $F(z)$ is analytic and bounded in a deleted neighborhood of $z = \infty$. Show that $\lim_{z \to \infty} F(z)$ exists.

7.4. POLES AND ZEROS OF MEROMORPHIC FUNCTIONS.   A function $f(z)$ which is analytic in a domain D, except at some points of D at which it has poles, is said to be *meromorphic in D*. A meromorphic function may have an essential singularity at $z = \infty$. We may consider the analytic functions in D as a special case among the meromorphic functions in D.

——*THEOREM* 7.4.1.   Let C be a simple closed contour. Let $G(z)$ be analytic on C and meromorphic in the interior of C, and let it have no zeros on C. Then

$$\frac{1}{2\pi i} \int_{C} \frac{G'(z)}{G(z)}\, dz = N - P, \qquad (7.4.1)$$

where N and P are the number of zeros and poles respectively of $G(z)$ interior to C, and the integral is taken in the positive direction along C. The order of each zero and of each pole is counted in determining N and P.

Proof. First of all observe (see Exercise 7.1.8) that the number of zeros and poles of $G(z)$ interior to C is finite. Suppose that $z = \alpha$ is a zero of order k of $G(z)$. Then from Remark 7.1.1 we have

$$G(z) = (z - \alpha)^k \lambda(z),$$

where $\lambda(z)$ is analytic at $z = \alpha$ and $\lambda(\alpha) \neq 0$. Thus

$$\frac{G'(z)}{G(z)} = \frac{k}{(z - \alpha)} + \frac{\lambda'(z)}{\lambda(z)}.$$

Observe that $\lambda'(z)/\lambda(z)$ is analytic at $z = \alpha$. Hence, $G'(z)/G(z)$ has a simple pole at $z = \alpha$ with residue equal to k.

Now, suppose that $z = \beta$ is a pole of order m of $G(z)$. Then utilizing again Remark 7.1.1 and proceeding as above, we find that $G'(z)/G(z)$ has a simple pole at $z = \beta$ with residue equal to $- m$. If α_i and β_i are the zeros and poles of $G(z)$ interior to the closed contour C, and k_i and m_i their orders respectively, then from Theorem 7.2.1 we have

$$\int_C \frac{G'(z)}{G(z)} \, dz = 2\pi i(\Sigma k_i - \Sigma m_i) = 2\pi i(N - P),$$

from which (7.4.1) now follows, and the theorem is established.

Let $C: z = f(t)$, $\alpha \leq t \leq \beta$, be a simple closed contour. Suppose that $H(z)$ is analytic on C and meromorphic in the interior of C. Suppose furthermore that $H(z) \neq \zeta_0$ for z on C. Consider the curve

$$\Gamma: \zeta = F(t), \qquad F(t) = H[f(t)], \qquad \alpha \leq t \leq \beta. \tag{7.4.2}$$

Remark 7.4.1.   The curve Γ in (7.4.2) is a contour since $F(t)$ is continuous, $F'(t) = H'(z)f'(t)$ is piecewise continuous and $F'(t)$ has only a finite number of zeros, $\alpha \leq t \leq \beta$. Also Γ does not pass through ζ_0; and Γ is closed since C is closed.

——**THEOREM** 7.4.2.   Let $C: z = f(t)$, $\alpha \leq t \leq \beta$, be a simple closed contour described in the positive direction. Suppose that $H(z)$ is analytic on C and meromorphic in the interior of C. Suppose furthermore that $H(z) \neq \zeta_0$ for z on C. Let Γ be the closed contour given in (7.4.2). Then

$$\nu(\Gamma, \zeta_0) = N - P, \tag{7.4.3}$$

where $\nu(\Gamma, \zeta_0)$ is the winding number of Γ about the point ζ_0, and N and P are respectively the number of zeros and poles of $H(z) - \zeta_0$ interior to C. The order of each zero and of each pole is counted in determining N and P.

Proof.   Setting $G(z) = H(z) - \zeta_0$ in Theorem 7.4.1, we get

$$\frac{1}{2\pi i} \int_C \frac{H'(z)}{H(z) - \zeta_0}\, dz = N - P.$$

By (5.4.2) and (5.2.9) we have

$$v(\Gamma, \zeta_0) = \frac{1}{2\pi i} \int_\Gamma \frac{d\zeta}{\zeta - \zeta_0} = \frac{1}{2\pi i} \int_\alpha^\beta \frac{F'(t)}{F(t) - \zeta_0}\, dt$$

$$= \frac{1}{2\pi i} \int_\alpha^\beta \frac{H'[f(t)]f'(t)}{H[f(t)] - \zeta_0}\, dt = \frac{1}{2\pi i} \int_C \frac{H'(z)}{H(z) - \zeta_0}\, dz = N - P,$$

thus establishing the theorem.

Theorem 7.4.2 is particularly useful when $H(z)$ is analytic within and on C. In this case, $P = 0$ and (7.4.3) becomes

$$v(\Gamma, \zeta_0) = N. \tag{7.4.4}$$

Usually, the contour Γ can be written as a formal sum of simple closed contours γ_j, that is, $\Gamma = \sum_{j=1}^n \gamma_j$ (see Remark 5.2.2), and by (5.4.6) we have

$$v(\Gamma, \zeta_0) = \sum_{j=1}^n v(\gamma_j, \zeta_0).$$

Each $v(\gamma_j, \zeta_0)$ can then be evaluated by inspection. If ζ_0 is exterior to γ_j, then by Theorem 5.5.2, $v(\gamma_j, \zeta_0) = 0$. If ζ_0 is interior to γ_j, then $v(\gamma_j, \zeta_0) = \pm 1$ according as γ_j is described in the positive or negative direction. (See Theorem 5.6.2.)

For example, if Γ is a contour given by $ABCDEFGHA$ as shown in Fig. 7.4.1,

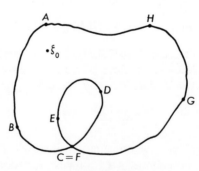

FIG. 7.4.1

then $\Gamma = \gamma_1 + \gamma_2$, where γ_1 and γ_2 are the simple closed contours given respectively by $ABCGHA$ and $CDEF$. Then for ζ_0 interior to γ_1 and exterior to γ_2, we have $v(\gamma_1, \zeta_0) = 1$ and $v(\gamma_2, \zeta_0) = 0$, respectively. Hence

$$v(\Gamma, \zeta_0) = v(\gamma_1, \zeta_0) + v(\gamma_2, \zeta_0) = 1.$$

As another example, let $C: z = e^{it}$, $0 \leq t \leq 2\pi$, describe the unit circle and let $G(z) = z^2$. Then Γ is given by $\zeta = (e^{it})^2 = e^{2it}$, $0 \leq t \leq 2\pi$ and we have $\Gamma = \gamma_1 + \gamma_2$, where γ_1 and γ_2 are simple closed contours given respectively by $\zeta = e^{2it}$, $0 \leq t \leq \pi$ and $\zeta = e^{2it}$, $\pi \leq t \leq 2\pi$. Both γ_1 and γ_2 are described in the positive direction and contain the point $\zeta_0 = 0$ in their interior. Hence $\nu(\Gamma, 0) = 2$, which agrees with the fact that in the interior of C, the function $G(z) = z^2$ has a zero of order two at $z = 0$ and does not vanish at any other point.

The following useful theorem is due to Rouché.

──**THEOREM** 7.4.3.   Let the functions $f(z)$ and $g(z)$ be analytic within and on a simple closed contour C. Suppose that $|g(z)| < |f(z)|$ for all z on C. Then the function $f(z) + g(z)$ has exactly as many zeros in the interior of C as the function $f(z)$.

Proof.   Observe that since $|g(z)| < |f(z)|$ for all z on C, it follows that neither $f(z)$ nor $f(z) + g(z)$ has a zero on C. Let N and N' denote the number of zeros of $f(z)$ and $f(z) + g(z)$ respectively, in the interior of C.

Recalling the definition of the variation, $\Delta_C \log G(z)$, of the logarithm of $G(z)$ along the contour C, we see from (5.3.9) and (7.4.1) with $P = 0$ that

$$2\pi i N = \Delta_C \log f(z) \tag{7.4.5}$$

and

$$2\pi i N' = \Delta_C \log [f(z) + g(z)] \tag{7.4.6}$$

$$= \Delta_C \log \left\{ f(z) \left[1 + \frac{g(z)}{f(z)} \right] \right\}.$$

It is not difficult to show (see Exercise 5.3.2) that

$$\Delta_C \log \left\{ f(z) \left[1 + \frac{g(z)}{f(z)} \right] \right\} = \Delta_C \log f(z) + \Delta_C \log \left[1 + \frac{g(z)}{f(z)} \right]. \tag{7.4.7}$$

Since $|g(z)/f(z)| < 1$ for all z on C, it follows from Lemma 5.3.1 that

$$\Delta_C \log \left[1 + \frac{g(z)}{f(z)} \right] = 0. \tag{7.4.8}$$

Utilizing (7.4.5) to (7.4.8) we have

$$2\pi i N' = \Delta_C \log f(z) = 2\pi i N.$$

Hence $N' = N$ and the theorem is established.

EXAMPLE 7.4.1.   Let us show that every polynomial of the nth degree has n zeros.

Solution.   Let

$$p(z) = a_n z^n + a_{n-1} z^{n-1} + \cdots + a_1 z + a_0, \qquad a_n \neq 0.$$

Let us take

$$f(z) = a_n z^n \quad \text{and} \quad g(z) = a_{n-1} z^{n-1} + \cdots + a_1 z + a_0.$$

Now we can choose a constant R sufficiently large so that

$$|a_n| R^n > |a_{n-1}| R^{n-1} + \cdots + |a_1| R + |a_0|. \qquad (7.4.9)$$

Consider the circle C_R with center at the origin and radius R. When z is on C_R we have

$$|f(z)| = |a_n| R^n \quad \text{and} \quad |g(z)| \leq |a_{n-1}| R^{n-1} + \cdots + |a_1| R + |a_0|.$$

$$(7.4.10)$$

Thus, for all z on C_R we have from (7.4.9) and (7.4.10)

$$|g(z)| < |f(z)|.$$

Therefore, by Theorem 7.4.3 we have that

$$p(z) = f(z) + g(z)$$

has as many zeros in the interior of the circle C_R as $f(z)$. But $f(z)$ has n zeros in the interior of C_R; namely, $z = 0$ is a zero of order n of $f(z)$. Hence, $p(z)$ has also n zeros in the interior of C_R. Since, in virtue of (7.4.9), $p(z)$ has no zeros exterior to or on C_R, it follows that $p(z)$ has n zeros.

EXAMPLE 7.4.2. Let us show that if $|a| > e$, the equation $az^n - e^z = 0$ has n roots in the interior of the unit circle C.

Solution. Let

$$f(z) = az^n \quad \text{and} \quad g(z) = -e^z.$$

Let $z = x + iy$ be any point on C, then $|z|^n = 1$ and $|x| \leq 1$. Consequently

$$|f(z)| = |a| |z|^n = |a| > e$$

and in virtue of (4.1.5)

$$|g(z)| = |e^z| = e^x \leq e.$$

Hence for all z on C, we have

$$|g(z)| < |f(z)|.$$

By Theorem 7.4.3

$$f(z) + g(z) = az^n - e^z$$

has as many zeros interior to C as $f(z)$. But $f(z)$ has n zeros in the interior of C. Hence $az^n - e^z$ has also n zeros in the interior of C.

EXERCISES 7.4

1. Let $f(z)$ be analytic within and on the circle $C: |z| = 1$. Suppose that $|f(z)| < 1$ when $|z| = 1$. Show that there is one and only one point z_0 interior to the circle C such that $f(z_0) = z_0$.

2. Let $S_n(z)$ denote the nth partial sum of the Taylor expansion $e^z = \sum_{n=0}^{\infty} z^n/n!$. Prove that for every $r > 0$ there exists an integer N, depending on r, such that $S_n(z) \neq 0$ for $n \geq N$ and all z interior to the circle $C: |z| = r$.

3. Show that the equation

$$ze^{a-z} = 1, \qquad a > 1$$

has only one root in the interior of the circle $C: |z| = 1$.

4. Let $\{f_n(z)\}$ be a sequence of analytic functions defined in a domain D and converging almost uniformly within D to a function $f(z)$. Let C be a simple closed contour interior to D. Suppose that $f(z) \neq 0$ for all z on C. Show that there exists a number N such that for $n \geq N$, $f_n(z)$ has the same number of zeros in the interior of C as $f(z)$.

7.5. THE EVALUATION OF THE INTEGRALS OF CERTAIN PERIODIC FUNCTIONS TAKEN BETWEEN THE LIMITS 0 AND 2π.

Suppose that we are given an integral of the form

$$I = \int_0^{2\pi} F(\sin \theta, \cos \theta) \, d\theta, \tag{7.5.1}$$

where $F(\sin \theta, \cos \theta)$ is a rational function of $\sin \theta$ and $\cos \theta$ which is finite on the range of integration. The above integral can be evaluated by substituting $e^{i\theta} = z$. Utilizing (4.2.2) we obtain

$$\sin \theta = \frac{1}{2i}(z - z^{-1}), \qquad \cos \theta = \frac{1}{2}(z + z^{-1}) \quad \text{and} \quad d\theta = -iz^{-1} \, dz. \tag{7.5.2}$$

Thus (7.5.1) can be written as

$$I = \int_C f(z) \, dz, \tag{7.5.3}$$

where $f(z)$ is a rational function of z that is finite on the path of integration C, and C is the unit circle. Using Theorem 7.2.1 we then have

$$I = \int_C f(z) \, dz = 2\pi i \sum_{n=1}^{k} \text{Res} \, [f(z), z_n], \tag{7.5.4}$$

where the z_n denote those poles of $f(z)$ which lie interior to the unit circle $C: |z| = 1$, and the integral along C is taken in the positive direction.

EXAMPLE 7.5.1.   Let us evaluate

$$I = \int_0^{2\pi} \frac{d\theta}{1 + a \cos \theta}, \qquad a^2 < 1.$$

Solution.   Using (7.5.2) we may write the foregoing integral as

$$I = \int_C \frac{2dz}{ai(z^2 + 2z/a + 1)} = \int_C \frac{2dz}{ai(z - z_1)(z - z_2)},$$

where

$$z_1 = \frac{-1 + \sqrt{1 - a^2}}{a} \quad \text{and} \quad z_2 = \frac{-1 - \sqrt{1 - a^2}}{a}.$$

The function $f(z) = 2/ai(z - z_1)(z - z_2)$ has simple poles at $z = z_1$ and $z = z_2$. Since $a^2 < 1$, it is evident that $|z_2| > 1$ and consequently z_2 is exterior to the unit circle C. Also, since $z_1 z_2 = 1$, it follows that z_1 is interior to C. From (7.5.4) we then have

$$I = 2\pi i \operatorname{Res} [f(z), z_1].$$

By (7.2.7) we obtain

$$\operatorname{Res} [f(z), z_1] = \lim_{z \to z_1} (z - z_1) f(z) = \frac{2}{ai(z_1 - z_2)} = \frac{1}{i \sqrt{1 - a^2}}.$$

Hence

$$\int_0^{2\pi} \frac{d\theta}{1 + a \cos \theta} = \frac{2\pi}{\sqrt{1 - a^2}}, \qquad a^2 < 1.$$

In the ensuing sections, we shall make use of the following

Definition 7.5.1.   Let p be a real number. A function $f(z)$ is said to be of *order* $1/|z|^p$ (in a neighborhood of the point at infinity), written as

$$f(z) = \mathcal{O}\left(\frac{1}{|z|^p}\right), \tag{7.5.5}$$

if there exists a constant K such that

$$|f(z)| \leq \frac{K}{|z|^p} \tag{7.5.6}$$

when $|z|$ is sufficiently large (that is, when $|z| \geq M$ for some constant $M > 0$).

We shall also need the notion of what is meant by the upper half plane $\mathscr{I}(z) > 0$. By this we mean the set of all points $z = x + iy$ such that $y > 0$. The lower half plane $\mathscr{I}(z) < 0$ consists of all z such that $y < 0$.

7.6.   THE EVALUATION OF CERTAIN TYPES OF INTEGRALS TAKEN BETWEEN THE LIMITS $-\infty$ TO ∞

——**THEOREM** 7.6.1. Suppose that $f(z)$ is meromorphic in the upper half plane and is analytic on the real axis. Also suppose that for $|z|$ sufficiently large $|f(z)| \leq K/|z|^p$, where $p > 1$ and K are constants. Then

$$\int_{-\infty}^{\infty} f(x)\, dx = 2\pi i \sum_{n=1}^{k} \text{Res}\,(z_n), \qquad (7.6.1)$$

where the z_n denote those poles of $f(z)$ that lie in the upper half plane.

Observe that the condition $|f(z)| \leq K\,|z|^{-p}$ for $|z|$ sufficiently large, $p > 1$, implies that $f(z)$ has only a finite number of poles (see Exercise 7.1.10).

Proof. Let C_R denote the upper half of the circle $|z| = R$ described in the positive direction, and take R sufficiently large so that all the poles z_n of $f(z)$ lie in its interior as shown in Fig. 7.6.1. Using Theorem 7.2.1 we then have

$$\int_{-R}^{R} f(x)\, dx + \int_{C_R} f(z)\, dz = 2\pi i \sum_{n=1}^{k} \text{Res}\,(z_n). \qquad (7.6.2)$$

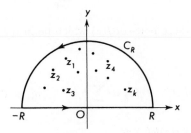

FIG. 7.6.1

Now, $|z| = R$ when z is on C_R. Thus, for R sufficiently large, we have from the hypothesis that for z on C_R, $|f(z)| \leq KR^{-p}$. Also

$$\left|\int_{C_R} f(z)\, dz\right| \leq \int_{C_R} |f(z)|\,|\,dz| \leq \frac{K}{R^p} \int_{C_R} |\,dz| = \frac{\pi K}{R^{p-1}}.$$

Thus, since $p > 1$

$$\int_{C_R} f(z)\, dz \to 0 \qquad \text{as } R \to \infty.$$

Hence letting $R \to \infty$, we obtain from (7.6.2)

$$\lim_{R \to \infty} \int_{-R}^{R} f(x)\, dx = 2\pi i \sum_{n=1}^{k} \text{Res}\,(z_n), \qquad (7.6.2)'$$

from which (7.6.1) now follows (see Remark 7.6.1 below), thus establishing the theorem.

Remark 7.6.1. By definition, the improper integral

$$\int_{-\infty}^{\infty} f(x)\ dx = \lim_{\substack{b \to \infty \\ a \to -\infty}} \int_{a}^{b} f(x)\ dx$$

(provided that the limit exists). In Theorem 7.6.1, since $f(z) = \mathcal{O}(1/|z|^p), p > 1$, it can be shown that $\int_{-\infty}^{\infty} f(x)\ dx$ exists. In particular, $\lim_{R \to \infty} \int_{-R}^{R} f(x)\ dx$ also exists in (7.6.2)′ and

$$\int_{-\infty}^{\infty} f(x)\ dx = \lim_{R \to \infty} \int_{-R}^{R} f(x)\ dx.$$

We shall use Theorem 7.6.1 to establish the following

——**THEOREM** 7.6.2.   Let $f(z) = p(z)/q(z)$, where $p(z)$ and $q(z)$ are relatively prime polynomials and $q(z)$ has no real zeros. If the degree of $q(z)$ is at least two greater than the degree of $p(z)$, then

$$\int_{-\infty}^{\infty} f(x)\ dx = 2\pi i \sum_{n=1}^{k} \operatorname{Res}\ (z_n), \qquad (7.6.3)$$

where the z_n denote those poles of $f(z)$ which lie in the upper half plane.

Proof.   Let

$$p(z) = \sum_{j=0}^{m} a_j z^j, \qquad q(z) = \sum_{i=0}^{n} b_i z^i, \qquad a_m \neq 0, \qquad b_n \neq 0. \quad (7.6.4)$$

We may write $f(z) = p(z)/q(z)$ as

$$f(z) = \frac{1}{z^{n-m}}\ R(z), \qquad (7.6.5)$$

where

$$R(z) = \frac{a_0/z^m + \cdots + a_{m-1}/z + a_m}{b_0/z^n + \cdots + b_{n-1}/z + b_n}. \qquad (7.6.6)$$

Now, for $|z|$ sufficiently large

$$|R(z)| \leqq \frac{|a_m| + |a_m|}{|b_n| - |b_n|/2} = K. \qquad (7.6.7)$$

Hence from (7.6.5) and (7.6.7) we get for $|z|$ sufficiently large

$$|f(z)| = \frac{|R(z)|}{|z|^{n-m}} \leqq \frac{K}{|z|^r},$$

where $r = n - m \geq 2$. Thus we see that $f(z)$ satisfies the hypotheses of Theorem 7.6.1. Therefore

$$\int_{-\infty}^{\infty} f(x)\, dx = \int_{-\infty}^{\infty} \frac{p(x)}{q(x)}\, dx = 2\pi i \sum_{n=1}^{k} \text{Res}\, (z_n), \qquad (7.6.8)$$

thus establishing the theorem.

If in Theorem 7.6.2, $f(x)$ is an even function, then

$$\int_{0}^{\infty} f(x)\, dx = \frac{1}{2} \int_{-\infty}^{\infty} f(x)\, dx = \pi i \sum_{n=1}^{k} \text{Res}\, (z_n). \qquad (7.6.9)$$

Observe that the poles of $f(z)$ in the upper half plane are precisely the roots of $q(z) = 0$ in the upper half plane.

EXAMPLE 7.6.1.   Let us evaluate

$$\int_{-\infty}^{\infty} \frac{x^2}{(x^2 + 1)(x^2 + 4)}\, dx.$$

Solution.   Let $f(z) = p(z)/q(z) = z^2/(z^2 + 1)(z^2 + 4)$. We see that $p(z)$ and $q(z)$ are relatively prime. Thus, in the upper half plane, the poles of $f(z)$ are given by the roots of $q(z) = (z^2 + 1)(z^2 + 4) = 0$. Hence, the poles of $f(z)$ in the upper half plane are $z = i$ and $z = 2i$. Clearly, $f(z)$ satisfies the conditions of Theorem 7.6.2. Since the poles of $f(z)$ are simple, by (7.2.7) we have

$$\text{Res}\, (i) = \lim_{z \to i} (z - i)\, f(z) = \lim_{z \to i} \left[\frac{z^2}{(z + i)(z^2 + 4)} \right] = -\frac{1}{6i},$$

$$\text{Res}\, (2i) = \lim_{z \to 2i} (z - 2i)\, f(z) = \lim_{z \to 2i} \left[\frac{z^2}{(z^2 + 1)(z + 2i)} \right] = \frac{1}{3i}.$$

Therefore

$$\int_{-\infty}^{\infty} \frac{x^2}{(x^2 + 1)(x^2 + 4)}\, dx = 2\pi i \left(-\frac{1}{6i} + \frac{1}{3i} \right) = \frac{\pi}{3}.$$

Also, since $f(x)$ is an even function, we have

$$\int_{0}^{\infty} \frac{x^2}{(x^2 + 1)(x^2 + 4)}\, dx = \frac{\pi}{6}.$$

In establishing the next theorem, we shall make use of the *Jordan Inequality*, given in (7.6.10) below. Observe that $\cos \theta$ is a decreasing function for $0 \leq \theta \leq \pi/2$. Therefore, the mean ordinate of the graph $y = \cos x$ over the range $0 \leq x \leq \theta$ also decreases steadily. This mean ordinate is given by

$$\frac{1}{\theta} \int_{0}^{\theta} \cos x\, dx = \frac{\sin \theta}{\theta}.$$

Hence, for $0 \leq \theta \leq \pi/2$, we have

$$1 \geq \frac{\sin \theta}{\theta} \geq \frac{2}{\pi}.$$

Thus

$$\frac{2\theta}{\pi} \leq \sin \theta \leq \theta, \qquad 0 \leq \theta \leq \frac{\pi}{2}. \tag{7.6.10}$$

We shall also need the following simple result:

$$\int_0^\pi e^{m \sin \theta} \, d\theta = 2 \int_0^{\pi/2} e^{m \sin \theta} \, d\theta, \tag{7.6.11}$$

where m is a constant.

Verification of (7.6.11):

$$\int_0^\pi e^{m \sin \theta} \, d\theta = \int_0^{\pi/2} e^{m \sin \theta} \, d\theta + \int_{\pi/2}^\pi e^{m \sin \theta} \, d\theta.$$

Using the substitution $\theta = \pi - \phi$ in the last integral above, we get

$$\int_{\pi/2}^\pi e^{m \sin \theta} \, d\theta = -\int_{\pi/2}^0 e^{m \sin(\pi-\phi)} \, d\phi = \int_0^{\pi/2} e^{m \sin \phi} \, d\phi = \int_0^{\pi/2} e^{m \sin \theta} \, d\theta,$$

thus establishing (7.6.11).

——**THEOREM** 7.6.3. Suppose that $f(z)$ is meromorphic in the upper half plane. Also suppose that there exist positive constants p, K and R_0 such that for $|z| \geq R_0$, $|f(z)| \leq K/|z|^p$. Then for every $m > 0$

$$\lim_{R \to \infty} \int_{C_R} e^{imz} f(z) \, dz = 0, \tag{7.6.12}$$

where C_R is the upper half of the circle $|z| = R$.

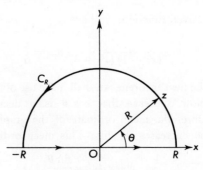

FIG. 7.6.2

Proof. Let z be on C_R. Then

$$z = Re^{i\theta} = R(\cos\theta + i\sin\theta),$$

(see Fig. 7.6.2). For z on C_R we have, in view of (4.1.5),

$$|e^{imz}| = |e^{imR(\cos\theta + i\sin\theta)}| = |e^{-mR\sin\theta}||e^{imR\cos\theta}| = e^{-mR\sin\theta}.$$

In view of (7.6.11) and (7.6.10), and taking $R \geq R_0$ so that $|f(z)| \leq KR^{-p}$ for z on C_R, we obtain

$$\left| \int_{C_R} e^{imz} f(z)\, dz \right|$$

$$= \left| \int_0^\pi e^{imz} f(z) \frac{dz}{d\theta}\, d\theta \right| = \left| \int_0^\pi e^{imz} f(z)\, Rie^{i\theta}\, d\theta \right| \leq \int_0^\pi |e^{imz}|\,|f(z)|\, R\, d\theta$$

$$\leq \frac{K}{R^p} \int_0^\pi e^{-mR\sin\theta} R\, d\theta \leq \frac{2K}{R^{p-1}} \int_0^{\pi/2} e^{-(2mR/\pi)\theta}\, d\theta = \frac{\pi K}{mR^p}(1 - e^{-mR}).$$

Since $m > 0$ and $p > 0$, we see that

$$\lim_{R\to\infty} \int_{C_R} e^{imz} f(z)\, dz = 0,$$

thus establishing the theorem.

We shall now establish the following useful

——**THEOREM** 7.6.4. Let $f(z) = p(z)/q(z)$, where $p(z)$ and $q(z)$ are relatively prime polynomials and $q(z)$ has no real zeros. If the degree of $q(z)$ exceeds that of $p(z)$ and $m > 0$, then

$$\int_{-\infty}^\infty f(x) e^{imx}\, dx = 2\pi i \sum_{n=1}^k \text{Res}\,[f(z) e^{imz}, z_n], \qquad (7.6.13)$$

where the z_n denote those poles of $f(z)e^{imz}$ which lie in the upper half plane.

Proof. Let C_R be the upper half of the circle $|z| = R$, and take R sufficiently large, say $R > R_0$, so that all the poles z_n of $f(z)e^{imz}$, which are located in the upper half plane, lie in its interior as shown in Fig. 7.6.3. From

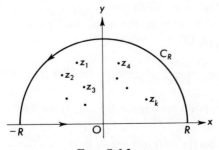

FIG. 7.6.3

Theorem 7.2.1 we then have

$$\int_{-R}^{R} f(x)\, e^{imx}\, dx + \int_{C_R} f(z)\, e^{imz}\, dz = 2\pi i \sum_{n=1}^{k} \mathrm{Res}\,[f(z)\, e^{imz},\, z_n].$$

(7.6.14)

Let the degree of $q(z)$ minus that of $p(z)$ be r. Then $r > 0$ and

$$f(z) = \mathcal{O}\left(\frac{1}{|z|^r}\right).$$

Thus the conditions of Theorem 7.6.3 are satisfied. Therefore

$$\lim_{R \to \infty} \int_{C_R} f(z)\, e^{imz}\, dz = 0.$$

Hence, upon letting $R \to \infty$ in (7.6.14), we obtain

$$\lim_{R \to \infty} \int_{-R}^{R} f(x)\, e^{imx}\, dx = 2\pi i \sum_{n=1}^{k} \mathrm{Res}\,[f(z)\, e^{imz},\, z_n].$$

It can be shown that the integral in (7.6.13) converges. Thus (see Remark 7.6.1), the theorem is established.

Observe that the poles of $f(z)e^{imz}$ in the upper half plane are precisely the roots of $q(z) = 0$ in the upper half plane.

Since $e^{imx} = \cos mx + i \sin mx$, by taking the real and imaginary parts of (7.6.13), we can evaluate integrals of the type

$$\int_{-\infty}^{\infty} f(x) \cos mx\, dx, \qquad \int_{-\infty}^{\infty} f(x) \sin mx\, dx. \qquad (7.6.15)$$

EXAMPLE 7.6.2.   Let us evaluate

$$\int_{0}^{\infty} \frac{x \sin x}{(x^2 + 1)(x^2 + 4)}\, dx.$$

Solution. We see that $f(z) = p(z)/q(z) = z/(z^2 + 1)(z^2 + 4)$ satisfies the conditions of Theorem 7.6.4. Thus, in the upper half plane, the poles of $f(z)e^{imz} = p(z)e^{imz}/q(z)$ are given by the roots of $q(z) = (z^2 + 1)(z^2 + 4) = 0$. Hence, the poles of $f(z)e^{imz}$ in the upper half plane are $z = i$ and $z = 2i$. Taking $m = 1$ in (7.6.13), we obtain

$$\int_{-\infty}^{\infty} \frac{xe^{ix}}{(x^2 + 1)(x^2 + 4)}\, dx = 2\pi i\,[\mathrm{Res}\,(i) + \mathrm{Res}\,(2i)].$$

Since the poles of $f(z)e^{iz}$ are simple, by (7.2.7) we have

$$\mathrm{Res}\,[f(z)\, e^{iz},\, i] = \lim_{z \to i}\,[(z - i)f(z)\, e^{iz}] = \lim_{z \to i} \frac{ze^{iz}}{(z + i)(z^2 + 4)} = \frac{1}{6e},$$

$$\text{Res}\,[f(z)\,e^{iz},\,2i] = \lim_{z \to 2i}[(z - 2i)f(z)\,e^{iz}] = \lim_{z \to 2i}\frac{ze^{iz}}{(z^2 + 1)\,(z + 2i)} = -\frac{1}{6e^2}.$$

Hence

$$\int_{-\infty}^{\infty}\frac{xe^{ix}}{(x^2 + 1)\,(x^2 + 4)}\,dx = \int_{-\infty}^{\infty}\frac{(x\cos x + ix\sin x)}{(x^2 + 1)\,(x^2 + 4)}\,dx = \frac{i\pi}{3e^2}\,(e - 1).$$

On equating the imaginary parts in the above expression, we obtain

$$\int_{-\infty}^{\infty}\frac{x\sin x}{(x^2 + 1)\,(x^2 + 4)}\,dx = \frac{\pi}{3e^2}\,(e - 1).$$

Since the integrand in the above integral is an even function, we have

$$\int_{0}^{\infty}\frac{x\sin x}{(x^2 + 1)\,(x^2 + 4)}\,dx = \frac{\pi}{6e^2}\,(e - 1).$$

Cauchy's principal value of an integral will now be defined. If $|f(x)| \to \infty$ as $x \to c$, then

$$\lim_{\substack{\epsilon \to +0 \\ \eta \to +0}}\left[\int_{a}^{c-\epsilon}f(x)\,dx + \int_{c+\eta}^{b}f(x)\,dx\right] \tag{7.6.16}$$

may exist; this limit (provided it exists) is also written as

$$\int_{a}^{b}f(x)\,dx$$

and is called an *improper integral*. However, it might happen that neither of the limits in (7.6.16) exists when $\epsilon \to 0$ and $\eta \to 0$ independently, but that

$$\lim_{\epsilon \to +0}\left[\int_{a}^{c-\epsilon}f(x)\,dx + \int_{c+\epsilon}^{b}f(x)\,dx\right] \tag{7.6.17}$$

exists. When this limit exists it is called the *Cauchy principal value of* $\int_{a}^{b}f(x)\,dx$ and is denoted for brevity by $P\int_{a}^{b}f(x)\,dx$, that is,

$$P\int_{a}^{b}f(x)\,dx = \lim_{\epsilon \to +0}\left[\int_{a}^{c-\epsilon}f(x)\,dx + \int_{c+\epsilon}^{b}f(x)\,dx\right]. \tag{7.6.18}$$

Note that if the limit exists in (7.6.16), then it also exists in the sense given in (7.6.17), that is, the Cauchy principal value of $\int_{a}^{b}f(x)\,dx$ exists (and the two limits are equal). Also, for $f(x) \geqq 0$, the converse holds.

When $f(x)$ is finite for all real values x, then by

$$P\int_{-\infty}^{\infty}f(x)\,dx$$

we mean

$$\lim_{R \to \infty} \int_{-R}^{R} f(x)\, dx, \tag{7.6.19}$$

(provided the limit exists).

More generally, when $|f(x)| \to \infty$ as $x \to a_k, k = 1, 2, \cdots, s, a_1 < a_2 < \cdots < a_s$, then by

$$P \int_{-\infty}^{\infty} f(x)\, dx$$

we mean

$$\lim_{\substack{R \to \infty \\ \max r_i \to 0}} \left[\int_{-R}^{a_1 - r_1} f(x)\, dx + \int_{a_1 + r_1}^{a_2 - r_2} f(x)\, dx + \cdots \right.$$

$$\left. + \int_{a_{s-1} + r_{s-1}}^{a_s - r_s} f(x)\, dx + \int_{a_s + r_s}^{R} f(x)\, dx \right], \tag{7.6.20}$$

(provided the limit exists).

EXAMPLE 7.6.3.   Let us show that for $a \neq 0$, a real,

$$P \int_{0}^{3a} \frac{dx}{x - a} = \log 2 \quad \text{but that} \quad \int_{0}^{3a} \frac{dx}{x - a}$$

does not exist as an improper integral.

Solution. Let $a > 0$. Then

$$P \int_{0}^{3a} \frac{dx}{x - a} = \lim_{\epsilon \to +0} \left(\int_{0}^{a - \epsilon} \frac{dx}{x - a} + \int_{a + \epsilon}^{3a} \frac{dx}{x - a} \right)$$

$$= \lim_{\epsilon \to +0} (\log \epsilon - \log a + \log 2a - \log \epsilon) = \log 2.$$

If we use (7.6.16), we obtain

$$\int_{0}^{3a} \frac{dx}{x - a} = \lim_{\substack{\epsilon \to +0 \\ \eta \to +0}} \left[\int_{0}^{a - \epsilon} \frac{dx}{x - a} + \int_{a + \eta}^{3a} \frac{dx}{x - a} \right]$$

$$= \lim_{\substack{\epsilon \to +0 \\ \eta \to +0}} [(\log \epsilon - \log a) + (\log 2a - \log \eta)]$$

$$= \log 2 + \lim_{\substack{\epsilon \to +0 \\ \eta \to +0}} \log \left(\frac{\epsilon}{\eta} \right).$$

The latter limit is indeterminate.

The proof that $P \int_{0}^{3a} dx/(x - a) = \log 2$ also for $a < 0$ is similar.

The integral

$$\int_{-\infty}^{\infty} \frac{4x^3}{x^4 + 1}\, dx$$

diverges, since its indefinite integral: $\log(x^4 + 1)$ becomes infinite as $x \to \infty$. However, since the integrand is an odd function, we have

$$P \int_{-\infty}^{\infty} \frac{4x^3}{x^4 + 1} \, dx = \lim_{R \to \infty} \int_{-R}^{R} \frac{4x^3}{x^4 + 1} \, dx = 0.$$

EXERCISES 7.6

Use the method of residues to verify that

1. $\displaystyle\int_0^\infty \frac{x^2}{(x^2 + 1)^2} \, dx = \frac{\pi}{4}.$

2. $\displaystyle\int_0^\infty \frac{x \sin x}{x^2 + 4} \, dx = \frac{\pi}{2} e^{-2}.$

3. $\displaystyle\int_0^\infty \frac{dx}{x^4 - 6x^2 + 25} = \frac{\pi}{20}.$

4. $\displaystyle\int_0^\infty \frac{\cos^2 x}{(x^2 + 1)^2} \, dx = \frac{\pi}{8}(1 + 3e^{-2}).$

5. $\displaystyle\int_0^\infty \frac{\cos ax}{(x^2 + b^2)^2} \, dx = \frac{\pi}{4b^3}(1 + ab)\, e^{-ab}, \qquad a \geqq 0, \quad b > 0.$

6. $\displaystyle\int_{-\infty}^\infty \frac{dx}{(x^2 + a^2)(x^2 + b^2)^2} = \frac{\pi(a + 2b)}{2ab^3(a + b)^2}, \qquad a > 0, \quad b > 0.$

7. $\displaystyle\int_{-\infty}^\infty \frac{\cos x}{(x^2 + a^2)(x^2 + b^2)} \, dx = \frac{\pi}{a^2 - b^2}\left(\frac{e^{-b}}{b} - \frac{e^{-a}}{a}\right), a > 0, b > 0, a \neq b.$

8. $\displaystyle\int_0^{2\pi} \frac{\sin n\theta}{1 + 2a \cos \theta + a^2} \, d\theta = 0, \qquad -1 < a < 1, \quad n \text{ is an integer.}$

9. $\displaystyle\int_0^{2\pi} \frac{\cos n\theta}{1 + 2a \cos \theta + a^2} \, d\theta = \frac{(-1)^n 2\pi a^n}{1 - a^2}, \qquad -1 < a < 1, \quad n = 0, 1, \cdots.$

10. $\displaystyle\int_0^\infty \frac{3x^2 - a^2}{(x^2 + b^2)^2} \cos mx \, dx = \frac{\pi e^{-mb}}{4b^3}[3b^2 - a^2 - mb(3b^2 + a^2)],$

    $b > 0, \quad m \geqq 0.$

11. $\displaystyle\int_0^\infty \frac{x^6}{(x^4 + a^4)^2} \, dx = \frac{3\sqrt{2}\pi}{16a}, \qquad a > 0.$

12. $\displaystyle\int_0^{2\pi} \frac{\cos^3 \theta}{1 - 2a \cos \theta + a^2} \, d\theta = \frac{\pi(a^3 + 3a)}{2(1 - a^2)}, \qquad -1 < a < 1.$

13. $\displaystyle\int_0^\pi \frac{\sin^2 \theta}{a + b \cos \theta} \, d\theta = \frac{\pi}{b^2}\left(a - \sqrt{a^2 - b^2}\right), \qquad a > |b| > 0.$

14. $\displaystyle\int_0^{2\pi} \frac{(1 + 2 \cos \theta)^n \cos n\theta}{3 + 2 \cos \theta} \, d\theta = \frac{2\pi}{\sqrt{5}}\left(3 - \sqrt{5}\right)^n, \qquad n = 0, 1, \cdots.$

15. $\int_0^\infty \dfrac{x(x^2 + 1) \sin x}{(x^4 + x^2 + 1)^2}\, dx = \dfrac{\pi}{6}\left(1 + \dfrac{2}{\sqrt{3}}\right) e^{-\sqrt{3}/2} \sin\left(\dfrac{1}{2}\right).$

16. $\int_{-\infty}^\infty \dfrac{dx}{(x^2 + 1)^{n+1}} = \dfrac{1 \cdot 3 \cdot 5 \cdots (2n - 1)\,\pi}{2 \cdot 4 \cdot 6 \cdots 2n}, \qquad n = 1, 2, \cdots.$

17. $\int_0^{2\pi} \dfrac{e^{m\cos\theta}}{1 + a^2 - 2a\sin\theta}\,[\cos\,(m\sin\theta) - a\sin\,(m\sin\theta + \theta)]\, d\theta = 2\pi\cos ma,$

$-1 < a < 1.$

18. $\int_0^{2\pi} (\cos x)^{2m}\, dx = \dfrac{\pi}{2^{2m-1}}\binom{2m}{m}, \qquad m = 1, 2, \cdots,$

where

$$\binom{n}{k} = \frac{n(n - 1)\,(n - 2)\cdots(n - k + 1)}{k!}, \qquad k = 1, 2, \cdots.$$

19. $\int_0^\infty \dfrac{x^{2m}}{1 + x^{2n}}\, dx = \dfrac{\pi}{2n \sin \dfrac{\pi(2m + 1)}{2n}}, \quad m, n \text{ integers}, \quad 0 \leqq m < n.$

7.7. INDENTED CONTOURS. We shall now extend Theorem 7.6.1 to the case where $f(z)$, besides being meromorphic in the upper half plane, may have simple poles on the real axis. Suppose first that the only singularity of $f(z)$ on the real axis is a simple pole at $z = a$. Consider the following indented contour C as shown in Fig. 7.7.1 (where $a > 0$). That is, C is the path consisting

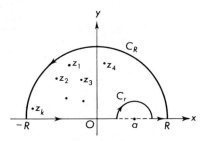

FIG. 7.7.1

of the semicircle C_R: $z = Re^{i\theta}$, $0 \leqq \theta \leqq \pi$, the interval $-R \leqq x \leqq a - r$, the inverse C_r of the semicircle Γ_r: $z = a + re^{i\theta}$, $0 \leqq \theta \leqq \pi$, and the interval $a + r \leqq x \leqq R$. As in Theorem 7.6.1, let $f(z)$ have a finite number of poles.

By taking R sufficiently large and r sufficiently small, we can make the contour C enclose all the poles of $f(z)$ in the upper half plane. By Theorem 7.2.1 we then have

$$\int_C f(z)\, dz = \int_{C_R} f(z)\, dz + \int_{-R}^{a-r} f(x)\, dx + \int_{C_r} f(z)\, dz + \int_{a+r}^R f(x)\, dx$$

$$= 2\pi i \sum_{n=1}^k \text{Res}\,(z_n). \tag{7.7.1}$$

To evaluate $\int_{C_r} f(z)\, dz$, we shall need the following

LEMMA 7.7.1.   Let

$$S_r:\quad z = a + re^{i\theta},\qquad \theta_1 \leq \theta \leq \theta_2, \tag{7.7.2}$$

be an arc of the circle with center at a and radius r. If $f(z)$ has a simple pole at $z = a$, then

$$\lim_{r\to 0} \int_{S_r} f(z)\, dz = i(\theta_2 - \theta_1)\, \text{Res}\,(a). \tag{7.7.3}$$

Proof.   Since $f(z)$ has a simple pole at $z = a$, its Laurent expansion about a is given by

$$f(z) = \frac{\text{Res}\,(a)}{z - a} + \lambda(z),$$

where $\lambda(z)$ is analytic at $z = a$. Thus

$$\int_{S_r} f(z)\, dz = \text{Res}\,(a) \int_{S_r} \frac{dz}{z - a} + \int_{S_r} \lambda(z)\, dz$$

$$= \text{Res}\,(a) \int_{\theta_1}^{\theta_2} \frac{rie^{i\theta}}{re^{i\theta}}\, d\theta + \int_{S_r} \lambda(z)\, dz \tag{7.7.4}$$

$$= i(\theta_2 - \theta_1)\, \text{Res}\,(a) + \int_{S_r} \lambda(z)\, dz.$$

Since $\lambda(z)$ is continuous at $z = a$, we can choose r sufficiently small so that for a given $\epsilon > 0$

$$|\lambda(z)| < |\lambda(a)| + \epsilon,\qquad \text{for } z \text{ on } S_r.$$

Thus as $r \to 0$

$$\left| \int_{S_r} \lambda(z)\, dz \right| \leq \int_{S_r} |\lambda(z)|\, |dz| < [|\lambda(a)| + \epsilon] \int_{S_r} |dz|$$

$$= [|\lambda(a)| + \epsilon]\,(\theta_2 - \theta_1)\, r \to 0. \tag{7.7.5}$$

Hence from (7.7.4) and (7.7.5) we obtain

$$\lim_{r\to 0} \int_{S_r} f(z)\, dz = i(\theta_2 - \theta_1)\, \text{Res}\,(a),$$

thus establishing (7.7.3).

Let us now return to (7.7.1). As in Theorem 7.6.1, let us suppose that for $|z|$ sufficiently large $|f(z)| \leq K/|z|^p$, where $p > 1$ and K are constants. Then as was seen in the proof of Theorem 7.6.1, we have

$$\lim_{R \to \infty} \int_{C_R} f(z)\, dz = 0. \tag{7.7.6}$$

Also, by definition

$$P \int_{-\infty}^{\infty} f(x)\, dx = \lim_{\substack{R \to \infty \\ r \to +0}} \left[\int_{-R}^{a-r} f(x)\, dx + \int_{a+r}^{R} f(x)\, dx \right]. \tag{7.7.7}$$

From (5.2.15) and Lemma 7.7.1, we obtain

$$\lim_{r \to 0} \int_{C_r} f(z)\, dz = - \lim_{r \to 0} \int_{\Gamma_r} f(z)\, dz$$

$$= - i(\pi - 0)\, \text{Res}\,(a) = - i\pi\, \text{Res}\,(a). \tag{7.7.8}$$

Utilizing (7.7.6), (7.7.7) and (7.7.8), we see that as $R \to \infty$ and $r \to 0$, equation (7.7.1) becomes

$$P \int_{-\infty}^{\infty} f(x)\, dx = 2\pi i \sum_{n=1}^{k} \text{Res}\,(z_n) + i\pi\, \text{Res}\,(a). \tag{7.7.9}$$

Now, suppose that a_j, $j = 1, 2, \cdots, s$ are simple poles of $f(z)$ along the real axis. Applying the above process to each a_j and using (7.6.20), we have the following

——**THEOREM** 7.7.1.   Let $f(z)$ be meromorphic in the upper half plane and analytic on the real axis except for simple poles. Suppose furthermore that for $|z|$ sufficiently large we have $|f(z)| \leq K/|z|^p$, where $p > 1$ and K are constants. Then

$$P \int_{-\infty}^{\infty} f(x)\, dx = 2\pi i \sum_{n=1}^{k} \text{Res}\,(z_n) + \pi i \sum_{j=1}^{s} \text{Res}\,(a_j) \tag{7.7.10}$$

where z_n, $n = 1, 2, \cdots, k$ are the poles of $f(z)$ in the upper half plane, a_j, $j = 1, 2, \cdots, s$ are the simple poles of $f(z)$ on the real axis, and $P \int_{-\infty}^{\infty} f(x)\, dx$ is as given in (7.6.20).

In a similar fashion, we may extend Theorem 7.6.4 to obtain the following

——**THEOREM** 7.7.2.   Let $f(z) = p(z)/q(z)$, where $p(z)$ and $q(z)$ are relatively prime polynomials and the degree of $q(z)$ exceeds that of $p(z)$. Suppose that on the real axis $f(z)$ has at most simple poles. Let z_n, $n = 1, 2, \cdots, k$ denote the poles of $f(z)$ which lie in the upper half plane. Let $a_j, j = 1, 2, \cdots, s$ denote the simple poles of $f(z)$ which lie on the real axis. If $m > 0$, then

$$P \int_{-\infty}^{\infty} f(x)\, e^{imx}\, dx = 2\pi i \sum_{n=1}^{k} \text{Res}\,[f(z)\, e^{imz}, z_n] + \pi i \sum_{j=1}^{s} \text{Res}\,[f(z)\, e^{imz}, a_j].$$

$$(7.7.11)$$

Note that the functions $f(z)$ and $f(z)\, e^{imz}$ have the same poles. However, $\text{Res}\,[f(z)\, e^{imz}, z_n]$ is not necessarily the same as $\text{Res}\,[f(z), z_n]$.

EXAMPLE 7.7.1. Let us show that

$$\int_0^{\infty} \frac{\sin mx}{x(x^2 + b^2)^2}\, dx = \frac{\pi}{2b^4}\left[1 - \frac{e^{-mb}}{2}(mb + 2)\right], \quad b > 0, \quad m > 0. \quad (7.7.12)$$

Solution. The function $f(z)\, e^{imz} = e^{imz}/z(z^2 + b^2)^2$ has the same poles in the upper half plane and along the real axis as $f(z) = p(z)/q(z) = 1/z(z^2 + b^2)^2$. The poles of $f(z)$ are given by the roots of $q(z) = z(z^2 + b^2)^2 = 0$. Hence $f(z)\, e^{imz}$ has a simple pole along the real axis at $z = 0$ and a pole of order two at $z = bi$ in the upper half plane. Utilizing formulas (7.2.7) and (7.2.6) we find

$$\text{Res}\,[f(z)\, e^{imz}, 0] = \lim_{z \to 0}[zf(z)\, e^{imz}] = \lim_{z \to 0} \frac{e^{imz}}{(z^2 + b^2)^2} = \frac{1}{b^4},$$

$$\text{Res}\,[f(z)\, e^{imz}, bi] = \lim_{z \to bi} \frac{d}{dz}[(z - bi)^2 f(z)\, e^{imz}] = \lim_{z \to bi} \frac{d}{dz}\left[\frac{e^{imz}}{z(z + bi)^2}\right]$$

$$= \frac{-e^{-mb}}{4b^4}(mb + 2).$$

Thus, from (7.7.11) we obtain

$$P \int_{-\infty}^{\infty} \frac{e^{imx}}{x(x^2 + b^2)^2}\, dx = P \int_{-\infty}^{\infty} \frac{(\cos mx + i \sin mx)}{x(x^2 + b^2)^2}\, dx$$

$$= \frac{i\pi}{b^4}\left[1 - \frac{e^{-mb}}{2}(mb + 2)\right].$$

On equating the imaginary parts in the above expression, we have

$$P \int_{-\infty}^{\infty} \frac{\sin mx}{x(x^2 + b^2)^2}\, dx = \frac{\pi}{b^4}\left[1 - \frac{e^{-mb}}{2}(mb + 2)\right]. \quad (7.7.13)$$

Since

$$\left|\frac{\sin mx}{x(x^2 + b^2)^2}\right| \leq \frac{1}{x^5}$$

for $x > 0$, and

$$\frac{\sin mx}{x(x^2 + b^2)^2} \to \frac{m}{b^4} \quad \text{as} \quad x \to 0,$$

the P before the integral is not necessary. Since the integrand in (7.7.13) is an even function, (7.7.12) now follows.

7.8. INTEGRALS INVOLVING MULTIPLE-VALUED FUNCTIONS.

Let us consider the integral

$$\int_0^\infty x^{\alpha-1} f(x)\, dx$$

where α is a real constant different from an integer, and $f(z)$ is a meromorphic function of z which has either no poles, or else only simple poles on the positive part of the real axis.

Let D and D_0 denote, respectively, the domains consisting of the z plane with the nonnegative and the nonpositive parts of the real axis removed. Since α is not an integer, the function

$$z^{\alpha-1} f(z) = e^{(\alpha-1)\log z} f(z)$$

is a multiple-valued function with a branch point at the origin. However, if we take the principal value of $z^{\alpha-1}$ (see Section 4.4), we obtain a single-valued function

$$F_0(z) = e^{(\alpha-1)\operatorname{Log} z} f(z) \tag{7.8.1}$$

which is meromorphic in the domain D_0.

If we take the principal value of $(-z)^{\alpha-1}$, we obtain another single-valued function

$$F(z) = e^{(\alpha-1)[\operatorname{Log}(-z)+i\pi]} f(z) \tag{7.8.2}$$

which is meromorphic in the domain D. Note that $F(z)$, as well as $F_0(z)$, is one of the values of $z^{\alpha-1} f(z)$. Observe that in D_0, $F_0(z)$ and $f(z)$ have the same poles, while in D, $F(z)$ and $f(z)$ have the same poles. Also (see Exercise 4.5.4) $F(z) = F_0(z)$ for $\mathscr{I}(z) > 0$, and $F(z) = e^{2\alpha\pi i} F_0(z)$ for $\mathscr{I}(z) < 0$.

One may easily show [see Exercise 4.4.3(c)] that

$$|F(z)| = |F_0(z)| = |z|^{\alpha-1} |f(z)|. \tag{7.8.3}$$

We shall now establish the following useful

——**THEOREM** 7.8.1. Let $f(z)$ be meromorphic in the complex plane and suppose that $f(z)$ has no poles on the positive real axis. Let α be a real constant different from an integer. Suppose further that

$$\lim_{z \to \infty} [|z|^\alpha |f(z)|] = 0 \quad \text{and} \quad \lim_{z \to 0} [|z|^\alpha |f(z)|] = 0.$$

Then

$$\int_0^\infty x^{\alpha-1} f(x)\, dx = -\frac{\pi e^{-\alpha\pi i}}{\sin \alpha\pi} \sum_{n=1}^{k} \text{Res}\, [F(z), z_n], \qquad (7.8.4)$$

where z_n, $n = 1, 2, \cdots, k$ denote the nonzero poles of $f(z)$, and $F(z)$ is the function given in (7.8.2).

Note: Since $\lim_{z\to\infty} [|\, z\,|^\alpha\, |\, f(z)\,|] = 0$, $f(z)$ has only a finite number of poles. (See hint to Exercise 7.1.10.)

Proof. Let the simple closed contour $C = C_R + L_2 + C_r + L_1$ be as in Fig. 7.8.1, where the radius R of C_R is sufficiently large, the radius r of C_r is sufficiently small and the segments L_1, L_2 are sufficiently close to the real axis so that all the nonzero poles z_1, z_2, $\cdots$, z_k of $f(z)$ are contained in the interior of C.

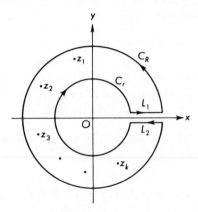

Fig. 7.8.1.

Since for z in D the poles of $F(z)$ are the same as the poles of $f(z)$, we have by Theorem 7.2.1

$$\int_C F(z)\, dz = \int_{C_R} F(z)\, dz + \int_{L_2} F(z)\, dz + \int_{C_r} F(z)\, dz + \int_{L_1} F(z)\, dz$$

$$= 2\pi i \sum_{n=1}^{k} \text{Res}\, [F(z), z_n]. \qquad (7.8.5)$$

For z on C_R, we have $|\, z\,| = R$. Utilizing (7.8.3) and (5.2.22), we obtain

$$\left| \int_{C_R} F(z)\, dz \right| \leq \int_{C_R} |\, F(z)\,|\, |\, dz\,| \leqq \int_{C_R} |\, z\,|^{\alpha-1} |\, f(z)\,|\, |\, dz\,|$$

$$= \int_{C_R} |\, z\,|^\alpha |\, f(z)\,|\, |\, z\,|^{-1} |\, dz\,|$$

$$\leqq \max_{|z|=R} [|\, z\,|^\alpha |\, f(z)\,|] \int_{C_R} |\, z\,|^{-1} |\, dz\,| < 2\pi \max_{|z|=R} [|\, z\,|^\alpha |\, f(z)\,|].$$

From the hypothesis, $\lim_{z \to 0} [| z |^{\alpha} | f(z) |] = 0$. Hence, given any $\epsilon > 0$, there exists a constant $R_0 > 0$ such that for $R > R_0$, we have

$$\left| \int_{C_R} F(z) \, dz \right| < \frac{\epsilon}{4}. \tag{7.8.6}$$

Now, $| z | = r$ for z on C_r. From the hypothesis, $\lim_{z \to \infty} [| z |^{\alpha} | f(z) |] = 0$. Proceeding as above we see that given any $\epsilon > 0$, there exists a constant $r_0 > 0$ such that for $r < r_0$, we have

$$\left| \int_{C_r} F(z) \, dz \right| < \frac{\epsilon}{4}. \tag{7.8.7}$$

Also in view of Exercise 4.5.4, we see that if $x > 0$, then $\lim_{z \to x} F(z) = x^{\alpha-1} f(x)$ when $z \to x$ from above the x axis and

$$\lim_{z \to x} F(z) = e^{2\pi i (\alpha-1)} x^{\alpha-1} f(x) = e^{2\alpha \pi i} x^{\alpha-1} f(x)$$

when $z \to x$ from below the x axis.

Thus, having fixed the values of R and r so that (7.8.6) and (7.8.7) are satisfied, we may take L_1 and L_2 sufficiently close to the x axis so that

$$\left| \int_r^R x^{\alpha-1} f(x) \, dx - \int_{L_1} F(z) \, dz \right| < \frac{\epsilon}{4},$$

$$\left| \int_R^r e^{2\alpha \pi i} x^{\alpha-1} f(x) \, dx - \int_{L_2} F(z) \, dz \right| < \frac{\epsilon}{4}. \tag{7.8.8}$$

From (7.8.5) to (7.8.8) we see that for any $\epsilon > 0$, we can choose $r_0 > 0$ sufficiently small and $R_0 > 0$ sufficiently large so that if $r < r_0$ and $R > R_0$, we have

$$\left| \int_r^R x^{\alpha-1} f(x) \, dx + \int_R^r e^{2\alpha \pi i} x^{\alpha-1} f(x) \, dx - 2\pi i \sum_{n=1}^{k} \text{Res} \, [F(z), z_n] \right| < \epsilon,$$

or

$$\left| (1 - e^{2\alpha \pi i}) \int_r^R x^{\alpha-1} f(x) \, dx - 2\pi i \sum_{n=1}^{k} \text{Res} \, [F(z), z_n] \right| < \epsilon.$$

Letting $r \to 0$ and $R \to \infty$ and noting that $e^{2\alpha \pi i} \neq 1$ when α is not an integer we obtain

$$\int_0^{\infty} x^{\alpha-1} f(x) \, dx = \frac{2\pi i}{1 - e^{2\alpha \pi i}} \sum_{n=1}^{k} \text{Res} \, [F(z), z_n].$$

Since

$$\frac{e^{\alpha \pi i} - e^{-\alpha \pi i}}{2i} = \sin \alpha \pi,$$

we have

$$\frac{2i}{1 - e^{2\alpha \pi i}} = -\frac{e^{-\alpha \pi i}}{\sin \alpha \pi}.$$

Therefore

$$\int_0^\infty x^{\alpha-1} f(x)\, dx = -\frac{\pi e^{-\alpha \pi i}}{\sin \alpha \pi} \sum_{n=1}^k \text{Res}\,[F(z), z_n],$$

and the theorem is established.

Suppose now that $f(z)$ has a simple pole at $z = a > 0$. Let the simple closed contour $C = C_R + L_3 + \Gamma_r' + L_4 + C_r + L_1 + \Gamma_r + L_2$ be as in Fig. 7.8.2, where the radius R of C_R is sufficiently large, the radius r of C_r, Γ_r' and Γ_r is sufficiently small, and the line segments L_1, L_2, L_3 and L_4 are sufficiently close to the positive real axis so that all the poles $z_1, z_2, \cdots, z_k$ not on the nonnegative x axis are contained in the interior of C.

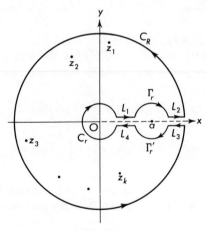

FIG. 7.8.2

Proceeding as in the proof of the foregoing theorem we have

$$\int_C F(z)\, dz = \int_{C_R} F(z)\, dz + \int_{L_3} F(z)\, dz + \int_{\Gamma_r'} F(z)\, dz + \int_{L_4} F(z)\, dz$$

$$+ \int_{C_r} F(z)\, dz + \int_{L_1} F(z)\, dz + \int_{\Gamma_r} F(z)\, dz + \int_{L_2} F(z)\, dz$$

$$= 2\pi i \sum_{n=1}^k \text{Res}\,[F(z), z_n].$$

For any $\epsilon > 0$, if r is sufficiently small, R sufficiently large and the segments L_i ($i = 1, 2, 3, 4$) sufficiently close to the x axis, we have

$$\left| \int_{C_R} F(z)\, dz \right| < \frac{\epsilon}{8} \quad \text{and} \quad \left| \int_{C_r} F(z)\, dz \right| < \frac{\epsilon}{8};$$

$$\left| \int_r^{a-r} x^{\alpha-1}\, f(x)\, dx - \int_{L_1} F(z)\, dz \right| < \frac{\epsilon}{8};$$

$$\left| \int_{a+r}^R x^{\alpha-1}\, f(x)\, dx - \int_{L_2} F(z)\, dz \right| < \frac{\epsilon}{8};$$

$$\left| \int_R^{a+r} e^{2\alpha\pi i}\, x^{\alpha-1}\, f(x)\, dx - \int_{L_3} F(z)\, dz \right| < \frac{\epsilon}{8};$$

$$\left| \int_{a-r}^r e^{2\alpha\pi i}\, x^{\alpha-1}\, f(x)\, dx - \int_{L_4} F(z)\, dz \right| < \frac{\epsilon}{8}.$$

Let $F_0(z)$ be as in (7.8.1). Utilizing Lemma 7.7.1, it is not difficult to show (see Exercise 7.8.22) that for any $\epsilon > 0$, if r is sufficiently small and the segments L_i ($i = 1, 2, 3, 4$) are sufficiently close to the x axis, we have

$$\left\{ \begin{aligned} &\left| - i\pi\, \text{Res}\,[F_0(z), a] - \int_{\Gamma_r} F(z)\, dz \right| < \frac{\epsilon}{8}, \quad \text{and} \\ &\left| - i\pi e^{2\alpha\pi i}\, \text{Res}\,[F_0(z), a] - \int_{\Gamma_r'} F(z)\, dz \right| < \frac{\epsilon}{8}. \end{aligned} \right. \tag{7.8.9}$$

Hence, for any $\epsilon > 0$, we can choose $r_0 > 0$ sufficiently small and $R_0 > 0$ sufficiently large so that if $r < r_0$ and $R > R_0$, we have

$$\left| \int_r^{a-r} x^{\alpha-1}\, f(x)\, dx + \int_{a+r}^R x^{\alpha-1}\, f(x)\, dx + \int_R^{a+r} e^{2\alpha\pi i}\, x^{\alpha-1}\, f(x)\, dx \right.$$

$$\left. + \int_{a-r}^r e^{2\alpha\pi i} x^{\alpha-1}\, f(x)\, dx - 2\pi i \sum_{n=1}^k \text{Res}\,[F(z), z_n] - i\pi(1 + e^{2\alpha\pi i})\, \text{Res}\,[F_0(z), a] \right| < \epsilon,$$

or

$$\lim_{\substack{r \to +0 \\ R \to \infty}} \left[(1 - e^{2\alpha\pi i}) \int_r^{a-r} x^{\alpha-1}\, f(x)\, dx + (1 - e^{2\alpha\pi i}) \int_{a+r}^R x^{\alpha-1}\, f(x)\, dx \right]$$

$$= 2\pi i \sum_{n=1}^k \text{Res}\,[F(z), z_n] + i\pi(1 + e^{2\alpha\pi i})\, \text{Res}\,[F_0(z), a].$$

Since $1 - e^{2\alpha\pi i} \neq 0$ for α not an integer, we have

$$P \int_0^\infty x^{\alpha-1} f(x) \, dx = \lim_{\substack{r \to +0 \\ R \to \infty}} \left[\int_r^{a-r} x^{\alpha-1} f(x) \, dx + \int_{a+r}^R x^{\alpha-1} f(x) \, dx \right]$$

$$= \frac{2\pi i}{1 - e^{2\alpha\pi i}} \sum_{n=1}^k \operatorname{Res} [F(z), z_n] + \frac{i\pi(1 + e^{2\alpha\pi i})}{1 - e^{2\alpha\pi i}} \operatorname{Res} [F_0(z), a]$$

$$= -\frac{\pi e^{-\alpha\pi i}}{\sin \alpha\pi} \sum_{n=1}^k \operatorname{Res} [F(z), z_n] - \pi \cot \pi\alpha \operatorname{Res} [F_0(z), a].$$

Finally suppose that a_j, $j = 1, 2, \cdots, s$ are simple poles of $f(z)$ along the positive real axis. Applying the foregoing process to each a_j, we have the following

——*THEOREM* 7.8.2. Let $f(z)$ be meromorphic in the complex plane and suppose that on the positive real axis $f(z)$ has only simple poles. Let α be a real constant different from an integer. Suppose further that

$$\lim_{z \to \infty} [| z |^\alpha | f(z) |] = 0 \quad \text{and} \quad \lim_{z \to 0} [| z |^\alpha | f(z) |] = 0.$$

Then

$$P \int_0^\infty x^{\alpha-1} f(x) \, dx = -\frac{\pi e^{-\alpha\pi i}}{\sin \alpha\pi} \sum_{n=1}^k \operatorname{Res} [F(z), z_n] - \pi \cot \pi\alpha \sum_{j=1}^s \operatorname{Res} [F_0(z), a_j],$$

$$(7.8.10)$$

where z_n, $n = 1, 2, \cdots, k$ are the poles of $f(z)$ in the complex plane except those along the nonnegative real axis, a_j, $j = 1, 2, \cdots, s$ are the simple poles of $f(z)$ along the positive real axis, and $F_0(z)$ and $F(z)$ are respectively the values of $z^{\alpha-1} f(z)$ given in (7.8.1) and (7.8.2).

EXAMPLE 7.8.1. Let us show that

$$\int_0^\infty \frac{x^\alpha}{(1 + x^2)^2} \, dx = \frac{\pi(1 - \alpha)}{4 \cos (\alpha\pi/2)}, \qquad -1 < \alpha < 3.$$

Solution.   For $\alpha \neq 0, 1, 2$. Here, $F(z) = z^\alpha/(1 + z^2)^2 = z^{\alpha-1} f(z)$, where $f(z) = z/(1 + z^2)^2$. Since $-1 < \alpha < 3$, we see that

$$\lim_{z \to 0} [| z |^\alpha | f(z) |] = 0 \quad \text{and} \quad \lim_{z \to \infty} [| z |^\alpha | f(z) |] = 0.$$

The function $f(z)$ has poles of order two at $z = i$ and $z = -i$. Using Theorem 7.8.1 we have

$$\int_0^\infty \frac{x^\alpha}{(1 + x^2)^2} \, dx = -\frac{\pi e^{-\alpha\pi i}}{\sin \alpha\pi} \{\operatorname{Res} [F(z), i] + \operatorname{Res} [F(z), -i]\}.$$

Utilizing formula (7.2.6), we find

$$\text{Res}\,[F(z),\,i] = \lim_{z \to i} \frac{d}{dz}\,[(z - i)^2 F(z)]$$

$$= \lim_{z \to i} \frac{d}{dz} \left\{ (z - i)^2\, e^{(\alpha-1)[\text{Log}(-z)+i\pi]} \cdot \frac{z}{(z - i)^2\,(z + i)^2} \right\}$$

$$= \lim_{z \to i} \frac{d}{dz} \left\{ \frac{e^{\alpha[\text{Log}(-z)+i\pi]}}{(z + i)^2} \right\} = \lim_{z \to i} \left\{ \frac{e^{\alpha[\text{Log}(-z)+i\pi]} \cdot [\alpha(z + i) - 2z]}{z(z + i)^3} \right\}$$

$$= \frac{2i(\alpha - 1)\, e^{\alpha(-\pi i/2 + i\pi)}}{8} = -\frac{i(1 - \alpha)\, e^{\alpha\pi i/2}}{4}.$$

$$\text{Res}\,[F(z),\,-i] = \lim_{z \to -i} \frac{d}{dz}\,[(z + i)^2 F(z)] = \lim_{z \to -i} \frac{d}{dz} \left\{ \frac{e^{\alpha[\text{Log}(-z)+i\pi]}}{(z - i)^2} \right\}$$

$$= \frac{i(1 - \alpha)\, e^{3\alpha\pi i/2}}{4}.$$

Hence

$$\int_0^\infty \frac{x^\alpha}{(1 + x^2)^2}\, dx = -\frac{\pi(1 - \alpha)\, i}{4 \sin \alpha\pi} \cdot \frac{e^{3\alpha\pi i/2} - e^{\alpha\pi i/2}}{e^{\alpha\pi i}}$$

$$= -\frac{\pi(1 - \alpha)\, i}{4} \frac{2i \sin(\alpha\pi/2)}{\sin \alpha\pi}$$

$$= \frac{\pi(1 - \alpha)}{4} \frac{2 \sin(\alpha\pi/2)}{2 \sin(\alpha\pi/2) \cos(\alpha\pi/2)} = \frac{\pi(1 - \alpha)}{4 \cos(\alpha\pi/2)}.$$

Remark 7.8.1. One should not conclude from the discussion given so far that circular contours are the only ones that can be used to evaluate integrals. In the following example, we shall evaluate an integral by using a *rectangular* path.

EXAMPLE 7.8.2. Let us show that

$$\int_{-\infty}^\infty \frac{e^{mx}}{1 + e^x}\, dx = \frac{\pi}{\sin \pi m}, \qquad 0 < m < 1,$$

by integrating the function $e^{mz}/(1 + e^z)$ around the rectangular path along the lines $y = 0$, $x = R$, $y = 2\pi$ and $x = -R$ (see Fig. 7.8.3) and then letting R tend to infinity.

Solution. Note that within the given rectangular region the function $f(z) = e^{mz}/(1 + e^z)$, $0 < m < 1$, has only one pole, namely, at $z = \pi i$. Using formula (7.2.8) with $p(z) = e^{mz}$ and $q(z) = 1 + e^z$, we find

$$\text{Res}\,(\pi i) = \frac{p(\pi i)}{q'(\pi i)} = \frac{e^{m\pi i}}{-1} = -e^{m\pi i}.$$

By Theorem 7.2.1 we then have

$$\int_{-R}^{R} \frac{e^{mx}}{1+e^x}\, dx + \int_{0}^{2\pi} \frac{e^{m(R+iy)}\, i}{1+e^{R+iy}}\, dy + \int_{R}^{-R} \frac{e^{m(x+2\pi i)}}{1+e^{x+2\pi i}}\, dx$$

$$+ \int_{2\pi}^{0} \frac{e^{m(-R+iy)}\, i}{1+e^{-R+iy}}\, dy = -2\pi i e^{m\pi i}. \qquad (7.8.11)$$

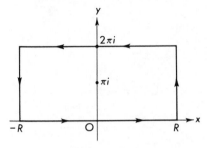

Fig. 7.8.3

Note that in virtue of (4.1.5) and (1.3.11) we have

$$|\,e^{m(R+iy)}\,| = e^{mR}, \qquad |\,e^{R+iy}+1\,| \geqq |\,e^{R+iy}\,| - 1 = e^R - 1.$$

Thus in view of (5.2.22) we obtain

$$\left|\int_{0}^{2\pi} \frac{e^{m(R+iy)}\, i}{1+e^{R+iy}}\, dy\right| \leqq \frac{e^{mR}}{e^R-1}\int_{0}^{2\pi} dy = \frac{2\pi e^{mR}}{e^R-1}.$$

Since $0 < m < 1$, we see that

$$\lim_{R\to\infty}\int_{0}^{2\pi} \frac{e^{m(R+iy)}\, i}{1+e^{R+iy}}\, dy = 0. \qquad (7.8.12)$$

Similarly, one finds that

$$\lim_{R\to\infty}\int_{2\pi}^{0} \frac{e^{m(-R+iy)}\, i}{1+e^{-R+iy}}\, dy = 0. \qquad (7.8.13)$$

Utilizing (7.8.12), (7.8.13), (4.1.6), we see that as $R \to \infty$, (7.8.11) becomes

$$P\int_{-\infty}^{\infty} \frac{e^{mx}}{1+e^x}\, dx + P\int_{\infty}^{-\infty} \frac{e^{mx}e^{2\pi m i}}{1+e^x}\, dx = -2\pi i e^{m\pi i},$$

or

$$P\int_{-\infty}^{\infty} \frac{e^{2m\pi i}-1}{1+e^x}\, e^{mx}\, dx = 2\pi i e^{m\pi i}.$$

Note that $e^{2\pi m i} \neq 1$ for $0 < m < 1$. Since $f(x) = e^{mx}/(1+e^x) > 0$, the P before the integral is not necessary. Hence

$$\int_{-\infty}^{\infty} \frac{e^{mx}}{1+e^x}\, dx = \frac{2i\pi}{e^{m\pi i}-e^{-m\pi i}} = \frac{\pi}{\sin m\pi}.$$

EXERCISES 7.8

1. Prove that

(a) $P \int_0^\infty \frac{x^4}{x^6 - 1} \, dx = \frac{\pi \sqrt{3}}{6}$;

(b) $\int_0^\infty \frac{\sin mx}{x} \, dx = \frac{\pi}{2}$, $m > 0$.

2. Prove that if $0 < \alpha < 1$,

(a) $\int_0^\infty \frac{x^{\alpha-1}}{x + 1} \, dx = \frac{\pi}{\sin \alpha\pi}$;

(b) $P \int_0^\infty \frac{x^{\alpha-1}}{1 - x} \, dx = \pi \cot \alpha\pi$.

3. Prove that if $0 < \alpha < 1$, $-\pi < \beta < \pi$,

$$\int_0^\infty \frac{x^{\alpha-1}}{x + e^{i\beta}} \, dx = \frac{\pi e^{(\alpha-1)\beta i}}{\sin \alpha\pi}.$$

4. Prove that if $-1 < \alpha < 1$, $-\pi < \theta < \pi$,

$$\int_0^\infty \frac{x^\alpha}{1 + 2x \cos \theta + x^2} \, dx = \frac{\pi}{\sin \alpha\pi} \frac{\sin \alpha\theta}{\sin \theta}.$$

5. Prove that if $0 < \alpha < 2$,

$$\int_0^\infty \frac{x^{\alpha-1}}{x^2 + x + 1} \, dx = \frac{2\pi}{\sqrt{3}} \cos \left(\frac{2\alpha\pi + \pi}{6} \right) \csc \alpha\pi.$$

6. Prove that

$$P \int_{-\infty}^\infty \frac{e^{mix}}{(x - a)(x - b)} \, dx = \frac{\pi i (e^{mbi} - e^{mai})}{(b - a)}$$

where a, b, m are real numbers, $a \neq b$, $m > 0$.

7. Prove that if $-1 < \alpha < 1$, $a > 0$, $b > 0$, $a \neq b$,

$$\int_0^\infty \frac{x^\alpha}{(x + a)(x + b)} \, dx = \frac{\pi (a^\alpha - b^\alpha)}{(a - b) \sin \alpha\pi}.$$

8. Prove that if $-1 < \alpha < 3$,

$$\int_0^\infty \frac{x^\alpha}{x^4 + 1} \, dx = \frac{\pi}{4} \csc \frac{\pi}{4} (\alpha + 1).$$

9. Prove that if $0 < \alpha < 2$, $b > 0$,

$$\int_0^\infty \frac{x^{\alpha-1}}{x^2 + b^2} \, dx = \frac{\pi b^{\alpha-2}}{2 \sin (\alpha\pi/2)}.$$

10. Given that $\int_0^\infty e^{-x^2}\, dx = \sqrt{\pi}/2$, integrate e^{-z^2} around a rectangle with vertices at $z = \pm R, \pm R + bi$, $R > 0$, $b > 0$, and letting $R \to \infty$, show that

$$\int_0^\infty e^{-x^2} \cos(2bx)\, dx = \frac{\sqrt{\pi}}{2} e^{-b^2}.$$

11. Integrate e^{iz}/z around the rectangle with vertices at $z = \pm R, \pm R + iR$, $R > 0$, indented at the origin, and show that

$$\int_{-\infty}^\infty \frac{\sin x}{x}\, dx = \pi.$$

12. Integrate $z/(1 - ae^{-iz})$ around the rectangle with vertices at $z = \pm \pi$, $\pm \pi + iR$, $R > 0$, and show that if $a > 1$

$$\int_0^\pi \frac{ax \sin x}{1 - 2a \cos x + a^2}\, dx = \pi \operatorname{Log}\left(1 + \frac{1}{a}\right).$$

Also show that if $0 < a < 1$, then

$$\int_0^\pi \frac{ax \sin x}{1 - 2a \cos x + a^2}\, dx = \pi \operatorname{Log}(1 + a).$$

13. Integrate $e^{az}/\cosh \pi z$ around a rectangle with vertices at $z = \pm R$, $-R + i, R + i$, $R > 0$, and show that if $-\pi < a < \pi$,

$$\int_{-\infty}^\infty \frac{e^{ax}}{\cosh \pi x}\, dx = \sec \frac{a}{2}.$$

Deduce from this expression that

$$\int_{-\infty}^\infty \frac{\cosh ax}{\cosh \pi x}\, dx = \sec \frac{a}{2}, \qquad -\pi < a < \pi.$$

14. Given that $\int_0^\infty e^{-x^2}\, dx = \sqrt{\pi}/2$, integrate the function e^{-z^2} around the boundary of the circular sector, $0 \le \theta \le \alpha$, $\alpha \le \pi/4$, $0 \le r \le R$, and letting $R \to \infty$ show that

(a) $\displaystyle \int_0^\infty e^{-r^2 \cos 2\alpha} \left[\cos(r^2 \sin 2\alpha)\right] dr = \frac{\sqrt{\pi}}{2} \cos \alpha$,

(b) $\displaystyle \int_0^\infty e^{-r^2 \cos 2\alpha} \left[\sin(r^2 \sin 2\alpha)\right] dr = \frac{\sqrt{\pi}}{2} \sin \alpha$.

In particular, when $\alpha = \pi/4$, obtain the *Fresnel Integrals*:

(c) $\displaystyle \int_0^\infty \cos(x^2)\, dx = \int_0^\infty \sin(x^2)\, dx = \frac{\sqrt{2\pi}}{4}.$

15. Integrate Log sin z around the rectangle with vertices at 0, π, $\pi + iR$, iR, $R > 0$, indented at 0 and π, and show that

$$\int_0^{\pi} \text{Log sin } x \, dx = -\pi \text{ Log } 2.$$

16. Integrate $e^{az}/\sinh(\pi z)$ around the rectangle with vertices at $z = \pm R$, $-R + i$, $R + i$, $R > 0$, indented at 0 and i, and show that

$$\int_0^{\infty} \frac{\sinh ax}{\sinh \pi x} \, dx = \frac{1}{2} \tan \frac{a}{2}, \qquad -\pi < a < \pi.$$

17. Show that the function $f(x) = \text{sech } (\sqrt{\pi/2}) \, x$ satisfies the equation

$$f(t) = \sqrt{\frac{2}{\pi}} \int_0^{\infty} f(x) \cos xt \, dx.$$

18. Show that

$$\int_0^{\infty} \frac{\cos x}{\sqrt{x}} \, dx = \int_0^{\infty} \frac{\sin x}{\sqrt{x}} \, dx = \sqrt{\frac{\pi}{2}}.$$

19. Let $f(z) = p(z)/q(z)$, where $p(z)$ and $q(z)$ are relatively prime polynomials, $q(z)$ has no real zeros, and $f(-z) = f(z)$. Let the degree of $q(z)$ be at least two greater than the degree of $p(z)$. Let C be the indented contour as shown in Fig. 7.7.1 with $a = 0$, that is, the semicircle C_r now has its center at the origin. Let $F(z) = p(z) (\text{Log } z)^n/q(z)$. Then from Theorem 7.2.1 we have

(a) $\displaystyle \int_C F(z) \, dz = \int_{C_R} F(z) \, dz + \int_{-R}^{-r} \frac{p(x)}{q(x)} (\text{Log } | x | + i\pi)^n \, dx$

$$+ \int_{C_r} F(z) \, dz + \int_r^R \frac{p(x)}{q(x)} (\text{Log } x)^n \, dx = 2\pi i \sum_{j=1}^{s} \text{Res } [F(z), z_j],$$

where z_j, $j = 1, 2, \cdots, s$, are the poles of $F(z)$ in the upper half plane. Note that the poles of $F(z)$ in the upper half plane are precisely the roots of $q(z) = 0$ in the upper half plane. Show that

(b) $\displaystyle \lim_{R \to \infty} \int_{C_R} F(z) \, dz = 0$ and $\displaystyle \lim_{r \to 0} \int_{C_r} F(z) \, dz = 0.$

Utilizing (b), show that (a) may be written as

(c) $\displaystyle \int_0^{\infty} \frac{p(x)}{q(x)} (\text{Log } x + i\pi)^n \, dx + \int_0^{\infty} \frac{p(x)}{q(x)} (\text{Log } x)^n \, dx$

$$= 2\pi i \sum_{j=1}^{s} \text{Res } [F(z), z_j].$$

In view of (c), we see that

$$\int_0^\infty \frac{p(x)}{q(x)} (\text{Log } x)^n \, dx$$

is expressible as a linear combination of integrals of the form

$$\int_0^\infty \frac{p(x)}{q(x)} (\text{Log } x)^k \, dx \qquad \text{with } k < n,$$

and $2\pi i \sum_{j=1}^s \text{Res}\,[F(z), z_j]$.

20. Show that

$$\int_0^\infty \frac{(\text{Log } x)^2}{(1+x^2)^2} \, dx = \frac{\pi^3}{16}.$$

21. Show that if $n = 2k + 1$, $k = 0, 1, 2, \cdots$, then

$$\int_0^\infty \frac{(\text{Log } x)^n}{1 + x^2} \, dx = 0.$$

22. Prove (7.8.9). Why cannot Lemma 7.7.1 be applied directly to $F(z)$ of (7.8.2)?

7.9. MITTAG-LEFFLER THEOREM. Suppose that we wish to construct a function $f(z)$ which is analytic in the entire finite complex plane, except at a finite number of points $z_1, z_2, \cdots, z_k$ where it has poles, with the principal part of each pole z_r $(r = 1, 2, \cdots, k)$ given in advance as

$$P(z, z_r) = \sum_{j=1}^{m_r} \frac{b_{jr}}{(z - z_r)^j}. \tag{7.9.1}$$

Then by Lemma 7.3.2 we know that such a function $f(z)$ can be constructed and each such function is given by

$$f(z) = \sum_{r=1}^k P(z, z_r) + \phi(z), \tag{7.9.2}$$

where $\phi(z)$ is a function analytic in the entire finite plane.

Suppose now, that we wish to construct a function analytic in the finite complex plane, except at an infinite set of points $z_1, z_2, \cdots$ where it has poles, with the principal part at each pole z_r $(r = 1, 2, \cdots)$ prescribed by

$$P(z, z_r) = \sum_{j=1}^{m_r} \frac{b_{jr}}{(z - z_r)^j}. \tag{7.9.3}$$

(Observe that the set $z_1, z_2, \cdots$ cannot have a finite accumulation point. For, if z_0 were an accumulation point of the sequence, then every neighborhood of z_0 would contain infinitely many poles; thus the point z_0 would be an essential singularity of our function. By the Bolzano-Weierstrass Theorem 2.5.2, the absence of a finite accumulation point implies that any bounded region contains only a finite number of the points $z_1, z_2, \cdots$.)

In this case, we cannot always form the sum

$$\sum_{r=1}^{\infty} P(z, z_r),$$

since this sum does not necessarily converge. This difficulty will be overcome by the following construction.

It is sufficient to consider the case where the origin is not a pole. For, if we can construct a function $f(z)$ for this case, then the function $f(z) + P(z, 0)$, where $P(z, 0)$ is the principal part at $z = 0$, will meet our requirements.

Let $C_\mu, \mu = 1, 2, \cdots$ be a sequence of concentric circles with centers at the origin and such that C_μ is interior to $C_{\mu+1}$, radius of $C_\mu \to \infty$ as $\mu \to \infty$, and no pole is interior to C_1 or on a C_μ, and none of the z_n are interior to C_1. Let $h_\mu(z)$ be a rational function whose poles are those members of the given sequence $z_1, z_2, \cdots$ which lie in the annular region between C_μ and $C_{\mu+1}$ and whose principal parts at these poles are the ones given in (7.9.3). [Such a function $h_\mu(z)$ may be obtained by adding the principal parts corresponding to the poles in the given annular region.] Then $h_\mu(z)$ is analytic in the interior of the circle C_μ and may be expanded about the origin in a power series

$$h_\mu(z) = A_0^{(\mu)} + A_1^{(\mu)}z + A_2^{(\mu)}z^2 + \cdots. \tag{7.9.4}$$

Now, the circle C_μ lies in the interior of a slightly larger concentric circle within which $h_\mu(z)$ is also analytic. Thus (see Theorem 6.3.1), the power series in (7.9.4) converges uniformly to $h_\mu(z)$ within (and on) C_μ. Hence there exists an integer n_μ such that for z interior to C_μ we have

$$\sum_{k=n_\mu+1}^{\infty} | A_k^{(\mu)}z^k | < \frac{1}{\mu^2}. \tag{7.9.5}$$

Put

$$p_\mu(z) = \sum_{k=0}^{n_\mu} A_k^{(\mu)}z^k \tag{7.9.6}$$

a polynomial in z. Then for z interior to C_μ, we have from (7.9.4), (7.9.6) and (7.9.5) that

$$| h_\mu(z) - p_\mu(z) | < \frac{1}{\mu^2}. \tag{7.9.7}$$

Let us form the function

$$f_0(z) = \sum_{\mu=1}^{\infty} [h_\mu(z) - p_\mu(z)]. \tag{7.9.8}$$

We shall now establish the following

LEMMA 7.9.1. The function $f_0(z)$ given in (7.9.8) is analytic in the entire finite complex plane except for poles at the points $z_1, z_2, \cdots$, and the principal part of $f_0(z)$ at each of these points z_r is equal to $P(z, z_r)$ as given in (7.9.3).

Proof. We shall show that if C is any circle, then $f_0(z)$ is analytic in the interior of C, except for those points of the set $z_1, z_2, \cdots$ contained in the interior of C at which $f_0(z)$ has poles with the principal part at each pole equal to $P(z, z_r)$ as given in (7.9.3).

Since the radius of $C_\mu \to \infty$ as $\mu \to \infty$, there exists an integer N such that C is interior to C_N. Consider the sum

$$f_1(z) = \sum_{\mu=N}^{\infty} [h_\mu(z) - p_\mu(z)]. \tag{7.9.9}$$

For z interior to C_N, each term of the series is analytic, since all the poles of $h_\mu(z)$, $\mu \geq N$, lie in the exterior of C_N. Moreover, in the interior of C_N, the series (7.9.9) converges uniformly, since by (7.9.7) each term $h_\mu(z) - p_\mu(z)$ is in absolute value less than the corresponding term of the convergent series

$$\sum_{\mu=N}^{\infty} \frac{1}{\mu^2}.$$

Hence, the series (7.9.9) is a uniformly convergent series of analytic functions for z interior to C, and by the Weierstrass Theorem 6.8.1 the sum is also analytic.

From the manner in which the $h_\mu(z)$ were constructed, we see that the sum

$$f_2(z) = \sum_{\mu=1}^{N-1} [h_\mu(z) - p_\mu(z)] \tag{7.9.10}$$

is analytic in the interior of C, except for the originally given poles, with the principal parts $P(z, z_r)$ at each pole as prescribed. Since $f_0(z) = f_1(z) + f_2(z)$, the same is true of $f_0(z)$. But C is an arbitrary circle. It follows that $f_0(z)$ is analytic everywhere in the finite plane, except for poles at $z_1, z_2, \cdots$, with the principal part at each z_r equal to $P(z, z_r)$ as given in (7.9.3). Thus the lemma is established.

We shall now state and prove the Mittag-Leffler theorem.

——**THEOREM** 7.9.1. Given a sequence of points $\{z_r\}$ having no finite accumulation point and for each r, $r = 1, 2, \cdots$, let $b_{jr}, j = 1, 2, \cdots, m_r$, be a finite number of nonzero constants. Let

$$P(z, z_r) = \sum_{j=1}^{m_r} \frac{b_{jr}}{(z - z_r)^j}. \tag{7.9.11}$$

Then there exists a function $f(z)$ analytic in the entire finite complex plane except for poles at $z_1, z_2, \cdots$, with the principal part at $z = z_r$ given by $P(z, z_r)$. Moreover, any other function $F(z)$ satisfies these conditions if, and only if, it has the form

$$F(z) = f(z) + \phi(z), \tag{7.9.12}$$

where $\phi(z)$ is a function analytic in the entire finite complex plane.

Proof. The proof of the first statement follows from Lemma 7.9.1. Concerning (7.9.12). Note that $F(z)$ and $f(z)$ both satisfy the conditions prescribed if, and only if, $F(z) - f(z)$ is analytic in the entire finite complex plane, that is, if, and only if, $F(z) = f(z) + \phi(z)$, where $\phi(z)$ is analytic. Thus the theorem is established.

EXAMPLE 7.9.1.   Let us show that

$$\frac{\pi^2}{(\sin \pi z)^2} = \sum_{n=-\infty}^{\infty} \frac{1}{(z - n)^2}. \tag{7.9.13}$$

Solution.   Consider the function

$$\cot \pi z = \frac{\cos \pi z}{\sin \pi z}.$$

Let $p(z) = \cos \pi z$ and $q(z) = \sin \pi z$. From Theorem 4.2.2 the zeros of $q(z)$ are given by $z_n = n$, and $q'(z_n) = \pi \cos (\pi z_n) \neq 0$, $n = 0, \pm 1, \pm 2, \cdots$. Consequently, by Theorem 7.2.3, the poles of $\cot \pi z$ are all simple. From (7.2.8) we see that the residue at each pole is the same, namely,

$$\text{Res} \left[\cot \pi z, z_n \right] = \frac{p(z_n)}{q'(z_n)} = \frac{\cos (\pi z_n)}{\pi \cos (\pi z_n)} = \frac{1}{\pi}, \qquad n = 0, \pm 1, \pm 2, \cdots.$$

It follows from the definition of the residue (see Section 7.2) that the principal part of $\cot \pi z$ at $z = z_n$ is equal to $(1/\pi) [1/(z - z_n)]$. Thus, in a neighborhood $0 < |z - z_n| < 1$ of each z_n, we have

$$\cot \pi z = \frac{1}{\pi} \frac{1}{z - z_n} + \phi_n(z),$$

where $\phi_n(z)$ is analytic for $|z - z_n| < 1$. Differentiating the above expression, we get

$$\frac{\pi^2}{(\sin \pi z)^2} = \frac{1}{(z - z_n)^2} - \pi \phi'_n(z). \tag{7.9.14}$$

It follows that the principal part at each pole z_n of $\pi^2/(\sin \pi z)^2$ is equal to $1/(z - n)^2$.

We now form the series

$$h(z) = \sum_{n=-\infty}^{\infty} \frac{1}{(z-n)^2}.$$ (7.9.15)

It is not difficult to show (see Exercise 7.9.5) that for each z not an integer, this series converges uniformly in a neighborhood of z. It follows from the Weierstrass Theorem 6.8.1 that the function $h(z)$ in (7.9.15) is analytic for $z \neq n$, $n = 0, \pm 1, \pm 2, \cdots$. Moreover, at $z = n$, the principal part $1/(z-n)^2$ of $h(z)$ is the same as that of $\pi^2/(\sin \pi z)^2$ in (7.9.14). Consequently, by Theorem 7.9.1, there exists a function

$$g(z) = \frac{\pi^2}{(\sin \pi z)^2} - \sum_{n=-\infty}^{\infty} \frac{1}{(z-n)^2}$$ (7.9.16)

which is analytic in the entire finite complex plane.

We shall now prove that $g(z) = 0$ by the following device due to H. Herglotz. Utilizing (7.9.16) we have

$$g\left(\frac{z}{2}\right) = \frac{\pi^2}{[\sin (\pi z/2)]^2} - \sum_{n=-\infty}^{\infty} \frac{4}{(z-2n)^2},$$

and

$$g\left(\frac{z+1}{2}\right) = \frac{\pi^2}{[\cos (\pi z/2)]^2} - \sum_{n=-\infty}^{\infty} \frac{4}{(z-2n+1)^2}.$$

Adding the above two series, we obtain

$$g\left(\frac{z}{2}\right) + g\left(\frac{z+1}{2}\right) = \frac{4\pi^2}{(\sin \pi z)^2} - \sum_{n=-\infty}^{\infty} \frac{4}{(z-n)^2} = 4g(z),$$ (7.9.17)

or

$$g(z) = \frac{1}{4}\left[g\left(\frac{z}{2}\right) + g\left(\frac{z+1}{2}\right)\right].$$

Put

$$M = \max |g(z)| \text{ for } |z| \leq 1.$$

Then for $|z| \leq 1$

$$|g(z)| = \frac{1}{4}\left|g\left(\frac{z}{2}\right) + g\left(\frac{z+1}{2}\right)\right| \leq \frac{1}{4}\left[\left|g\left(\frac{z}{2}\right)\right| + \left|g\left(\frac{z+1}{2}\right)\right|\right]$$

$$\leq \frac{1}{4}[M + M] = \frac{M}{2}.$$

Hence

$$M \leq \frac{M}{2},$$

thus $M = 0$ and $g(z) = 0$ for $|z| \leq 1$. It now follows (see Theorem 7.10.1) that $g(z) = 0$ for all z. Therefore (7.9.17) becomes

$$\frac{\pi^2}{(\sin \pi z)^2} = \sum_{n=-\infty}^{\infty} \frac{1}{(z-n)^2},$$

thus establishing (7.9.13).

EXERCISES 7.9

1. Show that $\dfrac{\pi^2}{(\cos \pi z)^2} = \displaystyle\sum_{n=-\infty}^{\infty} \frac{1}{(z - \frac{1}{2} - n)^2}$.

2. Show that $\pi \tan \pi z = -\displaystyle\sum_{n=0}^{\infty} \left[\frac{1}{z - n - \frac{1}{2}} + \frac{1}{z + n + \frac{1}{2}} \right]$

$$= \sum_{n=0}^{\infty} \frac{2z}{(n + \frac{1}{2})^2 - z^2}.$$

3. Show that $\pi \cot \pi z = \dfrac{1}{z} + \displaystyle\sum_{n=1}^{\infty} \frac{2z}{z^2 - n^2}$.

4. Show that $\dfrac{\pi}{\sin \pi z} = -\dfrac{1}{z} + \displaystyle\sum_{m=0}^{\infty} \frac{(-1)^m 2z}{z^2 - m^2}$.

5. Show that for each $z = z_0$ different from an integer, the series

$$\sum_{n=-\infty}^{\infty} \frac{1}{(z-n)^2}$$

converges uniformly in a neighborhood of z_0.

7.10. ANALYTIC FUNCTIONS DETERMINED BY THEIR VALUES NEAR A POINT.

As a consequence of Theorem 7.1.2, we have the following

LEMMA 7.10.1. Let $f(z)$ be analytic in a domain D and let z_0 be a point in D. If there exists a sequence $\{z_n\}$ in D with all the z_n different from z_0 such that $z_n \to z_0$ and $f(z_n) = 0$ for all n, then there exists a neighborhood $N(z_0)$ of z_0 such that $f(z) = 0$ for all z in $N(z_0)$.

Proof. Since $z_n \to z_0$ and $f(z_n) = 0$, it follows from the continuity of $f(z)$ that also $f(z_0) = 0$. (See Theorem 3.3.3.) Since every neighborhood of z_0 contains zeros of $f(z)$, we see from Theorem 7.1.2 that the Taylor series expansion of $f(z)$ about $z = z_0$ has all of its coefficients equal to zero. Thus the lemma is established.

——**THEOREM** 7.10.1.   Let $f(z)$ be analytic in a domain D. If $f(z) = 0$ in a subdomain D_0 of D, then $f(z) = 0$ for all z in D.

Proof.   Let z_1 be any point in D_0. Then $f(z) = 0$ in a neighborhood $N_1(z_1)$ of z_1. Let z_2 be any other point in D. We shall also show that $f(z_2) = 0$. This will prove the theorem.

Let Γ: $z = z(t)$, $t_1 \le t \le t_2$ be a contour in D joining z_1 to z_2, and let I denote the closed interval $[t_1, t_2]$ consisting of all t such that $t_1 \le t \le t_2$. Then, since $z(t)$ is continuous, there is a value t' in the interior of I such that for all t in the closed interval $[t_1, t']$, $z(t)$ is in $N_1(z_1)$ and consequently $f[z(t)] = 0$. In other words, there is a neighborhood of z_1 on the curve Γ in which $f(z) = 0$.

Consider the set S of all points t' in I such that $f(z) = 0$ for all z lying between $z_1 = z(t_1)$ and $z = z(t')$, that is, S is the set of all t' such that $f[z(t)] = 0$ for all t in the closed interval $[t_1, t']$. Then by the Dedekind Cut Property of Section 2.4, we have one of two cases. *Case* 1: All points of I belong to S. *Case* 2: There exists a point t_0, $t_1 < t_0 < t_2$, such that all points in I to the left of t_0 are in S, and all points in I to the right of t_0 are not in S. In Case 1, the result follows, since $f(z) = 0$ for all z on Γ and hence $f(z_2) = 0$. We shall now proceed to show that Case 2 leads to a contradiction, and thus the theorem will be established.

Suppose that Case 2 were true. Then, since $f[z(t)] = 0$ for all t in I to the left of t_0, we also have by continuity that $f(z_0) = 0$, where $z_0 = z(t_0)$. Thus $f(z) = 0$ for $z = z_0$ as well as for all z on Γ preceding z_0. It follows from Lemma 7.10.1 that there exists a neighborhood $N(z_0)$ of z_0 such that $f(z) = 0$ for z in $N(z_0)$.

Again, using the fact that $z = z(t)$ is continuous in t, there exists a neighborhood of z_0 on the contour Γ which is contained in $N(z_0)$. That is, there is a t'', $t_0 < t'' < t_2$, such that for all t in the closed interval $[t_0, t'']$, $z(t)$ is in $N(z_0)$ and consequently $f[z(t)] = 0$. Thus, t'' lying to the right of t_0 is also in S. This contradicts the definition of t_0 which asserted that points to the right of t_0 are not in S. The proof of the theorem is now complete.

Combining Theorem 7.10.1 and Lemma 7.10.1, we have

——**THEOREM** 7.10.2.   Let $f(z)$ be analytic in a domain D and let z_0 be a point in D. If there exists a sequence $\{z_n\}$ in D with all the z_n different from z_0 such that $z_n \to z_0$ and $f(z_n) = 0$ for all n, then $f(z) = 0$ for all z in D.

As an immediate corollary of this theorem, we have

——**THEOREM** 7.10.3.   Let $f_1(z)$ and $f_2(z)$ be analytic in a domain D and let z_0 be a point in D. If there exists a sequence $\{z_n\}$ in D with all the z_n different from z_0 such that $z_n \to z_0$ and $f_1(z_n) = f_2(z_n)$ for all n, then $f_1(z) = f_2(z)$ for all z in D.

   Proof. Let $f(z) = f_1(z) - f_2(z)$. Then, since $f_1(z_n) = f_2(z_n)$, we have $f(z_n) = 0$ for all n. By Theorem 7.10.2, $f(z) = 0$ for all z in D. Consequently, $f_1(z) = f_2(z)$ for all z in D.

   In particular, when $f_2(z)$ is equal to a constant in Theorem 7.10.3, we obtain

──**THEOREM** 7.10.4.   Let $f(z)$ be analytic in a domain D and let z_0 be any point in D. If there exists a sequence $\{z_n\}$ in D with all the z_n different from z_0 such that $z_n \to z_0$ and $f(z_n) = c$ for all n, where c is a constant, then $f(z) = c$ for all z in D.

EXERCISES 7.10

1. Suppose that $f(z)$ is an analytic nonconstant function in a domain D, and that z_0 is a point in D such that $f(z_0) = 0$. Using the result of Theorem 7.10.2, show that there exists a neighborhood $N(z_0)$ of z_0 in D such that if $z \neq z_0$ is in $N(z_0)$, then $f(z) \neq 0$.

2. Show that an analytic continuation between any two branches of a multiple-valued analytic function can be accomplished by means of a finite number of branches.

3. Suppose that $f(z)$ is an analytic function (not necessarily single-valued) in a domain D. Let $G_0(z)$ be a branch of $f(z)$ defined over a subdomain D_0 of D. Show that if $G_0(z) = c$ for all z in D_0, where c is a constant, then $f(z) = c$ for all z in D.

4. Suppose that $H(z)$ is an analytic function (not necessarily single-valued) in a domain D such that for some branch $h(z)$ of $H(z)$, with domain of definition D_h contained in D, we have $h'(z) = 0$ for all z in D_h. Show that $H(z)$ is constant in D.

5. Suppose that $H(z)$ is an analytic function (not necessarily single-valued) in a domain D. Let $F(z)$ be single-valued and analytic in D. Suppose further that for some branch $h(z)$ of $H(z)$, with domain of definition D_h contained in D, we have $h'(z) = F'(z)$ for all z in D_h. Show that $H(z)$ is also single-valued in D and differs from $F(z)$ by at most a constant.

6. Suppose that $H(z)$ is an analytic function (not necessarily single-valued) in a domain D such that the real part (or the imaginary part) of $H(z)$ is constant in D. Show that $H(z)$ is also constant in D.

7. Let D be the domain consisting of the finite complex plane with the point $z = 0$ removed. Let $u(z) = \text{Log}\,|z|$ for z in D. Show that we cannot have $u = \mathscr{R}[f(z)]$, where $f(z)$ is single-valued and analytic in D.

8. We shall define the sum $F(z) = F_1(z) + F_2(z)$ of two possibly multiple-valued functions $F_1(z)$ and $F_2(z)$ as follows: Let z be a point in the common domain of definition of the functions. Let w_1 be one of the values of $F_1(z)$ and w_2 one of the values of $F_2(z)$. Then, $w = w_1 + w_2$ is one of the values of $F(z)$.

(a) Show that a multiple-valued function equal to the sum of two multiple-valued analytic functions need not be analytic.

(b) Show that a multiple-valued function equal to the sum of a multiple-valued analytic function and a single-valued analytic function is analytic.

9. Obtain a chain rule (see Theorem 3.5.2) for multiple-valued analytic functions.

8

Conformal

Representation

8.1. ANALYTIC MAPPINGS. We recall from Section 2.9 that a mapping T of a set A into a set B assigns to each element in A a unique element in B. In this chapter, we shall be interested in the case where A and B are sets of complex numbers. The mapping T thus defines a single-valued function

$$w = F(z) \qquad (8.1.1)$$

which assigns to each z in A a unique number w in B. Conversely, a single-valued function (together with its domain of definition) completely determines a mapping T. (See Remark 3.1.1.)

In the sequel, we shall be particularly interested in the case where the set A is a domain D, and the function $F(z)$ is analytic* in D. We shall then say that the mapping given by $w = F(z)$ is *analytic*. By Theorem 3.4.1, $F(z)$ is also continuous in D, and hence the mapping determined by it is also continuous.

A mapping T of a set A is often called a *transformation* of A, and we shall use the terms mapping and transformation interchangeably. We shall use the notions of antecedent, image, one-to-one, onto, bicontinuous or topological mapping, inverse mapping, the product of mappings, and so on. For the definition of these concepts, we refer the reader to Section 2.9.

For clarity, we may regard the original set A as being given in one plane called the z plane, and its image in another plane called the w plane. If a succession of several mappings is involved, we may introduce additional planes.

***Definition* 8.1.1.** Let C: $z = h(t)$, $\alpha \le t \le \beta$, be a contour in the domain D and let $w = F(z)$ be analytic and not identically equal to a constant in D. Then the contour

$$\Gamma: w = H(t), \qquad \alpha \le t \le \beta, \qquad H(t) = F[h(t)],$$

induced by the mapping $w = F(z)$ is called the *image* of C under $w = F(z)$.

* In accordance with Remark 3.4.1, functions (including analytic functions) are to be considered single-valued, except where the contrary is indicated.

288

In virtue of Remark 7.4.1, we see that Γ is indeed a contour.

8.2. MAPPINGS OF DOMAINS.

We make the following observation before stating Lemma 8.2.1. The statement that a circle of arbitrarily small radius has a certain property shall be understood to mean, that given any $\epsilon > 0$, there exists a circle with radius $r < \epsilon$ having the property in question.

LEMMA 8.2.1.   Let the mapping $w = F(z)$ be analytic and not identically equal to a constant in a neighborhood of $z = z_0$. Let $w_0 = F(z_0)$ and let k be the least positive integer such that $F^{(k)}(z_0) \neq 0$. Then there exists a circle C of arbitrarily small radius with center at z_0, and a corresponding circle Γ with center at w_0, such that any point $w_1 \neq w_0$ interior to Γ has exactly k distinct antecedents $z_j, j = 1, 2, \cdots, k$, interior to C.

Proof.   Let

$$G(z) = F(z) - w_0. \qquad (8.2.1)$$

Since $G(z)$ and $G'(z)$ are both analytic at z_0, it follows (see Exercise 7.10.1) that there exists a neighborhood $N(z_0)$ of z_0 such that $G(z) \neq 0$ and $G'(z) \neq 0$ for every $z \neq z_0$ in $N(z_0)$. Let C be a circle of arbitrarily small radius in $N(z_0)$ with center at z_0. Since by hypothesis, $F(z_0) = w_0$ and $F^{(j)}(z_0) = 0$ for $j < k$ we have, by the Taylor expansion (6.4.1),

$$G(z) = F(z) - w_0 = \sum_{n=k}^{\infty} \frac{F^{(n)}(z_0)}{n!} (z - z_0)^n, \quad F^{(k)}(z_0) \neq 0. \qquad (8.2.2)$$

It follows from (7.1.10) that $z = z_0$ is a zero of order k of $G(z)$. Since $G(z) \neq 0$ for $z \neq z_0$ in $N(z_0)$, we see that the total number of zeros of $G(z)$ interior to C is equal to k.

Since C is a bounded and closed set, there exists (see Exercise 3.3.26) a point z' on C such that $|G(z')|$ is the minimum value of $|G(z)|$ on C. Since $|G(z)| \neq 0$ on C, it follows that $|G(z')| = m > 0$ and we have

$$|G(z)| \geq m \qquad \text{for all } z \text{ on } C. \qquad (8.2.3)$$

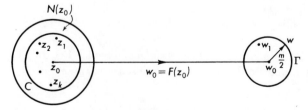

FIG. 8.2.1

Let Γ be the circle $|w - w_0| = m/2$. (See Fig. 8.2.1.) Let $w_1 \neq w_0$ be interior to Γ. Using (8.2.1), we see that

$$F(z) - w_1 = G(z) + (w_0 - w_1). \qquad (8.2.4)$$

Also we have

$$|w_0 - w_1| < \frac{m}{2}. \qquad (8.2.5)$$

Thus, from (8.2.3) and (8.2.5), we obtain

$$|G(z)| > |w_0 - w_1|$$

for all z on C. It follows from Rouché's Theorem 7.4.3 that the function $G(z) + (w_0 - w_1)$ has the same number of zeros interior to C as $G(z)$. In view of (8.2.4), $F(z) - w_1$ also has k zeros in the interior of C.

Let $z = z_1$ be any zero of $F(z) - w_1$ interior to C. Then, since $w_1 \neq w_0$, we have $z_1 \neq z_0$. Also, since $G'(z) \neq 0$ for $z \neq z_0$ in $N(z_0)$, we have $F'(z_1) = G'(z_1) \neq 0$. It follows that $z = z_1$ is a simple zero of $F(z) - w_1$, and is counted only once. Hence, there must be interior to C exactly k distinct points $z_j, j = 1, 2, \cdots, k$, such that $F(z_j) - w_1 = 0$. Thus the lemma is established.

LEMMA 8.2.2.   Let D_w be the image of a domain D_z under the analytic mapping $w = F(z)$, where $F(z)$ is not identically equal to a constant. Then D_w is an open set.

Proof.   To establish the lemma it is sufficient to show that if w_0 is any point in D_w, then there exists a circle Γ with center at w_0 such that the interior of Γ is contained in D_w.

Let w_0 be any point in D_w and let z_0 be an antecedent of w_0 in D_z. By Lemma 8.2.1, there exists a circle C in D_z and a circle Γ with centers at z_0 and w_0, respectively, such that for any point w_1 interior to Γ the function $F(z) - w_1$ has at least one zero, say z_1, interior to C. Thus $w_1 = F(z_1)$ is contained in the image D_w of D_z. Since w_1 is any point interior to Γ, the lemma is established.

——**THEOREM** 8.2.1.   Let D_w be the image of a domain D_z under the analytic mapping $w = F(z)$, where $F(z)$ is not identically equal to a constant. Then D_w is also a domain.

Proof.   By Lemma 8.2.2, D_w is an open set. Since D_z is connected (see Definition 2.2.5), it follows from Theorem 2.9.2 that D_w is also connected. Hence D_w is a domain.

As a corollary of Theorem 8.2.1, we have the following important

——**THEOREM** 8.2.2 (*Maximum modulus theorem*).   Let $f(z)$ be an analytic function in a domain D. If $|f(z)|$ attains its maximum in D, then $f(z)$ is constant in D.

Proof.   Suppose to the contrary that $|f(z)|$ attains its maximum in D and that $f(z)$ is not a constant. We shall show that this leads to a contradiction. Let z_0 be a point in D where $|f(z)|$ attains its maximum. By Theorem 8.2.1 the transformation $w = f(z)$ maps D onto a domain D_w containing the point $w_0 = f(z_0)$. Hence D_w, being an open set, contains a segment L given by

$w = w_0(1 + t)$, $0 < t \leq \epsilon$, for some $\epsilon > 0$. Consequently, for each point w on L there is a point z in D such that $w = f(z)$. But $|w| = (1 + t)|w_0| > |w_0|$. Hence $|f(z)| > |f(z_0)|$, contradicting our assumption that $|f(z)| \leq |f(z_0)|$ for all z in D. The theorem is thus established.

As a corollary to Theorem 8.2.2, we have the following

——THEOREM 8.2.3. Let R be a region consisting of a bounded domain D and its boundary B. Suppose that $f(z)$ is a function continuous on R and analytic in D. Then there exists a point z_0 on B such that $|f(z)| \leq |f(z_0)|$ for all z in R.

Proof. Since $|f(z)|$ is a continuous real-valued function on the closed and bounded set R, there exists a point z_0 in R such that $|f(z)| \leq |f(z_0)|$ for all z in R. (See Exercise 3.3.26.) If $f(z)$ is not constant in D, then by Theorem 8.2.2, z_0 cannot be in D and hence must be on B. If $f(z)$ is constant in D, then by continuity $f(z)$ is constant on all of R. Hence $|f(z)| \leq |f(z_0)|$ for any point z_0 on B and all z in R. Thus the theorem is established.

Remark 8.2.1. Unlike the maximum, the minimum of $|f(z)|$ may be attained at a point z_0 contained in D. For example, consider the function $f(z) = z$ defined in the domain $D: |z| < 1$. For all z in D, we have $|f(z)| \geq 0 = |f(0)|$, and yet $f(z)$ is not a constant in D. However, if $f(z)$ is a nonconstant analytic function such that $f(z)$ does not vanish at any point in D, then, since $1/f(z)$ is analytic in D, $1/|f(z)|$ cannot attain a maximum in D. Consequently $|f(z)|$ cannot attain a minimum in D. Thus, if R is a region consisting of a bounded domain D and its boundary B, and if $f(z)$ is a nonconstant function continuous on R, analytic in D, and such that $f(z)$ does not vanish at any point in D, then $|f(z)|$ attains its minimum on the boundary B.

The following theorem is found to be useful in the study of analytic mappings.

——THEOREM 8.2.4. Let C be a simple closed contour in the z plane and let Γ be its image in the w plane under the mapping $w = F(z)$, where $F(z)$ is not identically equal to a constant and is analytic on C and its interior. If Γ is simple closed, then $w = F(z)$ maps the interior of C one-to-one onto the interior of Γ.

Proof. Let us denote the interiors of C and Γ by D_z and D_w, respectively. We shall assume, without loss of generality, that C is described in the positive direction.

If w_0 is any point not on Γ, then by (7.4.4) we have

$$N = \nu(\Gamma, w_0), \qquad (8.2.6)$$

where N is the number of zeros of the function $F(z) - w_0$ interior to C and $\nu(\Gamma, w_0)$ is the winding number of Γ about the point w_0.

The remainder of the proof will consist of four steps.

1. No point exterior to Γ can be the image of a point in D_z. For, suppose

to the contrary that $F(z_0) = w_0$ for z_0 in D_z and w_0 is exterior to Γ. Then the function $F(z) - w_0$ has at least one zero interior to C. Hence, we have $N \geq 1$ in (8.2.6), while by Theorem 5.5.2, $\nu(\Gamma, w_0) = 0$. We are thus led to a contradiction.

2. No point on Γ can be the image of a point in D_z. For, suppose to the contrary that $F(z_0) = w_0$ for z_0 in D_z and w_0 is on Γ. By Lemma 8.2.2 there exists a circle γ with center at w_0 such that every point w_1 interior to γ is the image of a point in D_z. (See Fig. 8.2.2.) By the Jordan Theorem 5.5.1, there is a point w_1 interior to γ and exterior to Γ. Thus, a point exterior to Γ is the image of a point in D_z, contradicting 1.

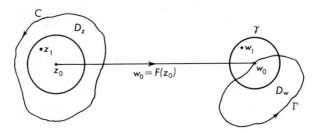

FIG. 8.2.2

3. It follows from 1 and 2 that the mapping $w = F(z)$ maps D_z into the interior of Γ.

4. The mapping $w = F(z)$ maps D_z one-to-one onto the interior of Γ. For, if w_0 is any point interior to Γ, then by (8.2.6) and Theorem 5.6.1 we have

$$\nu(\Gamma, w_0) = 1. \tag{8.2.7}$$

Consequently, there is exactly one point z_0 in D_z such that $F(z_0) - w_0 = 0$. This shows (1) that every point interior to Γ is the image of a point in D_z, that is, the mapping is onto, and (2) each point interior to Γ has only one antecedent in D_z, that is, the mapping is one-to-one. The theorem is thus established.

Remark 8.2.2. In Theorem 8.2.4, let C be described in the positive direction and let Γ be simple closed. It will then follow from (8.2.7) that Γ is also described in the positive direction.

——**THEOREM** 8.2.5. Suppose that $w = F(z)$ is analytic at $z = z_0$ and suppose that $F'(z_0) \neq 0$. Let $w_0 = F(z_0)$. Then there exists a neighborhood $N(w_0)$ of w_0 and a domain D_z containing z_0 such that $w = F(z)$ is a topological mapping of D_z onto $N(w_0)$.

Proof. Let $F(z)$ be analytic in the neighborhood $N(z_0)$ of z_0. Since by hypothesis $F'(z_0) \neq 0$, it follows from Lemma 8.2.1 that there exists a circle C in $N(z_0)$ and a circle Γ with center at w_0 such that any point w_1 interior to Γ

is the image of exactly one point z interior to C. Let us denote the interiors of C and Γ by $I(C)$ and $I(\Gamma)$, respectively. Let T denote the mapping of $I(C)$ into the w plane by the function $w = F(z)$. Let D_z denote the inverse image under T of $I(\Gamma)$. (See Fig. 8.2.3.) Since the inverse image of an open set under a continuous mapping is an open set (see Exercise 2.9.1), it follows that D_z is an open set.

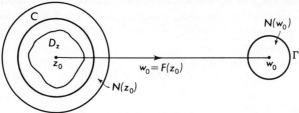

FIG. 8.2.3

Since every point of $I(\Gamma)$ has exactly one antecedent in $I(C)$ and this antecedent is in D_z, it follows that T maps D_z one-to-one onto $I(\Gamma)$. Moreover, the mapping T is continuous. By Lemma 8.2.2, the image under T of every open set in D_z is open. Consequently, T maps D_z topologically onto $N(w_0) \equiv I(\Gamma)$. (See Exercise 2.9.9.) Thus the theorem is established.

8.3. CONFORMAL MAPPING. We shall first discuss some preliminary concepts. For any complex constant $\lambda \neq 0$, the equation

$$z = z_0 + \lambda s, \qquad 0 \leq s < \infty, \tag{8.3.1}$$

defines a *ray* issuing from the point z_0. Two equations

$$z = z_0 + \lambda s \quad \text{and} \quad z = z_0 + \lambda' s, \quad \lambda \neq 0, \quad \lambda' \neq 0, \qquad 0 \leq s < \infty$$

define the same ray if

$$\lambda' = k\lambda, \qquad k > 0. \tag{8.3.2}$$

Suppose that we are given two rays issuing from the point z_0

$$L_1 \colon z = z_0 + \lambda_1 s \quad \text{and} \quad L_2 \colon z = z_0 + \lambda_2 s, \quad \lambda_1 \neq 0, \quad \lambda_2 \neq 0, \qquad 0 \leq s < \infty.$$

Then, setting $k = 1/|\lambda|$ in (8.3.2), we see that L_1 and L_2 are also given by the equations

$$L_1 \colon z = z_0 + \lambda_1' s \quad \text{and} \quad L_2 \colon z = z_0 + \lambda_2' s, \qquad 0 \leq s < \infty,$$

where

$$\lambda_1' = \frac{\lambda_1}{|\lambda_1|} \quad \text{and} \quad \lambda_2' = \frac{\lambda_2}{|\lambda_2|}.$$

Since $|\lambda_i'| = 1$, $i = 1, 2$, we have

$$\lambda_2'/\lambda_1' = e^{i\theta}. \tag{8.3.3}$$

The value of θ, determined up to a multiple of 2π in (8.3.3), is the angle through which the ray L_1 must be rotated about z_0 so that it will coincide with L_2, and we write $\theta = \angle(L_1, L_2)$. A counterclockwise rotation is assumed positive.

Note that in general the value of the angle depends not only upon the rays L_1 and L_2, but also upon their order, and we have

$$\angle(L_1, L_2) = -\angle(L_2, L_1). \tag{8.3.4}$$

Suppose now that

$$C_1: z = h_1(t), \quad \alpha_1 \leqq t \leqq \beta_1 \quad \text{and} \quad C_2: z = h_2(t), \quad \alpha_2 \leqq t \leqq \beta_2 \tag{8.3.5}$$

are two simple contours intersecting at

$$z_0 = h_1(t_1) = h_2(t_2), \quad \alpha_1 \leqq t_1 \leqq \beta_1, \quad \alpha_2 \leqq t_2 \leqq \beta_2 \tag{8.3.6}$$

and each having a tangent* at z_0. Then, in accordance with the definition of a tangent given in Section 5.1, the tangents to C_1 and C_2 are given by

$$L_1: z = z_0 + \lambda_1 s \quad \text{and} \quad L_2: z = z_0 + \lambda_2 s, \quad 0 \leqq s < \infty,$$

where

$$\lambda_i = \lim_{\eta \to 0} \frac{\eta}{|\eta|} \cdot \frac{h_i(t_i + \eta) - h_i(t_i)}{|h_i(t_i + \eta) - h_i(t_i)|}, \quad \eta \text{ real}, \quad i = 1, 2, \tag{8.3.7}$$

and consequently $|\lambda_i| = 1$, $i = 1, 2$.

By the *angle*, $\angle(C_1, C_2)$, between the contours C_1 and C_2 at z_0, we mean the angle between the tangent rays, namely, the value of θ, determined up to a multiple of 2π, by the equality

$$e^{i\theta} = \frac{\lambda_2}{\lambda_1}, \tag{8.3.8}$$

where λ_1 and λ_2 are given in (8.3.7).

——*THEOREM* 8.3.1.   Let $w = F(z)$ be analytic at $z = z_0$ with $F'(z_0) \neq 0$. Then there exists a neighborhood $N(z_0)$ of z_0 such that if C_1 and C_2 are simple contours in $N(z_0)$ intersecting at z_0, with tangents at z_0, then the images Γ_1 and Γ_2 of C_1 and C_2, respectively, are simple contours intersecting at $w_0 = F(z_0)$, with tangents at w_0, and

$$\angle(C_1, C_2) = \angle(\Gamma_1, \Gamma_2). \tag{8.3.9}$$

* Let z be a point on a contour C. Then z is contained in some section of C forming a simple contour. If C is a simple contour, then C has a unique tangent at all points on C, except possibly for a finite number of points on C where the tangent does not exist.

Proof. Let the simple contours C_1 and C_2 be as in (8.3.5). Then their images Γ_1 and Γ_2 are simple contours given by (see Definition 8.1.1 and Theorem 8.2.5)

$$\Gamma_1: z = H_1(t), \quad \alpha_1 \leq t \leq \beta_1 \quad \text{and} \quad \Gamma_2: z = H_2(t), \quad \alpha_2 \leq t \leq \beta_2,$$

where

$$H_1(t) = F[h_1(t)] \quad \text{and} \quad H_2(t) = F[h_2(t)]. \tag{8.3.10}$$

Since Γ_1 and Γ_2 intersect at $w_0 = F(z_0)$, we have from (8.3.6) and (8.3.10)

$$w_0 = F(z_0) = H_1(t_1) = H_2(t_2), \quad \alpha_1 \leq t_1 \leq \beta_1, \quad \alpha_2 \leq t_2 \leq \beta_2.$$

Let now δH_i and δh_i denote respectively the expressions

$$H_i(t_i + \eta) - H_i(t_i) \quad \text{and} \quad h_i(t_i + \eta) - h_i(t_i), \quad i = 1, 2, \text{ and } \eta \text{ real.}$$

Since $H_i(t) = F[h_i(t)]$, $i = 1, 2$, it follows that

$$\lim_{\eta \to 0} \frac{\delta H_i}{\delta h_i} = \lim_{\eta \to 0} \frac{F[h_i(t_i + \eta)] - F[h_i(t_i)]}{h_i(t_i + \eta) - h_i(t_i)} = F'[h_i(t_i)] = F'(z_0).$$

Since by hypothesis $F'(z_0) \neq 0$, we then have for η real

$$\lim_{\eta \to 0} \frac{\eta}{|\eta|} \cdot \frac{\delta H_i}{|\delta H_i|} = \lim_{\eta \to 0} \frac{\delta H_i}{\delta h_i} \cdot \lim_{\eta \to 0} \left| \frac{\delta h_i}{\delta H_i} \right| \cdot \lim_{\eta \to 0} \frac{\eta}{|\eta|} \cdot \frac{\delta h_i}{|\delta h_i|} = F'(z_0) \frac{1}{|F'(z_0)|} \lambda_i,$$

where λ_i, $i = 1, 2$, are given in (8.3.7).

It follows that each contour Γ_i has a tangent at w_0 given by $w = w_0 + \mu_i s$, where

$$\mu_i = \frac{F'(z_0)}{|F'(z_0)|} \lambda_i \quad \text{and} \quad |\mu_i| = 1, \quad i = 1, 2. \tag{8.3.11}$$

Hence, if $\phi = \angle(\Gamma_1, \Gamma_2)$, we then have

$$e^{i\phi} = \frac{\mu_2}{\mu_1} = \frac{\lambda_2}{\lambda_1} = e^{i\theta},$$

and the theorem is established.

It is to be understood that any equality as given in (8.3.9) is true up to a multiple of 2π.

Let now $w = F(z)$ be analytic in a neighborhood $N(z_0)$ of z_0. Let z_1, z_2 be two distinct points in $N(z_0)$, and w_1, w_2 be their respective images under the mapping $w = F(z)$. It is not difficult to show (see Exercise 8.3.3) that if $F'(z_0)$ exists, then given any $\epsilon > 0$, there exists a $\delta > 0$ such that when $|z_1 - z_0| < \delta$ and $|z_2 - z_0| < \delta$, we have

$$\left| \frac{|w_1 - w_2|}{|z_1 - z_2|} - |F'(z_0)| \right| < \epsilon. \tag{8.3.12}$$

Remark 8.3.1. Thus, for $F'(z_0) \neq 0$, figures contained in a sufficiently small neighborhood of z_0 are transformed under the mapping $w = F(z)$ into figures which are approximately similar and magnified in the ratio of $|F'(z_0)|$ to 1; $|F'(z_0)|$ is called the *ratio of magnification* at z_0. However, it should be remarked that since the ratio of magnification $|F'(z_0)|$ may vary from point to point, large figures may be transformed into figures which bear little resemblance to the original.

Suppose that $w = F(z)$ is a mapping of a domain containing z_0, and let $w_0 = F(z_0)$. If $\angle(C_1, C_2) = \angle(\Gamma_1, \Gamma_2)$ for any two simple contours C_1, C_2 intersecting at z_0, having tangents at z_0 and lying in a sufficiently small neighborhood of z_0, and their respective images Γ_1, Γ_2 intersecting at w_0, then the mapping $w = F(z)$ is said to be *conformal* at $z = z_0$.

Definition 8.3.1. If the mapping $w = F(z)$ is conformal at each point of a domain D, then the mapping is said to be *conformal in D*.

Remark 8.3.2. From Theorem 8.3.1 we see that if $F(z)$ is analytic and $F'(z) \neq 0$ in D, then the mapping $w = F(z)$ is conformal in D. We also see from Theorem 8.2.5 that such a mapping is "locally" topological or bicontinuous.* However, it is not generally true that a conformal mapping of a domain D_z onto D_w is one-to-one "in the large". For example, let D_z consist of the complex plane with the point $z = 0$ removed and $w = F(z) = z^2$, then the points $z = \pm z_1$ are both mapped into the point $w = z_1^2$. Hence D_z when considered as a whole is not mapped one-to-one. However, given any point z_0 in D_z, we may construct a small circle C with center at z_0 such that for any point z_1 interior to C, the point $-z_1$ is exterior to C. Then the interior of C will be mapped one-to-one.

EXERCISES 8.3

1. Suppose that $w = f(z)$ is analytic within and on the circle C: $|z - z_0| = R$. Show that if z_1 and z_2 are two distinct points interior to C, then

$$\frac{f(z_1) - f(z_2)}{z_1 - z_2} - f'(z_0) = \frac{1}{2\pi i} \int_C \left[\frac{1}{(\zeta - z_1)(\zeta - z_2)} - \frac{1}{(\zeta - z_0)^2} \right] f(\zeta)\, d\zeta.$$

2. Suppose that $f(z)$ is analytic in a neighborhood $N(z_0)$ of a point z_0. Show that for every $\epsilon > 0$ there exists a $\delta > 0$, depending only upon ϵ, such that if $|z_1 - z_0| < \delta$ and $|z_2 - z_0| < \delta$, $z_1 \neq z_2$, then z_1, z_2 are in $N(z_0)$ and

$$\left| \frac{f(z_1) - f(z_2)}{z_1 - z_2} - f'(z_0) \right| < \epsilon.$$

3. Show that the inequality of Exercise 2 above implies

$$\left| \left| \frac{f(z_1) - f(z_2)}{z_1 - z_2} \right| - |f'(z_0)| \right| < \epsilon.$$

* Recall that a topological or bicontinuous mapping is a continuous one-to-one mapping whose inverse is also continuous.

8.4. THE CASE $F'(z) = 0$

Definition 8.4.1.   A point z_0 is said to be *a critical point of the analytic transformation* $w = F(z)$ if $F'(z_0) = 0$.

The following theorem describes the nature of an analytic mapping in the neighborhood of a critical point.

——**THEOREM** 8.4.1.   Let the mapping $w = F(z)$ be analytic and not identically equal to a constant in a neighborhood of $z = z_0$. Let $w_0 = F(z_0)$ and let k be the least positive integer such that $F^{(k)}(z_0) \neq 0$. Then there exists a domain D_z containing z_0 and a neighborhood $N(w_0)$ of w_0 such that $w = F(z)$ maps D_z onto $N(w_0)$, and $F(z)$ can be obtained as a product of a one-to-one analytic mapping $\zeta = G(z)$ of D_z onto a neighborhood $N_\zeta : |\zeta| < \rho$ of $\zeta = 0$ followed by the mapping $w = w_0 + \zeta^k$ of N_ζ onto $N(w_0)$.

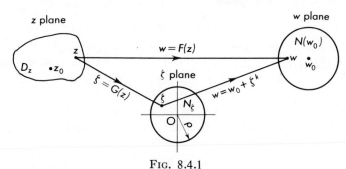

FIG. 8.4.1

Proof.   The Taylor expansion of $F(z)$ about $z = z_0$ is given by

$$F(z) = F(z_0) + \sum_{n=k}^{\infty} \frac{F^{(n)}(z_0)}{n!} (z - z_0)^n, \qquad F^{(k)}(z_0) \neq 0.$$

Since $w = F(z)$ and $w_0 = F(z_0)$, we have

$$w - w_0 = (z - z_0)^k \lambda(z), \qquad (8.4.1)$$

where

$$\lambda(z) = \sum_{n=k}^{\infty} \frac{F^{(n)}(z_0)}{n!} (z - z_0)^{n-k}$$

is by Theorem 6.6.2 analytic in a neighborhood of z_0. Moreover, by hypothesis

$$\lambda(z_0) = \frac{F^{(k)}(z_0)}{k!} \neq 0.$$

From Theorem 5.17.1, it follows (see Exercise 5.17.17) that there exists a neighborhood $N(z_0)$ of z_0 and an analytic function $\mu(z)$ such that

$$[\mu(z)]^k = \lambda(z) \qquad (8.4.2)$$

for z in $N(z_0)$. Let now

$$G(z) = (z - z_0)\,\mu(z) \qquad (8.4.3)$$

for z in $N(z_0)$. Then, from (8.4.1) to (8.4.3), we have

$$w - w_0 = [G(z)]^k. \qquad (8.4.4)$$

Consider the mapping

$$\zeta = G(z) \qquad (8.4.5)$$

where $G(z)$ is given in (8.4.3). Then, since $\lambda(z_0) \neq 0$, we have in virtue of (8.4.2) that $\mu(z_0) \neq 0$. Differentiating (8.4.3) we see that $G'(z_0) = \mu(z_0) \neq 0$. Also from (8.4.3), $\zeta_0 = G(z_0) = 0$. Hence by Theorem 8.2.5, there exists a domain D_z containing z_0 and a neighborhood N_ζ: $|\,\zeta\,| < \rho$ of $\zeta = 0$ such that $\zeta = G(z)$ maps D_z bicontinuously onto N_ζ. (See Fig. 8.4.1.)

Now consider the mapping

$$w = w_0 + \zeta^k. \qquad (8.4.6)$$

Since for any point ζ and its image w we have from (8.4.6) that $|\,w - w_0\,| = |\,\zeta\,|^k$, it is clear that every point in N_ζ: $|\,\zeta\,| < \rho$ has its image under the mapping (8.4.6) in $N(w_0)$: $|\,w - w_0\,| < \rho^k$. Conversely, every point $w = w_0 + re^{i\theta}$ in $N(w_0)$ is the image of a point $\zeta = r^{1/k}e^{i\theta/k}$ in N_ζ.

The mapping given in (8.4.5) followed by the mapping given in (8.4.6) transforms first every point z in D_z into the point $\zeta = G(z)$ in N_ζ, then takes the point ζ into the point

$$w = w_0 + \zeta^k = w_0 + [G(z)]^k = w_0 + (z - z_0)^k \lambda(z) = F(z).$$

Thus the mapping (8.4.5) followed by (8.4.6) yields the same transformation of D_z as the mapping $w = F(z)$. The theorem is now established.

Remark 8.4.1.   We may gain a better insight into the mapping described in Theorem 8.4.1 by examining more closely the mapping given in (8.4.6). If we subdivide the disk $|\,\zeta\,| \leq r$ into k equal sectors each having a central angle equal to $2\pi/k$, then the transformation (8.4.6) will map each sector together with its boundary onto the disk $|\,w - w_0\,| \leq r^k$. This mapping will be one-to-one except that each of the radial boundaries L_1 and L_2 of the sector is mapped onto the same segment L'. (See Fig. 8.4.2.)

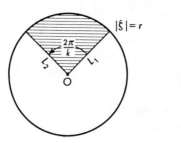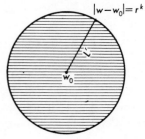

FIG. 8.4.2

Let us now take $r < \rho$ in Theorem 8.4.1 and let us subdivide the circle $\Gamma_\zeta\colon |\zeta| = r$ and its interior into k equal sectors. It is not difficult to show (see Exercise 8.4.2) that the inverse image of Γ_ζ is a simple closed contour C_z contained in D_z. (See Fig. 8.4.3 for the case when $k = 3$.) Also, the inverse

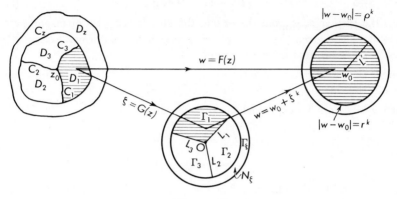

FIG. 8.4.3

image of the interior of Γ_ζ is the interior of C_z, and the inverse image of each radial line L_i is a contour C_i joining z_0 to a point on C_z, $i = 1, 2, \cdots, k$.

The contours C_i $(i = 1, 2, \cdots, k)$ subdivide the interior of C_z into k domains D_i each of which is mapped by (8.4.5) onto the interior Γ_i of a sector of Γ_ζ. The transformation (8.4.6) then maps one-to-one each Γ_i onto the interior of the circle $|w - w_0| = r^k$ with the segment L' removed. Thus $w = F(z)$ maps each of the domains D_i onto the interior of the circle $|w - w_0| = r^k$ with the segment L' removed. On the other hand, each of the contours C_i is first mapped by the transformation given in (8.4.5) onto one of the radial lines L_i and then all the L_i are mapped by (8.4.6) onto the segment L'.

To summarize, we may say that there exists a domain D_z containing z_0 which may be subdivided into k "sectors" by contours issuing from z_0. The transformation $w = F(z)$ maps each sector onto the interior, $N(w_0)$, of a circle $|w - w_0| = R$. The mapping of each sector is one-to-one except that the "radial" contours issuing from z_0, and separating the sectors, all map into the same radius of the circle $|w - w_0| = R$.

Remark 8.4.2. Let $w = f(z)$ be a mapping defined in a domain D. It follows from Theorems 8.3.1 and 8.4.1 that if the mapping $w = f(z)$ is analytic and locally one-to-one in D, then it is conformal in D. Conversely, it can be shown that if the mapping $w = f(z)$ is conformal in D and if $\mathcal{R}[f(z)]$ and $\mathcal{I}[f(z)]$ are continuous functions of x and y with continuous first derivatives for $z = x + iy$ in D, then $f(z)$ is analytic in D.

EXAMPLE 8.4.1. Let us discuss the transformation $w = z^2$. Since

$$w = u + iv = z^2 = (x + iy)^2 = x^2 - y^2 + 2xyi,$$

we have

$$u = x^2 - y^2, \qquad v = 2xy.$$

The ratio of magnification at any point $z_0 = x_0 + iy_0$ is

$$|f'(z_0)| = 2|z_0|.$$

Thus the further z_0 is from the origin, the greater the ratio of magnification. The mapping given by $w = z^2$ is everywhere conformal except when $f'(z_0) = 2z_0 = 0$, that is, at the origin.

Let

$$w = \rho e^{i\phi}, \qquad z = re^{i\theta}.$$

Then $w = z^2$ can be expressed in polar coordinates as

$$\rho e^{i\phi} = r^2 e^{2i\theta},$$

or

$$\rho = r^2, \qquad \phi = 2\theta.$$

Thus we see that the upper half of the z plane, that is, all points $z = re^{i\theta}$, $r > 0, 0 < \theta < \pi$, maps conformally one-to-one onto the domain D_0 consisting of the entire w plane with the nonnegative real axis removed. Similarly, the lower half plane maps conformally one-to-one onto D_0. The nonpositive and nonnegative halves of the x axis are each mapped onto the nonnegative half of the u axis.

The straight lines $x = c_1$ in the z plane map into a family of parabolas in the w plane

$$u = c_1^2 - y^2, \qquad v = 2c_1 y, \qquad -\infty < y < \infty,$$

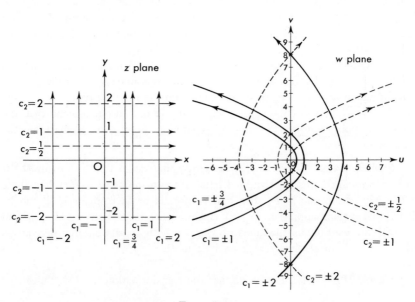

FIG . 8.4.4

or

$$v^2 = -4c_1^2(u - c_1^2). \tag{8.4.7}$$

The lines $y = c_2$ in the z plane map into a family of parabolas in the w plane

$$u = x^2 - c_2^2, \qquad v = 2c_2 x, \qquad -\infty < x < \infty,$$

or

$$v^2 = 4c_2^2(u + c_2^2). \tag{8.4.8}$$

Observe that the family of parabolas in (8.4.7) and (8.4.8), being images of an orthogonal system, also form an orthogonal system.

Fig. 8.4.4 shows how some of the lines $x = c_1$ and $y = c_2$ in the z plane map into parabolas in the w plane.

The region R_z, bounded by

$$y = 0; \qquad x = 2; \qquad x^2 - y^2 = 1, \qquad x \geq 0, \qquad y \geq 0,$$

is mapped by $w = z^2$ onto the region R_w, bounded by

$$v = 0; \qquad v^2 = -16(u - 4), \qquad v \geq 0; \qquad u = 1,$$

as shown in Fig. 8.4.5. Observe that the angles at A, B, C, are respectively

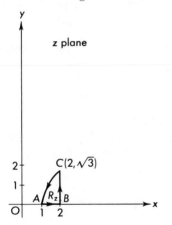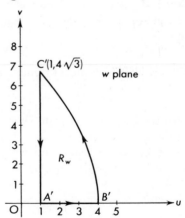

FIG. 8.4.5

equal to those at A', B', C'. Also, note that the region R_z does not have the same shape as R_w. As was remarked earlier, under a conformal mapping, a large region in the z plane does not necessarily map into a similar region in the w plane.

EXERCISES 8.4

1. Let $f(z)$ be analytic in a domain D_z and suppose that $w = f(z)$ maps D_z one-to-one onto a domain D_w. Let $z = g(w)$ define the inverse mapping of D_w onto D_z.

(a) Show that $f'(z) \neq 0$ in D_z.

(b) Show that $g(w)$ is continuous in D_w.

(c) Show that $g(w)$ is analytic in D_w.

2. Let $w = F(z)$ be a one-to-one analytic mapping of a domain D_z onto a domain D_w.

    (a) Show that if C_w is a contour in D_w, then its inverse image under $w = F(z)$ is a contour in D_z.

    (b) Show that if C_w is a simple closed contour in D_w, then its inverse image C_z is a simple closed contour in D_z, and the interior of C_z is the inverse image of the interior C_w^0 of C_w. (C_w^0 is assumed interior to D_w.)

8.5. THE LINEAR TRANSFORMATION. A simple example of a one-to-one analytic (and hence conformal) mapping is the linear transformation

$$w = Az + B, \tag{8.5.1}$$

where $A \neq 0$ and B are complex constants. The mapping given by the function in (8.5.1) may be studied by consideration of the following two special cases.

CASE 1. *Translation.* The general form is

$$w = z + B. \tag{8.5.2}$$

Each point z is displaced through the vector B, that is, if

$$z = x + iy, \qquad w = u + iv, \qquad B = b_1 + ib_2,$$

then the image of any point (x, y) in the z plane is the point $(x + b_1, y + b_2)$ in the w plane. Since $dw/dz = 1 \neq 0$, a domain D_z in the z plane is mapped by (8.5.2) conformally onto a congruent domain D_w in the w plane. [See Fig. 8.5.1, where $w = z + (2 + i)$.]

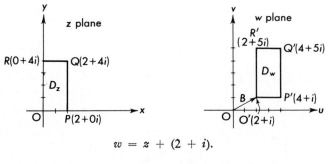

$$w = z + (2 + i).$$

FIG. 8.5.1

CASE 2. *Rotation-Magnification.* The general form is

$$w = Az, \qquad A \neq 0. \tag{8.5.3}$$

Let

$$A = ae^{i\alpha}, \quad z = re^{i\theta}, \quad w = \rho e^{i\phi}.$$

Then (8.5.3) becomes

$$\rho e^{i\phi} = are^{i(\theta+\alpha)}.$$

Thus

$$\rho = ar, \quad \phi = \theta + \alpha.$$

Hence the distances from the origin are magnified in the ratio a to 1, while all figures are rotated about the origin through the angle α. Thus, every domain D_z in the z plane is mapped conformally by this rotation and mangification onto a geometrically similar domain D_w in the w plane. [See Fig. 8.5.2,

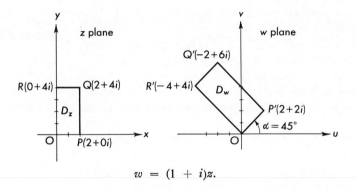

$$w = (1 + i)z.$$

FIG. 8.5.2

where $w = (1 + i)\,z$. Here, the magnification ratio is $\sqrt{2}$ to 1 and the rotation is through an angle of $\pi/4$.]

The transformation given in (8.5.1) may be written as

$$w = W + B, \tag{8.5.4}$$

where

$$W = Az. \tag{8.5.5}$$

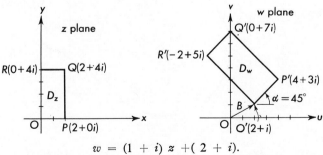

$$w = (1 + i)\,z + (2 + i).$$

FIG. 8.5.3

Thus, the mapping given in (8.5.1) may be obtained by performing the rotation-magnification given in (8.5.5) followed by the translation in (8.5.4). It follows that *the linear transformation* (8.5.1) *preserves the shapes of all figures.* [See Fig. 8.5.3 for the case when $w = (1 + i) z + (2 + i)$.]

8.6. INVERSION WITH RESPECT TO A CIRCLE. Let C be a circle of radius R with center at z_0. Let $p \neq z_0$ be any point at a distance ρ from z_0, and let q be a point on the radial line from z_0 through p at a distance r from z_0 as shown in Fig. 8.6.1. Note that the points z_0, p and q are collinear. If

$$\rho r = R^2, \tag{8.6.1}$$

then p and q are said to be *inverse points* with respect to the circle $C: |z - z_0| = R$; z_0 and R are called respectively the *center of inversion* and *radius of inversion*. Clearly, q is exterior to C, if and only if p is interior to C. If q is on C, then q coincides with p. In particular, when $z_0 = 0$ and $R = 1$, we have $\rho r = 1$. Then q and p are inverse points with respect to the unit circle; the center of inversion is at the origin.

Let p and q be inverse points with respect to the circle

$$C: \qquad |z - z_0| = R.$$

Then using (1.5.6) and (1.6.1), we have (see Fig. 8.6.1)

$$p = z_0 + \rho e^{i\lambda}, \qquad q = z_0 + \frac{R^2}{\rho} e^{i\lambda}.$$

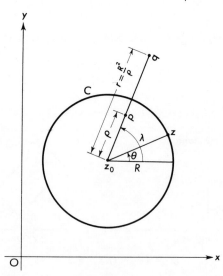

FIG. 8.6.1

If z is any point on C, then $z = z_0 + Re^{i\theta}$. It is not difficult to show (see Exercise 8.6.1) that for any point z on C

$$\left| \frac{z-p}{z-q} \right| = \frac{\rho}{R}. \tag{8.6.2}$$

Conversely, it can be shown (see Exercise 1.4.17) that

$$\left| \frac{z-p}{z-q} \right| = k, \tag{8.6.3}$$

where k is a real positive constant different from unity, represents a circle (known as the circle of Apollonius) with respect to which p and q are inverse points. When $k = 1$ in (8.6.3), z is equidistant from the points p and q and hence lies on the perpendicular bisector of the line joining them. Thus, the equation $|(z-p)/(z-q)| = 1$ represents a straight line forming the perpendicular bisector of the segment pq.

EXERCISES 8.6

1. Show that for $\rho > 0$ and $R > 0$, we have

$$\left| \frac{Re^{i\theta} - \rho e^{i\lambda}}{Re^{i\theta} - \dfrac{R^2}{\rho} e^{i\lambda}} \right| = \frac{\rho}{R}.$$

2. Show that two points p and q are inverse points with respect to the circle C: $|z - z_0| = R$ if, and only if, $(p - z_0)(\bar{q} - \bar{z}_0) = R^2$.

8.7. THE RECIPROCAL TRANSFORMATION:

$$w = \frac{1}{z}. \tag{8.7.1}$$

Instead of regarding corresponding values of z and w as being represented by points in different planes, it is convenient at times to think of the w plane as superposed upon the z plane. The numbers z and $1/z$ may then be represented by points P and Q, respectively, in the same plane.

Using polar coordinates, (8.7.1) may be written as

$$\rho e^{i\phi} = \frac{1}{r} e^{-i\theta} \quad \text{or} \quad \rho = \frac{1}{r}, \quad \phi = -\theta. \tag{8.7.2}$$

Thus, transformation (8.7.1) is the product of two consecutive transformations

$$z' = \frac{1}{r} e^{i\theta}, \quad w = \bar{z'}. \tag{8.7.3}$$

The first of these transformations, which is an inversion with respect to the unit circle C, is followed by a second transformation which is a reflection in the real axis as shown in Fig. 8.7.1. Thus, points exterior to C are mapped by

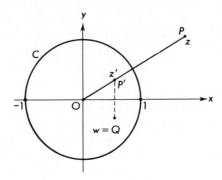

FIG. 8.7.1

$w = 1/z$ into points interior to C and conversely.

It is not difficult to show (see Exercise 1.4.8) that the equation of a circle in the z plane is given by

$$az\bar{z} + b\bar{z} + \bar{b}z + c = 0, \qquad (8.7.4)$$

where $a \neq 0$ and c are real constants and b is a complex constant. In particular, when $c = 0$, the circle goes through the origin ($z = 0$). When $a = 0$, (8.7.4) reduces to the equation of a straight line.

The transformation $w = 1/z$ maps the circle given in (8.7.4) into another circle given by

$$cw\bar{w} + \bar{b}\bar{w} + bw + a = 0 \qquad \text{if } c \neq 0,$$

or a straight line

$$\bar{b}\bar{w} + bw + a = 0 \qquad \text{if } c = 0.$$

Thus, $w = 1/z$ maps circles into circles except that circles passing through $z = 0$ are mapped into straight lines.

Putting $a = 0$ and $c \neq 0$ in (8.7.4), we see that lines not passing through the origin are mapped by $w = 1/z$ into the family

$$cw\bar{w} + \bar{b}\bar{w} + bw = 0$$

of circles passing through $w = 0$.

Finally, putting $a = 0$ and $c = 0$ in (8.7.4), we see that the lines going through $z = 0$ are mapped into lines

$$\bar{b}\bar{w} + bw = 0,$$

passing through $w = 0$.

We may summarize the foregoing results in the following

——**THEOREM** 8.7.1. The transformation $w = 1/z$ maps circles or straight lines into circles or straight lines.

In particular, let us observe that the lines $x = c_1 \neq 0$ and $y = c_2 \neq 0$ map into circles which are tangent respectively to the v axis and u axis at the origin. For,

$$w = u + iv = \frac{1}{x + iy}$$

gives the relation

$$u = \frac{x}{x^2 + y^2}, \qquad v = -\frac{y}{x^2 + y^2},$$

and noticing that $u^2 + v^2 = 1/(x^2 + y^2)$, we obtain

$$x = \frac{u}{u^2 + v^2}, \qquad y = -\frac{v}{u^2 + v^2}.$$

Thus when $x = c_1$ and $y = c_2$, we have

$$\frac{u}{u^2 + v^2} = c_1, \qquad -\frac{v}{u^2 + v^2} = c_2. \tag{8.7.5}$$

Upon completing the square in equations (8.7.5), we obtain

$$\left(u - \frac{1}{2c_1}\right)^2 + v^2 = \left(\frac{1}{2c_1}\right)^2, \qquad u^2 + \left(v + \frac{1}{2c_2}\right)^2 = \left(\frac{1}{2c_2}\right)^2,$$

which are the desired image circles of the lines $x = c_1 \neq 0$ and $y = c_2 \neq 0$, respectively. (See Fig. 8.7.2.)

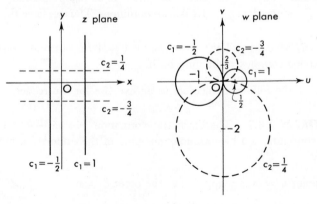

$$w = 1/z.$$

Fig. 8.7.2

We could also have arrived at the above result without resorting to computation. For example, the line $x = c$ is perpendicular to the x axis. Now, the

x axis is mapped by $w = 1/z$ onto the u axis. (Why?) Since the line $x = c$, $c \neq 0$, does not pass through $z = 0$, its image is a circle Γ passing through $w = 0$. The mapping $w = 1/z$ being conformal, it follows that Γ must be perpendicular to the u axis (at $w = 1/c$), and hence tangent to the v axis at $w = 0$.

8.8. THE POINT AT INFINITY. The mapping given by $\zeta = 1/z$ maps the finite z plane one-to-one onto the finite ζ plane, except for the point $z = 0$, which has no image, and the point $\zeta = 0$, which has no antecedent. However, as was seen in Section 2.12, we may obtain the extended z plane by adjoining to the finite complex plane an ideal point $z = \infty$. We also have found it natural to define a neighborhood of $z = \infty$ as the set of all finite z exterior to a circle $|z| = M$, $M > 0$, together with the point $z = \infty$. Similarly, we may speak of the extended ζ plane.

When we assign respectively the images $\zeta = \infty$ and $\zeta = 0$ to the points $z = 0$ and $z = \infty$, the transformation $\zeta = 1/z$ becomes a one-to-one mapping of the extended z plane onto the extended ζ plane.

To prove that this mapping is continuous, we need to verify that if ζ_0 is the image of z_0 and $N(\zeta_0)$ is any given neighborhood of ζ_0, then there exists a neighborhood $N(z_0)$ of z_0 which is mapped into $N(\zeta_0)$. For the case when ζ_0 and z_0 are both finite, this follows from the continuity of the function $1/z$ for z finite and not equal to zero. In case $z_0 = 0$ and $\zeta_0 = \infty$, $N(\zeta_0)$ consists of all ζ such that $|\zeta| > M$ for some constant $M > 0$. Clearly, the neighborhood $N(z_0)$ of $z_0 = 0$, which consists of all z such that $|z| < 1/M$, is mapped into $N(\zeta_0)$. Similarly, when $\zeta_0 = 0$ and $z_0 = \infty$, given $N(\zeta_0)$: $|\zeta| < M$, then the neighborhood $N(z_0)$: $|z| > 1/M$ is mapped into $N(\zeta_0)$.

In the same way, we can show that the inverse mapping which assigns to each point ζ its antecedent $z = 1/\zeta$ is also continuous. Thus we have the following

——**THEOREM** 8.8.1. The transformation $\zeta = 1/z$ is a bicontinuous mapping of the extended complex plane onto itself.

We leave the following theorem as an exercise for the reader.

——**THEOREM** 8.8.2. The linear transformation $\zeta = az + b$, where $a \neq 0$ and b are constants, is a bicontinuous mapping of the extended complex plane onto itself.

The point $z = \infty$ is mapped into the point $\zeta = \infty$.

Remark 8.8.1. In Section 7.3, we have seen that one may speak of a function $f(z)$ as being analytic or having a singularity at $z = \infty$, by resorting to a second coordinate w related to the z coordinate by the equation $z = 1/w$. Instead of considering directly the function $f(z)$ in the neighborhood of $z = \infty$, we consider the function $F(w) = f(1/w)$ in the neighborhood of $w = 0$.

Similarly, the derivatives of $f(z)$ at $z = \infty$, are defined in terms of the derivatives of $F(w)$ at $w = 0$.

The curve $C: z = f(t)$, $\alpha \leq t \leq \beta$, is said to be a contour passing through the point at infinity if

$$\Gamma: w = \frac{1}{z} = \frac{1}{f(t)} = g(t), \ \alpha \leq t \leq \beta,$$

is a contour such that $g(t_0) = 0$ for some t_0, $\alpha \leq t_0 \leq \beta$. Using w coordinates, it is perfectly natural to speak of the tangent to C at $z = \infty$, and the angle between two contours intersecting at $z = \infty$.

Many of the theorems which we have proved for the finite complex plane are valid also in the extended complex plane. Thus, for example, Theorems 8.2.1, 8.2.2, 8.2.3, 8.2.5, 8.3.1, 8.4.1 and 5.17.1 hold equally well in the extended complex plane. However, we shall not take up the details here.

8.9. THE LINEAR FRACTIONAL TRANSFORMATION. The transformation

$$w = \frac{az + b}{cz + d}, \qquad ad - bc \neq 0, \tag{8.9.1}$$

where a, b, c, d are complex constants and z is a complex variable, is called a *linear fractional transformation*. This transformation is also known as the *bilinear* or *Möbius transformation*. The expression

$$D = ad - bc = \begin{vmatrix} a & b \\ c & d \end{vmatrix}$$

is called the *determinant* of the transformation. Observe that if $D = 0$, then $a/c = b/d$ and (8.9.1) reduces to $w = $ constant. Thus, if $D = 0$, then all points in the z plane would be mapped into the same point in the w plane. By imposing the condition that $D \neq 0$, we are able to set aside this trivial case; the transformation $w = (az + b)/(cz + d)$, $D = ad - bc = 0$ will not be considered a linear fractional transformation.

The transformation given in (8.9.1) has an inverse which is also a linear fractional transformation for, solving for z in terms of w, we obtain

$$z = \frac{dw - b}{-cw + a}, \tag{8.9.2}$$

and

$$\begin{vmatrix} d & -b \\ -c & a \end{vmatrix} = ad - bc \neq 0.$$

Also a linear fractional transformation followed by a linear fractional transformation results again in a linear fractional transformation, for, let

$$w = \frac{az + b}{cz + d}, \quad D = \begin{vmatrix} a & b \\ c & d \end{vmatrix} \neq 0 \quad \text{and} \quad z = \frac{a'z' + b'}{c'z' + d'}, \quad D' = \begin{vmatrix} a' & b' \\ c' & d' \end{vmatrix} \neq 0;$$

then it follows by direct substitution that

$$w = \frac{Az' + B}{Cz' + D} \, , \tag{8.9.3}$$

where

$$\begin{vmatrix} A & B \\ C & D \end{vmatrix} = \begin{vmatrix} aa' + bc' & ab' + bd' \\ ca' + dc' & cb' + dd' \end{vmatrix} = \begin{vmatrix} a & b \\ c & d \end{vmatrix} \cdot \begin{vmatrix} a' & b' \\ c' & d' \end{vmatrix} = D \cdot D' \neq 0.$$

When $c = 0$, the linear fractional transformation (8.9.1) reduces to the linear transformation (8.5.1) discussed in Section 8.5. When $c \neq 0$, let

$$z' = cz + d, \qquad z'' = \frac{1}{z'} \, ,$$

then (8.9.1) can be written as

$$w = \frac{a}{c} + \frac{bc - ad}{c} z''.$$

Thus when $c \neq 0$, the transformation

$$w = \frac{az + b}{cz + d} \, , \qquad ad - bc \neq 0,$$

may be obtained by performing successively in the order given the following transformations

$$(1) \ z' = cz + d, \qquad (2) \ z'' = \frac{1}{z'} \, , \qquad (3) \ w = \frac{a}{c} + \frac{bc - ad}{c} z''. \tag{8.9.4}$$

The transformations (1) and (3) are linear mappings discussed in Section 8.5, while (2) is the reciprocal transformation discussed in Section 8.7. From Theorems 8.8.1 and 8.8.2, each of the transformations given in (8.9.4) is a bicontinuous mapping of the extended complex plane onto itself. Utilizing Exercise 2.9.5, we then have the following

———*THEOREM* 8.9.1.   The linear fractional transformation

$$w = \frac{az + b}{cz + d} \, , \qquad ad - bc \neq 0, \tag{8.9.1}$$

is a bicontinuous mapping of the extended complex plane onto itself.

The point $z = \infty$ is mapped into $w = a/c$ and the point $z = -d/c$ is mapped into $w = \infty$.

Remark 8.9.1.   Utilizing (8.9.2), (8.9.3), Theorem 8.9.1, and Exercise 2.9.12, we see that *the set of linear fractional transformations forms a group.*
We leave it as an exercise for the reader to establish the following

——**THEOREM** 8.9.2. The linear fractional transformation

$$w = \frac{az + b}{cz + d}, \qquad ad - bc \neq 0, \tag{8.9.1}$$

is a one-to-one analytic mapping of the extended complex plane onto itself. In view of Remark 8.4.2 and Theorem 8.9.2, transformation (8.9.1) is conformal.

Remark 8.9.2. Given a line L, then for any $M > 0$, there exists points z on L such that $|z| > M$. Thus the point $z = \infty$ is an accumulation point of L, and it is natural to regard $z = \infty$ as belonging to L. We shall often do so. For convenience, lines in the extended complex plane may also be referred to as circles. We leave it for the reader to show that the linear transformation (8.5.1) and the reciprocal transformation (8.7.1) map any circle one-to-one onto a circle. It follows that the linear fractional transformation (8.9.1), which is a product of the linear and reciprocal transformations in (8.9.4), also maps any circle one-to-one onto a circle.

8.10. INVARIANCE OF THE CROSS-RATIO. Suppose that the linear fractional transformation (8.9.1) maps four distinct finite points z_1, z_2, z_3, z_4 of the z plane respectively into four corresponding finite points w_1, w_2, w_3, w_4 of the w plane. Consider the equations

$$w_i - w_k = \frac{ad - bc}{(cz_i + d)(cz_k + d)}(z_i - z_k), \qquad i, k = 1, 2, 3, 4.$$

Taking $i = 1$, $k = 4$ and $i = 3$, $k = 2$ in the above equations, we get

$$(w_1 - w_4)(w_3 - w_2) = S(z_1 - z_4)(z_3 - z_2), \tag{8.10.1}$$

where

$$S = \frac{(ad - bc)^2}{(cz_1 + d)(cz_2 + d)(cz_3 + d)(cz_4 + d)}. \tag{8.10.2}$$

Since S is symmetric in z_1, z_2, z_3, z_4, we also have

$$(w_1 - w_2)(w_3 - w_4) = S(z_1 - z_2)(z_3 - z_4). \tag{8.10.3}$$

Since all the z_j's and w_j's $(j = 1, \cdots, 4)$ are distinct, we obtain upon dividing (8.10.1) by (8.10.3)

$$\frac{(w_1 - w_4)(w_3 - w_2)}{(w_1 - w_2)(w_3 - w_4)} = \frac{(z_1 - z_4)(z_3 - z_2)}{(z_1 - z_2)(z_3 - z_4)}. \tag{8.10.4}$$

The right-hand side of (8.10.4) is called the *cross-ratio* of the four points z_1, z_2, z_3, z_4 and is denoted by (z_1, z_2, z_3, z_4). Thus we may rewrite (8.10.4) as

$$(w_1, w_2, w_3, w_4) = (z_1, z_2, z_3, z_4). \tag{8.10.5}$$

Relation (8.10.5) asserts that under a linear fractional transformation, the cross-ratio of four distinct finite points which map into four finite points is invariant.

The definition of cross-ratio may be extended by continuity to the case when one of the points is the point at infinity. For example, the cross-ratio (∞, z_2, z_3, z_4) is defined as $\lim_{z_1 \to \infty} (z_1, z_2, z_3, z_4)$. Thus

$$(\infty, z_2, z_3, z_4) = \lim_{z_1 \to \infty} \frac{(1 - z_4/z_1)(z_3 - z_2)}{(1 - z_2/z_1)(z_3 - z_4)} = \frac{z_3 - z_2}{z_3 - z_4}. \qquad (8.10.6)$$

Similar expressions are obtained if z_2, z_3 or z_4 is the point at infinity. By taking the limit of both sides in (8.10.4), we see that the invariance of the cross-ratio also holds in case one of the z_i or w_i is equal to infinity. We thus have the following

——**THEOREM** 8.10.1.   The cross-ratio of four distinct points in the extended complex plane is invariant under the linear fractional transformation

$$w = \frac{az + b}{cz + d}, \qquad ad - bc \neq 0. \qquad (8.9.1)$$

Remark 8.10.1.   Let z_1, z_2, z_3 be three distinct points, not necessarily all finite, in the extended complex plane, and consider the mapping $\zeta = F(z)$, where $F(z) = (z_1, z_2, z_3, z)$. Although the cross-ratio (z_1, z_2, z_3, z) has been defined only for the case when z is distinct from z_i, $i = 1, 2, 3$, we can define $\zeta_i = F(z_i)$ as

$$\zeta_i = \lim_{z \to z_i} F(z) = F(z_i). \qquad (8.10.7)$$

Clearly, we then have $\zeta_1 = 0$, $\zeta_2 = 1$ and $\zeta_3 = \infty$.

We leave it as an exercise for the reader to verify that the mapping $\zeta = F(z)$ thus becomes a linear fractional transformation. In view of Theorem 8.9.1, it follows that ζ approaches the points 0, 1 and ∞ if, and only if, its antecedent z under F approaches the points z_1, z_2 and z_3, respectively.

——**THEOREM** 8.10.2.   Let z_i and w_i, $i = 1, 2, 3$, be distinct points in the extended z and w plane, respectively. Then there exists a unique linear fractional transformation mapping z_i respectively into w_i, $i = 1, 2, 3$.

Proof.   Note that the w_i and z_i are not required to be all finite. We first observe that if such a linear fractional transformation exists, and w denotes the image of z, then by the invariance of the cross ratio under a linear fractional transformation we must have

$$(w_1, w_2, w_3, w) = (z_1, z_2, z_3, z). \qquad (8.10.8)$$

Solving for w in (8.10.8), we obtain

$$w = \frac{\alpha z + \beta}{\gamma z + \delta}, \qquad \alpha\delta - \beta\gamma \neq 0, \qquad (8.10.9)$$

where α, β, γ and δ are complex constants depending upon z_i and w_i, $i = 1, 2, 3$. [See Exercise 8.10.16(b).]

If we let $z \to z_1$, **then the** right hand member of (8.10.8) approaches zero. In view of Remark **8.10.1**, it follows that w approaches w_1. Hence, if we let $z \to z_1$, then the value of w obtained from (8.10.9) approaches w_1. Similarly, if $z \to z_2$ or $z \to z_3$, then the value of w obtained from (8.10.9) approaches as a limit w_2 or w_3, respectively. Consequently, (8.10.9) is the desired linear fractional transformation mapping z_1, z_2 and z_3 into w_1, w_2 and w_3, respectively, thus establishing the theorem.

Remark 8.10.2. It now follows that *if C_z and C_w are any two circles in the z plane and w plane respectively, then a linear fractional transformation can always be found which will map C_z onto C_w.* (Here, by a "circle", we mean either a circle or a straight line.) To see this, we may choose three distinct points z_1, z_2, z_3 on C_z and three distinct points w_1, w_2, w_3 on C_w. Then the transformation which maps z_i respectively into w_i, $i = 1, 2, 3$, maps C_z onto the circle C_w passing through w_1, w_2 and w_3.

EXERCISES 8.10

1. Verify (8.10.2).

2. Show that under the transformation $w = iz + 1$ the image of the semi-infinite strip $x > c_1$, $c_2 < y < c_3$, is the semi-infinite strip $v > c_1$, $1 - c_3 < u < 1 - c_2$.

3. Under the transformation $w = 1/z$ show that the image of
   (a) the infinite strip $0 < y < 1/2c$, $c > 0$ is the domain

   $$u^2 + (v + c)^2 > c^2, \qquad v < 0;$$

   (b) the circle $|z - z_0| = |z_0| \neq 0$ is the line $\mathscr{R}(wz_0) = 1/2$;
   (c) the circle $|z| = r$ is the circle $|w| = 1/r$;
   (d) the hyperbola $x^2 - y^2 = 1$ is the lemniscate of Bernoulli, $\rho^2 = \cos 2\phi$, $(w = \rho e^{i\phi})$.

4. Under the transformation $w = z/(z - 1)$ show that the image of
   (a) the half plane $y \geq 0$ is the half plane $v \leq 0$;
   (b) the half plane $x \geq 0$ is the region $|w - 1/2| \geq 1/2$;
   (c) the disk $|z| \leq 1$ is the half plane $u \leq 1/2$;
   (d) the half plane $x \leq 1/2$ is the disk $|w| \leq 1$;
   (e) the line $x = 1$ is the line $u = 1$.

5. Under the transformation $w = (z - i)/(z + i)$ show that the image of
   (a) the half plane $y > 0$ is the disk $|w| < 1$;
   (b) the half plane $x > 0$ is the half plane $v < 0$;
   (c) the disk $|z| < 1$ is the half plane $u < 0$;
   (d) the line $y = -1$ is the line $u = 1$.

6. Show that if under the mapping $w = 1/z$ a circle C of radius r and center at z_0 is mapped onto a circle Γ of radius ρ and center w_0, then

$$\rho = \frac{r}{|\, z_0 \bar{z}_0 - r^2 \,|}, \qquad w_0 = \frac{\bar{z}_0}{z_0 \bar{z}_0 - r^2}.$$

7. Show that if under the transformation $w = az + b$, a circle C of radius r and center at z_0 is mapped onto a circle Γ of radius ρ and center at w_0, then

$$\rho = |\, a \,|\, r, \qquad w_0 = az_0 + b.$$

8. Show that if under the linear fractional transformation

$$w = \frac{az + b}{cz + d}, \qquad D = ad - bc \neq 0, \qquad c \neq 0,$$

a circle C of radius r and center at z_0 is mapped onto a circle Γ of radius ρ and center at w_0, then

$$\rho = \frac{r}{|\,|\, z_0 + d/c \,|^2 - r^2 \,|} \cdot \left| \frac{D}{c^2} \right|, \qquad w_0 = \frac{a}{c} - \frac{D}{c}\left[\frac{\overline{(cz_0 + d)}}{|\, cz_0 + d \,|^2 - |\, c \,|^2 r^2} \right].$$

9. Show that if, under an inversion with respect to a circle of radius R, a circle C with radius r is mapped onto a circle Γ of radius ρ, then

$$\rho = \frac{R^2 r}{|\, \sigma^2 - r^2 \,|},$$

where σ is the distance from the center of C to the center of inversion.

10. Show that under the linear fractional transformation

$$w = \frac{2z + 3}{z - 4},$$

the circle $C \colon |\, z - 2i \,| = 2$ is mapped onto the circle Γ:

$$\left|\, w - \left(-\frac{6 + 11i}{8} \right) \right| = \frac{11}{8}.$$

11. *The invariant points* (or *fixed points*) of a transformation $w = f(z)$ are given by the solutions of the equation $z = f(z)$. Suppose that we are given a linear fractional transformation

$$w = \frac{az + b}{cz + d}, \qquad D = ad - bc \neq 0, \tag{8.9.1}$$

which is not the identity transformation. Show that

(a) if $c = 0$ and $d \neq a$, then $z = \infty$ and $z = b/(d - a)$ are invariant points;

(b) if $c = 0$ and $d = a$, then the only invariant point is $z = \infty$.

Note that the transformation given in (8.9.1) has at most two invariant points. Suppose that the linear fractional transformation (8.9.1) has invariant points r and s. Establish the following results:

(c) if $(d + a)^2 = 4D$ and $c \neq 0$, then $r = s$;

(d) if $(d + a)^2 \neq 4D$ and $c \neq 0$, then $r \neq s$;

(e) if $r = s$ and $c \neq 0$, then (8.9.1) can be written as

$$\frac{1}{w - r} = \frac{1}{z - r} + \alpha,$$

where $\alpha \neq 0$ is a constant;

(f) if $r \neq s$ and $c \neq 0$, then (8.9.1) can be written as

$$\frac{w - r}{w - s} = \alpha \frac{z - r}{z - s},$$

where $\alpha \neq 0$ is a constant;

(g) express the relation

$$w = \frac{13iz + 75}{3z - 5i}$$

in the form (f) above.

12. Find the invariant points of the following transformations:

(a) $w = \dfrac{1}{z}$;

(b) $w = \dfrac{1}{1 - z}$;

(c) $w = \dfrac{z}{z - 1}$;

(d) $w = \dfrac{z + 1}{z - 1}$;

(e) $w = \dfrac{z + i}{z - i}$;

(f) $w = \dfrac{5z + 7}{5}$;

(g) $w = \dfrac{16z - 25}{z + 6}$;

(h) $w = \dfrac{5iz + 2}{4z + i}$;

(i) $w = \dfrac{z^2 - 4}{z^3 + 6z}$.

13. Find the linear fractional transformations which map respectively:

(a) $z_1 = 0,\ z_2 = i,\ z_3 = -i$ into $w_1 = 1,\ w_2 = -1,\ w_3 = 0$;

(b) $z_1 = 2,\ z_2 = i,\ z_3 = -2$ into $w_1 = 1,\ w_2 = i,\ w_3 = -1$;

(c) $z_1 = 1,\ z_2 = i,\ z_3 = 0$ into $w_1 = 0,\ w_2 = i,\ w_3 = 1$;

(d) $z_1 = 0,\ z_2 = \infty,\ z_3 = 1$ into $w_1 = \infty,\ w_2 = 0,\ w_3 = i$;

(e) $z = z_1,\ z = z_2,\ z = z_3$ ($z_1,\ z_2,$ and z_3 distinct) into $w_1 = 0,\ w_2 = 1,\ w_3 = \infty$;

(f) the cube roots of unity $z_1 = 1,\ z_2 = \omega,\ z_3 = \omega^2$ into $w_1 = 0,\ w_2 = 1,\ w_3 = \infty$.

14. Given the linear fractional transformation

$$w = \frac{az + b}{cz + d}, \qquad ad - bc \neq 0. \tag{8.9.1}$$

Prove that the family of circles through the two fixed points (assumed distinct) of (8.9.1) and the family of circles orthogonal to them each transforms under (8.9.1) into itself.

15. Show that under the transformation $w = (2z + 3)/(3z - 2)$ the center of the w circle passing through the points corresponding to $z = 0$, $z = i$, $z = -i$ is at $w = -5/12$ and its radius is $13/12$.

16. (a) Show that the cross-ratio

$$\lambda = (z_1, z_2, z_3, z) = \frac{(z_1 - z)(z_3 - z_2)}{(z_1 - z_2)(z_3 - z)} \qquad z_1, z_2, z_3 \text{ distinct}$$

can be written as

$$\lambda = \frac{az + b}{cz + d}, \qquad ad - bc \neq 0$$

where

$a = (z_2 - z_3)$, $b = z_1(z_3 - z_2)$, $c = (z_2 - z_1)$, $d = z_3(z_1 - z_2)$,
$ad - bc = (z_1 - z_2)(z_2 - z_3)(z_3 - z_1)$.

(b) Show that $\alpha\delta - \beta\gamma \neq 0$ in (8.10.9).

17. Show that

$$(0, 1, \infty, \lambda) = \lambda.$$

Use this result to show that four distinct points z_1, z_2, z_3, z_4 lie on a circle if, and only if, their cross-ratio (z_1, z_2, z_3, z_4) is a real number.

18. Prove that if four points z_1, z_2, z_3, z_4 are arranged in the given order around a circle, then the cross-ratio $(z_1, z_2, z_3, z_4) < 0$.

19. Prove that if we interchange the first two or last two points in the cross-ratio $(z_1, z_2, z_3, z_4) = \lambda$, then the cross-ratio is changed to $1 - \lambda$.

20. Show that if we form all possible cross-ratios of the four distinct numbers $0, 1, \infty, \lambda$, we obtain the six numbers

$$\lambda, \frac{1}{\lambda}, 1 - \lambda, \frac{1}{1 - \lambda}, \frac{\lambda}{\lambda - 1}, \frac{\lambda - 1}{\lambda},$$

(each occurring four times) and no others. More generally, let z_1, z_2, z_3, z_4 be four distinct points in the extended complex plane, and let $\lambda = (z_1, z_2, z_3, z_4)$. Show that by forming all permutations of z_1, z_2, z_3, z_4 in the expression for λ, we obtain the above six numbers.

21. Suppose that z_2 and z_4 are inverse points with respect to a circle C and z_1 and z_3 are two arbitrary points on C. Let $\lambda = (z_1, z_2, z_3, z_4)$. Prove that $|\lambda| = 1$.

22. Prove Ptolemy's theorem (see Exercise 1.6.18) using the properties of cross-ratios.

23. (a) Suppose that w_1 and w_2 are the images of z_1 and z_2 respectively under the transformation

$$w = R\frac{z - i}{z + i}, \qquad R > 0.$$

Show that if $z_2 = \overline{z_1}$, then $w_2 = R^2/\overline{w_1}$; and conversely;

(b) Show that the transformation

$$w = R\frac{z - i}{z + i}, \qquad R > 0,$$

maps the real axis of the z plane onto the circle $|w| = R$;

(c) Show that if $|w_1| \neq R$, $R > 0$, then any circle passing through the points w_1 and $R^2/\overline{w_1}$ is orthogonal to the circle $|w| = R$;

(d) Show that if z_1 and z_2 are two points such that every circle through z_1 and z_2 is orthogonal to the real axis, then $z_2 = \overline{z_1}$;

(e) Show that if w_1 and w_2 are two points such that any circle passing through them is perpendicular to the circle $|w| = R$, then $w_2 = R^2/\overline{w_1}$.

24. Given two circles Γ and γ tangent at a point z_0. Show that under an inversion with respect to a circle C with center at z_0, Γ and γ are transformed into two parallel lines.

25. Given two circles Γ and γ intersecting at the points z_0 and z_1. Show that under an inversion with respect to a circle C with center at z_0, Γ and γ are transformed into two lines intersecting at an angle equal to that formed by the circles Γ and γ.

26. Let $w = f(z)$ be a linear fractional transformation. Let C be a simple closed contour in the finite z plane, and Γ its image in the finite w plane. Show that Γ is a simple closed contour and that the exterior of C is mapped either onto the interior of Γ or onto the exterior of Γ.

8.11. SYMMETRY WITH RESPECT TO A CIRCLE. Two points z_1 and z_2 are said to be symmetric with respect to a line L, if L is the perpendicular bisector of the line segment joining z_1 to z_2. (See Fig. 8.11.1.) It is not difficult

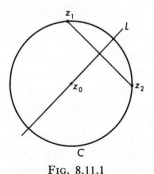

FIG. 8.11.1

to show that two points z_1 and $\dot{z}_2$ are symmetric with respect to a line L if, and only if, every circle C passing through z_1 and z_2 intersects L orthogonally. We shall take this property of orthogonality as a definition of symmetry of two points with respect to a line. Furthermore, we shall extend this definition to the case of a circle.

Definition 8.11.1.   Two points z_1 and z_2 are *symmetric with respect to a circle* Γ if every circle or straight line passing through z_1 and z_2 intersects Γ orthogonally.

We observe that, according to this definition, if z_1 is the center of Γ and $z_2 = \infty$, then z_1 and z_2 are symmetric with respect to Γ. For, the only "circles" passing through z_1 and z_2 are straight lines through the center of Γ, and they are clearly orthogonal to Γ.

——*THEOREM* 8.11.1.   Two finite points p and q are symmetric with respect to the circle Γ if, and only if, p and q are inverse points with respect to Γ.

Proof.   Suppose that p and q are inverse points with respect to the circle Γ with center at O, and let C be any circle passing through p and q. (See Fig. 8.11.2.) Let M be a point of intersection of C and Γ. Let the distances

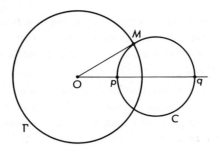

Fig. 8.11.2

from O to p and O to q be denoted by ρ and r, respectively. Then from (8.6.1) we have

$$(OM)^2 = \rho r. \qquad (8.11.1)$$

It is known from elementary geometry that if (8.11.1) is satisfied, then OM is tangent to the circle C. Hence Γ is orthogonal to C.

Conversely, suppose that p and q have the property that every circle or straight line passing through them is orthogonal to Γ, then the straight line pq must also be orthogonal to Γ and hence passes through the center O of Γ. Thus the points O, p and q are collinear. Let C be any circle passing through p and q, and let M be an intersection of C and Γ. (See Fig. 8.11.2.) Since OM is tangent to C, we have from geometry that $(OM)^2 = \rho r$. Hence p and q are inverse points with respect to Γ, and the theorem is established.

Since linear fractional transformations are conformal (see Theorem 8.9.2), it follows that orthogonal circles or straight lines are mapped into orthogonal circles or straight lines. Thus we have the following

——*THEOREM* 8.11.2. Let Γ be a circle or straight line. Then under a linear fractional transformation, the points z_1 and z_2 are symmetric with respect to Γ if, and only if, their respective images w_1, w_2 are symmetric with respect to the image of Γ.

8.12. SOME EXAMPLES OF LINEAR FRACTIONAL TRANSFORMATIONS

EXAMPLE 8.12.1. *To find all linear fractional transformations of the upper half plane $\mathcal{I}(z) > 0$ onto the upper half plane $\mathcal{I}(w) > 0$.*

Solution. Since the linear fractional transformation $w = (az + b)/(cz + d)$ is one-to-one and analytic in the extended complex plane (see Theorem 8.9.2), the boundary $\mathcal{I}(z) = 0$ must map onto the boundary $\mathcal{I}(w) = 0$. (Why?) Consequently, we search first for all linear fractional transformations mapping the line $\mathcal{I}(z) = 0$ onto the line $\mathcal{I}(w) = 0$.

Let $z = z_i$, $i = 1, 2, 3$, be the points on $\mathcal{I}(z) = 0$ which map respectively into $w = 0, 1, \infty$. Then, if w is the image of z, we have by the invariance of the cross-ratio (see Theorem 8.10.1), $(0, 1, \infty, w) = (z_1, z_2, z_3, z)$. But $(0, 1, \infty, w) = w$, hence $w = (z_1, z_2, z_3, z)$. Since z_1, z_2 and z_3 are all real, it follows that the linear fractional transformation mapping $\mathcal{I}(z) = 0$ onto $\mathcal{I}(w) = 0$ is given by

$$w = \frac{\alpha z + \beta}{\gamma z + \delta}, \qquad \alpha\delta - \beta\gamma \neq 0, \quad \alpha, \beta, \gamma, \text{ and } \delta \text{ are real.} \qquad (8.12.1)$$

Conversely, any linear fractional transformation (8.12.1) maps real z into real w, and maps $\mathcal{I}(z) = 0$ onto $\mathcal{I}(w) = 0$.

Let now $z = x + iy$, $y > 0$, be a point in the half plane $\mathcal{I}(z) > 0$, and let w be the image of z under the transformation (8.12.1). Then, as a simple computation shows, we have

$$\mathcal{I}(w) = \frac{(\alpha\delta - \beta\gamma)\,y}{(\gamma x + \delta)^2 + \gamma^2 y^2}. \qquad (8.12.2)$$

Hence $\mathcal{I}(w) > 0$ only if $\alpha\delta - \beta\gamma > 0$.

Conversely, if $\alpha\delta - \beta\gamma > 0$, then the transformation (8.12.1) maps $\mathcal{I}(z) > 0$ into $\mathcal{I}(w) > 0$, and it is not difficult to show (see Exercise 8.12.10) that this mapping is also onto.

EXAMPLE 8.12.2. *To find all linear fractional transformations that map the upper half plane $\mathcal{I}(z) > 0$ onto the interior of the circle $|w| = \rho$.*

Solution. As in Example 8.12.1, we first seek all linear fractional transformations

$$w = \frac{az + b}{cz + d}, \qquad ad - bc \neq 0, \tag{8.12.3}$$

which map the line $\mathscr{I}(z) = 0$ onto the circle $|w| = \rho$.

For z on $\mathscr{I}(z) = 0$, we have $\rho = |w| = |(az + b)/(cz + d)|$. Letting $z \to \infty$ we get $\rho = |a/c|$. Consequently, a and c are both different from zero, and we may write $a/c = \rho e^{i\alpha}$, where α is real. Thus (8.12.3) may be written as

$$w = \rho e^{i\alpha} \frac{z - z_0}{z - z_1}, \tag{8.12.4}$$

where $z_0 = -b/a$ and $z_1 = -d/c$.

The points $w = 0$ and $w = \infty$ are symmetric with respect to the circle $|w| = \rho$. Hence by Theorem 8.11.2, their respective antecedents $z = z_0$ and $z = z_1$ under the transformation (8.12.4) are symmetric with respect to the line $\mathscr{I}(z) = 0$. It follows that $z_1 = \overline{z_0}$. Also, since the image $w = 0$ of $z = z_0$ is interior to the circle $|w| = \rho$, z_0 is in the upper half plane. Hence, the desired transformation must be of the type

$$w = \rho e^{i\alpha} \frac{z - z_0}{z - \overline{z_0}}, \qquad \mathscr{I}(z_0) > 0. \tag{8.12.5}$$

Conversely, any transformation of the type (8.12.5) maps the line $\mathscr{I}(z) = 0$ onto the circle $|w| = \rho$. For, if z is real, then $z - \overline{z_0} = \overline{z - z_0}$ and consequently

$$|w| = \rho \frac{|z - z_0|}{|z - \overline{z_0}|} = \rho.$$

Moreover, since one point $z = z_0$ of $\mathscr{I}(z) > 0$ is mapped into the interior of $|w| = \rho$, it follows from Theorem 2.9.2 and Exercise 2.9.11 that the domain $\mathscr{I}(z) > 0$ is mapped onto the interior of the circle $|w| = \rho$.

EXAMPLE 8.12.3.   *To find all linear fractional transformations that map the interior of the circle $|z| = \rho$ onto the interior of the circle $|w| = \rho$.*

Solution. We begin by finding all linear fractional transformations

$$w = \frac{az + b}{cz + d}, \qquad ad - bc \neq 0, \tag{8.12.3}$$

that will map the circle $|z| = \rho$ onto the circle $|w| = \rho$.

If in (8.12.3) we had $a = 0$, then the antecedent of $w = 0$ would be $z = \infty$, but the antecedent of $w = 0$ is a point in the interior of $|z| = \rho$. It follows that $a \neq 0$.

We shall first deal with the case in which $b \neq 0$ and $c \neq 0$ in (8.12.3). The desired transformation then takes the form

$$w = \frac{a}{c} \frac{z - z_0}{z - z_1}, \tag{8.12.6}$$

where $z_0 = -b/a \neq 0$ and $z_1 = -d/c$.

The points $w = 0$ and $w = \infty$ are symmetric with respect to the circle $|w| = \rho$. From Theorem 8.11.2 their antecedents z_0 and z_1 are symmetric with respect to the circle $|z| = \rho$. Since z_0 and z_1 are finite points, from Theorem 8.11.1 the points z_0 and z_1 are inverse points with respect to the circle $|z| = \rho$. Hence $z_1 = \rho^2/\bar{z}_0$. (See Exercise 8.6.2.) Substituting this value of z_1 into (8.12.6), we get

$$w = \gamma \frac{z - z_0}{\bar{z}_0 z - \rho^2}, \tag{8.12.7}$$

where $\gamma = a\bar{z}_0/c$.

If $z = \rho e^{i\theta}$ is any point on the circle $|z| = \rho$, then its image under (8.12.7) is on the circle $|w| = \rho$ and we have

$$\rho = |w| = \left| \gamma \frac{\rho e^{i\theta} - z_0}{\rho e^{i\theta} \bar{z}_0 - \rho^2} \right| = \left| \frac{\gamma e^{-i\theta}}{-\rho} \right| \left| \frac{\rho e^{i\theta} - z_0}{\rho e^{-i\theta} - \bar{z}_0} \right| = \frac{|\gamma|}{\rho}.$$

Hence $|\gamma| = \rho^2$ and we may write $\gamma = \rho^2 e^{i\alpha}$, where α is a real number. Furthermore, since z_0 is the antecedent of $w = 0$ and $w = 0$ is interior to $|w| = \rho$, it follows that $|z_0| < \rho$. Thus the desired transformation must be of the form

$$w = \rho^2 e^{i\alpha} \frac{z - z_0}{\bar{z}_0 z - \rho^2}, \qquad \alpha \text{ real}, \quad |z_0| < \rho. \tag{8.12.8}$$

Conversely, any transformation of the type given in (8.12.8) maps $|z| < \rho$ onto $|w| < \rho$. We shall leave the verification for the reader.

In case $b = 0$ in (8.12.3), then the image of $z = 0$ is $w = 0$. It follows then from the preservation of symmetry (see Theorem 8.11.2) that the image of $z = \infty$ is $w = \infty$, and consequently we must have $c = 0$. However, if $c = 0$, the transformation (8.12.3) reduces to a linear mapping (8.5.1), and it is not difficult to show (see Exercise 8.10.7) that it is of the form $w = e^{i\alpha} z$, α real. However, this mapping may be obtained from (8.12.8) by setting $z_0 = 0$. Thus (8.12.8) gives us all the linear fractional transformations mapping the interior of the circle $|z| = \rho$ onto the interior of the circle $|w| = \rho$.

EXAMPLE 8.12.4. *To find all linear fractional transformations that map the region enclosed by two circular arcs onto the region enclosed by the sides of an angle in standard position.*

Solution. Let the circular arcs and the angle be as in Fig. 8.12.1, and let

$$w = F(z) = \frac{az + b}{cz + d}, \qquad ad - bc \neq 0, \tag{8.12.3}$$

be the desired transformation mapping the circular arcs C_1, C_2 respectively onto the sides L_1, L_2; and mapping z_1, z_2 the points of intersection of the circular arcs respectively into $w = 0$, $w = \infty$. The form of $F(z)$ is to be determined.

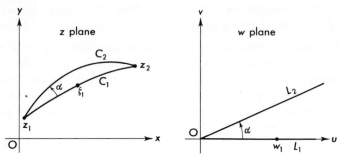

FIG. 8.12.1

Note that since the mapping (8.12.3) is conformal (see Theorem 8.9.2), we have $\angle(C_1, C_2) = \angle(L_1, L_2)$; note also that L_1 is the nonnegative real axis in the w plane. Since z_1, z_2 map respectively into $w = 0$, $w = \infty$, we have $z_1 = -b/a$, $z_2 = -d/c$, and $ac \neq 0$, and (8.12.3) becomes

$$w = \gamma \frac{z - z_1}{z - z_2},\tag{8.12.9}$$

where $\gamma = a/c$.

Let ζ_1, $\zeta_1 \neq z_1$ and $\zeta_1 \neq z_2$, be a fixed point on C_1. Let its image be $w = w_1$ for some arbitrary $w_1 > 0$. Substituting $z = \zeta_1$ into (8.12.9), we get

$$w_1 = \gamma \frac{\zeta_1 - z_1}{\zeta_1 - z_2}.\tag{8.12.10}$$

Let $\alpha_0 = \arg[(\zeta_1 - z_2)/(\zeta_1 - z_1)]$ and let $\rho = w_1 \,|\, (\zeta_1 - z_2)/(\zeta_1 - z_1)\,|$. We see that $\gamma = \rho e^{i\alpha_0}$ and that (8.12.9) must have the form

$$w = \rho e^{i\alpha_0} \frac{z - z_1}{z - z_2},\tag{8.12.11}$$

where (up to a multiple of 2π) α_0 is the fixed real number $\mathrm{Arg}\,[(\zeta_1 - z_2)/(\zeta_1 - z_1)]$ and ρ is any positive number.

Conversely, it is not difficult to show (see Exercise 8.12.2) that (8.12.11) is a transformation having the desired properties.

Remark 8.12.1.   From the characterization of (8.12.11) as the set of all linear fractional transformations mapping z_1, z_2, respectively, into $w = 0, \infty$ and mapping the region enclosed by C_1 and C_2 onto the angle α, it follows that α_0 is independent of the fixed point ζ_1 chosen on C_1, that is,

$$\alpha_0 = \mathrm{Arg}\left(\frac{\zeta - z_2}{\zeta - z_1}\right),$$

no matter what point ζ is taken on C_1. This is in agreement with the theorem of elementary geometry stating that the measure of an angle inscribed in a given arc of a circle does not depend on the position of the vertex.

We also observe that nothing is changed when the region to be mapped is enclosed by a circular arc and a line segment. The desired transformation is again given by (8.12.11). In particular, when in Fig. 8.12.1, C_1 is a line segment, we have

$$\alpha_0 = \text{Arg}\,\frac{\zeta_1 - z_2}{\zeta_1 - z_1} = \pi,$$

and (8.12.11) becomes

$$w = -\rho\,\frac{z - z_1}{z - z_2}. \tag{8.12.12}$$

EXERCISES 8.12

1. Show that every linear fractional transformation of the form

$$w = \frac{Az - B}{\bar{B}z - \bar{A}}, \qquad A \neq 0,$$

   is equivalent to the transformation (8.12.8) with $z_0 = B/A$, $\rho = 1$ and $\alpha = 2\,\text{Arg}\,A$.

2. Show that the transformation (8.12.11) maps the circular arcs C_1, C_2 respectively onto the lines L_1, L_2, and the interior of the crescent formed by C_1 and C_2 onto the interior of the angle formed by L_1 and L_2. (See Fig. 8.12.1.)

3. Show that the most general linear fractional transformation taking the circle $|z| = 2$ onto itself and the point 4 into the origin is given by

$$w = e^{i\alpha}\,\frac{z - 4}{z - 1}, \qquad \alpha \text{ real}.$$

4. Show that if $|c| = |d|$, then the linear fractional transformation

$$w = \frac{az + b}{cz + d}, \qquad ad - bc \neq 0,$$

   transforms the unit circle in the z plane into a straight line.

5. Find all linear fractional transformations mapping $z = 1$ into $w = 0$ and the region bounded by the x axis and the lower half of the unit circle onto the first quadrant of the w plane.

6. Show that the general linear fractional transformation of the interior of the circle $|z| = \rho$ onto the interior of the circle $|w| = r$ is given by

$$w = r\rho e^{i\alpha}\,\frac{z - z_0}{\bar{z}_0 z - \rho^2}, \qquad \alpha \text{ real and } |z_0| < \rho.$$

7. Find the linear fractional transformation which maps the interior of the circle $|z| = 1$ onto the interior of the circle $|w - 1| = 1$ and makes the points $w = 1/2, 0$ correspond to $z = 0, 1$, respectively.

8. Given the transformation

$$w = \frac{kz + 1}{z + k}, \qquad k \text{ real and } k \neq \pm 1.$$

Show that under this transformation the circle $|z| = 1$ is mapped onto the circle $|w| = 1$. Prove also that, if $z = e^{i\theta}$ and $\text{Arg}\,(w + 1) = \phi$, then

$$(k + 1) \tan \phi = (k - 1) \tan \tfrac{1}{2} \theta.$$

9. Show that the most general linear fractional transformation taking the imaginary z axis onto the unit circle is given by

$$w = e^{i\alpha}\, \frac{iz - z_0}{iz - \bar{z}_0}, \qquad \alpha \text{ real and } \mathscr{I}(z_0) \neq 0.$$

10. Let $w = (\alpha z + \beta)/(\gamma z + \delta)$ where α, β, γ, δ are real and $\alpha\delta - \beta\gamma > 0$. Show that this transformation maps the upper half plane $\mathscr{I}(z) > 0$ onto the upper half plane $\mathscr{I}(w) > 0$.

8.13. THE TRANSFORMATION

$$w = z + \frac{k^2}{z}, \qquad k > 0. \tag{8.13.1}$$

This transformation is of interest in fluid dynamics.

Note that w becomes infinite at $z = 0$, and

$$\frac{dw}{dz} = 1 - \frac{k^2}{z^2}$$

vanishes at $z = \pm k$. The points $z = \pm k$ play a special role in this transformation. Also observe that the ratio of magnification (see Remark 8.3.1)

$$\left| \frac{dw}{dz} \right| \to 1 \qquad \text{as } z \to \infty.$$

Thus, a figure far away from the origin in the z plane is mapped onto an almost identical figure at a distance far away from the origin in the w plane.

Substituting $\bar{z}$ for z in (8.13.1), we obtain

$$\bar{z} + \frac{k^2}{\bar{z}} = \overline{\left(z + \frac{k^2}{z} \right)} = \bar{w}.$$

This shows that if a point z is mapped into a point w, then $\bar{z}$ is mapped into $\bar{w}$, that is, conjugate points are mapped into conjugate points. Hence, if we know the image of the upper half of the z plane, we can get the image of the lower half of the z plane.

Furthermore, if we substitute $k^2/\bar{z}$ for z in (8.13.1), we again obtain

$$\frac{k^2}{\bar{z}} + \bar{z} = \bar{w}.$$

This shows that if z is mapped into a point w, its inverse point $k^2/\bar{z}$ with respect to the circle $|z| = k$ (see Exercise 8.6.2) is mapped into $\bar{w}$. In other words, inverse points map into conjugate points. Hence, if we know the image of the exterior of the circle $|z| = k$, we will also know the image of the interior of the circle $|z| = k$.

Also, if we substitute $-\bar{z}$ for z in (8.13.1), we obtain $-\bar{w}$. This shows that the points that are symmetric with respect to the y axis map into points that are symmetric with respect to the v axis. ($w = u + iv = z + k^2/z$, $k > 0$, $z = x + iy$.)

We shall now show that the set A_z, consisting of the points in the first quadrant of the z plane exterior to the circle $|z| = k$, is mapped in one-to-one fashion by the transformation (8.13.1) onto the set A_w, consisting of the points in the first quadrant of the w plane.

Let us consider the point

$$z = re^{i\theta}, \qquad r > 0. \tag{8.13.2}$$

Then its image w under the mapping (8.13.1) is given by

$$w = u + iv = re^{i\theta} + \frac{k^2}{r}e^{-i\theta} = \left(r + \frac{k^2}{r}\right)\cos\theta + i\left(r - \frac{k^2}{r}\right)\sin\theta.$$

Therefore

$$u = a\cos\theta, \qquad v = b\sin\theta, \tag{8.13.3}$$

where

$$a = \frac{r^2 + k^2}{r}, \qquad b = \frac{r^2 - k^2}{r}. \tag{8.13.4}$$

Let R_1 and R_2 be any two positive numbers such that $k < R_1 < R_2$. Let $r = R_2$ and let θ increase from 0 to $\pi/2$. Then the point z traverses in a counterclockwise direction a quadrant of the circle $|z| = R_2$, starting at $A: z = R_2$ and ending at $B: z = iR_2$, while the image point w describes counterclockwise the quadrant $A'B'$ of the ellipse (8.13.3), with

$$a = \frac{R_2^2 + k^2}{R_2} \quad \text{and} \quad b = \frac{R_2^2 - k^2}{R_2}.$$

(See Fig. 8.13.1.)

Now let us fix the value of θ at $\theta = \pi/2$ and let r decrease from $r = R_2$ to $r = R_1$. We see that the image of the point $z = re^{i\theta}$ describes downward the segment $B'C'$, where

$$B' = i\,\frac{R_2^2 - k^2}{R_2} \quad \text{and} \quad C' = i\,\frac{R_1^2 - k^2}{R_1}.$$

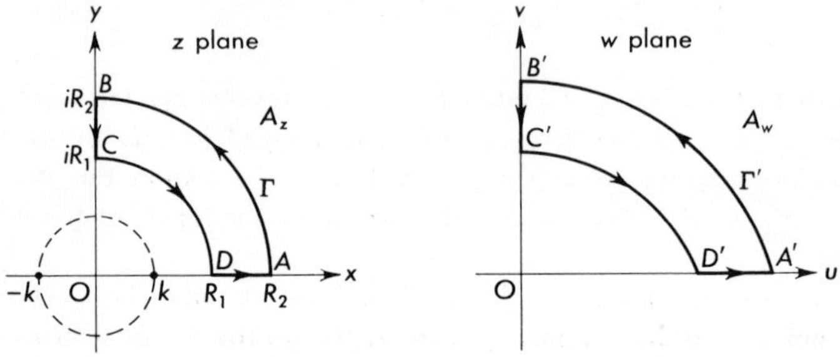

FIG. 8.13.1

Now, let $r = R_1$ and let θ decrease from $\pi/2$ to 0. The point z traverses clockwise the quadrant CD of the circle $|z| = R_1$, while the image point w describes clockwise the quadrant $C'D'$ of the ellipse (8.13.3), with

$$a = \frac{R_1^2 + k^2}{R_1} \quad \text{and} \quad b = \frac{R_1^2 - k^2}{R_1}.$$

Finally, we set $\theta = 0$ and let r increase from R_1 to R_2. We see that as z traverses the segment DA from left to right, the image point w traverses the segment $D'A'$ from left to right.

Let the contours $ABCDA$ and $A'B'C'D'A'$ be denoted respectively by Γ and Γ'. From the above discussion we see that the image of the simple closed contour Γ, under the transformation (8.13.1), is the simple closed contour Γ'. Since $w = z + k^2/z$ is an analytic function within and on Γ, we have from Theorem 8.2.4 that the region bounded by the contour Γ is mapped onto the region bounded by the contour Γ' in a one-to-one fashion.

It is clear from (8.13.2), (8.13.3) and (8.13.4) that under the transformation (8.13.1), each point of the set A_z, consisting of the points $|z| > k$ in the first quadrant, is mapped into a point of the first quadrant A_w in the w plane. We shall now show that this mapping is onto. Let w_0 be any point in A_w. Then, for R_1 sufficiently close to k and R_2 sufficiently large, w_0 is interior to Γ'. Hence w_0 is the image of some point z_0 interior to Γ. This shows that every point in A_w is the image of some point in A_z, and the mapping by (8.13.1) of A_z into A_w is onto.

We shall now show that the mapping of A_z onto A_w by (8.13.1) is one-to-one. Suppose that this were not so and that there existed two distinct points z_1 and z_2 in A_z whose image points were both equal to w_0 in A_w. Then, if we choose R_1 sufficiently close to k, and R_2 sufficiently large, z_1 and z_2 will be interior to Γ while their image point w_0 will be interior to Γ'. But this contradicts the fact that the interior of Γ is mapped onto the interior of Γ' in a one-to-one fashion.

In view of the foregoing results we have the following

——*THEOREM* 8.13.1.   Under the transformation

$$w = z + \frac{k^2}{z}, \qquad k > 0, \tag{8.13.1}$$

the upper and lower half of the z plane exterior to the circle $|z| = k$ map respectively onto the upper and lower half of the w plane, while the upper and lower half of the z plane interior to the circle $|z| = k$ map respectively onto the lower and upper half of the w plane.

Remark 8.13.1.   It is easy to see that the positive x and y axes exterior to the circle $|z| = k$ are mapped respectively onto the half lines $v = 0$, $u > 2k$ and $u = 0$, $v > 0$. Also, the negative x and y axes exterior to the circle $|z| = k$ are mapped, respectively, onto the half lines $v = 0$, $u < -2k$ and $u = 0$, $v < 0$.

To see how the circle $|z| = k$ itself is mapped under the transformation (8.13.1), put $r = k$ in (8.13.4). We obtain $a = 2k$ and $b = 0$. Thus $w = 2k \cos \theta$. As the point z traverses in a counterclockwise direction the upper half of the circle $|z| = k$ so that θ varies from 0 to π, the image point w will traverse the line segment $-2k \leq u \leq 2k$ on the u axis from right to left as shown in Fig. 8.13.2.

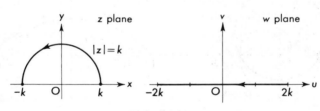

FIG. 8.13.2

Similarly, as z traverses the lower half of the circle $|z| = k$ in a counterclockwise direction, θ will vary from π to 2π and w will describe the same line segment from left to right. Also note that $z = 0$, $z = \infty$ each map into $w = \infty$.

Remark 8.13.2.   Thus, *the transformation (8.13.1) maps the extended z plane onto the extended w plane.*

8.14. THE TRANSFORMATION UNDER (8.13.1) OF CIRCLES PASSING THROUGH THE POINTS $z = \pm k$.

In the sequel, we shall need to know the image under (8.13.1) of any circle γ passing through the points $z = \pm k$ as well as the image of the exterior of γ. For definiteness, we shall take the center of γ above the x axis. The case where the center of γ is below the x axis may be treated similarly.

It is easily seen that the transformation

$$w = z + \frac{k^2}{z}, \qquad k > 0 \tag{8.13.1}$$

may be written in the following two forms

$$w - 2k = \frac{(z - k)^2}{z} \tag{8.14.1}$$

and

$$w + 2k = \frac{(z + k)^2}{z}. \tag{8.14.2}$$

Dividing (8.14.2) into (8.14.1) we obtain

$$\frac{w - 2k}{w + 2k} = \frac{(z - k)^2}{(z + k)^2}. \tag{8.14.3}$$

If we put $w - 2k = \rho_1 e^{i\phi_1}$, $w + 2k = \rho_2 e^{i\phi_2}$, $z - k = r_1 e^{i\theta_1}$ and $z + k = r_2 e^{i\theta_2}$ (see Fig. 8.14.1) equation (8.14.3) becomes

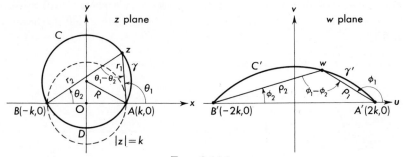

FIG. 8.14.1

$$\frac{\rho_1}{\rho_2} e^{i(\phi_1 - \phi_2)} = \left(\frac{r_1}{r_2}\right)^2 e^{2i(\theta_1 - \theta_2)}, \tag{8.14.4}$$

from which, upon equating arguments, we get

$$\phi_1 - \phi_2 = 2(\theta_1 - \theta_2) + 2n\pi, \qquad n = 0, \pm 1, \pm 2, \cdots. \tag{8.14.5}$$

Now, let $-\pi < \theta_1, \theta_2, \phi_1, \phi_2 \leqq \pi$ and let z describe counterclockwise the arc ACB of the circle γ. Then the image w under the transformation (8.13.1) describes the curve $A'C'B'$, starting at $w = 2k$ and ending at $w = -2k$. Since the arc ACB is in the upper half of the z plane exterior to the circle $|z| = k$, by Theorem 8.13.1 its image $A'C'B'$ is in the upper half of the

w plane. It follows that $0 < \theta_1 - \theta_2 < \pi$ and $0 < \phi_1 - \phi_2 < \pi$. Hence $n = 0$ in (8.14.5), and we have

$$\phi_1 - \phi_2 = 2(\theta_1 - \theta_2). \tag{8.14.6}$$

Furthermore, for z on the arc ACB, we have from elementary geometry

$$\theta_1 - \theta_2 = \frac{s}{2R}, \tag{8.14.7}$$

where R is the radius of the circle γ and s is the length of the lower arc ADB of γ. In view of (8.14.6) and (8.14.7), we then have

$$\phi_1 - \phi_2 = \frac{s}{R} = \text{constant.} \tag{8.14.8}$$

Consequently, the curve described by the image point w must be a circular arc $A'C'B'$, starting at $w = 2k$ and ending at $w = -2k$. (See Fig. 8.14.1.)

Let now z describe counterclockwise the lower arc BDA of the circle γ from $z = -k$ to $z = k$. Then the point z will be in the lower half of the z plane interior to the circle $|z| = k$. By Theorem 8.13.1, the image point w is again in the upper half of the w plane, and hence, $0 < \phi_1 - \phi_2 < \pi$. Now, for z on the arc BDA, we have

$$\theta_1 - \theta_2 = -\frac{t}{2R},$$

where $t = 2\pi R - s$ is the length of the upper arc ACB of γ. Consequently

$$\phi_1 - \phi_2 = 2(\theta_1 - \theta_2) + 2\pi = \frac{s}{R}. \tag{8.14.9}$$

Thus $\phi_1 - \phi_2$ has the same value as before, and it follows that as z describes the lower arc of γ from $z = -k$ to $z = k$, the image point w retraces its previous path from $w = -2k$ to $w = 2k$. Let us summarize the above result in the following

Remark 8.14.1.   *A circle γ with center above the x axis and passing through the points $z = \pm k$ is mapped by the transformation (8.13.1) onto a circular arc γ' on the w plane as shown in Fig. 8.14.1.*

Let now $E(\gamma)$ denote the exterior of the circle γ, and let $E(\gamma')$ denote the "exterior" of the circular arc γ', that is, the set of all points of the w plane which are not on the image γ' of γ. We shall establish the following

——**THEOREM** 8.14.1.   Under the transformation

$$w = z + \frac{k^2}{z}, \qquad k > 0, \tag{8.13.1}$$

$E(\gamma)$ is mapped one-to-one onto $E(\gamma')$.

Proof. First we show that the mapping is onto. Let w be any point in $E(\gamma')$. By Remark 8.13.2, the transformaton (8.13.1) maps the z plane onto the w plane. Hence, there exists a point z_0 whose image is w. If z_0 were on γ, then w would be on γ'. Hence z_0 is not on γ. In case z_0 is interior to γ, then [see Exercise 1.4.19(d)] k^2/z_0 is exterior to γ and consequently (see Exercise 8.15.4) k^2/z_0 has also the image w. Thus in any case, there is a point z exterior to γ whose image is w. Thus $E(\gamma)$ is mapped onto $E(\gamma')$.

To show that the mapping is one-to-one, suppose that two distinct points z_1 and z_2 have the same image w under (8.13.1). Then $z_1 z_2 = k^2$. (See Exercise 8.15.4.) It now follows [see Exercise 1.4.19(d)] that z_1 and z_2 cannot be both in $E(\gamma)$. Thus the mapping of $E(\gamma)$ onto $E(\gamma')$ is one-to-one.

8.15. THE JOUKOWSKI AIRFOIL.

Let Γ be a circle passing through the point $z = -k$ and containing the point $z = k$, $k > 0$, in its interior. (See Fig. 8.15.1.) We shall investigate in detail the image of Γ under the trans-

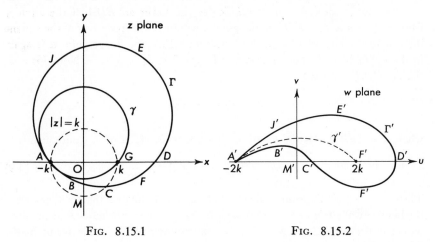

FIG. 8.15.1   FIG. 8.15.2

formation (8.13.1). This image, important in aerodynamics, resembles a section of an airplane wing and it is known as the Joukowski airfoil. (See Fig. 8.15.2.) We shall also show that the exterior of the circle Γ is mapped by (8.13.1) one-to-one onto the exterior of the Joukowski airfoil Γ'.

For definiteness, we take the center of the circle Γ to be above the x axis. The case where the center of Γ is below the x axis can be treated similarly. Let us draw a circle γ interior to Γ, passing through the point $z = k$ and tangent to Γ at $z = -k$. (See Fig. 8.15.1.) Note that the center of γ is located at the intersection of the y axis with the diameter of Γ containing the point $z = -k$.

As in the previous section, we shall denote respectively by $E(\gamma)$ and $E(\gamma')$ the exterior of the circle γ and the "exterior" of the circular arc γ', that is, the set of points in the w plane that are not on the image γ' of γ. We shall also denote respectively by $E(\Gamma)$ and $I(\Gamma, \gamma)$ the exterior of Γ and the domain lying exterior to γ and interior to Γ.

Remark 8.15.1. By Theorem 8.14.1, the transformation (8.13.1) maps $E(\gamma)$ one-to-one onto $E(\gamma')$. Since, except for the point $z = -k$, Γ lies in $E(\gamma)$, it is easily seen that (8.13.1) maps Γ in a one-to-one manner onto its image Γ'. Hence Γ' does not cross itself and is therefore a simple closed contour.

Let us now denote the exterior of Γ' by $E(\Gamma')$ and the set of points interior to Γ' but not on γ' by $I(\Gamma', \gamma')$. We shall now establish the following

——**THEOREM** 8.15.1.   The transformation

$$w = z + \frac{k^2}{z}, \qquad k > 0, \tag{8.13.1}$$

maps $E(\Gamma)$ one-to-one onto $E(\Gamma')$.

Proof. Since $E(\Gamma)$ is contained in $E(\gamma)$, it follows from Theorem 8.14.1 that under the transformation (8.13.1), $E(\Gamma)$ is mapped one-to-one onto its image. We shall now show that the image of $E(\Gamma)$ is $E(\Gamma')$.

Let $E_1(\gamma)$ denote the union of the two disjoint domains $I(\Gamma, \gamma)$ and $E(\Gamma)$. Similarly, let $E_1(\gamma')$ denote the union of the two disjoint domains $I(\Gamma', \gamma')$ and $E(\Gamma')$. Now, (8.13.1) is a one-to-one continuous mapping of $E_1(\gamma)$ onto $E_1(\gamma')$. It follows (see Exercise 2.9.11) that the image of $E(\Gamma)$ is either $E(\Gamma')$ or $I(\Gamma', \gamma')$. But for $|z|$ sufficiently large, z is in $E(\Gamma)$ and its image under (8.13.1) is a point in $E(\Gamma')$. Hence the image of $E(\Gamma)$ is $E(\Gamma')$, and the theorem is established.

We shall now give a detailed discussion of the mapping of the circle Γ under the transformation (8.13.1). The arc $AJED$ on Γ is mapped onto the arc $A'J'E'D'$ on Γ' in the upper half of the w plane, since by Theorem 8.13.1 the upper half plane exterior to the circle $|z| = k$ is mapped by (8.13.1) onto the upper half of the w plane. Note that the image of A ($z = -k$) is A' ($w = -2k$). Also note that the image of the point D ($z = x + 0i$, $x > k$) is D' ($w = u + 0i$, $u > 2k$). The arc DFC on Γ maps onto the arc $D'F'C'$ on Γ' in the lower half of the w plane, since by Theorem 8.13.1 the transformation (8.13.1) maps the exterior of the circle $|z| = k$ in the lower half of the z plane onto the lower half of the w plane. The point C' is to the left of G' ($w = 2k$) on the u axis, since by Remark 8.13.1 the part of the circle $|z| = k$ below the x axis maps under the transformation (8.13.1) in a one-to-one fashion onto the segment $A'G'$ on the u axis. Since $C = ke^{i\theta}$, we have

$$C' = ke^{i\theta} + \frac{k^2}{ke^{i\theta}} = 2k \cos \theta.$$

Thus C' is to the right or left of the v axis according as C is to the right or left of the y axis. The arc CBA on Γ is mapped onto the arc $C'B'A'$ above the u axis, since by Theorem 8.13.1 the transformation (8.13.1) maps the interior of the circle $|z| = k$ in the lower half of the z plane onto the upper half of the w plane. Since Γ' does not cross itself, the arc $C'B'A'$ cannot have any point in common with the arc $A'J'E'D'$ except at A', and consequently the arc $C'B'A'$ lies in the region between the arc $A'J'E'D'$ and the u axis.

Thus we have shown that the image of the circle Γ under the transformation (8.13.1) is a profile of the type given in Fig. 8.15.2. We shall now show that the Joukowski airfoil has a cusp at the point $w = -2k$.

Since

$$w = z + \frac{k^2}{z}, \qquad k > 0, \tag{8.13.1}$$

we have

$$w + 2k = \frac{(z + k)^2}{z}. \tag{8.15.1}$$

Let us write

$$w + 2k = \rho e^{i\phi}, \qquad z + k = Re^{i\theta}, \qquad z = re^{i\lambda}.$$

Thus we may write (8.15.1) as

$$\rho e^{i\phi} = \frac{R^2 e^{i2\theta}}{re^{i\lambda}},$$

or

$$e^{i(\phi - 2\theta + \lambda)} = \frac{R^2}{\rho r}. \tag{8.15.2}$$

Since the right-hand member of (8.15.2) is a positive number, the left-hand member must also be positive. Consequently, we have

$$\phi - 2\theta + \lambda = 0,^*$$

or

$$\phi = 2\theta - \lambda. \tag{8.15.3}$$

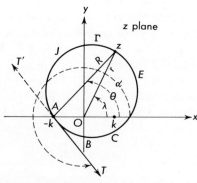

FIG. 8.15.3

---

* Note that we are defining angles up to a multiple of 2π.

Let us now consider the case when z describes the arc EJA, while its image w describes the arc $E'J'A'$. Since the arc EJA has a tangent T at the point A, forming an angle, say α, with the positive x axis, we see that as $z \to -k$ along the arc EJA, $\theta \to \alpha - \pi$ and $\lambda \to \pi$. (See Fig. 8.15.3.) Using (8.15.3) we see that as $w \to -2k$ along the arc $E'J'A'$, ϕ approaches the value

$$2\alpha - 3\pi = 2\alpha - \pi.$$

Hence, the arc $E'J'A'$ has a tangent at A' forming with the positive u axis an angle equal to 2α.

Similarly, as z describes the arc CBA while its image w describes the arc $C'B'A'$, we see that as $z \to -k$, the angle θ in (8.15.3) approaches the value α and the angle λ approaches π. Consequently, the limit of the angle ϕ as $w \to -2k$ along the arc $C'B'A'$ is equal to $2\alpha - \pi$. Therefore (see Fig. 8.15.2) the tangent at A' to the arc $C'B'A'$ forms an angle with the positive u axis which is equal to 2α. Thus, the two tangents coincide, since they both begin at A' and their angles with the positive u axis are equal. Hence, the arc $E'J'A'$ and the arc $C'B'A'$ form a cusp at the point A' ($w = -2k$).

Remark 8.15.2. Note that we could have written

$$w = z + \frac{k^2}{z}, \qquad k > 0, \tag{8.13.1}$$

as three successive transformations:

$$(1)\ z' = \frac{z}{k}, \qquad (2)\ w' = z' + \frac{1}{z'}, \qquad (3)\ w = kw'. \tag{8.15.4}$$

Since (1) and (3) involve merely a change of scale, there would have been no loss of generality if we had considered from the beginning of Section 8.13 the transformation

$$w = z + \frac{1}{z}$$

instead of the transformation given in (8.13.1).

In Section 8.17, we shall utilize the transformation

$$w = \frac{1}{2}\left(z + \frac{1}{z}\right). \tag{8.15.5}$$

This transformation may be obtained by performing successively the transformations

$$(1)\ w' = z + \frac{1}{z}, \qquad (2)\ w = \frac{1}{2}w'. \tag{8.15.6}$$

The transformation (1) is obtained by setting $k = 1$ in (8.13.1). Transformation (2) is simply a shrinkage. Thus (see Theorem 8.13.1 and Remarks 8.13.1,

8.13.2) the transformation (8.15.5) maps the z plane onto the w plane as indicated in Figures 8.15.4. and 8.15.5.

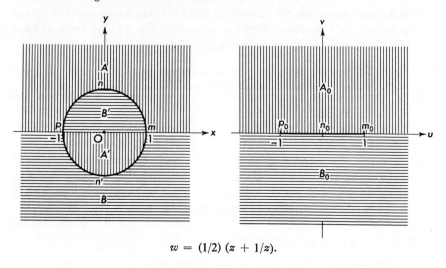

$$w = (1/2)\,(z + 1/z).$$

FIG. 8.15.4   FIG. 8.15.5

Each of the domains A and A' in Fig. 8.15.4 is mapped one-to-one onto the domain A_0 of Fig. 8.15.5, and each of the domains B and B' maps one-to-one onto the domain B_0. Note also that the upper half mnp and the lower half $mn'p$ of the circle $|z| = 1$ are each mapped one-to-one onto the line segment $m_0 n_0 p_0$ of the u axis.

EXERCISES 8.15

1. Show that if under the linear fractional transformation

$$w = i\,\frac{z+k}{z-k}, \qquad k \text{ real and } k \neq 0,$$

the point z_1 is mapped into the point w_1, then the point k^2/z_1 is mapped into the point $-w_1$.

2. Show that under the linear fractional transformation

$$w = i\,\frac{z+k}{z-k}, \qquad k \text{ real and } k \neq 0,$$

the circle passing through the points z_1, k^2/z_1 and $-k$ is mapped into a straight line.

3. Using the transformation given in Exercise 2 above show that if a circle passes through the points z_1, k^2/z_1 and $-k$, then it must also pass through the point $z = k$.

4. Show that under the transformation (8.13.1) two distinct points z_1, z_2 are mapped into the same point if, and only if, $z_2 = k^2/z_1$.

5. Show that under the transformation (8.13.1) a circle passing through the point $z = -k$ and containing the point $z = k$ in its interior is mapped into the w plane in a one-to-one fashion.

6. Show that the circles $|z| = r$, $r > k$, are mapped by the transformation (8.13.1) into a family of confocal ellipses with foci at $w = \pm 2k$.

7. Show that an ellipse in the w plane with foci at $w = \pm 2k$ and parametric equations $u = a \cos \theta$, $v = b \sin \theta$, $a > 0$, $b > 0$ is the image under the transformation (8.13.1) of the circle $|z| = (a + b)/2$.

8. Let the circle Γ be as in Figure 8.15.1 with center at z_0 and radius r, passing through the point $z = -k$ and having the point $z = k$ in its interior. Show that the location of the point C' on the Joukowski airfoil (see Fig. 8.15.2) is independent of $|z_0|$ and depends only on Arg z_0. Also show that as Arg $z_0 \to 0$, $C' \to -2k$.

9. Let the circle Γ be given as in Exercise 8 above. Show that if the point C (see Fig. 8.15.1) is given by $z = ke^{i\theta}$, then as $|z_0| \to \infty$, Arg z_0 fixed, the limiting position of the arc $A'B'C'$ (see Fig. 8.15.2) is given by

$$w = k\left(-2 + \frac{t^2\gamma^2}{t\gamma - 1}\right), \qquad 0 \leqq t \leqq 1,$$

where $\gamma = 1 + e^{i\theta}$.

10. Let w be the image of z under the transformation (8.13.1). Give a geometric construction for locating the point w.

11. Discuss the mapping of the x and y axes under transformation (8.13.1).

12. Let the circle Γ pass through the point $z = ki$, $k > 0$, and have the point $z = -ki$ in its interior. Show that the transformation

$$w = z - \frac{k^2}{z}, \qquad k > 0,$$

maps the circle Γ onto a Joukowski airfoil.

13. Show that for $u = x + k^2/x$, $k > 0$, that $du/dx < 0$ or $du/dx > 0$ according as $0 < x < k$ or $x > k$. Now show that under the transformation (8.13.1) the segment $0 < x \leq k$ and the half line $x \geq k$ each map onto the half line $w \geq 2k$ in a one-to-one fashion. State and prove a similar result for the negative half of the x axis.

14. Show that under the transformation $w = (1/2)(z + 1/z)$, one half of the circle $|w| = 1$ is the image of the circle $|z - i| = \sqrt{2}$, and the other half is the image of the circle $|z + i| = \sqrt{2}$.

15. Determine the images of the exterior and interior of the circle $|z| = 2k$ under the transformation

$$w = \frac{1}{4}z + \frac{k^2}{z}, \qquad k > 0.$$

16. *Symmetric Joukowski Airfoil.* Let $k > 0$. Consider the circles

$$\Gamma: \ |z| = k,$$

$$\Gamma_1: \ |z + a| = k - a, \qquad -\infty < a < k, \qquad a \neq 0, k/2.$$

$$\Gamma_2: \ \left|z + \frac{k}{2}\right| = \frac{k}{2}$$

as shown in Fig. 8.15.6 (with $0 < a < k/2$ for Γ_1).

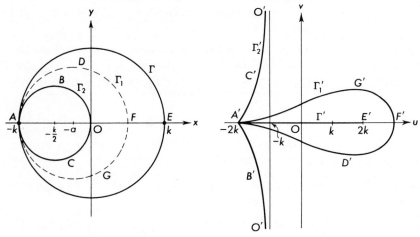

FIG. 8.15.6   FIG. 8.15.7

Show that under the transformation (8.13.1)

(a) The circle Γ_2 and the line $x = -k$ are both mapped into the curve Γ_2': $O'B'A'C'O'$ with a cusp at A' and the line $u = -k$ as its asymptote. (See Fig. 8.15.7.)

(b) The circle Γ_1 is mapped into the symmetric airfoil Γ_1': $A'G'F'D'A'$ with cusp at A'. (See Fig. 8.15.7.)

(c) The interior of the circle Γ_1: $|z + a| = k - a$, $0 < a < k/2$, is mapped one-to-one onto the exterior of the airfoil Γ_1'. Also discuss the cases when $-\infty < a < 0$, and $k/2 < a < k$.

The image Γ' of Γ was discussed in Remark 8.13.1.

17. Show that under the transformation

$$w = \left(\frac{z^n + 1}{z^n - 1}\right)^2, \qquad n \text{ a positive integer},$$

the image of the sector $|z| < 1$, $z = |z| e^{i\theta}$, $0 < \theta < \pi/n$, is the upper half of the w plane.

18. Let Γ be a circle passing through the point $z = -k, k > 0$, and containing the point $z = k$ in its interior. Let γ be a circle interior to Γ, passing through the point $z = k$ and tangent to Γ at $z = -k$. Let $z = bi$, $b > 0$, be the center of γ. (See Fig. 8.15.1.) The circular arc γ' (see Fig. 8.15.2) is the image of γ under the mapping (8.13.1). Let d be the distance between the centers of the circles Γ and γ. Let α denote the angle which the circular arc γ' forms with the positive direction of the u axis at $w = -2k$.

(a) Show that if h is the height of the circular segment bounded by γ' and the chord joining the points $w = \pm 2k$, then $h = 2b$.

(b) Show that as b increases from 0 to ∞, α increases from 0 to π.

(c) Show that if b is fixed and d increases from 0 to ∞, the area of the interior of the Joukowski airfoil increases from 0 to ∞.

19. Let C be a contour and let Γ be its image under the transformation (8.13.1). Show that if C has a tangent at $z = -k$ or at $z = k$, then Γ has a cusp, respectively, at $w = -2k$ or at $w = 2k$.

8.16. THE EXPONENTIAL TRANSFORMATION

$$w = e^z. \tag{8.16.1}$$

This transformation is useful and important. Since $dw/dz = e^z$ is different from zero for all z, the mapping is conformal everywhere in the complex plane.
   Putting $z + 2k\pi i$, $k = \pm 1, \pm 2, \cdots$ instead of z in (8.16.1), we obtain

$$w = e^{z+2k\pi i} = e^z.$$

Hence the point $z + 2k\pi i$, $k = \pm 1, \pm 2, \cdots$ has the same image as the point z. The strip given by

$$-\pi + 2k\pi < y \leq \pi + 2k\pi, \qquad -\infty < x < \infty, \qquad k = \pm 1, \pm 2, \cdots$$

is mapped the same way as the *fundamental strip:*

$$-\pi < y \leq \pi, \qquad -\infty < x < \infty. \tag{8.16.2}$$

The z plane may thus be divided into horizontal strips of width equal to 2π, and the mapping will repeat itself on each strip. It is, therefore, sufficient to consider the mapping of the fundamental strip.
   We have

$$w = e^z = e^{x+iy} = e^x e^{iy}.$$

Therefore

$$w = e^x(\cos y + i \sin y). \tag{8.16.3}$$

First we shall consider the case when $y = \pi$. Then $w = -e^x$, and as x

varies from $-\infty$ to ∞, w varies from 0 to $-\infty$. Hence the line $y = \pi$ is mapped one-to-one by the transformation (8.16.1) onto the negative half of the u axis.

We shall now consider the mapping under (8.16.1) of the interior, $-\pi < \mathscr{I}(z) < \pi$, of the fundamental strip.

Let y have the fixed value $\pi - \epsilon$, $\epsilon > 0$, and let x vary from R to $-R$, $R > 0$. As the point z traverses the segment abc from right to left (see Fig.8.16.1.),

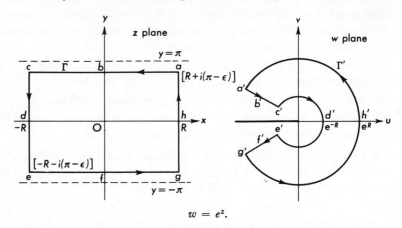

$$w = e^z.$$

FIG. 8.16.1

we see from (8.16.3) that the image point w traverses the segment $a'b'c'$.

Now, let x have the fixed value $x = -R$ and let y vary from $(\pi - \epsilon)$ to $-(\pi - \epsilon)$. The point z now traverses the segment cde while the image point w describes the circular arc $c'd'e'$. In a similar fashion we see that as z describes the segments efg and gha, the image point w describes respectively the segment $e'f'g'$ and the circular arc $g'h'a'$.

We shall now establish the following

——THEOREM 8.16.1.   Under the transformation

$$w = e^z,   \tag{8.16.1}$$

the interior, $-\pi < \mathscr{I}(z) < \pi$, of the fundamental strip is mapped one-to-one onto the domain D_w consisting of the w plane with the nonpositive half of the u axis removed.

Proof.   Let Γ and Γ' denote respectively the simple closed contours $abcdefgha$ and $a'b'c'd'e'f'g'h'a'$. (See Fig. 8.16.1.) From Theorem 8.2.4, we see that the transformation (8.16.1) maps the interior of Γ one-to-one onto the interior of Γ'.

To see that the mapping is onto, suppose that w_0 is any point in D_w. Then by making R sufficiently large and ϵ sufficiently small (see Fig. 8.16.1), w_0 will be contained in the interior of Γ'. Consequently, there is a point z_0 in the interior of Γ whose image is w_0. Hence, every point in D_w is an image point of some point in the interior of the fundamental strip and the mapping is onto.

We shall now show that the mapping is one-to-one. Suppose that two distinct points z_1 and z_2 in the interior of the fundamental strip are mapped into the same point w_0. Then by taking R sufficiently large and ϵ sufficiently small, z_1 and $\bar{z}_2$ will be in the interior of Γ, while w_0 is interior to Γ'. But this contradicts the fact that the interior of Γ is mapped onto the interior of Γ' in a one-to-one fashion. Thus the theorem is established.

Remark 8.16.1.   Let us now consider separately the four cases determined by $x > 0$, $x < 0$ and

$$-\pi < y < 0, \qquad 0 < y < \pi.$$

The strip given in (8.16.2) will be subdivided into four domains plus their boundaries as shown in Fig. 8.16.2. However, the line $y = -\pi$ is not part of the fundamental strip. It is easy to show that the four domains A_1, A'_1, B_1, B'_1 in Fig. 8.16.2 are mapped by the transformation (8.16.1) respectively into the corresponding domains A, A', B, B' in Fig. 8.15.4. For instance, to show that A_1 of Fig. 8.16.2 goes into A of Fig. 8.15.4 note that if z is in A_1, then $x > 0$ and $0 < y < \pi$. Consequently $|w| = e^x > 1$ and $0 < \text{Arg } w < \pi$.

Similarly, we can show that the domain A'_1 of Fig. 8.16.2 is mapped into

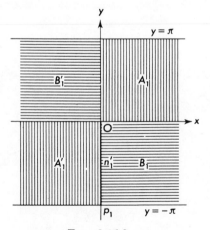

FIG. 8.16.2

the domain A' of Fig. 8.15.4, and so on. We may further verify that the boundaries between the domains A_1, B_1; A_1, B'_1; and so on, are mapped into the corresponding boundaries between the domains A, B; A, B'; and so on, of Fig. 8.15.4.

From Theorem 8.16.1, the transformation (8.16.1) maps the interior of the fundamental strip (8.16.2) one-to-one onto the w plane, with the non-positive half of the real axis removed. It follows (see Exercise 2.9.10) that the mapping of each domain A_1, A'_1, $\cdots$, of Fig. 8.16.2 into the corresponding domain A, A', $\cdots$, of Fig. 8.15.4 is one-to-one and onto. Also, the mapping of the boundary between each pair of domains in Fig. 8.16.2 into the boundary between the corresponding domains in Fig. 8.15.4 is one-to-one and onto, except that the boundary between A_1', B_1' maps one-to-one onto that part of the boundary between A', B' for which $0 < x \leq 1$, $y = 0$; and the boundary between A_1, B_1 maps one-to-one onto that part of the boundary between A and B for which $x \geq 1$, $y = 0$. The line $y = \pi$ maps under (8.16.1) one-to-one onto the half line in Fig. 8.15.4 for which $x < 0$, $y = 0$.

EXERCISES 8.16

1. Show that under the transformation $w = e^z$ the segment $-\pi < y \leq \pi$, $x = a$, is mapped onto a circle with center at the origin.

2. Find the image under the transformation $w = e^z$ of the half line $0 \leq x < \infty$, $y = a$.

3. Show that under the transformation $w = ie^{iz}$, the image of the semi-infinite strip

$$0 \leq x \leq \pi, \qquad 0 \leq y < \infty$$

is a semicircle and its interior excluding the point $w = 0$, as shown in Fig. 8.16.3.

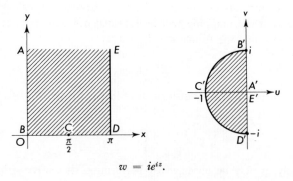

$$w = ie^{iz}.$$

FIG. 8.16.3

4. Show that under the transformation $w = e^z$ the rectangular region

$$k_1 \leq x \leq k_2, \qquad 0 \leq y \leq \pi$$

is mapped one-to-one onto a semiring as shown in Fig. 8.16.4.

5. Under the transformation $w = e^z$, determine the image of the rectangular region bounded by
   (a) $x = c_1$, $x = c_2$, $y = c_3$, $y = c_4$, $(0 < c_4 - c_3 < 2\pi)$;
   (b) the same rectangle, but with $c_4 - c_3 = 2\pi$.

6. Under the transformation $w = z + e^z$ determine the image of the strip

$$-\pi < y < \pi, \qquad -\infty < x < \infty.$$

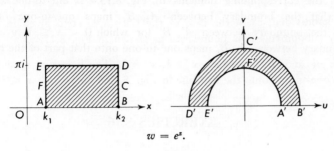

$$w = e^z.$$

FIG. 8.16.4

8.17. THE TRANSFORMATION

$$w = \cos z. \tag{8.17.1}$$

Since $\cos z$ is periodic with period 2π, we have

$$w = \cos(z + 2k\pi) = \cos z, \qquad k = 0, \pm 1, \pm 2, \cdots.$$

Thus the point $z + 2k\pi$ is mapped into the same image as the point z. Consequently, we may divide the z plane into parallel vertical strips of width equal to 2π, and the mapping will be repeated on each strip. It is, therefore, sufficient to examine the fundamental strip

$$-\pi < x \leqq \pi, \qquad -\infty < y < \infty. \tag{8.17.2}$$

In view of (4.2.2), the transformation (8.17.1) may be written

$$w = \frac{1}{2}\left(e^{iz} + \frac{1}{e^{iz}}\right). \tag{8.17.3}$$

Consequently, it may be obtained by performing successively the transformations

$$(1)\ z' = iz, \qquad (2)\ z'' = e^{z'}, \qquad (3)\ w = \frac{1}{2}\left(z'' + \frac{1}{z''}\right). \tag{8.17.4}$$

The transformation $z' = iz$ is a counterclockwise rotation of 90 degrees, that is, the image of each point z may be obtained by rotating z counterclockwise about the origin through a 90 degree angle. Transformation (2) is the same as (8.16.1) and transformation (3) is the same as (8.15.5).

Let us consider separately the four cases determined by $y > 0$, $y < 0$ and

$$-\pi < x < 0, \qquad 0 < x < \pi.$$

We see that the vertical strip

$$-\pi < x \le \pi, \qquad -\infty < y < \infty$$

may be subdivided, as in the case of the horizontal strip given in (8.16.2), into four subdomains plus boundaries as shown in Fig. 8.17.1.

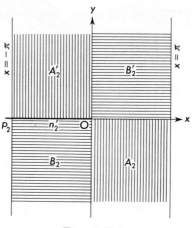

FIG. 8.17.1

It is easy to see that by means of transformation $z' = iz$ each of the domains A_2, B_2, A_2' and B_2' in Fig. 8.17.1 is mapped respectively one-to-one onto the correspondingly labeled domains A_1, B_1, A_1' and B_1' of Fig. 8.16.2. From Remark 8.16.1, the transformation (2) in (8.17.4) maps each of the domains A_1, B_1, A_1' and B_1' of Fig. 8.16.2 respectively one-to-one onto the domains A, B, A' and B' of Fig. 8.15.4. From Remark 8.15.2, the transformation (3) in (8.17.4) maps each of the domains A and A' in Fig. 8.15.4 one-to-one onto the domain A_0 of Fig. 8.15.5, and each of the domains B and B' one-to-one onto B_0. It follows that as a result of performing successively the transformations (1), (2), (3) of (8.17.4), each of the domains A_2 and A_2' of Fig. 8.17.1 is mapped one-to-one onto the domain A_0 of Fig. 8.15.5. Similarly, each member of the pair of domains B_2 and B_2' of Fig. 8.17.1 is mapped one-to-one onto the domain B_0 of Fig. 8.15.5.

It is also easy to trace how each boundary between the domains A_2, B_2; A_2, B_2'; $\cdots$, is mapped. For instance, the segment $0n_2'p_2$ of Fig. 8.17.1 is mapped by the transformation (1) of (8.17.4) one-to-one onto the segment $0n_1'p_1$ of Fig. 8.16.2. The transformation (2) of (8.17.4) maps this latter segment, which forms the boundary between the domains A_1' and B_1 onto the semicircumference $mn'p$ of Fig. 8.15.4, which forms the boundary between the domains A' and B. Finally, the transformation (3) of (8.17.4) maps the circular arc $mn'p$ one-to-one onto the segment $m_0n_0p_0$ of Fig. 8.15.5 which forms a part of the common boundary between the domains A_0 and B_0. This last result may be obtained directly by noticing that $\cos x$ varies from 1 to -1 as x varies from 0 to $-\pi$.

Let us now consider the transformation

$$w = \sin z. \tag{8.17.5}$$

Since $\sin z$ is periodic with period 2π, we have

$$\sin(z + 2k\pi) = \sin z, \qquad k = 0, \pm 1, \pm 2, \cdots.$$

Hence, it is sufficient to consider any vertical strip of width 2π, say

$$-\frac{\pi}{2} < x \leq \frac{3}{2}\pi, \qquad -\infty < y < \infty. \tag{8.17.6}$$

Utilizing (4.2.16) we obtain

$$\sin z = \cos\left(z - \frac{\pi}{2}\right). \tag{8.17.7}$$

Hence, the transformation (8.17.5) may be obtained by performing successively the transformations

$$(1) \ z' = z - \frac{\pi}{2}, \qquad (2) \ w = \cos z'. \tag{8.17.8}$$

Transformation (1) is simply a translation leftward by $\pi/2$. Hence it maps the vertical strip

$$-\frac{\pi}{2} < x \leq \frac{3}{2}\pi, \qquad -\infty < y < \infty$$

into the strip

$$-\pi < x \leq \pi, \qquad -\infty < y < \infty.$$

Thus we see that the transformation $w = \sin z$ maps the strip

$$-\frac{\pi}{2} < x \leq \frac{3}{2}\pi, \qquad -\infty < y < \infty$$

in the same manner as the transformation $w = \cos z$ maps the strip

$$-\pi < x \leq \pi, \qquad -\infty < y < \infty.$$

EXERCISES 8.17

1. Show that under the transformation $w = \cos z$ the half line $x = \pi$, $-\infty < y \leq 0$ is mapped one-to-one onto the half line $-\infty < u \leq -1$, $v = 0$.

2. Under the transformation $w = \cos z$ determine the image of the half line $x = \pi$, $0 \leq y < \infty$.

3. Show that the transformation $w = \sin z$ may be obtained by performing successively the transformations

(a) $z' = e^{iz}$,   (b) $z'' = z' - \dfrac{1}{z'}$,   (c) $w = \dfrac{1}{2i}\, z''$.

4. Under the transformation $w = \sin z$, show that the semi-infinite strip

$$0 \le x \le \frac{\pi}{2}, \qquad 0 \le y < \infty,$$

maps one-to-one onto the first quadrant together with its boundary as shown in Fig. 8.17.2.

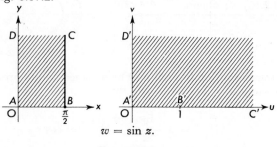

$$w = \sin z.$$

FIG. 8.17.2

5. Under the transformation $w = \sin z$, show that the rectangular region

$$-\frac{\pi}{2} \le x \le \frac{\pi}{2}, \qquad 0 \le y \le k,$$

maps one-to-one onto a semielliptic region as shown in Fig. 8.17.3.

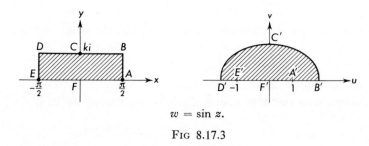

$$w = \sin z.$$

FIG 8.17.3

Show that the equation of $B'C'D'$ is given by

$$\frac{u^2}{\cosh^2 k} + \frac{v^2}{\sinh^2 k} = 1, \qquad v \ge 0.$$

6. Show that under the transformation $w = \sin z$, the line $x = p$, where $2p/\pi$ is not an integer, maps onto a branch of the hyperbola:

$$|\, w + 1 \,| - |\, w - 1 \,| = 2 \sin p.$$

7. Show that under the transformation $w = \sin z$, the rectangular region

$$- \pi < x \leqq \pi, \qquad 0 < k_1 \leqq y \leqq k_2,$$

maps onto a region bounded by two confocal ellipses as shown in Fig. 8.17.4. Also note that the line $x = \pi$ maps onto the line segment

$$u = 0, \qquad v = -\sinh y, \qquad k_1 \leqq y \leqq k_2.$$

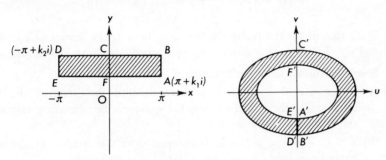

$$w = \sin z.$$

Fig. 8.17.4

8. Show that under the transformation $w = \tan^2 \frac{1}{2} z$, the semi-infinite strip

$$0 \leqq x \leqq \frac{\pi}{2}, \qquad -\infty < y \leqq 0,$$

is mapped onto the region bounded by the segment, $-1 \leqq u \leqq 1, v = 0$, and the lower half of the circle $|w| = 1$.

9. Show that under the transformation $w = \tan^2 (1/2)z$, the line $x = \pi/4$ is mapped onto a simple closed contour cutting the u axis at $w = -1$ and $w = 3 - 2\sqrt{2}$.
(Note: $\lim_{y \to \pm\infty} \tan^2 [(1/2)(\pi/4 + iy)] = -1$. The point $w = -1$ has been adjoined to the contour.)

10. Given the transformation $w = \cosh z$.
 (a) Show that the line $x = k$ $(k \neq 0)$ is mapped onto the ellipse $u^2/\cosh^2 k + v^2/\sinh^2 k = 1$.
 (b) Show that the line $y = c$, $2c/\pi$ not an integer, is mapped one-to-one onto a branch of the hyperbola

$$\frac{u^2}{\cos^2 c} - \frac{v^2}{\sin^2 c} = 1.$$

 (c) Determine the image of each of the rectangular regions

 (1) $0 < k_1 \leqq x \leqq k_2, \qquad 0 < c_1 \leqq y \leqq c_2 < \pi/2;$
 (2) $0 < k_1 \leqq x \leqq k_2, \qquad -\pi/2 < c_1 \leqq y \leqq c_2 < 0;$

(3) $k_1 \leq x \leq k_2 < 0,$ $\pi/2 < c_1 \leq y \leq c_2 < \pi;$
(4) $k_1 \leq x \leq k_2 < 0,$ $-\pi < c_1 \leq y \leq c_2 < -\pi/2.$

[Note: By utilizing equation (4.3.1), the transformation $w = \cosh z$ may be obtained by applying successively the transformations

$$(1)\ z' = e^z, \qquad (2)\ w = \frac{1}{2}\left(z' + \frac{1}{z'}\right).]$$

11. Show that under the transformation $w = \tanh z$, the lines $x = c$ ($c \neq 0$) and $y = k$ ($k \neq n\pi/2$, n an integer) are mapped into circles and circular arcs.

12. Show that under the transformation $w = \tanh z$ the domain

(a) $0 < x < c,\ 0 < y < \pi/2$, is mapped onto that part of the first quadrant in the w plane which lies outside a certain circle having its center on the real axis;

(b) $x > c,\ -\pi/2 < y \leq \pi/2$, is mapped onto the interior of the same circle as in part (a) with the point $w = 1$ excluded.

13. Show that under the transformation $w = \mathrm{Log}\ [(z-1)/(z+1)]$, the half plane $\mathscr{I}(z) \geq 0$, $z \neq \pm 1$, is mapped onto the infinite strip

$$-\infty < u < \infty, \qquad 0 \leq v \leq \pi,$$

as shown in Fig. 8.17.5.

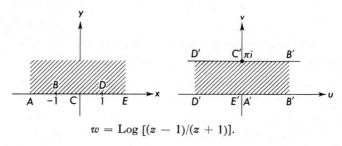

$$w = \mathrm{Log}\ [(z-1)/(z+1)].$$

FIG. 8.17.5

What is the image of the half plane $\mathscr{I}(z) \leq 0$?

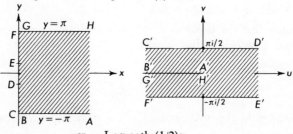

$$w = \mathrm{Log}\ \coth\ (1/2)z.$$

FIG. 8.17.6

14. Determine the image of the arc of the circle $x^2 + y^2 - 2y \cot k = 1$, $0 < k < \pi$, under the transformation $w = \text{Log}\,[(z - 1)/(z + 1)]$.

15. Determine the image of the upper half plane $\mathscr{I}(z) > 0$ under the transformation $w = \pi i + z - \text{Log}\,z$.

16. Show that under the transformation $w = \text{Log} \coth \frac{1}{2} z$, the semi-infinite strip $0 \leqq x < \infty$, $-\pi \leqq y \leqq \pi$, $z \neq 0$, is mapped onto a region as indicated in Fig. 8.17.6.

8.18. FUNCTIONS INDUCED BY THE MAPPING OF ONE DOMAIN INTO ANOTHER. Suppose that we are given a mapping G which assigns to each point w in a set D_w a point $z = G(w)$ in a set D_z. Then, to any function $F(z)$ on D_z there corresponds a function $H(w)$ on D_w defined as follows: the value $H(w_0)$ of the function $H(w)$ at any point w_0 in D_w is equal to the value of $F(z_0)$ of the function $F(z)$ at the image point $z_0 = G(w_0)$ of w_0, and we write

$$H(w) = F[G(w)], \qquad \text{for } w \text{ in } D_w. \tag{8.18.1}$$

[See Fig. 8.18.1, where $\zeta = F(z)$ lies in the set D_ζ.] Clearly, the function H will be respectively real- or complex-valued whenever F is real- or complex-valued.

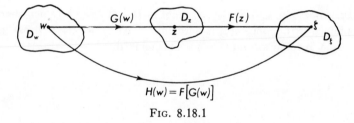

$$H(w) = F[G(w)]$$

FIG. 8.18.1

We also see that if to the functions $\phi(z)$ and $\psi(z)$ there correspond respectively the functions $\lambda(w)$ and $\mu(w)$, then to the function $a\phi(z) + b\psi(z)$, where a and b are constants, there will correspond the function $a\lambda(w) + b\mu(w)$. Consequently, if $F(z) = \phi(z) + i\psi(z)$, where $\phi(z)$ and $\psi(z)$ are real-valued functions, then the function $H(w)$ corresponding to $F(z)$ will be given by $H(w) = \lambda(w) + i\mu(w)$, where $\lambda(w)$ and $\mu(w)$ are the real-valued functions corresponding to $\phi(z)$ and $\psi(z)$, respectively.

***Remark* 8.18.1.** If the sets D_w and D_z are domains and the mapping G of D_w into D_z given by

$$z = G(w) \tag{8.18.2}$$

is analytic in D_w, and if $F(z)$ is analytic in D_z, then the corresponding function $H(w)$ will also be analytic in D_w, since $H(w) = F[G(w)]$ is an analytic function of an analytic function. (See Theorem 3.5.2.)

8.19. SOME BASIC PROPERTIES OF HARMONIC FUNCTIONS.

Let us recall (see Definition 3.7.1) that a real-valued function $u(x, y)$ in a domain D of the z plane is called harmonic in D, if it has continuous partial derivatives of the second order and $u_{xx} + u_{yy} = 0$ in D. As observed in Remark 3.1.2, $u(x, y)$ may be regarded as a real-valued function of the complex variable $z = x + iy$. Thus we may write $u(z)$ instead of $u(x, y)$.

Definition 8.19.1.   A real-valued function $u(z)$ is said to be *harmonic at the point* z_0 if $u(z)$ is harmonic in a domain D containing z_0.

Recall (see Theorem 3.7.1) that if $u = \mathscr{R}[f(z)]$, where $f(z)$ is single-valued and analytic in D, then u is harmonic in D. Using the function $u = \mathscr{R}(\log z)$, which is harmonic in the domain D consisting of all points $z \neq 0$, it can be shown that the converse of Theorem 3.7.1 is not valid. That is, if $u(z)$ is harmonic in a domain D, it does not follow that $u = \mathscr{R}[f(z)]$ for some single-valued analytic function $f(z)$ in D. (See Exercise 7.10.7.) However, the converse of Theorem 3.7.1 is true in the following "local" sense.

——**THEOREM** 8.19.1.   Let $u(z)$ be harmonic in a domain D and let z_0 be any point in D. Then there exists a neighborhood $N(z_0)$ of z_0 contained in D and a function $f(z)$ single-valued and analytic in $N(z_0)$ such that $u = \mathscr{R}[f(z)]$ for z in $N(z_0)$.

Proof.   Let $z_0 = x_0 + iy_0$ be any point in D. Let $N(z_0)$ be a neighborhood of z_0 contained in D. Since $u(z)$ is harmonic in $N(z_0)$, we have $(\partial/\partial x)\,(u_x) = (\partial/\partial y)\,(-\,u_y)$. It follows from Green's Theorem* that

$$\int_C -\,u_y\,dx + u_x\,dy = 0,$$

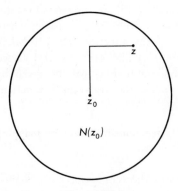

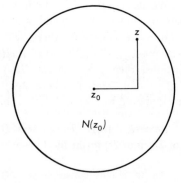

FIG. 8.19.1   FIG. 8.19.2

* See R. C. Buck, *Advanced Calculus*, p. 338. New York: McGraw-Hill, 1956.

when C describes the perimeter of a rectangle in $N(z_0)$. Consequently

$$v(z) = \int_{(x_0, y_0)}^{(x, y)} - u_y \, dx + u_x \, dy \qquad (8.19.1)$$

has the same value when the path of integration, lying in $N(z_0)$, is as given in Fig. 8.19.1 or in Fig. 8.19.2.

As in the proof of Lemma 5.8.4, we find that $v_x = - u_y$ and $v_y = u_x$. Since $u(z)$ is harmonic, u_x and u_y are continuous. Thus the function

$$f(z) = u(z) + iv(z)$$

satisfies the conditions of Theorem 3.6.2 and consequently is analytic in $N(z_0)$. Hence $u = \mathscr{R}[f(z)]$ for z in $N(z_0)$, and the theorem is established.

We shall now prove the following important

——**THEOREM** 8.19.2.   Let $u(z)$ be harmonic in a domain D. If $u(z)$ attains a maximum or a minimum in D, then $u(z)$ is constant in D.

Proof.   Suppose that $u(z)$ attains a maximum at a point $z = z_0$ in D. By Theorem 8.19.1, there exists a neighborhood $N(z_0)$ of z_0 in D and an analytic function $f(z)$ in $N(z_0)$ such that $u = \mathscr{R}[f(z)]$. We shall now show that $f(z)$, and consequently $u(z)$, is constant in $N(z_0)$. It will then follow (see Exercise 8.19.5) that $u(z)$ is constant in D.

For, suppose to the contrary that $f(z)$ were not constant in $N(z_0)$, then by Theorem 8.2.1, the image D_w of $N(z_0)$ under the analytic mapping $w = f(z)$ is a domain.

Let $w_0 = u_0 + iv_0$ be the image of z_0 under the analytic mapping $w = u + iv = f(z)$. Then, since D_w is an open set, it contains a segment parallel to the u axis and having w_0 in its interior. Since every point on this segment is the image of some point z in $N(z_0)$, it follows that there are points in $N(z_0)$ whose images $u + iv$ have values of u greater than $u(z_0)$. This contradicts the assumption that $u(z_0) \geq u(z)$ for all z in D. Hence, $f(z)$ is constant in $N(z_0)$, and consequently $u(z)$ is also constant in $N(z_0)$. Therefore $u(z)$ is constant in D.

Concerning the minimum value of $u(z)$: If $u(z)$ attains a minimum at a point z_0 in D, then the harmonic function $- u(z)$ attains a maximum at $z = z_0$. It follows by the foregoing result that $- u(z)$ is constant in D. Consequently, $u(z)$ is also constant in D. The theorem is thus established.

An immediate consequence of the foregoing theorem is that the maximum and minimum values of an harmonic function are attained on the boundary. More precisely, we have the following

——**THEOREM** 8.19.3.   Let R be a closed bounded region consisting of a domain D and its boundary B. Let $u(z)$ be a function continuous on R and harmonic in D. Then there exist two points z_1 and z_2 on B such that

$$u(z_1) \leq u(z) \leq u(z_2) \tag{8.19.2}$$

for all z in R.

Proof. If $u(z) = k$ for all z in D, where k is a constant, then by continuity $u(z) = k$ also for z on the boundary B. Thus (8.19.2) holds for any z_1 and z_2 on B and all z in R.

We shall assume therefore, that $u(z)$ is not constant in D. Since R is a closed and bounded set, $u(z)$ attains its maximum and minimum value in R. (See Exercise 3.3.26.) Hence there exist points z_1 and z_2 in R such that

$$u(z_1) \leq u(z) \leq u(z_2), \qquad \text{for all } z \text{ in } R.$$

By Theorem 8.19.2, z_1 and z_2 cannot be in D. Hence they are on the boundary B. Thus the theorem is established.

As an immediate consequence of the foregoing theorem, we have

——**THEOREM** 8.19.4.   Let R be a bounded closed region consisting of a domain D and its boundary B. Let $u(z)$ be a function continuous on R and harmonic in D. If $u(z) = k$ for all z on the boundary B, where k is a constant, then $u(z) = k$ for all z in R.

Proof.   By Theorem 8.19.3, there exist two points z_1 and z_2 on the boundary B such that

$$u(z_1) \leq u(z) \leq u(z_2), \qquad \text{for all } z \text{ in } R.$$

But $u(z_1) = u(z_2) = k$. Therefore $u(z) = k$ for all z in R.

We shall need the following two lemmas:

LEMMA 8.19.1.   Let $z = G(w)$ be an analytic mapping of a domain D_w in the w plane into a domain D_z of the z plane. Let $\phi(z)$ be harmonic in D_z. Let $\lambda(w) = \phi[G(w)]$ be the function induced on D_w by $\phi(z)$ under the mapping $z = G(w)$. Then $\lambda(w)$ is harmonic in D_w.

Proof.   Let w_0 be any point in D_w. We shall show that $\lambda(w)$ is harmonic in a neighborhood of w_0. This will imply that $\lambda(w)$ is harmonic in D_w. Let $z_0 = G(w_0)$. Then by Theorem 8.19.1, there exists a neighborhood $N(z_0)$ of z_0 contained in D_z and an analytic function $f(z)$ defined in $N(z_0)$ such that

$$\phi(z) = \mathscr{R}[f(z)], \qquad \text{for } z \text{ in } N(z_0).$$

Let now $N(w_0)$ be a neighborhood of w_0 which is mapped by $G(w)$ into $N(z_0)$. (Since $G(w)$ is continuous, such a neighborhood always exists.) Under the mapping $z = G(w)$, the functions $f(z)$ and $\phi(z)$ defined on the image of $N(w_0)$ induce respectively in $N(w_0)$ the functions $H(w) = f[G(w)]$ and $\lambda(w) = \phi[G(w)]$. Clearly, we have $\lambda(w) = \mathscr{R}[H(w)]$. Moreover (see Remark 8.18.1) $H(w)$ is analytic in $N(w_0)$. Hence, $\lambda(w)$ being the real part of the analytic function $H(w)$, is harmonic in $N(w_0)$. Thus the lemma is established.

EXAMPLE 8.19.1.   The function $\phi(x, y) = e^{-ky} \cos kx$, where k is a real number, being the real part of the analytic function e^{ikz}, is harmonic in the z plane. Under the analytic mapping $z = G(w) = w^3$, we have $x = u^3 - 3uv^2$, $y = 3u^2v - v^3$, where $z = x + iy$ and $w = u + iv$, and hence the corresponding function

$$\lambda(u, v) = e^{k(v^3 - 3u^2 v)} \cos k(u^3 - 3uv^2)$$

is harmonic in the w plane, that is

$$\nabla^2 \lambda = \frac{\partial^2 \lambda}{\partial u^2} + \frac{\partial^2 \lambda}{\partial v^2} = 0.$$

Definition 8.19.2.   A real valued function $u(z)$ is said to be *harmonic at* $z = \infty$, if the function $u(1/w)$ is harmonic in a neighborhood of $w = 0$.

We leave as an exercise for the reader to show that if a function is harmonic at $z = \infty$, then there exists a neighborhood N of $z = \infty$ and a function $f(z)$ analytic in N such that $u(z) = \mathscr{R}[f(z)]$ for z in N. Also, one may show that a function harmonic at $z = \infty$ cannot attain a maximum or a minimum at this point.

LEMMA 8.19.2.   If $u(z)$ is harmonic at $z = \infty$, then $u(\alpha + k/w)$ where $k \neq 0$ and α are constants, is harmonic at $w = 0$.

Proof.   By hypothesis, $u(1/\zeta)$ is harmonic at $\zeta = 0$. Consider the mapping of the w plane onto the ζ plane given by

$$\zeta = \frac{w}{\alpha w + k} . \tag{8.19.3}$$

Note that the mapping given in (8.19.3) is analytic at $w = 0$. By Lemma 8.19.1, the function $u(1/\zeta)$ being harmonic in a neighborhood of $\zeta = 0$, induces under the mapping (8.19.3) a function $u(\alpha + k/w)$ which is harmonic in the corresponding neighborhood of $w = 0$.

——*THEOREM* 8.19.5.   Let R denote the region consisting of a simple closed contour C and its exterior D, where D contains the point $z = \infty$. If $u(z)$ is a function continuous on R, harmonic in D and constant on C, then $u(z)$ is constant on R.

Proof. Let $z = \alpha$ be any point interior to C, and take $\rho > 0$ so that the disk $|z - \alpha| \leqq \rho$ is also interior to C. Consider the linear fractional transformation

$$w = \frac{\rho^2}{z - \alpha}. \tag{8.19.4}$$

For any point z in R, we have $|z - \alpha| > \rho$. Consequently, its image under (8.19.4) satisfies the condition $|w| < \rho$. Hence, the image of R lies within the circle $|w| = \rho$. Let Γ denote the image under (8.19.4) of the simple closed contour C. (See Fig. 8.19.3.) The exterior D of C, is mapped either entirely

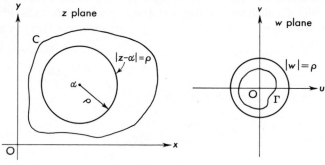

FIG. 8.19.3

onto the interior of Γ or else entirely onto its exterior. (See Exercise 8.10.26.) The second alternative is not possible, since D is mapped into the interior of the circle $|w| = \rho$. It follows that under the mapping (8.19.4), the exterior D of C corresponds to the interior of Γ. Hence, under the inverse mapping

$$z = \alpha + \frac{\rho^2}{w}, \tag{8.19.5}$$

the interior of Γ is mapped onto D. Since $u(z)$ is harmonic in D, it induces in the interior of Γ the harmonic function $U(w) = u(\alpha + \rho^2/w)$. (See Lemmas 8.19.1 and 8.19.2.) By hypothesis, $u(z)$ is constant on C. Consequently, $U(w)$ is constant on Γ, and by Theorem 8.19.4 it is also constant in the interior of Γ. Hence, $u(z)$ is constant on R, and the theorem is established.

EXERCISES 8.19

1. Suppose that $u(z)$ is harmonic in a domain D. Show that there exists an analytic function (not necessarily single-valued) in D such that $u(z) = \mathscr{R}[f(z)]$.

2. Suppose that $u(z)$ is harmonic in a simply connected domain D. Show that there exists a function $f(z)$, single-valued and analytic in D, such that $u(z) = \mathscr{R}[f(z)]$.

3. Let $u(z)$ be harmonic in a domain D. Show that if $u(z) = 0$ for all z in a subdomain D_0 of D, then $u(z) = 0$ for all z in D.

4. Let $u_1(z)$ and $u_2(z)$ be functions harmonic in a domain D. Show that if $u_1(z) = u_2(z)$ for all z in a subdomain D_0 of D, then $u_1(z) = u_2(z)$ for all z in D.

5. Let $u(z)$ be harmonic in a domain D. Show that if $u(z) = c$ in a subdomain D_0 of D, where c is a constant, then $u(z) = c$ for all z in D.

6. Show that if $u(z)$ is harmonic throughout the z plane and $\lim_{z \to \infty} u(z) = 0$, then $u(z)$ is identically zero.

7. Suppose that the real function $u(z)$ is continuous on the region $R: \mathscr{I}(z) \geq 0$, harmonic in the domain $\mathscr{I}(z) > 0$, and equal to a constant k on the boundary $\mathscr{I}(z) = 0$. Furthermore, suppose that $\lim_{z \to \infty} u(z) = k$. Show that $u(z)$ is constant on R.

8. Derive the maximum modulus Theorem 8.2.2 from Theorem 8.19.2.

9. Let $u(z)$ be harmonic in the complex plane with the point $z = 0$ removed. Suppose that $u = u(r)$, where $r = |z| = (x^2 + y^2)^{1/2}$. Show that $u = A \operatorname{Log} r + B$, where A and B are real constants.

10. Let $f(z)$ be analytic in a domain D. Suppose that $f(z) \neq 0$ in D. Show that $\operatorname{Log} |f(z)|$ is harmonic in D.

9

Application of
Analytic Functions
to the Theory
of Flows

9.1. INTRODUCTION. The theory of two-dimensional flow is closely related to the theory of analytic functions, especially to the theory of conformal mapping. Analytic function methods turn out to be very useful in solving problems related to two-dimensional flows, with applications to various fields such as aerodynamics, conduction of heat, electricity, and hydrodynamics. On the other hand, the picture given by the flow is an aid in understanding the properties of analytic functions.

In the ensuing discussion, we shall assume a two-dimensional flow, that is, (1) the velocities of all particles of the moving fluid are parallel to one plane which we may conveniently choose as the xy plane, and (2) all particles having the same x and y coordinates have equal velocities. Such cases arise when a very thin sheet of liquid is flowing in some manner over a plane, or when a thick layer of liquid circulates over a plane in such a way that there is no motion and no variation of motion normal to the plane. Also we shall assume an "ideal fluid," that is, one that is incompressible and frictionless. For an incompressible fluid, the density is constant. A frictionless fluid has zero viscosity, that is, it cannot sustain a shear stress at any point. Thus the fluid force acting on any elemental surface in the fluid is normal to that surface.

The concept of an ideal fluid greatly simplifies the mathematical treatment of flows. Although an ideal fluid does not actually exist, many real fluids have small viscosities, and the effects of compressibility may be small. Thus, for example, many conclusions concerning the motion of a solid through an ideal fluid are applicable with slight modifications to the motion of airships and submarines at speeds which are not too high.

9.2. FUNDAMENTALS OF THE THEORY OF FLOWS.

A two-dimensional *vector field* over a domain D in the xy plane is defined by a pair of real-valued functions

$$[q_1(x, y), q_2(x, y)], \tag{9.2.1}$$

each continuously differentiable in D; that is, the partial derivatives of the first order of q_1 and q_2 exist and are continuous in D. These functions define a unique vector $q = [q_1, q_2]$ at each point of D. Such a vector field can be given a physical interpretation if we consider a fluid flowing over D, and define the vector $q = [q_1, q_2]$ as the *velocity* of the fluid at each point (x, y), q_1 and q_2 being respectively the x and y components of velocity. We then say that (9.2.1) defines a *velocity field* or a *flow* over D.

We shall concern ourselves with flows in which the velocity vector q^* does not vary with time, that is, a *steady-state* type of flow. In such a flow the lines of motion are called *streamlines* and they are identical with the family of curves determined by the field of velocity vectors, that is, the family of curves such that the direction of the tangent at each point (x, y) on a curve of the family coincides with that of the vector $[q_1(x, y), q_2(x, y)]$. The members of the family orthogonal to the family of streamlines are called *equipotential lines*. It can be shown that exactly one streamline and one equipotential line pass through each point (x, y) in D where $q_1^2 + q_2^2 \neq 0$.

Suppose that a flow given by (9.2.1) is defined over a domain D, and let C be a contour in D. Let T be a tangent at a point (x, y) on C, and let the real variable $q_t(x, y)$ denote the projection on the tangent T of the velocity vector q at (x, y). If s is the arc length along C, then the line integral

$$\int_C q_t \, ds \tag{9.2.2}$$

is called the *circulation* of the fluid along C. If $q_t = 0$ along C, then C is an equipotential line.

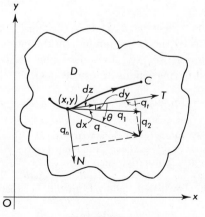

FIG. 9.2.1

* The velocity q will also be referred to as the velocity vector q.

It is convenient to denote the vector $q = [q_1, q_2]$ by

$$q = q_1 + iq_2. \tag{9.2.3}$$

By the scalar product $\alpha \cdot \beta$ of two vectors $\alpha = [a, b] = a + ib$ and $\beta = [c, d] = c + id$, we mean the real number

$$ac + bd = |\alpha| |\beta| \cos \theta,$$

where θ is the angle between the two vectors α and β.

Let the complex number $dz = dx + i\, dy$* (see Fig. 9.2.1) represent a vector along the tangent T to the contour $C: z = z(t)$, $t_1 \leq t \leq t_2$, at the point (x, y). Furthermore, let the arc length s of C be measured so that it increases with t. Then the length of the vector dz is equal to ds. Since q_t is the projection of q on the tangent T, we have

$$q \cdot dz = |q| |dz| \cos \theta = q_t |dz| = q_t \, ds.$$

Also

$$q \cdot dz = [q_1, q_2] \cdot [dx, dy] = q_1 \, dx + q_2 \, dy.$$

Thus we may write the circulation of the fluid along C given by (9.2.2) as

$$\int_C q_t \, ds = \int_C q_1 \, dx + q_2 \, dy. \tag{9.2.4}$$

Now, let q_n denote the component of q in the direction of the normal N, at the point (x, y) to the contour C. (See Fig. 9.2.1.) By the direction of the normal we mean the direction obtained by rotating the tangent 90 degrees in a clockwise direction. The line integral

$$\int_C q_n \, ds \tag{9.2.5}$$

is called the *flux* of the fluid across C. If $q_n = 0$ along C, then C is a streamline.

The product of ds by the projection of q on the normal vector is the scalar product of the vector $q = [q_1, q_2]$ by the vector $-idz = [dy, -dx]$ lying along the normal and having length ds. Consequently

$$q_n \, ds = [q_1, q_2] \cdot [dy, -dx] = -q_2 \, dx + q_1 \, dy, \tag{9.2.6}$$

---

* The reader may interpret such statements as "the length of the vector $dz = dx + i\, dy$ is equal to ds" to mean "the length of the vector $dz/dt = dx/dt + i\, dy/dt$ is equal to ds/dt". Similarly, such formulas as "$q \cdot dz = q_1 \, dx + q_2 \, dy$" may be interpreted as "$q \cdot dz/dt = q_1 \, dx/dt + q_2 \, dy/dt$". The equations (9.2.4) and (9.2.7) in the sequel will then follow from the fact that

$$\int_C F \cdot dz = \int_{t_1}^{t_2} \left(F \cdot \frac{dz}{dt} \right) dt,$$

where $F = F(z) = F[z(t)]$.

and the flux across C is given by

$$\int_C q_n \, ds = \int_C -q_2 \, dx + q_1 \, dy. \tag{9.2.7}$$

If C is a closed contour,* then the line integral (9.2.7) taken in the positive direction along C (see Definition 5.6.3 and Theorem 5.6.2) represents the total amount of fluid flowing out of the interior across C in unit time (assuming that the fluid has unit density). If the flux integral (9.2.7) vanishes for every closed contour C in D, then we say that there are no *sources* (points from which fluid issues) and no *sinks* (negative sources—that is, points into which the fluid is absorbed) in D. Such a flow is called *source free*.

If for some closed contour C in D the circulation (9.2.4) is not equal to zero, then we say that the fluid has a *vortex*[†] inside of C, and the value of the circulation gives a measure of the vorticity. A fluid for which the circulation integral (9.2.4) vanishes for every closed contour C in D is called *circulation free* or *irrotational*. We shall now establish the following essential

——THEOREM 9.2.1. Let $q_1 = q_1(x, y)$ and $q_2 = q_2(x, y)$ be a pair of continuous functions defined in a domain D. Then q_1 and q_2 define a source free and circulation free flow $q = [q_1, q_2]$ in D if, and only if, there exists in D a single-valued and analytic function

$$F(z) = \phi(x, y) + i\psi(x, y) \tag{9.2.8}$$

such that

$$F'(z) = q_1 - iq_2. \tag{9.2.9}$$

Proof. Suppose that the flow is source free and circulation free so that

$$\int_C q_1 \, dx + q_2 \, dy = 0 \quad \text{and} \quad \int_C -q_2 \, dx + q_1 \, dy = 0$$

for every closed contour C in D. Thus, each of these integrals is independent of the path of integration. Consequently, the functions

$$\phi(x, y) = \int_{(x_0, y_0)}^{(x, y)} q_1 \, dx + q_2 \, dy \quad \text{and} \quad \psi(x, y) = \int_{(x_0, y_0)}^{(x, y)} -q_2 \, dx + q_1 \, dy \tag{9.2.10}$$

are single-valued for (x_0, y_0) fixed and (x, y) varying in D. By following the method used in the proof of Theorem 5.11.1, one may show (see Exercise 9.2.1) that ϕ and ψ are both differentiable in D and that

$$\phi_x = \psi_y = q_1, \qquad \phi_y = -\psi_x = q_2.$$

* In this chapter, closed contours are understood to be simple closed contours, except where the contrary is indicated.

† Points at which there are sources, sinks, or vortices are excluded from the domain D.

Since q_1 and q_2 are continuous in D and the Cauchy-Riemann equations are satisfied, it follows from Theorem 3.6.2 that the complex function

$$F(z) = \phi(x, y) + i\psi(x, y)$$

is analytic in D and

$$F'(z) = \phi_x + i\psi_x = q_1 - iq_2.$$

Conversely, let

$$F(z) = \phi(x, y) + i\psi(x, y)$$

be a single-valued analytic function in a domain D. Then we have for any closed contour C in D

$$\int_C F'(z)\, dz = \int_{z_1}^{z_2} F'(z)\, dz = F(z_2) - F(z_1) = 0,$$

where z_1 and z_2 are respectively the initial and terminal points on C and thus $z_1 = z_2$. Let $\phi_x = q_1$ and $\psi_x = -q_2$ so that

$$F'(z) = q_1 - iq_2.$$

Then

$$0 = \int_C F'(z)\, dz = \int_C (q_1 - iq_2)\,(dx + i\, dy)$$

$$= \int_C q_1\, dx + q_2\, dy + i \int_C - q_2\, dx + q_1\, dy.$$

Hence for the vector field defined by $q = [q_1, q_2]$, we have

$$\int_C q_1\, dx + q_2\, dy = 0 \quad \text{and} \quad \int_C - q_2\, dx + q_1\, dy = 0$$

for every closed contour C in D. Consequently, the flow determined by $[q_1, q_2]$ is source free and circulation free in D. The theorem is thus established.

The function $F(z)$ given in (9.2.8) is called the *complex potential*, and is determined up to an additive constant by the velocity field $[q_1, q_2]$. Its derivative $F'(z)$, given in (9.2.9), is called the *complex velocity*. The conjugate of the complex velocity is equal to the velocity

$$\overline{F'(z)} = q_1 + iq_2 = q. \tag{9.2.11}$$

The speed, or magnitude of the velocity, is given by

$$|q| = \sqrt{q_1^2 + q_2^2} = |F'(z)|. \tag{9.2.12}$$

Let $\mathscr{C}$ and $\mathscr{F}$ denote respectively the circulation and flux given by (9.2.4) and (9.2.7). Now

$$\int_C F'(z)\,dz = \int_C (q_1 - iq_2)\,(dx + i\,dy)$$

$$= \int_C q_1\,dx + q_2\,dy + i\int_C - q_2\,dx + q_1\,dy.$$

Thus

$$\int_C F'(z)\,dz = \mathscr{C} + i\mathscr{F} \tag{9.2.13}$$

and is called the *total circulation* of the fluid along C. Also

$$\mathscr{C} = \mathscr{R}\left[\int_C F'(z)\,dz\right] \quad \text{and} \quad \mathscr{F} = \mathscr{I}\left[\int_C F'(z)\,dz\right]. \tag{9.2.14}$$

If the flow q is source free and circulation free, the functions

$$\phi(x, y) = \int_{(x_0, y_0)}^{(x,y)} q_t\,ds = \int_{(x_0, y_0)}^{(x,y)} q_1\,dx + q_2\,dy \tag{9.2.15}$$

and

$$\psi(x, y) = \int_{(x_0, y_0)}^{(x,y)} q_n\,ds = \int_{(x_0, y_0)}^{(x,y)} - q_2\,dx + q_1\,dy, \tag{9.2.16}$$

being the real and imaginary parts of the single-valued analytic function $F(z)$, are harmonic in the domain D and satisfy Laplace's equation

$$\nabla^2 u = u_{xx} + u_{yy} = 0, \tag{9.2.17}$$

with $u = \phi(x, y)$ or $u = \psi(x, y)$.

We shall now establish the following

——**THEOREM** 9.2.2. Suppose that a flow q is source free and circulation free in a domain D. A contour C in D is a streamline if, and only if, the function $\psi(x, y)$ given in (9.2.16) is constant along C.

Proof. Suppose that C is a streamline and that (x_1, y_1), (x_2, y_2) are any two points on C contained in D. Then from (9.2.16) we have

$$\psi(x_2, y_2) - \psi(x_1, y_1) = \int_{(x_1, y_1)}^{(x_2, y_2)} q_n\,ds,$$

where the path of integration may be taken along C. Since $q_n = 0$ at each point of C, we have $\psi(x_2, y_2) = \psi(x_1, y_1)$ and thus $\psi(x, y)$ is constant on C.

Conversely, it can be shown (see Exercise 9.2.2) that if C is any contour in D such that $\psi(x, y) = $ constant on C, then $q_n = 0$ at each point of C. Thus the velocity vector q at each point is tangent to C and C is a streamline.

Similarly, one may establish the following

——**THEOREM** 9.2.3. Suppose that a flow q is source free and circulation free in a domain D. A contour C in D is an equipotential line if, and only if, the function $\phi(x, y)$ given in (9.2.15) is constant along C.

The proof is left as an exercise for the reader.

The functions $\phi(x, y)$ and $\psi(x, y)$ given in (9.2.15) and (9.2.16) are known respectively as the *equipotential function* and *stream function* of the flow.

EXERCISES 9.2

1. Prove that the functions $\phi(x, y)$ and $\psi(x, y)$ given in (9.2.10) are differentiable in their domain of definition D and that $\phi_x = \psi_y = q_1$ and $\phi_y = -\psi_x = q_2$ in D.

2. Let the velocity vector $q = [q_1, q_2]$ define a flow over a domain D, and let C be a contour in D such that the function $\psi(x, y)$ given in (9.2.16) is constant on C. Let q_n denote the component of q in the direction of the normal. Show that $q_n = 0$ at each point of C.

3. Prove Theorem 9.2.3.

9.3. LOCALLY CIRCULATION AND SOURCE FREE FLOWS. For a flow defined over a domain D there may exist closed contours in D for which the circulation and flux do not vanish. However, such a flow may be locally circulation and source free in the following sense:

Definition 9.3.1. A flow is said to be *locally circulation and source free in a domain D* if for every point z_0 in D, there exists a neighborhood $N(z_0)$ such that the circulation and flux vanish for every closed contour Γ contained in $N(z_0)$.

Corresponding to Theorem 9.2.1, we have the following theorem for flows which are locally circulation and source free.

——**THEOREM** 9.3.1. Let $q_1 = q_1(x, y)$ and $q_2 = q_2(x, y)$ be a pair of continuous functions defined in a domain D. Then q_1 and q_2 define a locally circulation and source free flow $q = [q_1, q_2]$ in D if, and only if, there exists in D a (not necessarily single-valued) analytic function

$$F(z) = \phi(x, y) + i\psi(x, y) \qquad (9.3.1)$$

with a single-valued derivative given by

$$F'(z) = q_1(x, y) - iq_2(x, y). \qquad (9.3.2)$$

Proof. Suppose that $q = q_1 + iq_2$ defines a locally circulation and source free flow in D. Let

$$F(z) = \phi(z) + i\psi(z)$$

where

$$\phi(z) = \int_{z_0}^{z} q_t \, ds = \int_{z_0}^{z} q_1 \, dx + q_2 \, dy \qquad (9.3.3)$$

and

$$\psi(z) = \int_{z_0}^{z} q_n \, ds = \int_{z_0}^{z} - q_2 \, dx + q_1 \, dy, \qquad (9.3.4)$$

with z_0 fixed and z varying in D^*. Since the flow may not be entirely circulation and source free in D, the values of the integrals in (9.3.3) and (9.3.4) may vary with the path of integration, and thus $F(z)$ may be multiple-valued. To show that $F(z)$ is a (possibly multiple-valued) analytic function in D, we must verify that the two conditions given in Definition 4.5.4 are satisfied.

Let z_1 be a point in D and let $F_\alpha(z_1)$ be one of the values of the function $F(z)$ at $z = z_1$, that is,

$$F_\alpha(z_1) = \int_{z_0}^{z_1} q_t \, ds + i \int_{z_0}^{z_1} q_n \, ds, \qquad (9.3.5)$$

where the integration is taken along some path γ_α in D joining z_0 to z_1. Let $N(z_1)$ be a neighborhood of the point z_1 contained in D such that the circulation and flux around every closed contour Γ in $N(z_1)$ are equal to zero. We shall now show that there exists in $N(z_1)$ a branch $G_\alpha(z)$ of the function $F(z)$ such that $G_\alpha(z_1) = F_\alpha(z_1)$. Let

$$H(z) = \int_{z_1}^{z} q_t \, ds + i \int_{z_1}^{z} q_n \, ds, \qquad (9.3.6)$$

where the path of integration γ joining z_1 to z lies entirely in $N(z_1)$. Since the flow is circulation and source free in $N(z_1)$, it follows from Theorem 9.2.1, that $H(z)$ is a single-valued analytic function in $N(z_1)$, and

$$H'(z) = q_1 - iq_2. \qquad (9.3.7)$$

Let

$$G_\alpha(z) = F_\alpha(z_1) + H(z), \qquad \text{for } z \text{ in } N(z_1). \qquad (9.3.8)$$

From (9.3.6), we have that $H(z_1) = 0$. Hence $G_\alpha(z_1) = F_\alpha(z_1)$.

It remains to show that $G_\alpha(z)$ is a branch in $N(z_1)$ of $F(z)$. First of all, since $F_\alpha(z_1)$ is a constant, $G_\alpha(z)$ is a single-valued analytic function in $N(z_1)$.

---

*In view of Remark 3.1.2, we may write $q(z)$, $\phi(z)$ and $\psi(z)$ instead of $q(x, y)$, $\phi(x, y)$ and $\psi(x, y)$. The function $F(z)$ given in (9.3.1) is also called the complex potential. The derivative $F'(z)$ of $F(z)$ is defined in terms of the derivatives of the branches of $F(z)$.

We shall now show that for each z in $N(z_1)$, $G_\alpha(z)$ is one of the values of $F(z)$. (See Definition 4.5.1.) In view of (9.3.5), (9.3.6) and (9.3.8), we have

$$G_\alpha(z) = \int_{z_0}^z q_t \, ds + i \int_{z_0}^z q_n \, ds, \qquad (9.3.9)$$

where the integral is taken along the path consisting of γ_α followed by γ. Thus $G_\alpha(z)$ is one of the values of $F(z)$. We have shown that condition (1) in Definition 4.5.4 is satisfied. We leave it as an exercise for the reader (see Exercise 9.3.1) to show that condition (2) of Definition 4.5.4 is also satisfied. The proof that $F(z)$ is an analytic function in D will then be established.

To prove that $F'(z)$ is a single-valued function, we observe from (9.3.7) and (9.3.8) that $G'_\alpha(z) = q_1 - iq_2$. Thus no matter what branch of $F(z)$ we consider, the derivative is the same, and is given by

$$F'(z) = q_1(z) - iq_2(z).$$

Conversely, suppose that we are given a (possibly multiple-valued) analytic function $F(z) = \phi(z) + i\psi(z)$ in D so that $F'(z)$ is single-valued. Let $\phi_x = q_1$ and $\psi_x = -q_2$ so that $F'(z) = q_1 - iq_2$. Let $G_\alpha(z)$ be a branch of $F(z)$ defined in a neighborhood $N(z_1)$ of the point z_1 in D. Let Γ be any closed contour contained in $N(z_1)$. Then

$$\int_\Gamma F'(z) \, dz = \int_\Gamma G'_\alpha(z) \, dz = G_\alpha(z_2) - G_\alpha(z_1),$$

where z_1 and z_2 are respectively the initial and terminal points of Γ. Since $z_1 = z_2$ and $G_\alpha(z)$ is single-valued in $N(z_1)$, it follows that $G_\alpha(z_1) = G_\alpha(z_2)$ and consequently

$$\mathscr{R} \left[\int_\Gamma F'(z) \, dz \right] = \mathscr{I} \left[\int_\Gamma F'(z) \, dz \right] = 0.$$

Thus the flow in D defined by the vector field $[q_1, q_2]$ is locally circulation and source free. The theorem is now established.

Remark 9.3.1.   We consider a complex potential to be uniquely determined if it is determined up to an additive constant. A complex potential uniquely determines a (possibly locally) circulation and source free flow and conversely. (See Exercise 9.3.3.)

Remark 9.3.2.   *If D is a simply connected domain, then any locally circulation and source free flow in D is entirely circulation and source free in D.* For, if $F(z)$ is the complex potential of this flow with derivative $F'(z)$, then by the foregoing theorem, $F'(z)$ is single-valued in D. Furthermore, each value of $F(z)$ is given by

$$F(z) = \int_{z_0}^z F'(z) \, dz, \qquad (9.3.10)$$

where the integration is taken along a contour in D joining z to a fixed point z_0. Since D is simply connected and $F'(z)$ is single-valued and analytic in D, the integral given in (9.3.10) is independent of the path by Theorem 5.10.1. (See also Remark 5.8.1.) Consequently, the function $F(z)$ is single-valued. Thus, from Theorem 9.2.1, it follows that the flow is entirely circulation and source free in D.

Remark 9.3.3. In case the flow is only locally source free, so that $\psi(x, y)$ is multiple-valued, Theorem 9.2.2 no longer holds. However, using the concept of a branch of an analytic function along a contour (see Definition 4.5.2), one may prove the following

——**THEOREM** 9.3.2. Suppose that a flow q is only locally source free in a domain D. A contour C in D is a streamline if, and only if, for every branch $f(z)$ along C of the complex potential $F(z), \mathscr{I}[f(z)]$ is constant along C.

The proof will be left as an exercise for the reader.

EXERCISES 9.3

1. Show that if $G_1(z)$ and $G_2(z)$ are any two branches of the multiple-valued function

$$F(z) = \int_{z_0}^{z} q_t \, ds + i \int_{z_0}^{z} q_n \, ds,$$

where $q = [q_1, q_2]$ defines a locally circulation and source free flow in a domain D, then $G_2(z)$ is an analytic continuation of $G_1(z)$ along some curve C in D.

2. Prove Theorem 9.3.2.

3. Let $F_1(z)$ and $F_2(z)$ be (possibly multiple-valued) imaginary potentials for a given flow. Show that for some constant c, $F_2(z) = F_1(z) + c$.

9.4. EXAMPLES OF FLOWS ARISING FROM CERTAIN FAMILIAR COMPLEX POTENTIALS

EXAMPLE 9.4.1. $F(z) = Az$, where A is a real and positive number. From (9.2.8) we then have $\phi(x, y) = Ax$ and $\psi(x, y) = Ay$. Thus the stream-lines $\psi = $ constant are parallel to the x axis, and the equipotential lines $\phi = $ constant are parallel to the y axis. Also from (9.2.11), the velocity is given by

$$q = q_1 + iq_2 = \overline{F'(z)} = A,$$

so that $q_1 = A, q_2 = 0$ and $|q| = A$. Thus we have a uniform flow with velocity A parallel to the x axis as shown in Fig. 9.4.1.

If $A \neq 0$ is a complex number, say $A = a_1 + ia_2$, then

$$F(z) = Az = a_1 x - a_2 y + i(a_1 y + a_2 x),$$

and

$$\phi(x, y) = a_1 x - a_2 y \quad \text{and} \quad \psi(x, y) = a_1 y + a_2 x.$$

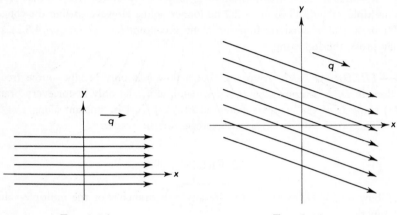

FIG. 9.4.1   FIG. 9.4.2

Also

$$q = q_1 + iq_2 = \overline{F'(z)} = a_1 - ia_2,$$

so that $q_1 = a_1$ and $q_2 = -a_2$. The streamlines are lines parallel to the vector $q = a_1 - ia_2$ as shown in Fig. 9.4.2, for the case when a_1 and a_2 are both positive numbers.

Thus, in all cases, $F(z) = Az$ defines a flow along parallel lines with constant speed. There is, consequently, no loss of generality in assuming that A is a positive real constant. Making A complex only introduces a rotation of the whole stream pattern through some angle.

EXAMPLE 9.4.2. $F(z) = (A/2) z^2$, where A is a real and positive number. Then

$$\phi(x, y) = \frac{A}{2} (x^2 - y^2) \quad \text{and} \quad \psi(x, y) = Axy.$$

The streamlines $\psi = $ constant form a family of rectangular hyperbolas with the coordinate axes as asymptotes, while $\phi = $ constant give the orthogonal family of rectangular hyperbolas whose asymptotes are the lines $y = x$ and $y = -x$. (See Fig. 3.8.2.)

Parts of this diagram can sometimes be of practical significance; one half of it, for example, depicts the case of a flow against a plate (see Fig. 9.4.3), and one-quarter of it is the flow inside a corner (see Fig. 9.4.4). Also we have

$$q = q_1 + iq_2 = \overline{F'(z)} = A\bar{z} = Ax - Aiy,$$

so that $q_1 = Ax$ and $q_2 = -Ay$. The speed is

$$|q| = \sqrt{q_1^2 + q_2^2} = A\sqrt{x^2 + y^2} = A|z|.$$

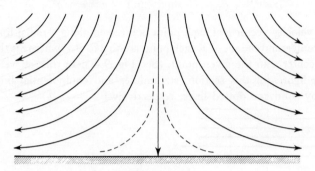

Fig. 9.4.3

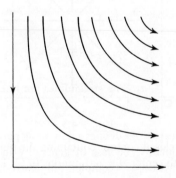

Fig. 9.4.4

Hence, if we consider a series of concentric circles with the origin as center, the speed at any point is proportional to the radius of the circle through that point, and is the same for all points on the circle.

EXAMPLE 9.4.3. $F(z) = A \log(z - \alpha)$, where A is a real and positive number. $F(z)$ is defined in the domain D consisting of all points $z \neq \alpha$. Although $F(z)$ is not single-valued in D, $F'(z) = A/(z - \alpha)$ is single-valued in D. By Theorem 9.3.1, $F(z)$ determines a locally circulation and source free flow in D. Let $z - \alpha = re^{i\theta}$, then (up to a multiple of $2\pi Ai$),

$$F(z) = A \operatorname{Log} r + A\theta i$$

so that the equipotential lines $\phi = A \operatorname{Log} r = \text{constant}$ (or $r = \text{constant}$) constitute a family of concentric circles with center at α. By Theorem 9.3.2, we see that the streamlines are given by $\psi = A\theta = \text{constant}$ (or $\theta = \text{constant}$), and constitute a family of radial lines orthogonal to the equipotential lines.

Also

$$q = q_1 + iq_2 = \overline{F'(z)} = \frac{A}{\overline{z - \alpha}} = \frac{A}{r} e^{i\theta} = \frac{A}{r} (\cos \theta + i \sin \theta),$$

so that

$$q_1 = \frac{A}{r} \cos \theta, \qquad q_2 = \frac{A}{r} \sin \theta \quad \text{and} \quad |q| = \sqrt{q_1^2 + q_2^2} = \frac{A}{r}.$$

Thus the velocity vector q at each point is directed along a radial line outward from the center, and the speed at each point is equal to A/r, where r is the distance from the center α to the given point. (See Fig. 9.4.5. In this, as well as in the remaining figures of this section, streamlines and equipotential lines will be denoted by solid and dotted lines, respectively.)

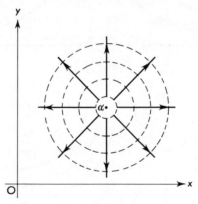

FIG. 9.4.5

Now, let C be any closed contour containing the point $z = \alpha$ in its interior, and let Γ be a circle with center at α and interior to C. Then by Theorem 5.10.3 and Example 5.2.2, we have

$$\int_C F'(z) \, dz = \int_\Gamma F'(z) \, dz = \int_\Gamma \frac{A \, dz}{z - \alpha} = 2\pi A i.$$

It follows from (9.2.14) that the circulation $\mathscr{C}$ along C is equal to

$$\mathscr{R} \left[\int_C F'(z) \, dz \right] = 0,$$

and the flux $\mathscr{F}$ across C is equal to

$$\mathscr{I} \left[\int_C F'(z) \, dz \right] = 2\pi A.$$

We say that the point $z = \alpha$ is a source of strength $m = 2\pi A$. The *strength* m is the rate at which a fluid of unit density will flow across any closed contour containing α in its interior. When A is negative, the flow is inward, and we say that there is a sink at $z = \alpha$ of strength $m = -2\pi A$.

On the other hand, if C is any closed contour in D not containing the point $z = \alpha$ in its interior, then by Theorem 5.10.2

$$\int_C F'(z)\, dz = 0.$$

Thus the circulation and the flux across C are equal to zero, verifying directly that the flow is locally circulation and source free in D.

EXAMPLE 9.4.4. $F(z) = -iB \log(z - \alpha)$, where B is a real and positive number. As in Example 9.4.3, $F(z)$ is the complex potential of a flow in a domain D consisting of all points $z \neq \alpha$. Setting $z - \alpha = re^{i\theta}$, we have (up to a multiple of $2\pi B$)

$$F(z) = B\theta - iB \operatorname{Log} r.$$

Thus the family of concentric circles with center at α constitute the streamlines, while the family of radial lines orthogonal to the streamlines form the equipotential lines.

Also

$$q = q_1 + iq_2 = \overline{F'(z)} = \frac{iB}{z - \alpha} = \frac{iB}{r} e^{i\theta} = \frac{B}{r}(-\sin\theta + i\cos\theta),$$

so that

$$q_1 = -\frac{B}{r}\sin\theta, \qquad q_2 = \frac{B}{r}\cos\theta \quad \text{and} \quad |q| = \frac{B}{r}.$$

Thus the velocity vector q at each point z is directed along the tangent to the circle $|z - \alpha| = r$ in a counterclockwise direction, and the speed at each point is equal to B/r, where r is the distance from the center $z = \alpha$ to the given point. (See Fig. 9.4.6.)

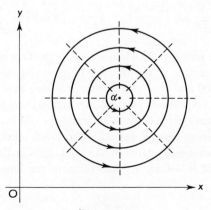

FIG. 9.4.6

If C is any closed contour in D containing the point $z = \alpha$ in its interior, then proceeding as in Example 9.4.3, we find that

$$\int_C F'(z)\, dz = 2\pi B.$$

Consequently, the flux $\mathscr{F}$ across C is equal to

$$\mathscr{I}[2\pi B] = 0,$$

while for the circulation $\mathscr{C}$ about C, we have

$$\mathscr{C} = \mathscr{R}[2\pi B] = 2\pi B.$$

The point $z = \alpha$ is called a vortex of strength $n = 2\pi B$. When B is negative, the circulation about any closed contour C in D containing α in its interior will be in a clockwise direction.

As in Example 9.4.3, if C is any closed contour in D not containing the point $z = \alpha$ in its interior, then

$$\int_C F'(z)\, dz = 0,$$

and thus we verify directly that the flow is locally circulation and source free in D.

Conversely, for flows of the type derived in Examples 9.4.3 and 9.4.4 with a source of strength $m = \mathscr{F}$ or a vortex of strength $n = \mathscr{C}$ at $z = \alpha$, the complex potentials must necessarily be of the type given in these examples. (See Exercises 9.4.1 and 9.4.2).

EXAMPLE 9.4.5.   Suppose that the complex potential of a flow is given by

$$F_\alpha(z) = \frac{m}{2\pi} \log\left(\frac{z - \alpha}{z}\right) = \frac{m}{2\pi} \log (z - \alpha) - \frac{m}{2\pi} \log z, \qquad (9.4.1)$$

where m is a positive number. By Theorem 9.3.1, the flow given by F_α is locally circulation and source free in the domain D consisting of the complex plane with the points $z = 0$ and $z = \alpha$ removed. It is easy to show that the points $z = 0$ and $z = \alpha$ are, respectively, a sink of strength m and a source of strength m.

Now, if the distance between the source and the sink is allowed to approach zero, the effects of the source and sink will cancel each other, unless we increase the intensity of the sink and source in the same ratio as the distance between them decreases. That is, let m vary according to the formula

$$m = \frac{\mu}{|\alpha|}, \qquad (9.4.2)$$

where $|\alpha|$ is the distance between the sink and the source and μ is a positive constant. Let

$$\alpha = |\alpha| e^{i\lambda}, \tag{9.4.3}$$

where λ is constant. We may express (9.4.1) as

$$F_\alpha(z) = -\frac{\mu}{2\pi} e^{i\lambda} \left[\frac{\log(z-\alpha) - \log(z)}{-\alpha} \right].$$

Denoting by $F(z)$ the limit of $F_\alpha(z)$ as $\alpha \to 0$, we get

$$F(z) = \lim_{\alpha \to 0} F_\alpha(z) = -\frac{\mu e^{i\lambda}}{2\pi} \cdot \frac{d}{dz}(\log z) = -\frac{\mu e^{i\lambda}}{2\pi} \cdot \frac{1}{z}. \tag{9.4.4}$$

We say that there is a *doublet* at the point $z = 0$. To this doublet there corresponds the vector $\mu e^{i\lambda}$. The length of this vector, μ, called the *strength* of the doublet, is equal to the constant product of the variable strength m by the variable distance $|\alpha|$ between the sink and the source. The unit vector $e^{i\lambda}$, called the *axis* (or *orientation*) of the doublet, gives the constant direction from the sink to the source as the latter moves towards coincidence with the former.

Let $z = re^{i\theta}$; then (9.4.4) may be written as

$$F(z) = -\frac{\mu}{2\pi r} e^{-i(\theta-\lambda)} = -\frac{\mu}{2\pi r} [\cos(\theta-\lambda) - i \sin(\theta-\lambda)], \tag{9.4.5}$$

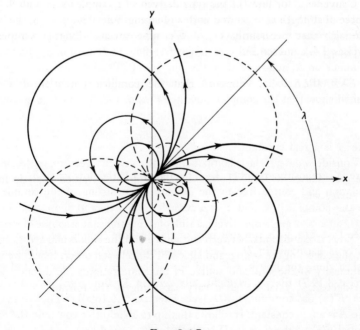

FIG. 9.4.7

so that

$$\phi = -\frac{\mu}{2\pi r}\cos(\theta - \lambda) \quad \text{and} \quad \psi = \frac{\mu}{2\pi r}\sin(\theta - \lambda).$$

We leave the following observations as an exercise for the reader. (See Exercise 9.4.3.) The streamlines $\psi = $ constant are circles passing through the origin and tangent to the axis of the doublet, while the equipotential lines $\phi = $ constant are circles passing through the origin and perpendicular to the axis of the doublet. (See Fig. 9.4.7.)

Also, we have

$$q = q_1 + iq_2 = \overline{F'(z)} = \frac{\mu e^{-i\lambda}}{2\pi} \cdot \frac{1}{\bar{z}^2}$$

$$= \frac{\mu}{2\pi r^2}e^{i(2\theta - \lambda)} = \frac{\mu}{2\pi r^2}[\cos(2\theta - \lambda) + i\sin(2\theta - \lambda)],$$

so that

$$q_1 = \frac{\mu}{2\pi r^2}\cos(2\theta - \lambda), \qquad q_2 = \frac{\mu}{2\pi r^2}\sin(2\theta - \lambda)$$

and the speed $|q|$ at any point is equal to $\mu/2\pi r^2$, where r is the distance from the doublet to the given point.

EXAMPLE 9.4.6. Let D denote the domain of all points $z = x + iy$, $y > 0$ and let R denote the region consisting of D and its boundary $y = 0$. Suppose that there is a source and circulation free flow $q = [q_1, q_2]$ defined on R such that the boundary $y = 0$ is a streamline. By this we mean that $q = [q_1, q_2]$ is a source and circulation free flow in D with $q_1(x, y)$ and $q_2(x, y)$ continuous on R, and $q_2 = 0$ on the line $y = 0$. Furthermore, we assume that as $z \to \infty$, the velocity vector q approaches parallelism with the line $y = 0$. We shall show that the complex potential $F(z)$ of the flow in D is given by

$$F(z) = Az, \tag{9.4.6}$$

where A is a real constant.

Consider $q_2(x, y)$, the y component of the velocity vector $q = [q_1, q_2]$ in R. Since (see Theorem 9.2.1) there exists in D a single-valued analytic function $F(z)$ such that

$$F'(z) = q_1 - iq_2,$$

we see that $q_2(x, y)$ is the real part of the analytic function $iF'(z)$, and consequently is harmonic in D. Also, by assumption, $q_2(x, y)$ is continuous in R, vanishes along the line $y = 0$, and approaches zero as $z \to \infty$. It follows (see Exercise 8.19.7) that q_2 is identically zero in R. But $F'(z)$ is analytic in D, hence $F'(z)$ is constant in D [see Exercise 3.6.16(a)]. Thus $F'(z) = A$, where A is a real constant. It follows that up to an additive constant, the complex potential $F(z)$ of the flow in D is given by $F(z) = Az$.

EXERCISES 9.4

1. Suppose that we have a flow in a domain D consisting of all $z \neq \alpha$ such that (a) the magnitude $|q|$ of the velocity vector at each point z depends only on the distance $r = |z - \alpha|$ of z from the point $z = \alpha$, (b) the velocity vector at each point z is directed radially away from $z = \alpha$, and (c) the flux $\mathscr{F}$ across every circle with center at $z = \alpha$ is equal to a constant m. Show that $m > 0$ and that the complex potential of the flow is given by

$$F(z) = \frac{m}{2\pi} \log (z - \alpha).$$

2. Suppose that we have a flow in a domain D consisting of all $z \neq \alpha$ such that (a) the magnitude $|q|$ of the velocity vector at each point z depends only on the distance $r = |z - \alpha|$ of z from the point $z = \alpha$, (b) the velocity vector at each point $z = \alpha + re^{i\theta}$ is directed counterclockwise tangentially to the circle $|z - \alpha| = r$, and (c) the circulation $\mathscr{C}$ around every circle with center at $z = \alpha$ is equal to a constant n. Show that $n > 0$ and that the complex potential of the flow is given by

$$F(z) = -\frac{in}{2\pi} \log (z - \alpha).$$

3. Show that the equation $(\mu/2\pi r) \sin (\theta - \lambda) = c$, where μ, λ and c are real constants, represents a circle passing through the origin with center on the line $y = -(\cot \lambda) x$. Hence, show that the circle is tangent to the line $y = (\tan \lambda) x$. Similarly, show that the equation $(\mu/2\pi r) \cos (\theta - \lambda) = c$ represents a circle passing through the origin and perpendicular to the line $y = (\tan \lambda) x$.

4. Let $F(z) = (A + iB) \log (z - \alpha)$, A and B real, $AB \neq 0$, be the complex potential of a flow in a domain D consisting of all points $z \neq \alpha$. Show that

(a) the flow is locally circulation and source free in D;

(b) for any closed contour Γ containing the point $z = \alpha$ in its interior, the circulation and flux across Γ are equal to $-2\pi B$ and $2\pi A$, respectively;

(c) the equipotential lines and the streamlines are given respectively by

$$r = c_1 e^{(B/A)\theta} \quad \text{and} \quad r = c_2 e^{-(A/B)\theta},$$

where c_1 and c_2 are arbitrary constants and $z - \alpha = re^{i\theta}$;

(d) the families of curves given in (c) are orthogonal to each other (sketch a few of these curves);

(e) the velocity vector q is given by

$$q = \frac{(A - iB) e^{i\theta}}{r}.$$

5. Let $F(z) = A(ze^{-i\lambda} + k^2/ze^{-i\lambda})$, $z \neq 0$, $A > 0$ and $k > 0$, be the complex potential of a flow.

(a) Show that if $z = ke^{i\theta}$, then the velocity vector at z is given by

$$q = 2A \sin (\lambda - \theta) \, e^{i(\theta + \pi/2)}.$$

(b) Using part (a), show that the velocity vector at any point on the circle $|z| = k$ is tangent to the circle, and that $q = 0$ when $z = \pm \, ke^{i\lambda}$.

(c) Show that the equipotential lines and streamlines are given respectively by

$$\left(r + \frac{k^2}{r}\right) \cos (\theta - \lambda) = c_1 \quad \text{and} \quad \left(r - \frac{k^2}{r}\right) \sin (\theta - \lambda) = c_2,$$

where $z = re^{i\theta}$, and c_1 and c_2 are arbitrary constants.

(d) Sketch a few equipotential lines and streamlines given in part (c). Note the orthogonality.

6. Suppose that we are given a complex potential

$$F_\alpha(z) = \frac{m}{2\pi} \log \frac{z - \alpha}{z - \beta},$$

where the points $z = \alpha$ and $z = \beta$ are respectively a source and sink of equal strength m. Let $\alpha = \beta + |\alpha - \beta| \, e^{i\lambda}$, where β and λ are fixed. Show that if $|\alpha - \beta| \to 0$ and $m = \mu/|\alpha - \beta|$, where μ is a constant, then $F_\alpha(z)$ approaches as a limit the complex potential

$$F(z) = - \frac{\mu e^{i\lambda}}{2\pi} \cdot \frac{1}{z - \beta}.$$

7. Show that the streamlines in Exercise 9.4.6 are circles passing through the point $z = \beta$ and tangent to the line $y - \beta_2 = (\tan \lambda) (x - \beta_1)$, where $\beta = \beta_1 + i\beta_2$ and λ real. Also show that the equipotential lines are circles passing through $z = \beta$ and perpendicular to the line $y - \beta_2 = (\tan \lambda)(x - \beta_1)$.

9.5. FLOW AROUND A CYLINDRICAL OBJECT. If we say there is a two-dimensional flow around a cylindrical object, we mean that both the object and the flow appear exactly the same in any section made by a member of a family of parallel planes. This two-dimensional section will then completely characterize the flow.

Suppose that a steady-state flow is given over the xy plane around a cylindrical object with generators perpendicular to the plane of flow. We may treat this problem as a flow in the region R consisting of a closed contour C (the boundary of the object), together with the domain D, of all points of the finite z plane exterior to C. (See Fig. 9.5.1.) By this we mean that a velocity vector $q = [q_1, q_2]$ is given at each point (x, y) of R such that $q_1(x, y)$ and $q_2(x, y)$ are continuous in R and continuously differentiable in D.

We shall make the following additional assumptions:*

(1) The closed contour C is a streamline.
(2) The integral $\int_\Gamma q_n \, ds = 0$ for every closed contour Γ lying in R.
(3) The circulation around every closed contour having its interior in D is zero.
(4) As $z \to \infty$, the velocity vector q approaches a finite limit.

$$(9.5.1)$$

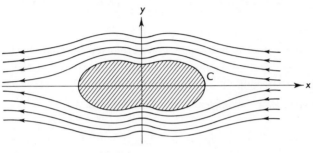

FIG. 9.5.1

Observe that conditions (2) and (3) imply respectively that the flow is source free and locally circulation free in D.† It may be shown (see Exercise 9.5.2), that the circulation around every closed contour Γ containing C in its interior is equal to a constant $\mathscr{C}$. In particular, if $\mathscr{C} = 0$, then the circulation around every closed contour Γ in D is zero. Consequently, the flow is entirely circulation and source free in D, and by Theorem 9.2.1 the flow has a complex potential $F(z) = \phi(z) + i\psi(z)$ which is single-valued and analytic in D. If $\mathscr{C} \neq 0$, then by Theorem 9.3.1, there exists a multiple-valued analytic function $F(z)$ in D with a single-valued derivative $F'(z) = q_1(z) - iq_2(z)$, where q_1 and q_2 are the components of the velocity vector q. In either case, the flow is by (2) entirely source free. Since the integral

$$\int_\Gamma q_n \, ds = 0$$

for every closed contour Γ in R, the integral

$$\psi(z) = \int_{z_0}^z q_n \, ds = \int_{z_0}^z - q_2 \, dx + q_1 \, dy \qquad (9.5.2)$$

is independent of the path in R. Furthermore, for z in D, we have

$$\psi(z) = \mathscr{I}[F(z)]. \qquad (9.5.3)$$

* From physical observation it is known that conditions (9.5.1) can be approximated by introducing a cylindrical obstacle into a fluid with uniform flow.
† The continuity of q_1 and q_2 and conditions (2) and (3) imply that q_1 and q_2 are harmonic, and hence continuously differentiable in D. (See Theorem 9.3.1.)

It follows that $\psi(z)$ is single-valued, continuous on R, and harmonic in D. Furthermore, for any two points z_1 and z_2 on C, we have

$$\psi(z_2) - \psi(z_1) = \int_{z_1}^{z_2} q_n \, ds,$$

where the path of integration may be taken along C. Since by assumption (1), C is a streamline, $q_n = 0$ on C, and consequently $\psi(z_2) = \psi(z_1)$ for any two points on C; that is, $\psi(z)$ is a constant along C. Thus we have established

——**THEOREM** 9.5.1.   Let a region R consist of a closed contour C together with the domain D of all points of the z plane exterior to C. If a flow q on R satisfies conditions (1) to (3) of (9.5.1), then the stream function $\psi(z)$ given in (9.5.3) is continuous on R, harmonic in D and constant on C.

We shall now establish the following important

——**THEOREM** 9.5.2.   Let a region R consist of a closed contour C and its exterior D. Then any flow q in R satisfying conditions (1) to (4) of (9.5.1) is uniquely determined by the value of

$$\lim_{z \to \infty} q(z) = Q_1 + iQ_2 \qquad (9.5.4)$$

and by the constant $\mathscr{C}$ of circulation around any closed contour containing C in its interior.

Proof.   Let $F(z)$ be the complex potential of a flow q in R with q satisfying conditions (9.5.1) and (9.5.4). Since $F'(z)$ is single-valued and analytic in the exterior of C, it is single-valued and analytic in a neighborhood of $z = \infty$, except possibly at $z = \infty$. Moreover, by (9.5.4) we have

$$\lim_{z \to \infty} F'(z) = \lim_{z \to \infty} \bar{q}(z) = Q_1 - iQ_2. \qquad (9.5.5)$$

If we define the value of $F'(z)$ at $z = \infty$ to be equal to this limit, then by Exercise 7.3.4, $F'(z)$ will also be analytic at $z = \infty$. Thus in some neighborhood of $z = \infty$, we have (see Exercise 7.3.1)

$$F'(z) = Q_1 - iQ_2 + \frac{a_1}{z} + \frac{a_2}{z^2} + \frac{a_3}{z^3} + \frac{a_4}{z^4} + \cdots. \qquad (9.5.6)$$

Furthermore, if Γ is a circle with center at the origin and of sufficiently large radius, the expansion given in (9.5.6) will converge uniformly on Γ, and consequently may be integrated over Γ term by term (see Exercise 7.3.2). We thus obtain

$$\int_\Gamma F'(z) \, dz = \int_\Gamma \left(Q_1 - iQ_2 + \frac{a_1}{z} + \frac{a_2}{z^2} + \frac{a_3}{z^3} + \frac{a_4}{z^4} + \cdots \right) dz$$

$$= \int_\Gamma (Q_1 - iQ_2) \, dz + \int_\Gamma \frac{a_1}{z} \, dz + \int_\Gamma \frac{a_2}{z^2} \, dz + \int_\Gamma \frac{a_3}{z^3} \, dz + \int_\Gamma \frac{a_4}{z^4} \, dz + \cdots.$$

But (see Example 5.2.2)

$$\int_\Gamma (Q_1 - iQ_2)\, dz = \int_\Gamma \frac{a_2}{z^2}\, dz = \int_\Gamma \frac{a_3}{z^3}\, dz = \int_\Gamma \frac{a_4}{z^4}\, dz = \cdots = 0$$

and

$$\int_\Gamma \frac{a_1}{z}\, dz = 2\pi i a_1.$$

Therefore

$$\int_\Gamma F'(z)\, dz = 2\pi i a_1.$$

From (9.2.13) we have

$$\int_\Gamma F'(z)\, dz = \mathscr{C} + i\mathscr{F},$$

where $\mathscr{C}$ is the circulation along Γ and $\mathscr{F}$ is the flux across Γ. By condition (2) of (9.5.1), $\mathscr{F} = 0$. Consequently, $2\pi i a_1 = \mathscr{C}$ and we may write (9.5.6) as

$$F'(z) = Q_1 - iQ_2 + \frac{\mathscr{C}}{2\pi i}\frac{1}{z} + \frac{a_2}{z^2} + \frac{a_3}{z^3} + \frac{a_4}{z^4} + \cdots, \qquad (9.5.7)$$

valid in a neighborhood of $z = \infty$.

To show that this flow is uniquely determined by $Q_1 + iQ_2$ and $\mathscr{C}$, it is sufficient to prove that under conditions (1) to (4) of (9.5.1), two complex potentials $F_1(z)$ and $F_2(z)$, whose derivatives may be expressed as in (9.5.7), determine identical flows. To this end, suppose that in a neighborhood N_∞ of $z = \infty$ we have

$$F_1'(z) = Q_1 - iQ_2 + \frac{\mathscr{C}}{2\pi i}\frac{1}{z} + \frac{a_2}{z^2} + \frac{a_3}{z^3} + \frac{a_4}{z^4} + \cdots$$

and

$$F_2'(z) = Q_1 - iQ_2 + \frac{\mathscr{C}}{2\pi i}\frac{1}{z} + \frac{b_2}{z^2} + \frac{b_3}{z^3} + \frac{b_4}{z^4} + \cdots.$$

Hence, for z in N_∞,

$$F_1'(z) - F_2'(z) = \frac{c_2}{z^2} + \frac{c_3}{z^3} + \frac{c_4}{z^4} + \cdots, \qquad (9.5.8)$$

where

$$c_j = a_j - b_j, \qquad j = 2, 3, \cdots.$$

Let

$$G(z) = -\frac{c_2}{z} - \frac{c_3}{2z^2} - \frac{c_4}{3z^3} - \cdots, \qquad z \text{ in } N_\infty. \qquad (9.5.9)$$

Then, in view of (9.5.8), we have

$$G'(z) = F_1'(z) - F_2'(z).$$

It follows (see Exercise 9.5.3) that for z in N_∞ we have $\mathscr{I}[G(z)] = \psi_1(z) - \psi_2(z)$ where ψ_1 and ψ_2 are the stream functions of the flows determined by $F_1(z)$ and $F_2(z)$. Since $G(z)$ is analytic at $z = \infty$ it follows that $\psi_1(z) - \psi_2(z)$ is harmonic at $z = \infty$. Let now R_∞ and D_∞ denote respectively the region and domain obtained by adjoining the point $z = \infty$ to the region R and domain D. Thus $\psi_1(z) - \psi_2(z)$ is single-valued, harmonic in D_∞, continuous on R_∞, and constant on C. It follows from Theorem 8.19.5 that $\psi_1(z) - \psi_2(z)$ is constant in D_∞.

Thus

$$\mathscr{I}\left[F_1'(z) - F_2'(z)\right] = \psi_1'(z) - \psi_2'(z) = 0$$

for z in D. Hence [see Exercise 3.6.16(a)], $F_1'(z) - F_2'(z) = c$, where c is a constant. In view of (9.5.8), we then have

$$c = \lim_{z \to \infty} [F_1'(z) - F_2'(z)] = 0.$$

Thus, $F_1'(z) = F_2'(z)$, and the flows determined by the complex potentials $F_1(z)$ and $F_2(z)$ are identical. The theorem is now established.

EXAMPLE 9.5.1. We shall now determine the complex potential of a flow satisfying conditions (1) to (4) of (9.5.1) for the case when the circulation $\mathscr{C}$ is equal to zero and C is a circle of radius $k > 0$ with center at the origin.

Since the flow is, by assumption, entirely circulation and source free, the complex potential $F(z) = \phi(z) + i\psi(z)$ is by Theorem 9.2.1 single-valued in the domain D consisting of the exterior of the circle C. Since the velocity q is continuous in the region R consisting of the domain D and its boundary C,

$$F(z) = \int_{z_0}^{z} q_t \, ds + i \int_{z_0}^{z} q_n \, ds$$

is also continuous on R. Hence

$$w = F(z) \qquad (w = u + iv) \tag{9.5.10}$$

may be regarded as defining a mapping of R into the w plane which is continuous on R and analytic in D. Furthermore, since C is a streamline, the stream function $\psi(z) = \mathscr{I}[F(z)]$ is constant on C. Consequently, the image of C under the mapping given in (9.5.10) lies on a line parallel to the u axis. Therefore, in seeking a complex potential $F(z)$, we search for a mapping of R into the w plane such that the image of C lies on a line parallel to the u axis and such that

$$\lim_{z \to \infty} q(z) = \lim_{z \to \infty} \overline{F'(z)} = Q_1 + iQ_2.$$

We shall first consider the case when $\lim_{z \to \infty} q(z) = \lim_{z \to \infty} \overline{F'(z)} = 1$. A desired mapping is then given by (8.13.1), namely,

$$w = F(z) = z + \frac{k^2}{z}, \qquad k > 0. \tag{9.5.11}$$

For

$$\lim_{z \to \infty} q(z) = \lim_{z \to \infty} \overline{F'(z)} = \lim_{z \to \infty} \left(1 - \frac{k^2}{\bar{z}^2} \right) = 1.$$

Furthermore, since $F(z)$ maps the circle $C: |z| = k$ onto the segment $- 2k \leq u \leq 2k$ of the real axis (see Remark 8.13.1), $\mathscr{I}[F(z)]$ is constant on C and thus C is a streamline. And finally, since the complex potential $F(z)$ is single-valued, the circulation $\mathscr{C}$ is equal to zero.

In case $\lim_{z \to \infty} q(z) = Q$, where Q is any real number, then obviously a complex potential of the flow will be given by

$$w = F(z) = Q \left(z + \frac{k^2}{z} \right), \qquad k > 0. \tag{9.5.12}$$

However, if Q is complex, say $Q = Ae^{i\lambda}$, $A > 0$, then the mapping given in (9.5.12) will take the circle $C: |z| = k$ into a segment making an angle λ with the positive u axis. We therefore consider the mapping

$$w = F(z) = A \left(ze^{-i\lambda} + \frac{k^2}{ze^{-i\lambda}} \right), \tag{9.5.13}$$

which is obtained by performing successively the mappings

$$\zeta = ze^{-i\lambda}$$

which transforms the circle C into itself, followed by the mapping

$$w = A \left(\zeta + \frac{k^2}{\zeta} \right)$$

which transforms the circle C into the segment $- 2Ak \leq u \leq 2Ak$ of the real axis. Consequently, $F(z)$ as given in (9.5.13) is a desired complex potential. For

(a) $q(z) = \overline{F'(z)}$ is continuous on R,

(b) $\lim_{z \to \infty} q(z) = \lim_{z \to \infty} \overline{F'(z)} = \lim_{z \to \infty} A \left(e^{i\lambda} - \frac{k^2}{\bar{z}^2 e^{i\lambda}} \right) = Ae^{i\lambda} = Q$,

(c) since the complex potential $F(z)$ is single-valued, the circulation $\mathscr{C}$ is equal to zero,

and

(d) since $F(z)$ maps the circle C into a segment of the real axis, $\mathscr{I}[F(z)]$ is constant on C and therefore C is a streamline.

By Theorem 9.5.2, the complex potential $F(z)$ is uniquely determined whenever the circulation $\mathscr{C}$ and $\lim_{z \to \infty} q(z)$ are given. Therefore, the function $F(z)$ given in (9.5.13) is the complex potential of the given flow.

EXAMPLE 9.5.2. We shall now determine the complex potential of a flow satisfying conditions (1) to (4) of (9.5.1) for the case in which C is the circle $|z| = k > 0$, the circulation is equal to a nonzero constant $\mathscr{C}$, and

$$\lim_{z \to \infty} q(z) = Q = Ae^{i\lambda}, \qquad A > 0.$$

It is easy to show (see Exercises 9.5.4 and 9.5.5) that if a contour C is a streamline of two flows which are determined respectively by the complex potentials $F_1(z)$ and $F_2(z)$, and if $F(z)$ is a complex potential such that $F'(z) = F_1'(z) + F_2'(z)$, then C is also a streamline of the flow determined by $F(z)$. Also, if $\mathscr{C}_1$ and $\mathscr{C}_2$ are the circulations around a closed contour C determined respectively by the flows with complex potentials $F_1(z)$ and $F_2(z)$, then the circulation around C determined by a complex potential $F(z)$ such that $F'(z) = F_1'(z) + F_2'(z)$ is equal to $\mathscr{C}_1 + \mathscr{C}_2$.

Now, let $F_1(z)$ and $F_2(z)$ denote respectively the complex potentials of the flows given in Examples 9.5.1 and 9.4.4, where in Example 9.4.4 we take $\alpha = 0$ and $B = \mathscr{C}/2\pi$, that is, let

$$F_1(z) = A\left(ze^{-i\lambda} + \frac{k^2}{ze^{-i\lambda}}\right) \quad \text{and} \quad F_2(z) = -\frac{i\mathscr{C}}{2\pi}\log z.$$

Since both of these flows have the circle $C: |z| = k$ as a streamline,

$$F(z) = A\left(ze^{-i\lambda} + \frac{k^2}{ze^{-i\lambda}}\right) - \frac{i\mathscr{C}}{2\pi}\log z \qquad (9.5.14)$$

will also have C as a streamline. Moreover, since the circulations of $F_1(z)$ and $F_2(z)$ are respectively equal to zero and $\mathscr{C}$, the circulation of $F(z)$ will also be equal to $\mathscr{C}$. We have furthermore

$$\lim_{z \to \infty} q(z) = \lim_{z \to \infty} \overline{F'(z)} = Ae^{i\lambda}.$$

By Theorem 9.5.2, the function $F(z)$ given in (9.5.14) is the unique complex potential satisfying the given conditions.

The equipotential lines and the streamlines of the flow in (9.5.14) are given respectively by

$$\left(r + \frac{k^2}{r}\right)\cos(\theta - \lambda) + \frac{\mathscr{C}\theta}{2\pi A} = c_1$$

and

$$\left(r - \frac{k^2}{r}\right)\sin(\theta - \lambda) - \frac{\mathscr{C}}{2\pi A}\log r = c_2,$$

$$(9.5.15)$$

where $z = re^{i\theta}$, and c_1 and c_2 are arbitrary constants. For later use, we shall determine the *stagnation points*, that is, the points at which the velocity $q = \overline{F'(z)}$ is equal to zero. These are obtained by solving the equation $F'(z) = 0$. We shall concern ourselves only with stagnation points that lie on the circle $\mid z \mid = k$. From (9.5.14), we obtain

$$F'(z) = A \left(e^{-i\lambda} - \frac{k^2}{z^2 e^{-i\lambda}} \right) - i \frac{\mathscr{C}}{2\pi} \frac{1}{z}. \qquad (9.5.16)$$

Putting $z = ke^{i\sigma}$ in (9.5.16), and setting the resulting expression equal to zero, we get after simplification

$$\left[e^{i(\sigma - \lambda)} - \frac{1}{e^{i(\sigma - \lambda)}} \right] = \frac{i\mathscr{C}}{2\pi A k}. \qquad (9.5.17)$$

Utilizing (4.2.2), (9.5.17) becomes

$$\mathscr{C} = 4\pi A k \sin (\sigma - \lambda). \qquad (9.5.18)$$

Observe that if $Q = Ae^{i\lambda}$ and a stagnation point on the circle $\mid z \mid = k$ are given, then the circulation $\mathscr{C}$ is uniquely determined. Conversely, if $\mid \mathscr{C}/4\pi A k \mid \leq 1$, then $\mathscr{C}$ determine two stagnation points on the circle $\mid z \mid = k$, which coincide when $\mid \mathscr{C}/4\pi A k \mid = 1$.

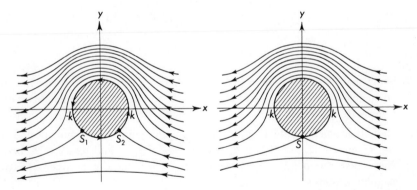

FIG. 9.5.2. $0 < \mathscr{C}/4\pi A < k$; stagnation points S_1 and S_2 are on the cylinder.

FIG. 9.5.3. $\mathscr{C}/4\pi A = k$; stagnation points S_1, $S_2(= S)$ coincide on the cylinder.

Figures 9.5.2 and 9.5.3 show the appearance of the streamlines for $0 < \mathscr{C}/4\pi A < k$ and $\mathscr{C}/4\pi A = k$ for the case when $Q = Ae^{i\pi}$, $A > 0$.

EXERCISES 9.5

1. Suppose that the velocity vector $q = [q_1, q_2]$ defines a flow in a domain D consisting of the exterior of a closed contour C such that the circulation around every closed contour having its interior in D is zero. Let Γ_1 and Γ_2

be two closed contours both containing C in their interiors, and such that Γ_1 is contained in the interior of Γ_2. Show that the circulation around Γ_1 and Γ_2 are equal.

2. With the notation of Exercise 9.5.1, let Γ_1 and Γ_2 be two closed contours containing C in their interiors, where Γ_1 is not necessarily contained in the interior of Γ_2. Prove that the circulation around Γ_1 and Γ_2 are equal.

3. Let $G(z)$, $F_1(z)$ and $F_2(z)$ be complex potentials and let $\psi(z)$, $\psi_1(z)$ and $\psi_2(z)$, where $\psi_1(z)$ and $\psi_2(z)$ are single-valued, be their respective stream functions. Suppose that $G'(z) = F_1'(z) - F_2'(z)$. Show that $\psi(z) = \psi_1(z) - \psi_2(z)$.

4. (a) Let $F_1(z)$ and $F_2(z)$ be complex potentials with single-valued stream functions, and let C be a streamline for the flows determined by $F_1(z)$ and $F_2(z)$. Suppose furthermore that $F(z)$ is a complex potential such that $F'(z) = F_1'(z) + F_2'(z)$. Show that C is a streamline of the flow determined by $F(z)$.

(b) Prove part (a) above without assuming the stream functions to be single-valued.

5. Show that if $\mathscr{C}_1$ and $\mathscr{C}_2$ are the circulations around a closed contour C determined respectively by the flows with complex potentials $F_1(z)$ and $F_2(z)$, then the circulation around C determined by a complex potential $F(z)$ such that $F'(z) = F_1'(z) + F_2'(z)$ is equal to $\mathscr{C}_1 + \mathscr{C}_2$.

6. Show that the stagnation points of the flow in (9.5.14) are given by

$$z = e^{i\lambda}[ti \pm \sqrt{k^2 - t^2}], \quad \text{where} \quad t = \frac{\mathscr{C}}{4\pi A}.$$

7. Show that if for the flow in (9.5.14) we have $|\,\mathscr{C}/4\pi A\,| > k$, then there are no stagnation points on the circle $|\,z\,| = k$, and exactly one stagnation point exterior to the circle $|\,z\,| = k$.

8. Show that when $|\,\mathscr{C}/4\pi A\,| \le k$, the stagnation points of the flow in (9.5.14) are given by $z = ke^{i(\pi/2 + \lambda \pm \theta)}$, where $0 \le \theta \le \pi$ and $\cos\theta = \mathscr{C}/4\pi Ak$. Show that the point $z = (\mathscr{C}/4\pi A)e^{i(\pi/2 + \lambda)}$ lies midway between the two stagnation points.

9. Suppose that $H(z)$ is an analytic function (not necessarily single-valued) in a domain D such that for some branch $h(z)$ of $H(z)$, with domain of definition D_h contained in D, we have $h'(z) = q_1(z) - iq_2(z)$ for all z in D_h, where $q = [q_1, q_2]$ defines a circulation and source-free flow in D. Show that $H(z)$ is also single-valued in D.

9.6. FLOW AROUND AN OBSTACLE (CONTINUED). Let R be the region consisting of a closed contour C (the boundary of an obstacle) together with the domain D, of all points of the finite z plane exterior to C. (See Fig. 9.5.1.) It is not difficult to show (see Exercise 9.6.1) that for a flow in a region R, conditions (1) to (4) of (9.5.1) are equivalent to the following:

(1) There exists a complex potential $F(z)$ analytic (and possibly multiple-valued) on the domain D, with a single-valued derivative $F'(z)$ such that $F'(z)$ may be extended by continuity* to all of R. We shall denote the extended function also by $F'(z)$.

(2) For any closed contour Γ in R, we have

$$\int_\Gamma F'(z)\,dz = \begin{cases} 0, & \text{if the interior of } \Gamma \text{ is in } D, \\ \mathscr{C}, & \text{if the interior of } \Gamma \text{ is not in } D, \mathscr{C} \text{ real.} \end{cases}$$

(3) The stream function $\mathscr{I}[\int_{z_0}^z F'(z)\,dz]$ is constant on C.

(4) $\lim_{z\to\infty} F'(z)$ exists.

$$\left. \right\} \quad (9.6.1)$$

Let D_z and D_w denote respectively the exteriors of the closed contours C_z and C_w in the z and w planes. Also, let R_z and R_w denote the regions consisting of C_z and D_z, and C_w and D_w, respectively. Suppose that we are given a complex potential $F(z)$ on R_z having C_z as a streamline which satisfies conditions (1) to (4) of (9.6.1). We shall indicate a method for determining a complex potential $H(w)$ on R_w which also satisfies conditions (1) to (4) of (9.6.1).

Suppose that $z = g(w)$ is continuous on R_w, analytic in D_w and

$$\lim_{w\to\infty} g(w) = \infty, \qquad \lim_{w\to\infty} g'(w) = \bar{P} \qquad (9.6.2)$$

where $P \neq 0$ is a complex number. Suppose also that $z = g(w)$ defines a one-to-one mapping of D_w onto D_z and of C_w onto C_z. Then the function

$$H(w) = F[(g(w)]$$

on R_w induced by the mapping $z = g(w)$ is analytic (and possibly multiple-valued) in D_w. (See Section 8.18.)

Using the functions defined above, we shall establish the following

——THEOREM 9.6.1.   If the mapping $z = g(w)$ is such that

$$H'(w) = F'[g(w)]\,g'(w) \qquad (9.6.3)$$

can be extended so that it is continuous on all of R_w, then $H(w)$ will also satisfy conditions (1) to (4) of (9.6.1), with the same value of the circulation $\mathscr{C}$.

Proof. By hypothesis $H(w)$ satisfies condition (1). To show that condition (2) is satisfied, let Γ_w be a closed contour in R_w and let Γ_z be

* By this we mean that (a) $\lim_{\zeta\to z} F'(\zeta)$ exists for each point z on C, and (b) the function

$$f(z) = \begin{cases} F'(z), & z \text{ in } D \\ \lim_{\zeta\to z} F'(\zeta), & z \text{ on } C \end{cases}$$

is continuous on R.

its image in R_z under the mapping $z = g(w)$. Then it is not difficult to show (see Exercise 9.6.2) that

$$\int_{\Gamma_w} H'(w) \, dw = \int_{\Gamma_z} F'(z) \, dz. \tag{9.6.4}$$

If the interior of Γ_w is in D_w, then from Theorem 8.2.4, it follows that the interior of Γ_z will be in D_z, and hence

$$\int_{\Gamma_w} H'(w) \, dw = 0.$$

If, however, the interior of Γ_w is not in D_w, then the interior of Γ_z cannot be contained in D_z, and consequently

$$\int_{\Gamma_w} H'(w) \, dw = \int_{\Gamma_z} F'(z) \, dz = \mathscr{C}.$$

That condition (3) is satisfied is seen immediately from the relation $\mathscr{I}[H(w)] = \mathscr{I}\{F[g(w)]\}$. If w_1 and w_2 are any two points on C_w, then $z_i = g(w_i)$, $i = 1, 2$, are on C_z; and since $\mathscr{I}[F(z_1)] = \mathscr{I}[F(z_2)]$, it follows that

$$\mathscr{I}[H(w_1)] = \mathscr{I}[H(w_2)].$$

That condition (4) is also satisfied follows from (9.6.2), since

$$\lim_{w \to \infty} H'(w) = \lim_{w \to \infty} F'[g(w)] \cdot \lim_{w \to \infty} g'(w) = \lim_{z \to \infty} F'(z) \cdot \lim_{w \to \infty} g'(w).$$

EXAMPLE 9.6.1.   We shall now determine the complex potential $H(w)$ of a flow in the w plane satisfying conditions (1) to (4) of (9.6.1) for the case when C_w is the circle $|w - w_0| = k$ with center at w_0 and radius $k > 0$. Further, we shall require that

$$\lim_{w \to \infty} \overline{H'(w)} = Ae^{i\lambda}, \tag{9.6.5}$$

where $A > 0$.

By Example 9.5.2, the flow q around the circle $|z| = k$ with circulation $\mathscr{C}$ and $\lim_{z \to \infty} q(z) = Ae^{i\lambda}$ is given by

$$F(z) = A\left(ze^{-i\lambda} + \frac{k^2}{ze^{-i\lambda}}\right) - \frac{i\mathscr{C}}{2\pi} \log z. \tag{9.6.6}$$

The mapping $z = g(w) = w - w_0$ transforms the circle C_w and its exterior onto the circle $|z| = k$ and its exterior. We now form the function

$$H(w) = F[g(w)] = A\left[(w - w_0)e^{-i\lambda} + \frac{k^2}{(w - w_0)e^{-i\lambda}}\right] - \frac{i\mathscr{C}}{2\pi} \log(w - w_0). \tag{9.6.7}$$

Clearly, $H'(w) = F'[g(w)]\,g'(w)$ is defined and continuous in the region R_w consisting of the circle C_w and its exterior. It follows from Theorem 9.6.1, that $H(w)$ satisfies conditions (1) to (4) of (9.6.1), and that the circulation around C_w will also be equal to $\mathscr{C}$. Moreover,

$$\lim_{w \to \infty} \overline{H'(w)} = \lim_{z \to \infty} \overline{F'(z)} \cdot \lim_{w \to \infty} \overline{g'(w)} = A e^{i\lambda} \cdot 1 = A e^{i\lambda}.$$

By Theorem 9.5.2, the complex potential $H(w)$ is unique.

For later use, we shall restate the above result, in somewhat different notation, in the following

——**THEOREM** 9.6.2. Given any circle Γ: $|z - z_0| = \rho$. The complex potential $F(z)$ of the flow around Γ satisfying conditions (1) to (4) of (9.5.1) with circulation $\mathscr{C}$ and

$$\lim_{z \to \infty} \overline{F'(z)} = Q = A e^{i\lambda},\ A > 0,$$

is given by

$$F(z) = A\left[(z - z_0)\,e^{-i\lambda} + \frac{\rho^2}{(z - z_0)\,e^{-i\lambda}}\right] - \frac{i\mathscr{C}}{2\pi}\log(z - z_0). \quad (9.6.8)$$

It is easily shown (see Exercise 9.6.3) that if $z = z_0 + \rho e^{i\sigma}$ is a stagnation point on the circle Γ, then the circulation $\mathscr{C}$ is given by

$$\mathscr{C} = 4\pi A\rho \sin(\sigma - \lambda). \quad (9.6.9)$$

EXAMPLE 9.6.2. *Flow Around the Joukowski Airfoil.* Let Γ denote a circle with center at z_0, passing through the point $z = -k$ and containing the point $z = k$, $k > 0$, in its interior. Let Γ' denote the image of Γ under the transformation

$$w = z + \frac{k^2}{z}, \quad (9.6.10)$$

(See Figs. 8.15.1 and 8.15.2). Let D_z and D_w denote the domains exterior to Γ and Γ' respectively. Also, let R_z and R_w denote the regions consisting of Γ and D_z, and Γ' and D_w, respectively.

Suppose we have a flow in R_w satisfying conditions (1) to (4) of (9.6.1), with Γ' as a streamline and the velocity at infinity equal to $A e^{i\lambda}$. Let $H(w)$ be the corresponding complex potential in D_w. As we have seen in Section 8.15, the transformation (9.6.10) maps D_z and Γ one-to-one onto D_w and Γ' respectively. It consequently induces in D_z the complex potential $F(z) = H(z + k^2/z)$, and we have

$$F'(z) = H'\left(z + \frac{k^2}{z}\right) \cdot \left(1 - \frac{k^2}{z^2}\right). \quad (9.6.11)$$

It is easy to show that since $H'(w)$ can be extended by continuity to all of R_w, $F'(z)$ can also be extended by continuity to all of R_z. The other prerequisites of Theorem 9.6.1 are also fulfilled, and thus $F(z)$ determines a flow in R_z satisfying conditions (9.6.1) with the circle Γ as a streamline and the circulation $\mathscr{C}$ equal to that of the original flow in R_w. By Theorem 9.5.2 this flow in R_z is unique, and its complex potential is therefore given by (9.6.8). Putting $z = -k$ in (9.6.11) we find $F'(-k) = 0$. Thus $z = -k$ is a stagnation point of the induced flow, and it follows (see Exercise 9.6.4) that

$$\mathscr{C} = 4\pi A \, | \, k + z_0 \, | \, \sin \, [\lambda - \arg \, (k + z_0)]. \tag{9.6.12}$$

Taking into account Theorem 9.5.2, we have the following result:

A flow around a Joukowski airfoil satisfying conditions (9.5.1) is uniquely determined by the velocity $Q = Ae^{i\lambda}$ at infinity. The value of the circulation is given in (9.6.12), where z_0 is the center of the circle Γ which is the antecedent of the Joukowski airfoil under the mapping (9.6.10).

So far we have not yet shown that a flow around the Joukowski airfoil satisfying conditions (9.5.1) actually exists. This we now proceed to do.

Consider the flow on R_z with complex potential (9.6.8) and a stagnation point at $z = -k$. The circulation is consequently given by (9.6.12). Consider the mapping $z = g(w)$, inverse to the transformation (9.6.10), mapping D_w and Γ' one-to-one onto D_z and Γ, respectively. It is not difficult to show (see Exercise 9.6.7) that $z = g(w)$ is continuous and, except for $w = -2k$, analytic on R_w. It is also easy to show (see Exercise 9.6.8) that

$$\lim_{w \to \infty} z = \lim_{w \to \infty} g(w) = \infty. \tag{9.6.13}$$

Furthermore, we have

$$g'(w) = \frac{dz}{dw} = \left(\frac{dw}{dz} \right)^{-1} = \frac{z^2}{z^2 - k^2}. \tag{9.6.14}$$

From (9.6.13) and (9.6.14) we obtain

$$\lim_{w \to \infty} g'(w) = \lim_{z \to \infty} \frac{z^2}{z^2 - k^2} = 1. \tag{9.6.15}$$

Consider now the complex potential

$$H(w) = F[g(w)] = A \left\{ [g(w) - z_0] \, e^{-i\lambda} + \frac{\rho^2}{[g(w) - z_0] \, e^{-i\lambda}} \right\}$$

$$- \frac{i\mathscr{C}}{2\pi} \log \, [g(w) - z_0] \tag{9.6.16}$$

induced in D_w by the complex potential (9.6.8). (Observe that $\rho = | \, z_0 + k \, |$.) In order that $H(w)$ define a flow, it is necessary that $H'(w) = F'[g(w)] \, g'(w)$ can be extended by continuity to all of R_w. Let w_0 be any point in R_w. If

$w_0 \neq -2k$, then $g(w)$ is analytic at w_0; and since $F'(z)$ is analytic everywhere on R_z it follows that $H'(w)$ is defined and continuous at w_0. There remains for consideration the point $w_0 = -2k$ at which $g'(w)$ is not defined.

We now recall that, by assumption, $z = -k$ is a stagnation point of the flow in R_z, and hence $F'(-k) = 0$. By Remark (7.1.1) we have $F'(z) = (z+k)f(z)$, where $f(z)$ is analytic in a neighborhood of $z = -k$. From the continuity of $z = g(w)$ on R_w, it follows that $z \to -k$ as $w \to -2k$. Hence by (9.6.14) we have

$$\lim_{w \to -2k} H'(w) = \lim_{z \to -k} \left[F'(z) \frac{z^2}{z^2 - k^2} \right] = \lim_{z \to -k} \left[(z+k) f(z) \frac{z^2}{z^2 - k^2} \right]$$

$$= -\frac{k}{2} f(-k)$$

is finite. Thus $H'(w)$ can be extended by continuity to all of R_w. This, with (9.6.13) and (9.6.15), fulfills the requirements of Theorem 9.6.1, and hence there exists a flow around the Joukowski profile, satisfying conditions (9.5.1), whose velocity at infinity is given by $Q = Ae^{i\lambda}$, and whose complex potential

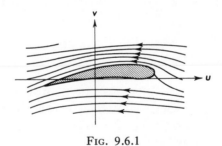

FIG. 9.6.1

Flow around the Joukowski Airfoil.

is given in (9.6.16). Fig. 9.6.1 shows the appearance of the streamlines for the case $\lambda = \pi$ and $\mathscr{C} > 0$.

EXERCISES 9.6

1. Let R be the region consisting of a closed contour C and its exterior D. (a) Show that if $q = [q_1, q_2]$ defines a flow in R satisfying conditions (1) to (4) of (9.5.1), then there exists a complex potential $F(z)$ satisfying conditions (1) to (4) of (9.6.1) such that $F'(z) = q_1 - iq_2$ in D. (b) Conversely, show that if $F(z)$ is a function satisfying conditions (1) to (4) of (9.6.1), then there exists a flow in R given by $q = [q_1, q_2]$ satisfying conditions (1) to (4) of (9.5.1) such that $F'(z) = q_1 - iq_2$ in D.

2. Verify (9.6.4).

3. Show that if in the flow given in (9.6.8), a point $z = z_0 + \rho e^{i\sigma}$ on the circle $\Gamma: |z - z_0| = \rho$ is a stagnation point, then the circulation $\mathscr{C}$ is given by

$$\mathscr{C} = 4\pi A\rho \sin(\sigma - \lambda).$$

4. Show that if in the flow given in (9.6.8), the point $z = -k, \; k > 0$ is a stagnation point on the circle $\Gamma: |z - z_0| = \rho$, then the circulation $\mathscr{C}$ is given by

$$\mathscr{C} = 4\pi A \, |k + z_0| \sin[\lambda - \arg(k + z_0)].$$

5. Suppose that $F(z)$ is the complex potential of a circulation and source free flow in a domain D_z in the z plane. Suppose further that $z = g(w)$ defines a one-to-one analytic mapping of a domain D_w in the w plane onto D_z. Let $H(w) = F[g(w)]$ be the induced complex potential in D_w. Show that if Γ_w is a streamline in D_w, then the image Γ_z of Γ_w under the mapping $z = g(w)$ is a streamline in D_z. Also show that every streamline Γ_z in D_z is the image under the mapping $z = g(w)$ of a streamline Γ_w in D_w.

6. Prove Exercise 9.6.5 for the case when the flow in D_z is merely locally circulation and source free.

7. Show that the function $z = g(w)$ in Example 9.6.2 is continuous and, except for the point $w = -2k$, analytic in R_w.

8. Show that the function $z = g(w)$ in Example 9.6.2 satisfies the condition $\lim_{w \to \infty} g(w) = \infty$.

9.7. THE EULER AND BERNOULLI EQUATIONS IN HYDRO-DYNAMICS.

Let a two-dimensional steady-state flow be defined in a domain D by the velocity vector $q = [q_1, q_2]$, where $q_1 = q_1(x, y)$ and $q_2 = q_2(x, y)$ are real-valued and continuously differentiable in D. We shall assume that the fluid is incompressible and frictionless, and that the pressure $p(x, y)$ is also continuously differentiable in D.

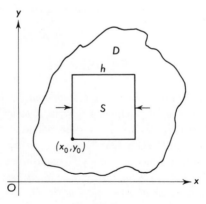

FIG. 9.7.1

Suppose that (x_0, y_0) is any point in D. Let S be a square lying in D with sides, of length h, parallel to the x and y axes, and such that the coordinates of its lower left-hand corner are (x_0, y_0). (See Fig. 9.7.1.) We consider horizontal (or vertical) forces acting to the right (or upward) as positive, and those acting to the left (or downward) as negative. Also we suppose that no external forces act on S perpendicular to the xy plane. Then the net horizontal force acting on the square is given by

$$F_x = \int_{y_0}^{y_0+h} p(x_0, y)\, dy - \int_{y_0}^{y_0+h} p(x_0 + h, y)\, dy$$

$$= -\int_{y_0}^{y_0+h} [p(x_0 + h, y) - p(x_0, y)]\, dy,$$

and by the mean value theorem, we obtain

$$F_x = -h \int_{y_0}^{y_0+h} \frac{\partial p(x_0 + \theta h, y)}{\partial x}\, dy, \qquad 0 < \theta < 1.$$

This expression may also be written as

$$F_x = -h \int_{y_0}^{y_0+h} \frac{\partial p(x_0, y_0)}{\partial x}\, dy - h \int_{y_0}^{y_0+h} \lambda\, dy, \tag{9.7.1}$$

where

$$\lambda = \frac{\partial p(x_0 + \theta h, y)}{\partial x} - \frac{\partial p(x_0, y_0)}{\partial x}.$$

Integrating the first term on the right-hand side of (9.7.1), we get

$$F_x = -h^2 \frac{\partial p(x_0, y_0)}{\partial x} - h \int_{y_0}^{y_0+h} \lambda\, dy. \tag{9.7.2}$$

Let δ denote the density of the fluid. Then the mass of the fluid in the square is equal to δh^2. According to Newton's second law of motion, it follows that the total horizontal force acting on the square is also given by

$$F_x = \delta h^2 \left[\frac{d^2x}{dt^2} \Big|_{(x_0, y_0)} + \mu \right], \tag{9.7.3}$$

where [see (9.7.7)] $\mu \to 0$ as $h \to 0$. Equating (9.7.2) and (9.7.3) and then dividing by h^2, we get

$$\delta \frac{d^2x}{dt^2} \Big|_{(x_0, y_0)} + \delta\mu = -\frac{\partial p}{\partial x} \Big|_{(x_0, y_0)} - \frac{1}{h} \int_{y_0}^{y_0+h} \lambda\, dy. \tag{9.7.4}$$

Now

$$\left| \frac{1}{h} \int_{y_0}^{y_0+h} \lambda \, dy \right| \leq \frac{1}{h} \cdot h \cdot \max_{\substack{|x-x_0| \leq h \\ |y-y_0| \leq h}} \left| \frac{\partial p(x, y)}{\partial x} - \frac{\partial p(x_0, y_0)}{\partial x} \right|,$$

and since the first-order partial derivatives of $p(x, y)$ are assumed to be continuous, it follows that

$$\lim_{h \to 0} \frac{1}{h} \int_{y_0}^{y_0+h} \lambda \, dy = 0.$$

Letting $h \to 0$ in (9.7.4) we obtain, since (x_0, y_0) is any arbitrary point in D

$$\delta \frac{d^2x}{dt^2} = - \frac{\partial p(x, y)}{\partial x} \tag{9.7.5}$$

for all points (x, y) in D.

Similarly, the net vertical force acting on the square S is given by

$$\delta \frac{d^2y}{dt^2} = - \frac{\partial p(x, y)}{\partial y} \tag{9.7.6}$$

at all points (x, y) in D. Since

$$\frac{dx}{dt} = q_1(x, y) \quad \text{and} \quad \frac{dy}{dt} = q_2(x, y),$$

upon differentiating these functions with respect to t, we find

$$\frac{d^2x}{dt^2} = \frac{\partial q_1}{\partial x} \frac{dx}{dt} + \frac{\partial q_1}{\partial y} \frac{dy}{dt} = q_1 \frac{\partial q_1}{\partial x} + q_2 \frac{\partial q_1}{\partial y},$$
$$\frac{d^2y}{dt^2} = \frac{\partial q_2}{\partial x} \frac{dx}{dt} + \frac{\partial q_2}{\partial y} \frac{dy}{dt} = q_1 \frac{\partial q_2}{\partial x} + q_2 \frac{\partial q_2}{\partial y}. \tag{9.7.7}$$

From (9.7.5), (9.7.6) and (9.7.7), we get

$$\delta \left(q_1 \frac{\partial q_1}{\partial x} + q_2 \frac{\partial q_1}{\partial y} \right) = - \frac{\partial p}{\partial x},$$
$$\delta \left(q_1 \frac{\partial q_2}{\partial x} + q_2 \frac{\partial q_2}{\partial y} \right) = - \frac{\partial p}{\partial y}. \tag{9.7.8}$$

Equations (9.7.8) are known as the *Euler equations in hydrodynamics*.

Suppose now that the flow is locally irrotational in D, that is, for each point z in D, there exists a neighborhood $N(z)$ contained in D such that

$$\int_C q_1 \, dx + q_2 \, dy = 0$$

for every closed contour C in $N(z)$. As in the proof of Theorem 9.2.1, this condition implies that

$$\frac{\partial q_1}{\partial y} = \frac{\partial q_2}{\partial x}.$$

The equations given in (9.7.8) then become

$$\delta\left(q_1\frac{\partial q_1}{\partial x} + q_2\frac{\partial q_2}{\partial x}\right) = -\frac{\partial p}{\partial x}, \qquad \delta\left(q_1\frac{\partial q_1}{\partial y} + q_2\frac{\partial q_2}{\partial y}\right) = -\frac{\partial p}{\partial y}. \qquad (9.7.9)$$

These equations can also be written as

$$\frac{\delta}{2}\frac{\partial}{\partial x}(q_1^2 + q_2^2) = -\frac{\partial p}{\partial x},$$

$$\frac{\delta}{2}\frac{\partial}{\partial y}(q_1^2 + q_2^2) = -\frac{\partial p}{\partial y},$$

which upon integration give

$$\frac{\delta}{2}(q_1^2 + q_2^2) + p(x, y) = k, \qquad (9.7.10)$$

where k is a constant determined by known conditions of velocity and pressure. This is the *Bernoulli equation for a steady-state, locally irrotational flow.* Observe that for a given flow, the smaller the magnitude $\sqrt{q_1^2 + q_2^2}$ of the velocity, the greater the pressure will be, and the pressure is at its maximum when the velocity is zero. If in addition to being locally irrotational, the flow is also locally source free, then from (9.3.2) we have

$$q_1^2 + q_2^2 = |F'(z)|^2, \qquad (9.7.12)$$

where $F(z)$ is the complex potential given in (9.3.1). Thus we see that for a steady, locally irrotational and source free flow in D, the maximum pressure is attained for those values of z for which $F'(z) = 0$. That is, the maximum pressure is attained at the stagnation points of the flow.

9.8. FORCE EXERTED BY A FLOW AROUND A CYLINDRICAL OBJECT.

As before, we consider a flow q in the xy plane exterior to a closed contour C and satisfying conditions (1) to (4) of (9.5.1). This flow causes certain forces to act on C. We wish to express these forces in terms of $Q_1 + iQ_2 = \lim_{z \to \infty} q(z)$ and the constant circulation $\mathscr{C}$ around any closed contour containing C in its interior.

Let the closed contour C be given by the parametric equations $x = x(s)$, $y = y(s)$, $0 \leq s \leq L$, where $s(x, y)$ is the arc length measured in the positive direction along C from a fixed point (x_0, y_0) to the variable point (x, y) on C. Let $p(x, y)$ denote the pressure normal to C at the point (x, y) on C. Then, since the direction cosines of the normal directed towards the interior of C are $(- \, dy/ds, \, dx/ds)$, the horizontal and vertical components of pressure exerted by the fluid at (x, y) are respectively equal to

$$- p(x, y) \frac{dy}{ds} \quad \text{and} \quad p(x, y) \frac{dx}{ds}.$$

Thus the total horizontal and vertical forces on C are given respectively by

$$X = - \int_0^L \left(p \frac{dy}{ds} \right) ds = - \int_C p \, dy, \quad Y = \int_0^L \left(p \frac{dx}{ds} \right) ds = \int_C p \, dx, \quad (9.8.1)$$

where the integral along C is taken in the positive direction, and L is the length of the contour C.

Let us define the *complex force* V by

$$V = Y + iX. \tag{9.8.2}$$

Hence in view of (9.8.1), we have

$$V = \int_C p \, dx - ip \, dy.$$

Since we are assuming the flow to be locally circulation free and source free, we have from (9.7.10)

$$p = - \frac{\delta}{2} (q_1^2 + q_2^2) + k, \qquad k \text{ is a constant.}$$

But

$$\int_C k \, dx - ik \, dy = 0,$$

therefore

$$V = - \frac{\delta}{2} \int_C (q_1^2 + q_2^2) \, (dx - i \, dy)$$

$$= - \frac{\delta}{2} \int_C (q_1 - iq_2) \, (q_1 + iq_2) \, (dx - i \, dy). \tag{9.8.3}$$

Now consider the integral

$$J = - \frac{\delta}{2} \int_C (q_1 - iq_2)^2 \, (dx + i \, dy)$$

$$= - \frac{\delta}{2} \int_C (q_1 - iq_2) \, \overline{[(q_1 + iq_2) \, (dx - i \, dy)]}. \tag{9.8.4}$$

Using (9.8.3), (9.8.4), (9.2.6) and (1.3.6), we obtain

$$V - J = - \frac{\delta}{2} \int_C (q_1 - iq_2) \, 2i \mathscr{I}[(q_1 + iq_2) \, (dx - i \, dy)]$$

$$= i\delta \int_C (q_1 - iq_2) \, [- q_2 \, dx + q_1 \, dy] = i\delta \int_C (q_1 - iq_2) \, q_n \, ds.$$

Since, by assumption, C is a streamline, $q_n = 0$ on C, and consequently we have $V = J$. Thus

$$V = -\frac{\delta}{2} \int_C (q_1 - iq_2)^2 \, dz. \tag{9.8.5}$$

Let Γ be a circle containing C in its interior and of radius sufficiently large so that the expansion given in (9.5.7) is valid and converges uniformly on Γ. Now, the function $(q_1 - iq_2)^2 = [F'(z)]^2$ is continuous on the region R bounded by Γ and C, and is analytic in the interior of R. Hence, by Theorem 5.10.3 and Remark 5.10.1, we have

$$V = -\frac{\delta}{2} \int_C (q_1 - iq_2)^2 \, dz = -\frac{\delta}{2} \int_\Gamma (q_1 - iq_2)^2 \, dz.$$

Thus

$$V = -\frac{\delta}{2} \int_\Gamma [F'(z)]^2 \, dz. \tag{9.8.6}$$

By (9.5.7), for z on Γ, we have

$$F'(z) = Q_1 - iQ_2 + \frac{\mathscr{C}}{2\pi i}\frac{1}{z} + g(z),$$

where

$$g(z) = \frac{a_2}{z^2} + \frac{a_3}{z^3} + \frac{a_4}{z^4} + \cdots.$$

Consequently

$$[F'(z)]^2 = (Q_1 - iQ_2)^2 + \frac{(Q_1 - iQ_2)\,\mathscr{C}}{\pi i} \cdot \frac{1}{z} + h(z),$$

where

$$h(z) = \frac{d_2}{z^2} + \frac{d_3}{z^3} + \frac{d_4}{z^4} + \cdots,$$

and d_j, $j = 2, 3, \cdots$, are constants. Hence

$$V = -\frac{\delta}{2} \int_\Gamma [F'(z)]^2 \, dz$$

$$= -\frac{\delta(Q_1 - iQ_2)^2}{2} \int_\Gamma dz - \frac{\delta\mathscr{C}}{2\pi i}(Q_1 - iQ_2) \int_\Gamma \frac{dz}{z} - \frac{\delta}{2} \int_\Gamma h(z) \, dz.$$

But (see Example 5.2.2)

$$\int_\Gamma dz = \int_\Gamma h(z) \, dz = 0 \quad \text{and} \quad \int_\Gamma \frac{dz}{z} = 2\pi i.$$

Therefore

$$V = - \frac{\delta \mathscr{C}}{2\pi i} (Q_1 - iQ_2) \int_\Gamma \frac{dz}{z} = - \delta \mathscr{C}(Q_1 - iQ_2). \qquad (9.8.7)$$

From (9.8.7) and (9.8.2), we obtain

$$Y + iX = - \delta \mathscr{C}(Q_1 - iQ_2).$$

Hence

$$X = \delta \mathscr{C} Q_2 \quad \text{and} \quad Y = - \delta \mathscr{C} Q_1, \qquad (9.8.8)$$

where

$$Q_1 = \lim_{z \to \infty} q_1(z) \quad \text{and} \quad Q_2 = \lim_{z \to \infty} q_2(z).$$

If the x and y axes are so chosen that the flow approaches parallelism with the x axis as $z \to \infty$, that is, so as to have $Q_2 = 0$; then we have

$$X = 0 \quad \text{and} \quad Y = - \delta \mathscr{C} Q_1. \qquad (9.8.9)$$

The result (9.8.9) is applied to the following situation, already discussed in Section 9.5. Suppose that a steady flow with uniform velocity is given over the xy plane, and a cylindrical obstacle with generators perpendicular to the plane of flow is introduced. We may choose the coordinate axis so that the direction of the flow is in the positive direction of the x axis. Denoting by C the cross-sectional outline of the obstacle, we have a flow in the xy plane around C, which in conformity with physical observation is assumed to satisfy conditions (1) to (4) of (9.5.1) with $\lim_{z \to \infty} q = Q = Q_1 + iQ_2$, where $Q_2 = 0$, $Q_1 > 0$ and Q is equal to the given uniform velocity of the flow before the obstacle was introduced. In view of the result given in (9.8.9), we then have the following

——*THEOREM* 9.8.1. A uniform flow of a frictionless, incompressible fluid around a cylindrical obstacle, introduced into the fluid and with generators perpendicular to the flow, exerts a force against the obstacle whose magnitude is equal to $\delta |\mathscr{C}| |Q|$, where δ is the density of the fluid, $\mathscr{C}$ is the circulation around the obstacle, and Q is the constant velocity defining the given uniform flow. The direction of this force is normal to that of the given uniform flow.

The relations (9.8.9), fundamental in aerodynamics, are due to Kutta and Joukowski. If Q_1 is positive and the circulation $\mathscr{C}$ is negative, then there will be according to (9.8.9) a *lift* in the positive y direction. It might be expected that since the flow is in the positive x direction, there would be a horizontal force exerted against the obstacle, but according to (9.8.9), there is none, nor would there be any in actual practice if the surface of the obstacle were perfectly smooth. This is known as *Laplace's Paradox*. One also sees why it is reasonable to expect a force in the y direction. Suppose, for example, that $\mathscr{C}$ is negative and

Q_1 is positive. The circulation around C is clockwise and the flow is from left to right. Thus, underneath the cylinder the circulation works against the flow, reducing the velocity, and hence by the Bernoulli equation (9.7.10) increases the pressure. Whereas, above the cylinder the circulation serves to increase the velocity, thus reducing the pressure. The difference in pressure above the cylinder and below results in a net upward force.

EXERCISES 9.8

1. Find the x and y components and magnitude of the lifting force on the Joukowski airfoil; show that these depend only on the shape and size of the airfoil and on the velocity at infinity of the flow.

9.9. THE SCHWARZ-CHRISTOFFEL TRANSFORMATION.

We shall now consider the problem of mapping the upper half plane one-to-one and analytically onto the interior of a polygon. Recall (see Remarks 8.3.2 and 8.4.2) that an analytic mapping $w = f(z)$ defined over a domain D with $f'(z) \neq 0$ for z in D is locally one-to-one and conformal in D.

Let the function $g(z)$ be defined by

$$g(z) = (z - x_1)^{-\alpha_1} (z - x_2)^{-\alpha_2} \cdots (z - x_n)^{-\alpha_n}, \qquad z \text{ in } D, \qquad (9.9.1)$$

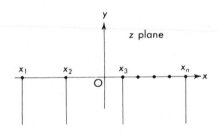

FIG. 9.9.1

where the domain D consists of the z plane with the half lines $x_j + iy$, $y \leq 0$, omitted (see Fig. 9.9.1); the x_j's are points on the real axis such that

$$x_1 < x_2 < \cdots < x_n;$$

the α_j's are real numbers with $-1 < \alpha_j < 1$, $\alpha_j \neq 0$; $-1 < 2 - \sum_{j=1}^{n} \alpha_j < 1$; and $-\pi/2 < \arg(z - x_j) < (3/2)\pi$; $j = 1, 2, \cdots, n$.

Remark 9.9.1. In (9.9.1), $\arg(z - x)^\alpha$ is taken to be equal to $\alpha \arg(z - x)$. We see that in its domain of definition D, the function $g(z)$ is single-valued, analytic, and $g(z) \neq 0$.

Consider the transformation

$$w = f(z) = A \int_{z_0}^{z} g(\zeta)\, d\zeta + B, \qquad z \text{ in } D \qquad (9.9.2)$$

where D and $g(z)$ are as in (9.9.1), $\mathscr{I}(z_0) > 0$, $A \neq 0$, and B are complex constants,

LEMMA 9.9.1. The transformation $w = f(z)$ of (9.9.2) is analytic and $f'(z) \neq 0$ in its domain of definition D. Moreover, $\lim_{z \to x_j} f(z)$ exists for $j = 1, 2, \cdots, n$.

Proof. Since D is simply connected and $g(z) \neq 0$ and

$$f'(z) = Ag(z), \qquad z \text{ in } D, \tag{9.9.3}$$

it follows that $f(z)$ is single-valued, the transformation $w = f(z)$ is analytic, and $f'(z) \neq 0$ for z in D. (See Theorem 5.11.1.)

To show that $\lim_{z \to x_1} f(z)$ exists, we may, without loss of generality, take $A = 1$ in (9.9.2) and let $z \to x_1$. Let x_j, α_j, arg $(z - x_j)$, and domain D be as in (9.9.1), and let us define the functions $h(z)$ and $\phi(z)$ by

$$h(z) = (z - x_1)^{-\alpha_1} (x_1 - x_2)^{-\alpha_2} \cdots (x_1 - x_n)^{-\alpha_n}, \qquad z \text{ in } D, \tag{9.9.4}$$

and

$$\phi(z) = g(z) - h(z), \qquad z \text{ in } D. \tag{9.9.5}$$

Observe that $h(z)$ and $\phi(z)$ are single-valued and analytic in D, and (see Exercise 9.9.1)

$$\lim_{z \to x_1} \phi(z) = 0. \tag{9.9.6}$$

In view of (9.9.2), (9.9.4) and (9.9.5), we have for z_1 and z_2 in D

$$f(z_2) - f(z_1) = \int_{z_1}^{z_2} h(\zeta) \, d\zeta + \int_{z_1}^{z_2} \phi(\zeta) \, d\zeta$$

$$= \frac{(z - x_1)^{1-\alpha_1}}{1 - \alpha_1} (x_1 - x_2)^{-\alpha_2} \cdots (x_1 - x_n)^{-\alpha_n} \Big|_{z=z_1}^{z=z_2} + \int_{z_1}^{z_2} \phi(\zeta) \, d\zeta.$$

Since $\alpha_1 < 1$, we have $\lim_{z_i \to x_1} (z_i - x_1)^{1-\alpha_1} = 0$, $i = 1, 2$. Also, (see Exercise 9.9.2)

$$\lim_{\substack{z_1 \to x_1 \\ z_2 \to x_1}} \int_{z_1}^{z_2} \phi(\zeta) \, d\zeta = 0. \tag{9.9.7}$$

It follows that

$$\lim_{\substack{z_1 \to x_1 \\ z_2 \to x_1}} [f(z_2) - f(z_1)] = 0.$$

Consequently (see Exercise 3.3.32), $\lim_{z \to x_1} f(z)$ exists.

Similarly $\lim_{z \to x_j} f(z)$ exists for $j = 2, 3, \cdots, n$.

Remark 9.9.2. By an *extended set* we shall mean a set of points in the complex plane with the point at infinity adjoined. Thus, the extended real axis denotes the real axis with the point at infinity adjoined; the extended half plane

$\mathscr{I}(z) \geq 0$ denotes the half plane $\mathscr{I}(z) \geq 0$ with the point at infinity z_∞ adjoined; and so on.

LEMMA 9.9.2. Let $f(z)$ be defined as in (9.9.2). If z is restricted to the half plane $\mathscr{I}(z) \geq 0$, $z \neq x_j$, $j = 1, 2, \cdots, n$, then $\lim_{z \to z_\infty} f(z)$ exists.

Proof. Let z be restricted to the half plane $\mathscr{I}(z) \geq 0$, $z \neq x_j$ and let $g(z)$ be as in (9.9.1). Now, (9.9.1) may be written as

$$g(z) = z^{-\Sigma_{j=1}^n \alpha_j} \left(1 - \frac{x_1}{z}\right)^{-\alpha_1} \cdots \left(1 - \frac{x_n}{z}\right)^{-\alpha_n}, \quad \mathscr{I}(z) \geq 0, \quad z \neq x_j. \quad (9.9.8)$$

We see that

$$\lim_{z \to z_\infty} z^{\Sigma_{j=1}^n \alpha_j} g(z) = 1. \quad (9.9.9)$$

Since (by hypothesis) $\sum_{j=1}^n \alpha_j > 1$, it follows (see Exercise 9.9.3) that $\lim_{z \to z_\infty} f(z)$ exists, thus establishing the lemma.

In view of Lemmas 9.9.1 and 9.9.2, we may modify the domain of definition of transformation (9.9.2) and obtain*

$$w = f(z) = A \int_{z_0}^z (\zeta - x_1)^{-\alpha_1} (\zeta - x_2)^{-\alpha_2} \cdots (\zeta - x_n)^{-\alpha_n} d\zeta + B, \quad (9.9.10)$$

$$\mathscr{I}(z) \geq 0 \quad \text{or} \quad z = z_\infty,$$

where the domain of definition of $f(z)$ is now the extended half plane $\mathscr{I}(z) \geq 0$. A summary of the foregoing results is contained in the following

LEMMA 9.9.3. Transformation (9.9.10) is continuous on its domain of definition consisting of the extended half plane $\mathscr{I}(z) \geq 0$; and is analytic, with derivative nowhere equal to zero, in the upper half plane $\mathscr{I}(z) > 0$.

Remark 9.9.3. In view of Lemma 9.9.1, transformation (9.9.10) can also be considered analytic, with $f'(z) \neq 0$, everywhere on the real axis, except for the points $z = x_j$, $j = 1, 2, \cdots, n$.

Remark 9.9.4. Let w_1, w_2 be two distinct points in the w plane. By the expression $[w_1, w_2]$ we mean the line segment with initial point w_1 and terminal point w_2.

By a *closed polygonal line* we mean a closed (not necessarily simple closed) contour consisting of line segments. By a *polygon* we mean a simple closed contour consisting of line segments.

For z real, the function $g(z)$ of (9.9.1) may be expressed as follows:

$$g(x) = (x - x_1)^{-\alpha_1} (x - x_2)^{-\alpha_2} \cdots (x - x_n)^{-\alpha_n}, \quad x \neq x_j. \quad (9.9.11)$$

* In (9.9.2), we let $f(z) = \lim_{\zeta \to z} f(\zeta)$, $z = x_1, x_2, \cdots, x_n, z_\infty$, and we say that $f(z)$ is continuous at $z = z_\infty$ as well as at $z = x_1, x_2, \cdots, x_n$.

For ξ real

$$\arg(x - \xi) = \begin{cases} \pi, & \text{for } x < \xi, \\ 0, & \text{for } x > \xi. \end{cases} \tag{9.9.12}$$

We see that $\arg(x - \xi)$ is constant for $x < \xi$ and for $x > \xi$, but abruptly decreases by π as x increases through ξ. Thus in (9.9.11) for $k = 1, 2, \cdots, n$, $\arg(x - x_k)$ is constant over each of the intervals $-\infty < x < x_1$; $x_j < x < x_{j+1}$, $j = 1, \cdots, n - 1$; $x_n < x < \infty$. Utilizing (9.9.12), we see that the function $g(x)$ of (9.9.11) may be expressed as follows:

$$g(x) = e^{i\theta_j} \, | \, g(x) \, |, \qquad x_j < x < x_{j+1}, \qquad j = 0, 1, \cdots, n, \tag{9.9.13}$$

where $x_0 = -\infty$, $x_{n+1} = \infty$,

$$\theta_j = -\pi \sum_{k=j+1}^{n} \alpha_k \qquad j = 0, 1, \cdots, n, \text{ with } \theta_n = 0.$$

LEMMA 9.9.4.   Under transformation (9.9.10) the segment $x_j \leqq x \leqq x_{j+1}$ of the real axis is mapped one-to-one onto the line segment $[f(x_j), f(x_{j+1})]$, $j = 1, 2, \cdots, n - 1$; the extended half line $-\infty < x \leqq x_1$ is mapped one-to-one onto the line segment $[f(z_\infty), f(x_1)]$; and the extended half line $x_n \leqq x < \infty$ is mapped one-to-one onto the line segment $[f(x_n), f(z_\infty)]$.

Proof.   For fixed j ($j = 1, 2, \cdots, n - 1$), let ξ_j and ξ'_j be points on the real axis such that $x_j < \xi_j < \xi'_j < x_{j+1}$. Then from (9.9.10), we have

$$f(\xi'_j) - f(\xi_j) = A \int_{\xi_j}^{\xi'_j} (x - x_1)^{-\alpha_1} (x - x_2)^{-\alpha_2} \cdots (x - x_n)^{-\alpha_n} \, dx. \tag{9.9.14}$$

Observing that θ_j is constant in (9.9.13) for $x_j < x < x_{j+1}$, we obtain

$$f(\xi'_j) - f(\xi_j) = A e^{i\theta_j} \int_{\xi_j}^{\xi'_j} | \, g(x) \, | \, dx, \qquad x_j < \xi_j < \xi'_j < x_{j+1}. \tag{9.9.15}$$

Since $g(x) \neq 0$ for $\xi_j \leqq x \leqq \xi'_j$, it follows that $f(\xi'_j) \neq f(\xi_j)$.

Let $\xi_j \to x_j$ and $\xi'_j \to x_{j+1}$. Then utilizing (9.9.15) and Lemma 9.9.3, we see that the image of the line segment $x_j \leqq x \leqq x_{j+1}$ is the line segment $[f(x_j), f(x_{j+1})]$, and that the correspondence is one-to-one.

Since $f(z)$ is continuous at $z = z_\infty$, a similar argument holds for each of the extended half lines $-\infty < x \leqq x_1$ and $x_n \leqq x < \infty$. The lemma is thus established.

An immediate consequence of Lemmas 9.9.3 and 9.9.4 is the following

LEMMA 9.9.5.   Transformation (9.9.10) maps the extended real axis onto a closed polygonal line.

LEMMA 9.9.6.   Let $w = f(z)$ be the transformation given in (9.9.10). Then

$$\arg [f(x_{j+1}) - f(x_j)] - \arg [f(x_j) - f(x_{j-1})] = \pi\alpha_j, \, j = 1, 2, \cdots, n,$$

and

$$\arg [f(x_1) - f(z_\infty)] - \arg [f(z_\infty) - f(x_n)] = \pi\alpha_{n+1}, \qquad (9.9.16)$$

where

$$x_0 = x_{n+1} = z_\infty \quad \text{and} \quad \alpha_{n+1} = 2 - \sum_{k=1}^{n} \alpha_k \, .$$

Proof.   Let $\xi_0, \xi_1, \cdots, \xi_n, \xi_0', \xi_1', \cdots, \xi_n'$ be points on the real axis such that $-\infty < \xi_0 < \xi_0' < x_1; \, x_j < \xi_j < \xi_j' < x_{j+1}, j = 1, 2, \cdots, n - 1;$ $x_n < \xi_n < \xi_n' < \infty.$

Utilizing (9.9.13) and (9.9.15), we obtain $\arg[f(\xi_j') - f(\xi_j)] = -\pi \sum_{k=j+1}^{n} \alpha_k + \arg A,$ $j = 0, 1, \cdots, n.$ Thus we have (see Fig. 9.9.2),

$$\arg [f(\xi_j') - f(\xi_j)] - \arg [f(\xi_{j-1}') - f(\xi_{j-1})] = \pi\alpha_j, \quad j = 1, 2, \cdots, n. \quad (9.9.17)$$

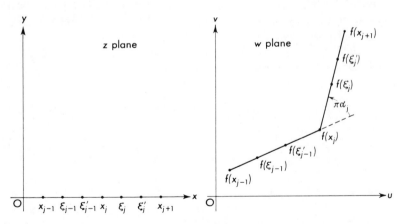

FIG. 9.9.2

Letting $j = 1, 2, \cdots, k, 1 \leq k \leq n$, in (9.9.17) and summing, we obtain

$$\arg [f(\xi_k') - f(\xi_k)] - \arg [f(\xi_0') - f(\xi_0)] = \sum_{j=1}^{k} \pi\alpha_j, \quad k = 1, 2, \cdots, n. \quad (9.9.18)$$

In particular, when $k = n$ in (9.9.18), we obtain (up to a multiple of 2π)

$$\arg\left[f(\xi_0') - f(\xi_0)\right] - \arg\left[f(\xi_n') - f(\xi_n)\right] = -\sum_{j=1}^{n} \pi\alpha_j = \pi\left(2 - \sum_{j=1}^{n} \alpha_j\right).$$

(9.9.19)

Letting $\xi_j \to x_j$, $\xi_j' \to x_{j+1}$, $j = 0, 1, \cdots, n$, and utilizing (9.9.17), (9.9.19) and Lemmas 9.9.3, 9.9.4, the lemma now follows.

From Lemmas 9.9.4 and 9.9.6, we obtain the following

LEMMA 9.9.7. Let $\alpha_j, j = 1, 2, \cdots, n$ be as in (9.9.10). If $2 - \sum_{j=1}^{n} \alpha_j = 0$, then transformation (9.9.10) maps the union of the extended line segments $x_n \leqq x < \infty$ and $-\infty < x \leqq x_1$ one-to-one onto the line segment $[f(x_n), f(x_1)]$.

We shall now place a restriction on transformation (9.9.10). Let

$$w = f(z) = A \int_{z_0}^{z} (\xi - x_1)^{-\alpha_1} (\xi - x_2)^{-\alpha_2} \cdots (\xi - x_n)^{-\alpha_n} d\xi + B, \qquad (9.9.20)$$

$$\mathscr{I}(z) \geqq 0 \quad \text{or} \quad z = z_\infty$$

be the same as transformation (9.9.10) with the α_j's and x_j's further restricted so that the following condition is satisfied: Except for the common end point of two consecutive sides, no two sides of the image of the extended real axis have a point in common. In view of Lemmas 9.9.4 to 9.9.7, we have the following

LEMMA 9.9.8. Transformation (9.9.20) maps the extended real axis one-to-one onto a polygon such that (a) if $2 - \sum_{j=1}^{n} \alpha_j \neq 0$, then the polygon has $n + 1$ sides with exterior angles $\pi\alpha_j$ at vertices $f(x_j)$, $1 \leqq j \leqq n$; and with exterior angle $\pi(2 - \sum_{j=1}^{n} \alpha_j)$ at vertex $f(z_\infty)$; (b) if $2 - \sum_{j=1}^{n} \alpha_j = 0$, then the polygon has n sides with exterior angles $\pi\alpha_j$ at vertices $f(x_j)$, $1 \leqq j \leqq n$. [See Fig. 9.9.3 for a polygon satisfying condition (a).]

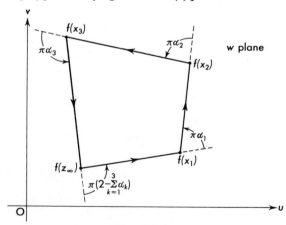

FIG. 9.9.3

Remark 9.9.5.   Let Γ: $w = w(t)$ be a polygon and let

$$w_{j-1} = w(t_{j-1}), \quad w_j = w(t_j), \quad w_{j+1} = w(t_{j+1}), \quad t_{j-1} < t_j < t_{j+1},$$

be three successive vertices. The *exterior angle* of the polygon at vertex w_j is defined by $\arg(w_{j+1} - w_j) - \arg(w_j - w_{j-1})$. Thus, the exterior angle β_j at vertex $f(x_j)$ of the polygon in Lemma 9.9.8 is given by

$$\beta_j = \arg[f(x_{j+1}) - f(x_j)] - \arg[f(x_j) - f(x_{j-1})], \tag{9.9.21}$$

and according to Lemma 9.9.6, $\beta_j = \pi\alpha_j$. Note that if $\alpha_{n+1} = 0$, then $j = 1, 2, \cdots, n$; if $\alpha_{n+1} \neq 0$, then $j = 1, 2, \cdots, n+1$, with $x_{n+2} = x_1$, in (9.9.21).

——***THEOREM*** 9.9.1.   Transformation (9.9.20) maps the extended half plane $\mathscr{I}(z) \geq 0$ one-to-one and continuously onto a set consisting of a polygon and its interior. The upper half plane $\mathscr{I}(z) > 0$ is mapped analytically onto the interior of the polygon. Conversely, given a polygon, there exists a transformation (9.9.20) that maps the extended real axis onto the given polygon.

Proof.   By Lemma 9.9.8, transformation (9.9.20) maps the extended real axis one-to-one onto a polygon, Γ. By Lemma 9.9.3, the mapping is continuous on the extended half plane $\mathscr{I}(z) \geq 0$, and is analytic in the upper half plane $\mathscr{I}(z) > 0$.

We shall now show that transformation (9.9.20) maps the upper half plane $\mathscr{I}(z) > 0$ one-to-one onto the interior of the polygon Γ. Let the extended real axis be indented at the points x_j ($j = 1, 2, \cdots, n$) and at z_∞. The indentation at each point x_j is a semicircle lying in the upper half plane $\mathscr{I}(z) > 0$, with center at x_j and radius r. The indentation at z_∞ is a semicircle lying in the upper half plane $\mathscr{I}(z) > 0$ with center at the origin and radius $1/r$.

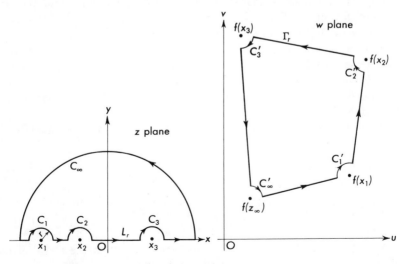

FIG. 9.9.4

Let L_r denote the indented extended real axis. (See Fig. 9.9.4.) If r is small, then (see Exercise 9.9.4) transformation (9.9.20) maps the contour L_r one-to-one onto its image Γ_r. It follows (see Theorem 8.2.4) that the interior of L_r maps one-to-one onto the interior of Γ_r. Now, L_r coincides with the extended real axis, except for neighborhoods of x_j and of z_∞. Letting $r \to 0$, L_r approaches coincidence with the extended real axis, and Γ_r approaches coincidence with the polygon Γ. Thus, as in the proof of Theorem 8.16.1, the upper half plane maps one-to-one onto the interior of the polygon.

For a proof of the converse part of the theorem, see Z. Nehari, *Conformal Mapping*, pp. 189-196, New York: McGraw-Hill, 1952.

Remark 9.9.6.   In view of Theorem 9.9.1 and Remark 8.4.2, transformation (9.9.20) maps the upper half plane $\mathscr{I}(z) > 0$ one-to-one and conformally onto the interior of a polygon.

Let us consider the problem of finding a transformation of the form (9.9.20) for a given polygon. The α_j's in (9.9.20) are determined by the exterior angles of the polygon. Let the given polygon have m sides with exterior angles $\beta_j, j = 1, 2, \cdots, m$. Since the sum of the exterior angles of a polygon equals 2π, we have $\sum_{j=1}^{m} \beta_j = 2\pi$. In (9.9.20) we may take $n = m$ or $n = m - 1$. If we take $n = m$ and $\alpha_j = \beta_j/\pi, j = 1, 2, \cdots, n$, we obtain $\sum_{j=1}^{n} \alpha_j = 2$. However, if we take $n = m - 1$ and $\alpha_j = \beta_j/\pi, j = 1, 2, \cdots, n$, we obtain $\sum_{j=1}^{n} \alpha_j = 2 - \beta_m/\pi$, with the image of z_∞ being a vertex at which the exterior angle is equal to β_m.

It can be shown that the positions of three of the x_j's in (9.9.20) may be chosen arbitrarily. One of the three x_j's may be placed at z_∞, in which case the corresponding factor $(z - x_j)^{\alpha_j}$ does not appear in (9.9.20). That there are at least three arbitrary choices for the x_j's follows readily from Theorem 8.10.2.

The constant B in (9.9.20) is determined by the position of the polygon and the choice of z_0. The modulus and the argument of A are determined respectively by the size and the orientation of the polygon.

If the polygon is a triangle, the x_j's in (9.9.20) may all be chosen arbitrarily; however, the integrals that arise are not elementary. The integrals are elliptic if the triangle is equilateral, right-angled isosceles, or $30° - 60° - 90°$. If the polygon is not a triangle, the determination of the x_j's and the integration may both be difficult.

We shall now weaken the restriction on the α_j's in (9.9.10) to obtain

$$w = f(z) = A \int_{z_0}^{z} (\zeta - x_1)^{-\alpha_1} (\zeta - x_2)^{-\alpha_2} \cdots (\zeta - x_n)^{-\alpha_n} \, d\zeta + B, \qquad (9.9.22)$$

$$\mathscr{I}(z) \geq 0 \quad \text{or} \quad z = z_\infty,$$

where $-1 \leq \alpha_j \leq 3$, $\alpha_j \neq 0$, $j = 1, 2, \cdots, n$; $-1 \leq 2 - \sum_{j=1}^{n} \alpha_j \leq 3$.

Also the x_j's and α_j's in (9.9.22) are restricted so that the image of the extended real axis forms the boundary of a simply connected domain.

Transformation (9.9.22) is known as the *Schwarz-Christoffel transformation*. Transformation (9.9.22) includes transformation (9.9.20) as a special case, and retains many of the properties of transformation (9.9.20). For example, for both (9.9.20) and (9.9.22), the image of the line segment L: $x_j < x < x_{j+1}$ is linear (see proof of Lemma 9.9.4). However, in (9.9.22) the image of the line segment L may be a line or a half line, as well as a line segment.

The boundaries of certain unbounded simply connected domains, such as infinite strips, semi-infinite strips, and so on, may be considered as degenerate, unbounded polygons.*

We shall consider several examples in which we desire to obtain a one-to-one analytic mapping of the upper half plane onto a given domain whose boundary is an unbounded polygon. We shall not develop a general theory of such mappings, but shall in each case assume that the mapping is of the Schwarz-Christoffel type (9.9.22). We shall choose values for the x_j's and α_j's using methods appropriate for bounded domains and ordinary polygons. If we can verify that the transformation so obtained has the desired properties, then we shall consider solved the problem posed in the given example.

EXAMPLE 9.9.1.   Mapping of a half plane onto a semi-infinite strip. Let us map the upper half plane $\mathscr{I}(z) > 0$ one-to-one and analytically onto the interior of the semi-infinite strip $w_{1\infty}w_2w_3w_{4\infty}$ of breadth b in the w plane, as shown in Fig. 9.9.5. We consider the boundary of the strip to be an unbounded

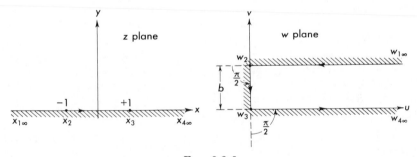

FIG. 9.9.5

triangle with an exterior angle equal to π at w_∞. Choosing three points in the z plane arbitrarily, we map $x_{1\infty} = z_\infty$, $x_2 = -1$, $x_3 = 1$, $x_{4\infty} = z_\infty$, respectively, into $w_{1\infty} = w_\infty$, $w_2 = ib$, $w_3 = 0$, $w_{4\infty} = w_\infty$. Since the exterior angles at w_2 and w_3 are each equal to $\pi/2$, we have $\alpha_2 = \alpha_3 = 1/2$ in (9.9.22); and since $x_{1\infty}$ and $x_{4\infty}$ do not appear in (9.9.22), we obtain

$$w = f(z) = A \int \frac{dz}{\sqrt{z^2 - 1}} + B = A \cosh^{-1} z + B.$$

* We may think of an unbounded polygon P as a "polygon" in the extended complex plane with a vertex, possibly multiple, at the point at infinity. The interior of P may be considered as the limit of the interior of a polygon with a fixed number of sides as some (or all) of its vertices recede to infinity.

Since $w = 0$ when $z = 1$, and $w = ib$ when $z = -1$, it follows that $B = 0$ and $A = b/\pi$. Thus

$$w = \frac{b}{\pi} \cosh^{-1} z, \qquad 0 \leqq \mathscr{I} (\cosh^{-1} z) \leqq \pi. \tag{9.9.23}$$

The inverse map is given by

$$z = \cosh\left(\frac{\pi w}{b}\right).$$

It is easy to verify that transformation (9.9.23) maps the upper half plane $\mathscr{I}(z) > 0$ one-to-one and analytically onto the interior of the given semi-infinite strip.

EXAMPLE 9.9.2. Let us utilize the Schwarz-Christoffel transformation (9.9.22) to find a complex potential $F(w)$ for the flow of a fluid over a step in the bed of a deep stream, with velocity at infinity equal to q, $q > 0$. The bed $w_{1\infty} w_2 w_3 w_{4\infty}$, with $w_{1\infty} = w_{4\infty} = w_\infty$, $w_2 = ib$, $w_3 = 0$, is shown in Fig. 9.9.6. The bed is taken to be a streamline.

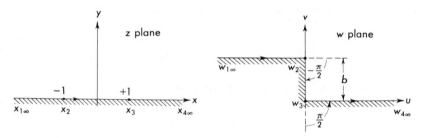

FIG. 9.9.6

Let us map $x_{1\infty} = z_\infty$, $x_2 = -1$, $x_3 = 1$, $x_{4\infty} = z_\infty$, respectively, into $w_{1\infty}, w_2, w_3, w_{4\infty}$. Since the exterior angles at w_2 and w_3 are respectively equal to $-\pi/2$ and $\pi/2$, we have $\alpha_2 = -1/2$ and $\alpha_3 = 1/2$ in (9.9.22); and since $x_{1\infty}$ and $x_{4\infty}$ do not appear in (9.9.22), we obtain

$$w = f(z) = A \int \frac{(z+1)^{1/2}}{(z-1)^{1/2}} \, dz + B = A \left[\sqrt{z^2 - 1} + \cosh^{-1} z\right] + B.$$

Since $w = ib$ when $z = -1$, and $w = 0$ when $z = 1$, we find that $B = 0$ and $A = b/\pi$. Hence

$$w = f(z) = \frac{b}{\pi}[\sqrt{z^2 - 1} + \cosh^{-1} z], \tag{9.9.24}$$

where

$$\arg \sqrt{z^2 - 1} = (\tfrac{1}{2}) [\arg (z + 1) + \arg (z - 1)], \qquad 0 \leqq \mathscr{I} (\cosh^{-1} z) \leqq \pi.$$

Now $H(z) = F[f(z)]$ will define a complex potential on the half plane $\mathscr{I}(z) \geqq 0$, with the real axis $\mathscr{I}(z) = 0$ as a streamline. Utilizing (9.9.24) we have

$$\frac{dH}{dz} = \frac{dF}{dw} \cdot \frac{dw}{dz} = \frac{b}{\pi} \sqrt{\frac{z+1}{z-1}} \frac{dF}{dw} \to \frac{bq}{\pi} \quad \text{as } z \to \infty.$$

Thus (see Example 9.4.6) $H(z) = (bq/\pi)z$. Since $H(z) = F(w)$ and $z = f^{-1}(w)$, we see that the desired complex potential is given by

$$F(w) = \frac{bq}{\pi} f^{-1}(w) = \frac{bq}{\pi} z. \qquad (9.9.25)$$

EXAMPLE 9.9.3. Let us utilize the Schwarz-Christoffel transformation (9.9.22) to determine the electrostatic potential due to a (uniformly distributed) line charge situated between two semi-infinite grounded planes intersecting at an angle θ, the line charge being parallel to the line of intersection of the planes.

First, let $V(x, y)$ be the electrostatic potential* in a domain D, due to line charges perpendicular to the z plane, piercing it in points not in D. It follows from Coulomb's Law† that $V(x, y)$ is harmonic in D. Let

$$F(z) = U(x, y) + iV(x, y)$$

be an analytic function such that $\mathscr{I}(F) = V$. The functions U and F may be multiple-valued in D.

Now, let V be the electrostatic potential due to a line charge of density q, the line charge being perpendicular to the z plane and going through the origin. Since V is harmonic, is independent of direction with respect to the origin, and is determined up to an additive constant, we have $V = -2q \operatorname{Log} r$, where $r = |z|$. (See Exercise 8.19.9.) Here, the coefficient $-2q$ is obtained by utilizing Coulomb's Law. We also have

$$F(z) = U + iV = -2qi \log z. \qquad (9.9.26)$$

Now, let q be a line charge perpendicular to the z plane going through the point z_0, with $\mathscr{I}(z_0) \neq 0$; and let $-q$ be another line charge perpendicular

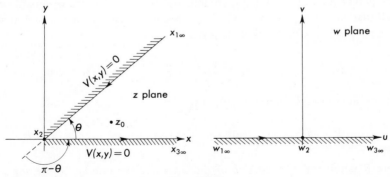

FIG. 9.9.7

* The electrostatic field is given by $E = -\bigtriangledown V$.

† Coulomb's Law: Let r be the distance between two electric point charges q and q'. If the charges are alike they repel, and if unlike they attract each other with a force equal to qq'/r^2 acting along the line containing the two charges.

to the z plane going through the point $\bar{z}_0$. Since the potential due to two charges is the sum of the potentials due to the individual charges, we have, in view of equation (9.9.26)

$$F(z) = U + iV = -2qi \operatorname{Log} \frac{z - z_0}{z - \bar{z}_0}. \qquad (9.9.27)$$

Also, we may easily verify that if $z = x$ in (9.9.27), then $F(z)$ is real; thus $V = \mathscr{I}(F) = 0$ on the x axis. Hence, V in (9.9.27) is the electrostatic potential due to an infinite grounded plate and a line charge q, both perpendicular to the z plane, and piercing it respectively in the x axis and at the point z_0. Here, V is defined in the half plane bounded by the x axis and containing the point z_0.

Now, let two semi-infinite planes, both perpendicular to the z plane, intersect at an angle θ; let q be a line charge perpendicular to the z plane, piercing it at the point $z = z_0$ with z_0 interior to the angle θ, as shown in Fig. 9.9.7.

We shall map the upper half plane $\mathscr{I}(w) > 0$ one-to-one and analytically onto the interior of the angle θ, with $w_{1\infty}$, w_2, $w_{3\infty}$ mapping respectively into $x_{1\infty}$, x_2, $x_{3\infty}$ as shown in Fig. 9.9.7. We shall now utilize the Schwarz-Christoffel transformation (9.9.22), with w and z interchanged. Since the exterior angle at x_2 is equal to $\pi - \theta$, we have $\alpha_2 = 1 - \theta/\pi$; and since $w_{1\infty} = w_{3\infty} = w_\infty$, and $w_2 = 0$, we obtain

$$z = A \int w^{-1+\theta/\pi}\, dw + B = A_1 w^{\theta/\pi} + B.$$

Since $z = x_2 = 0$ when $w = w_2 = 0$, we have $B = 0$. Thus $z = A_1 w^{\theta/\pi}$. Then, the inverse mapping is given by

$$w = f(z) = A_2 z^{\pi/\theta}, \qquad A_2 > 0. \qquad (9.9.28)$$

We see that transformation (9.9.28) maps the sides of the angle θ onto the u axis, and maps the point z_0 into the point $w_0 = A_2 z_0^{\pi/\theta}$. Let V_1 be the electrostatic potential due to an infinite grounded plate and a line charge q both perpendicular to the w plane and piercing it respectively in the u axis and at the point w_0. Then [see (9.9.27)] V_1 is given by

$$F_1(w) = U_1 + iV_1 = -2qi \operatorname{Log} \frac{w - w_0}{w - \bar{w}_0}, \qquad \mathscr{I}(w) \geqq 0.$$

It then follows (see Exercise 9.9.19) that

$$U + iV = F(z) = F_1[f(z)] = -2qi \operatorname{Log} \frac{z^{\pi/\theta} - z_0^{\pi/\theta}}{z^{\pi/\theta} - \bar{z}_0^{\pi/\theta}}, \qquad z \text{ in } R,$$

where R is the region consisting of the sides and the interior of the angle θ. Hence

$$V(x, y) = \mathscr{I} \left[-2qi \operatorname{Log} \frac{z^{\pi/\theta} - z_0^{\pi/\theta}}{z^{\pi/\theta} - \bar{z}_0^{\pi/\theta}} \right], \qquad z \text{ in } R. \qquad (9.9.29)$$

The desired potential $V(x, y)$ is given in (9.9.29).

EXERCISES 9.9

1. Verify equation (9.9.6).

2. Verify equation (9.9.7).

3. Using (9.9.8) and (9.9.9), show that $\lim_{z \to z_\infty} f(z)$ exists, where z is restricted to the half plane $\mathscr{I}(z) \geq 0$.

4. Let L_r be the contour defined in the proof of Theorem 9.9.1. Show that when r is small, transformation (9.9.20) maps L_r one-to-one onto its image.

5. Show that if in (9.9.10), $0 < \alpha_j < 1$, $j = 1, 2, \cdots, n$, and

$$0 \leq 2 - \sum_{j=1}^{n} \alpha_j < 1,$$

then transformation (9.9.10) maps the extended real axis one-to-one onto its image.

6. Let x_j, α_j, $j = 1, 2, \cdots, n$ be as in (9.9.22), and let $x_{n+1} = z_\infty$ and

$$\alpha_{n+1} = 2 - \sum_{j=1}^{n} \alpha_j.$$

Show that in (9.9.22), for $j = 1, 2, \cdots, n + 1$,

(a) $\lim_{z \to x_j} f(z)$ exists, if $\alpha_j < 1$;

(b) $f(z) \to w_\infty$ as $z \to x_j$, if $\alpha_j \geq 1$.

(These results are also valid if in (9.9.22), the α_j's are allowed to assume any real values.)

7. Show that z_0 in formula (9.9.20) may be any point in the extended half plane $\mathscr{I}(z) \geq 0$.

8. Show that when $\sum_{j=1}^{n} \alpha_j = 2$, transformation (9.9.20) is conformal at $z = z_\infty$, with respect to the extended half plane $\mathscr{I}(z) \geq 0$.

9. Let $w = f(z)$ of (9.9.20) be a Schwarz-Christoffel transformation for a given polygon P.

(a) Show that if in (9.9.20) $\sum_{j=1}^{n} \alpha_j = 2$, then $F(\zeta) = f(x_n - 1/\zeta)$, $\mathscr{I}(\zeta) \geq 0$ or $\zeta = \zeta_\infty$, can be expressed as a Schwarz-Christoffel transformation for the polygon P, in which α_j appears for $j = 1, 2, \cdots, n - 1$, but does not appear for $j = n$.

(b) Show that if in (9.9.20) $\alpha_{n+1} = 2 - \sum_{j=1}^{n} \alpha_j \neq 0$ and x_{n+1} is a point on the real axis such that $x_{n+1} > x_n$, then

$$F(\zeta) = f\left(\frac{1}{x_{n+1} - \zeta}\right), \qquad \mathscr{I}(\zeta) \geq 0 \quad \text{or} \quad \zeta = \zeta_\infty,$$

can be expressed as a Schwarz-Christoffel transformation for the polygon P, in which α_j appears for $j = 1, 2, \cdots, n + 1$.

10. Show that the transformation

$$w = \int_0^z \frac{d\zeta}{(1 - \zeta^2)^{2/3}}$$

maps the upper half plane $\mathscr{I}(z) > 0$ one-to-one and analytically onto the interior of an equilateral triangle.

11. Find a Schwarz-Christoffel transformation (9.9.20) that maps the upper half plane $\mathscr{I}(z) > 0$ one-to-one and analytically onto the interior of a right-angled isosceles triangle.

12. Show that the transformation

$$w = \int_0^z \frac{d\zeta}{\sqrt{(1 - \zeta^2)(1 - k^2\zeta^2)}} \qquad (0 < k < 1)$$

maps the upper half plane $\mathscr{I}(z) > 0$ one-to-one and analytically onto the interior of a rectangle.

13. Show that the transformation

$$w = \int_0^z \frac{d\zeta}{\sqrt{\zeta}\sqrt{\zeta^2 - 1}}$$

maps the upper half plane $\mathscr{I}(z) > 0$ one-to-one and analytically onto the interior of a square.

14. Utilize the Schwarz-Christoffel transformation (9.9.22) to arrive at the transformation $w = (b/\pi) \operatorname{Log} z$ that maps the upper half plane $\mathscr{I}(z) > 0$ one-to-one and analytically onto the interior of the infinite strip shown in Fig. 9.9.8, with $z = 1$ mapping into $w = 0$.

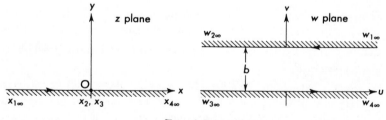

FIG. 9.9.8

15. Utilize the Schwarz-Christoffel transformation (9.9.22) to arrive at the transformation

$$w = \frac{b}{\pi} \operatorname{Log}(2\sqrt{z^2 + z} + 2z + 1)$$

that maps the upper half plane $\mathscr{I}(z) > 0$ one-to-one and analytically onto the interior of the semi-infinite strip shown in Fig. 9.9.9.

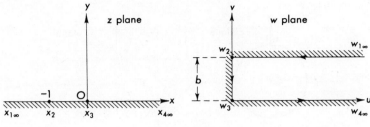

FIG. 9.9.9

16. Utilize the Schwarz-Christoffel transformation (9.9.22) to arrive at the transformation $z = w^{1/m}$ that maps the interior of the angular region $0 \leq \arg w \leq m\pi$ $(0 < m < 1)$, one-to-one and analytically onto the upper half plane $\mathscr{I}(z) > 0$ as shown in Fig. 9.9.10.

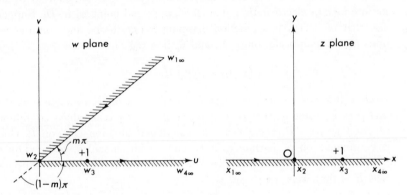

FIG. 9.9.10

17. Consider the transformation

$$w = f(z) = A \int_{z_0}^{z} (\zeta - \zeta_1)^{-\alpha_1} \cdots (\zeta - \zeta_n)^{-\alpha_n} \, d\zeta + B, \qquad |z| \leq 1,$$

where the ζ_j's are distinct and lie on the unit circle; $\arg (\zeta - \zeta_j)$ is continuous on the unit disk $|\zeta| \leq 1$, except for the point $\zeta = \zeta_j$; A, B, and the α_j's are as given in (9.9.1). Suppose that $f(z)$ maps the unit circle one-to-one onto its image. Show that $f(z)$ maps the disk $|z| \leq 1$ bicontinuously onto the set consisting of a polygon and its interior, and maps the disk $|z| < 1$ analytically onto the interior of the polygon.

18. Utilize the transformation of Exercise (9.9.17), with the α_j's as in (9.9.22), to arrive at the transformation $w = \text{Log} \, [(1 + z)/(1 - z)]$ which maps the unit disk $|z| < 1$ one-to-one and analytically onto the interior of the infinite strip shown in Fig. 9.9.11, with $z = \pm 1$ mapping into w_∞.

19. In the z plane, let R be a region consisting of a simple closed contour B and its interior D. Let $V(x, y)$ be the electrostatic potential in R due to

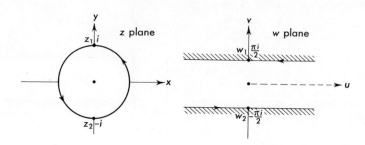

an infinite grounded cylinder and a line charge of density q, both perpendicular to the z plane piercing it respectively in B and z_0, where z_0 is a point in D. Suppose that a similar condition holds in the w plane with a line charge of the same density q, for the region R_1, simple closed contour B_1 and its interior D_1, electrostatic potential $V_1(u, v)$ and point w_0 in D_1. Suppose also that $w = f(z)$ is a function mapping R one-to-one and continuously onto R_1, D analytically onto D_1, and z_0 into w_0. Show that

$$V(x, y) = \mathscr{I}\{F_1[f(z)]\},$$

where $F_1(w) = U_1 + iV_1$ is a (multiple-valued) analytic function such that $\mathscr{I}(F_1) = V_1$. Assume that B is such that given any real-valued continuous function $g(z)$ on B, there exists a real-valued function $G(z)$ on R which is continuous on R, harmonic in D, and which coincides with $g(z)$ on B. [The problem of finding a $G(z)$ is known as the *Dirichlet problem*. Suppose that B is the circle: $|z| = \rho$. Let

$$g(z) = g(\rho e^{i\theta}) = h(\theta).$$

Then in D: $|z| = |re^{i\theta}| < \rho$, $G(z)$ is given by the Poisson integral formula

$$G(z) = H(r, \theta) = \frac{\rho^2 - r^2}{2\pi} \int_0^{2\pi} \frac{h(\varphi)\, d\varphi}{\rho^2 - 2r\rho \cos(\varphi - \theta) + r^2} \bigg].$$

The conclusion also holds if the boundaries B and B' and the mapping $w = f(z)$ are as in Example 9.9.3.

20. Find the electrostatic potential due to a line charge q placed midway between two infinite grounded plates as shown in Fig. 9.9.12.

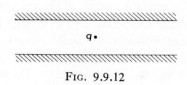

FIG. 9.9.12

Bibliography

Ahlfors, L. V. *Complex Analysis. An Introduction to the Theory of Analytic Functions of One Complex Variable.* New York: McGraw-Hill Book Company, Inc., 1953.

Apostol, T. M. *Mathematical Analysis.* Reading, Mass.: Addison-Wesley Publishing Company, Inc., 1957.

Birkhoff, G. and MacLane, S. *A Brief Survey of Modern Algebra.* New York: Macmillan Company, 1953.

Buck, R. C. *Advanced Calculus.* New York: McGraw-Hill Book Company, Inc., 1956.

Caratheodory, C. *Theory of Functions.* New York: Chelsea Publishing Company, 1954.

Churchill, R. V. *Complex Variables and Applications,* 2d ed. New York: McGraw-Hill Book Company, Inc., 1960.

Copson, E. T. *An Introduction to the Theory of Functions of a Complex Variable.* Oxford: Clarendon Press, 1935.

Franklin, P. *Functions of Complex Variables.* Englewood Cliffs, New Jersey: Prentice-Hall, Inc., 1958.

Graves, L. M. *The Theory of Functions of Real Variables,* 2d. ed. New York: McGraw-Hill Book Company, Inc., 1956.

Green, S. L. *The Theory and Use of the Complex Variable.* London: Sir Isaac Pitman and Sons, Ltd., 1948.

Hille, E. *Analytic Function Theory,* Vol. I. Boston: Ginn and Company, 1959.

Kaplan, W. *Advanced Calculus.* Reading, Mass.: Addison-Wesley Publishing Company, Inc., 1957.

Knopp, K. *Theory and Application of Infinite Series.* London and Glasgow: Blackie and Son Ltd., 1947.

———. *Funktionentheorie,* 2d. ed. (2 vols. plus 2 vols. of problems). Berlin: Sammlung Goschen, 1918-1928. Translated by Bagemihl, F., as *Theory of Functions.* New York: Dover Publications, Inc., 1945.

Kober, H. *Dictionary of Conformal Representations.* London: Admiralty Computing Service, British Admiralty, 1945.

MacRobert, T. M. *Functions of a Complex Variable.* London: MacMillan and Company, Ltd., 1938.

Miller, K. S. *Advanced Complex Calculus*. New York: Harper and Brothers, 1960.

Nehari, Z. *Conformal Mapping*. New York: McGraw-Hill Book Company, Inc., 1952.

Phillips, E. G. *Functions of a Complex Variable with Applications*, 6th ed. Edinburgh: Oliver and Boyd Limited, 1949.

Saks, S., and Zygmund, A. *Analytic Functions*. Warsaw and Wroclaw: Monografie Matematyczne, Vol. 28, 1952.

Streeter, V. L. *Fluid Dynamics*. New York: McGraw-Hill Book Company, Inc., 1948.

Thron, W. J. *Introduction to the Theory of Functions of a Complex Variable*. New York: John Wiley and Sons, Inc., 1953.

Titchmarsh, E. C. *The Theory of Functions*, 2d. ed. London: Oxford University Press, 1939.

Whittaker, E. T., and Watson, G. N. *A Course of Modern Analysis*, 4th. ed. London: Cambridge University Press, 1952.

Answers and Hints

CHAPTER 1

EXERCISES 1.2

1. $12 - i$.　　　　**2.** $-1 - 2i$.　　**3.** $106 + 18i$.　　**4.** $\dfrac{18}{13} + \dfrac{25}{13} i$.

5. $3i$.　　　　　　**6.** $-4i$.　　　　**7.** -4.

EXERCISES 1.3

3. Write $z_1 = (z_1/z_2)\, z_2$. Now apply (1.3.8).

4. $\dfrac{\sqrt{9x^2 + (3y + 1)^2}}{9x^2 + (3y - 1)^2}$.

7. Use Exercise 1.3.2.(a).

10. First, replace z_1 in (1.3.9) by $z_1 - z_2$. Thus $|z_1| - |z_2| \leq |z_1 - z_2|$. Next, replace z_2 in (1.3.9) by $z_2 - z_1$.

11. Replace z_1 in (1.3.11) by $z_1 + z_2$.

16. First show that

$$\left| \sum_{j=1}^{n} \alpha_j \beta_j \right|^2 = \sum_{j=1}^{n} |\alpha_j \beta_j|^2 + \sum_{1 \leq j < k \leq n} (\alpha_j \beta_j \overline{\alpha_k \beta_k} + \alpha_k \beta_k \overline{\alpha_j \beta_j}).$$

Next show that

$$\sum_{j=1}^{n} |\alpha_j \beta_j|^2 = \sum_{j=1}^{n} |\alpha_j|^2 \sum_{j=1}^{n} |\beta_j|^2 - \sum_{1 \leq j < k \leq n} (\alpha_j \beta_k \overline{\alpha_j \beta_k} + \alpha_k \beta_j \overline{\alpha_k \beta_j}).$$

Now substitute this latter relation into the former and simplify.

17. Use Exercise 1.3.16.

18. $\displaystyle\sum_{j=1}^{n} |\alpha_j + \beta_j|^2 \leq \sum_{j=1}^{n} |\alpha_j|\,|\alpha_j + \beta_j| + \sum_{j=1}^{n} |\beta_j|\,|\alpha_j + \beta_j|$. Now use Exercise 1.3.17.

EXERCISES 1.4

5. (a) The points $z = 1 \pm i$.

(b) All points in the complex plane except the points interior to the circle with center at $(- 5/3, 0)$ and radius $4/3$.

(c) All points interior and on the ellipse $\dfrac{x^2}{4} + \dfrac{y^2}{3} = 1$.

9. $\left| \dfrac{\alpha - \beta}{1 - \bar{\beta}\alpha} \right| = \left| \dfrac{\alpha\bar{\alpha} - \beta\bar{\alpha}}{1 - \bar{\beta}\alpha} \right| = \left| \dfrac{1 - \beta\bar{\alpha}}{1 - \bar{\beta}\alpha} \right| = 1.$

10. Let $\alpha = \alpha_1 + i\alpha_2$, then $|\alpha_1| < 1$. Consequently $1 + \alpha_1 > 0$.

12. Square the terms of the inequality. Expand $(|x| - |y|)^2 \geqq 0$.

14. Three points z_1, z_2, z_3 are collinear if, and only if, they all lie on the same line, that is, $z_3 - z_1 = k(z_2 - z_1)$, where k is a real constant.

15. Use Exercise 1.4.14.

16. Let $z_j = x_j + iy_j$, $j = 1, 2, 3$. Note that if $z_2 z_3 - 1 = 0$, then the result follows. (Why?) Assume that $z_2 z_3 - 1 \neq 0$. Then

$$z_1 = \frac{z_2 + z_3}{z_2 z_3 - 1} = \frac{|z_2|^2\, \bar{z}_3 - z_3 + |z_3|^2\, \bar{z}_2 - z_2}{D},$$

where $D = (z_2 z_3 - 1)(\bar{z}_2 \bar{z}_3 - 1) > 0$. Next show that

$$y_1 = \mathscr{I}(z_1) = -k_1 y_3 - k_2 y_2,$$

where

$$k_1 = \frac{|z_2|^2 + 1}{D} > 0 \quad \text{and} \quad k_2 = \frac{|z_3|^2 + 1}{D} > 0.$$

If $y_3 > 0$ and $y_2 > 0$, then $y_1 < 0$; if $y_3 < 0$ and $y_2 < 0$, then $y_1 > 0$.

18. (a) Note that $|z_1 + z_2| = |z_1| + |z_2|$ implies that $\mathscr{R}(z_1 \bar{z}_2) = |z_1 \bar{z}_2|$. Hence $z_1 \bar{z}_2 = \rho$, $\rho \geqq 0$. Therefore $z_1 = rz_2$, where $r = \rho/|z_2|^2 \geqq 0$.

19. (a) The center of Γ lies on the perpendicular bisector of the line segment $y = 0$, $-k \leqq x \leqq k$. Hence, the equation of Γ is $|z - bi|^2 = k^2 + b^2$; z will be exterior to, on, or interior to Γ according as $|z - bi|^2 = (z - bi)(\bar{z} + bi)$ is greater than, equal to, or less than $k^2 + b^2$, from which the conclusion may now be obtained.

(b) The circle determined by $-k, k, z_1$ is given by

$$z\bar{z} + ibz - ib\bar{z} = k^2, \quad b \text{ real}.$$

Since z_1 is on the circle, this equation is satisfied when we substitute z_1 for z. Show that this equation is also satisfied when we substitute k^2/z_1 for z.

(c) Since the three points lie on a circle, we have $z_1 = x_1 + iy_1$, where $y_1 \neq 0$. (Why?) Now apply part (b).

(d) We assume $z \neq 0$. Let z be interior to Γ. Then by part (a) we have

$$z\bar{z} - 2b\mathscr{I}(z) < k^2.$$

Multiplying this expression by the positive real number $k^2/z\bar{z}$, we get

$$k^2 - 2b\mathcal{I}\overline{\left(\frac{k^2}{z}\right)} = k^2 + 2b\mathcal{I}\left(\frac{k^2}{z}\right) < \frac{k^4}{z\bar{z}},$$

and, consequently,

$$\left(\frac{k^2}{z}\right)\overline{\left(\frac{k^2}{z}\right)} - 2b\mathcal{I}\left(\frac{k^2}{z}\right) > k^2.$$

Thus, by part (a), k^2/z is exterior to Γ. Since all of the above steps are reversible, the converse is also true.

EXERCISES 1.6

1. $z = 2\sqrt{2}\,e^{i(3/4)\pi}$. **2.** $z = 2e^{-i(\pi/3)}$. **3.** $z = 3e^{i\pi}$.

4. $z = 2e^{i(\pi/2)}$. **5.** $z = 2\sqrt{7}\,e^{i(2/3)\pi}$. **6.** $e^{i(2/3)\pi} = -\frac{1}{2} + i\frac{\sqrt{3}}{2}$

7. $4e^{i(2/3)\pi} = -2 + i2\sqrt{3}$. **8.** $\sqrt{2}\,e^{i(3/4)\pi} = -1 + i$.

9. Real part: $\dfrac{1 + \cos\theta + \cos\phi + \cos(\theta - \phi)}{2 + 2\cos\phi}$,

Imaginary part: $\dfrac{\sin\theta - \sin\phi + \sin(\theta - \phi)}{2 + 2\cos\phi}$,

Modulus: $\left(\dfrac{1 + \cos\theta}{1 + \cos\phi}\right)^{1/2}$.

12. $(z - z_0)\overline{(z - z_0)} = r^2$. See Remark 1.4.3.

13. If triangle $z_1 z_2 z_3$ is similar to triangle $z_4 z_5 z_6$, then

$$\frac{z_1 - z_2}{z_3 - z_2} = \frac{z_4 - z_5}{z_6 - z_5}. \quad \text{(Why?)}$$

This expression can be written as the determinant given in the problem.

14. Show that $|z_3 - z_2|^2 = 4|z_3 - z_1||z_1 - z_2|\sin^2(\alpha/2)$ and

$$\arg[(z_3 - z_2)^2] = \arg[(z_3 - z_1)(z_1 - z_2)].$$

It is sufficient to prove the latter equality for the case when the vector $(z_3 - z_2)$ has the same direction as the positive half of the x axis. (Why?)

17. Let $\theta_1 = \text{Arg}\left(\dfrac{z_1 - z_2}{z_3 - z_2}\right)$, that is, θ_1 is the angle through which the vector $z_3 - z_2$ must be rotated to coincide with the vector $z_1 - z_2$. Similarly, let $\theta_2 = \text{Arg}\left(\dfrac{z_3 - z_1}{z_2 - z_1}\right)$. Since the triangle is equilateral, we have $\theta_1 = \theta_2$

and $\left|\dfrac{z_1 - z_2}{z_3 - z_2}\right| = \left|\dfrac{z_3 - z_1}{z_2 - z_1}\right|$. Thus $\dfrac{z_1 - z_2}{z_3 - z_2} = \dfrac{z_3 - z_1}{z_2 - z_1}$. (Why?)

18. We shall indicate a proof of the necessity. Note that if we remove the absolute value signs from the given expression it becomes an identity. We shall now show that if the four points z_1, z_2, z_3, z_4 lie on a circle in that order, the absolute value signs may be removed. Let us write the given expression as

(a) $\qquad \left| -\dfrac{(z_2 - z_1)(z_4 - z_3)}{(z_4 - z_1)(z_2 - z_3)} \right| + 1 = \left| \dfrac{(z_4 - z_2)(z_3 - z_1)}{(z_3 - z_2)(z_4 - z_1)} \right|.$

Let $\theta_1 = \text{Arg}\left(\dfrac{z_2 - z_1}{z_4 - z_1}\right)$, that is, θ_1 is the smallest angle through which

the vector $z_4 - z_1$ must be rotated (either clockwise or counterclockwise) to coincide with the vector $z_2 - z_1$. Similarly, let

$$\theta_2 = \text{Arg}\left(\frac{z_4 - z_3}{z_2 - z_3}\right), \qquad \theta_3 = \text{Arg}\left(\frac{z_4 - z_2}{z_3 - z_2}\right), \qquad \theta_4 = \text{Arg}\left(\frac{z_3 - z_1}{z_4 - z_1}\right).$$

Then

$$\text{Arg}\left[\left(\frac{z_2 - z_1}{z_4 - z_1}\right)\left(\frac{z_4 - z_3}{z_2 - z_3}\right)\right] = |\,\theta_1 + \theta_2\,| = \pi$$

and

$$\text{Arg}\left[\left(\frac{z_4 - z_2}{z_3 - z_2}\right)\left(\frac{z_3 - z_1}{z_4 - z_1}\right)\right] = \theta_3 + \theta_4 = 0. \qquad \text{(Why?)}$$

Thus, the absolute value signs may be removed from (a). (Why?)

EXERCISES 1.8

1. $\dfrac{\sqrt{2}}{2}(1 + i), \ -\dfrac{\sqrt{2}}{2}(1 + i).$ **2.** $1, i, -1, -i.$

3. $2e^{i[(\pi/5)+k(2\pi/5)]}, \ k = 0, 1, \cdots, 4.$

4. $\dfrac{\sqrt{2} + i\sqrt{6}}{2}, \quad \dfrac{-\sqrt{6} + i\sqrt{2}}{2}, \quad -\dfrac{\sqrt{2} + i\sqrt{6}}{2}, \quad \dfrac{\sqrt{6} - i\sqrt{2}}{2}.$

5. $\cos\dfrac{\pi}{9} + i\sin\dfrac{\pi}{9}, \quad \cos\dfrac{13}{9}\pi + i\sin\dfrac{13}{9}\pi, \quad \cos\dfrac{7}{9}\pi + i\sin\dfrac{7}{9}\pi.$

6. $x = -2316 \approx -2300, \ y = -2097 \approx -2100.$

7. $\dfrac{\sqrt{2}}{2}(1 + i), \quad \dfrac{\sqrt{2}}{2}(-1 + i), \quad -\dfrac{\sqrt{2}}{2}(1 + i), \quad \dfrac{\sqrt{2}}{2}(1 - i).$

8. $-1, i, -i.$

9. For the first part, proceed as in Example 1.8.1. For the second part, let $z = x + iy$. Then $32z^5 = (z+1)^5$ implies that $4(x^2 + y^2) = (x+1)^2 + y^2$, from which we obtain $(x - 1/3)^2 + y^2 = (2/3)^2$.

16. $\left[\dfrac{1 + \sin\theta + i\cos\theta}{1 + \sin\theta - i\cos\theta}\right]^n = \left[\dfrac{(1 + \sin\theta + i\cos\theta)^2}{2(1 + \sin\theta)}\right]^n = (\sin\theta + i\cos\theta)^n.$

17. $2\sqrt[3]{2}\cos\dfrac{\pi}{9}, \quad 2\sqrt[3]{2}\cos\dfrac{7}{9}\pi, \quad 2\sqrt[3]{2}\cos\dfrac{13}{9}\pi.$

18. $7 + 2\sqrt{3} + i(4 + 3\sqrt{3}), \quad 7 - 2\sqrt{3} + i(4 - 3\sqrt{3}).$

19. Let z_1, z_2, z_3 be the roots of $z^3 - 3pz^2 + 3qz - r = 0$. Then

$$(z - z_1)(z - z_2)(z - z_3) = 0,$$

which gives

$$z^3 - (z_1 + z_2 + z_3)z^2 + (z_1z_2 + z_2z_3 + z_3z_1)z - z_1z_2z_3 = 0.$$

Thus $p = (1/3)(z_1 + z_2 + z_3)$. Why is p the centroid of the triangle? Let z_1, z_2, z_3 be the vertices of the equilateral triangle ABC. Utilize Exercise 1.6.17 to show that $p^2 = q$.

20. $\displaystyle\sum_{k=0}^{n} \cos k\theta + i\sum_{k=1}^{n} \sin k\theta = \dfrac{1 - (\cos\theta + i\sin\theta)^{n+1}}{1 - \cos\theta - i\sin\theta}$

$$= \frac{1}{2} + \frac{\sin(n+1)\theta\cos\theta/2 - \cos(n+1)\theta\sin\theta/2}{2\sin\theta/2}$$

$$+ \left[\frac{1}{2}\cot\frac{\theta}{2} - \frac{\sin(n+1)\theta\sin\theta/2 + \cos(n+1)\theta\cos\theta/2}{2\sin\theta/2}\right]i.$$

21. (b) $(2\cos\theta)^n = \left(z + \dfrac{1}{z}\right)^n = z^n + \dfrac{n}{1!}z^{n-1}\left(\dfrac{1}{z}\right) + \dfrac{n(n-1)}{2!}z^{n-2}\left(\dfrac{1}{z^2}\right) +$

$$\cdots + \frac{n(n-1)\cdots 3}{(n-2)!}z^2\left(\frac{1}{z^{n-2}}\right) + \frac{n(n-1)\cdots 2}{(n-1)!}z\left(\frac{1}{z^{n-1}}\right) + \frac{1}{z^n}$$

$$= \left(z^n + \frac{1}{z^n}\right) + \frac{n}{1!}\left(z^{n-2} + \frac{1}{z^{n-2}}\right) + \frac{n(n-1)}{2!}\left(z^{n-4} + \frac{1}{z^{n-4}}\right) + \cdots$$

$$= 2\cos n\theta + 2\frac{n}{1!}\cos(n-2)\theta + 2\frac{n(n-1)}{2!}\cos(n-4)\theta + \cdots.$$

CHAPTER 2

Exercises 2.2

9. Suppose that S is separated into the sets T_1 and T_2 and that the common point z_0 is in T_1. Show that every S_α is in T_1 and hence T_2 is empty.

10. Suppose that F is separated into the sets F_1 and F_2. Then E must be either contained entirely in F_1 or entirely in F_2. (Why?) Suppose that E is contained in F_1. Then each accumulation point of E must also be in F_1. (Why?)

11. All points interior and on the circle $(x - 1)^2 + y^2 = 1$.

12. All points exterior and on the circle $(x - 1)^2 + y^2 = 1$.

13. All points to the right of the y axis.

14. All points interior to the infinite strip $-\infty < x < \infty,\ 0 \leqq y \leqq 2\pi$.

15. All points interior and on the lemniscate $(x^2 + y^2)^2 = 2(x^2 - y^2)$.

16. All points interior and on the oval $(x^2 + y^2)^2 - 2(x^2 - y^2) = 24$.

17. The complex plane excluding the domain with boundary $x^2 - y^2 = 9$.

18. The complex plane excluding the domain with boundary $2xy = 9$.

19. All points interior to the annulus of two concentric circles of radius 2 and 4 respectively, both with center at $(1, 0)$, plus the points on the circumference of these circles.

20. All points exterior and on the circle $(x - 31/15)^2 + y^2 = 16/225$.

21. All points of the complex plane.

22. All points interior and on the ellipse $x^2/4 + y^2/3 = 1$.

23. All points in the first quadrant to the right and on the line $y = x$.

24. All points in the infinite strip $-\infty < y < \infty,\ 0 \leqq x < 2\pi$. Note that the points on the line $x = 0$ are included, but those on the line $x = 2\pi$ are excluded.

25. All points interior and on the oval $(x^2 + y^2)\,[(x - 1)^2 + y^2] = 1$.

26. All points in the half plane $x \geqq 0$.

27. All points exterior and on the closed polar curve
$$4r^2 + r\cos\theta - 9r + 4 = 0.$$

28. All points interior and on the circle $(x - 1)^2 + (y - 2)^2 = 9$.

29. All points exterior and on the circle $(x + 2/3)^2 + (y - 8/3)^2 = 32/9$.

30. All points exterior and on the circle $(x - 3/2)^2 + y^2 = 1/4$.

Exercises 2.3

3. Suppose that there were two distinct points z_1 and z_2 common to all the S_n. Then we would have diameter $(S_n) \geqq |\,z_2 - z_1\,|$ for all n.

4. Suppose that $z_n \to z_0$. Then for any $\epsilon > 0$, there exists an integer N such that $|z_n - z_0| < \epsilon/2$ and $|z_m - z_0| < \epsilon/2$ for all $m > N$ and $n > N$. Consequently $|z_n - z_m| < \epsilon$ for all $m > N$ and $n > N$.

5. Let z_1 be a point in S. Then there exists a point z_2 such that $|z_1 - z_2| \geq 1$. For, otherwise, all points of S would be interior to a circle of unit radius and center at z_1. Similarly, there exists a point z_3 such that $|z_1 - z_3| \geq 1$ and $|z_2 - z_3| \geq 1$. (Why?) Continuing this process we obtain the desired sequence.

6. If $\{z_n\}$ had an accumulation point z_0, then by Exercise 2.3.1 $z'_m \to z_0$ for some subsequence $\{z'_m\}$ of $\{z_n\}$, and by Exercise 2.3.4 $\{z'_m\}$ would be a Cauchy sequence.

7. For any $\epsilon > 0$, choose $N_0 = N_0(\epsilon)$ so that $|z_k - z_0| < \epsilon/2$ for $k > N_0$. With N_0 fixed, choose $N_1 > N_0$ so that

$$(1/n)\left|\sum_{k=1}^{N_0}(z_k - z_0)\right| < \epsilon/2 \text{ for } n > N_1.$$ Then, for $n > N_1$, we have

$$|\zeta_n - z_0| = \left|\frac{1}{n}\sum_{k=1}^{n}(z_k - z_0)\right| \leqq \left|\frac{1}{n}\sum_{k=1}^{N_0}(z_k - z_0)\right| + \left|\frac{1}{n}\sum_{k=N_0+1}^{n}(z_k - z_0)\right|$$

$$< \frac{\epsilon}{2} + \frac{\epsilon}{2} = \epsilon.$$

8. Let the sequence $\{z_n\}$ converge to z_0. Then for any n,

$$|z_n| = |(z_n - z_0) + z_0| \leqq |z_n - z_0| + |z_0|.$$

Take $\epsilon = 1$ in (2.3.2) and let N be such that $|z_n - z_0| < 1$ for all $n > N$. Then $|z_n| < 1 + |z_0|$ for all $n > N$. Let

$$M = \max(|z_1|, |z_2|, \cdots, |z_N|, 1 + |z_0|).$$

Then $|z_n| \leqq M$ for all n. Thus the sequence $\{z_n\}$ is bounded.

EXERCISES 2.4

2. Suppose A is a set of real numbers such that if t_1 and t_2 are in A, then all t, $t_1 \leqq t \leqq t_2$ are also in A. Let t_0 be any point in A, and let A_1 be the set of all t in A such that $t \leqq t_0$. Then by Exercise 2.4.1, A_1 has a greatest lower bound α, finite or infinite. Similarly, if A_2 is the set of all t in A such that $t \geqq t_0$, then A_2 has a least upper bound β. Show that the set A consists of the open interval (α, β) together with none, one, or both of its boundary points. (It is assumed that A contains at least two points.)

4. Consider two cases. Case 1. The sequence $\{x_n\}$ contains only a finite number of distinct points. Then one of these points occurs an infinite number of times, and consequently is an accumulation point of the sequence. Case 2.

The sequence $\{x_n\}$ contains an infinite number of distinct points. For this case, apply the Bolzano-Weierstrass Property (4) of Section 2.4 for real numbers.

5. Use the method employed in Exercise 2.4.4.

7. Suppose first that I is not an interval. By Exercise 2.4.2 there exist two points t_1, t_2 in I, and a point t_0, $t_1 < t_0 < t_2$ such that t_0 is not in I. Let S_1 denote the points of I less than t_0, and S_2 the points of I greater than t_0. Show that the set I is separated in the sense of Definition 2.2.3 into the sets S_1 and S_2. Conversely, suppose that I_0 is a closed interval $[\alpha, \beta]$, where α and β are finite, and that I_0 is the union of two disjoint nonempty sets S_1 and S_2. Subdivide I_0 into two equal closed subintervals. Then one of them, say I_1, contains points of S_1 and S_2. (Why?) Continuing this process we arrive at a nested sequence of closed intervals $I_0 \supset I_1 \supset I_2 \supset \cdots$, such that each interval I_n contains points both of S_1 and S_2 and the length of I_n approaches zero. By the Nested Interval Property of Section 2.4, there exists a point t_0 common to all the intervals I_n. The point t_0 is an accumulation point of S_1 and S_2. (Why?) But t_0 belongs to S_1 or S_2. Thus, one of the sets S_1 or S_2 contains an accumulation point of the other. Hence I_0 cannot be separated and is therefore connected. Finally, suppose that I is an interval (not necessarily closed). Then I is the union of a family of finite closed intervals having at least one point in common. By the preceding discussion, each of these closed intervals is connected. By Exercise 2.2.9 their union is connected. (It is assumed I contains at least two points.)

EXERCISES 2.5

1. To show that S is closed, note that its complement is open. (Why?) Now use Exercise 2.2.3.

3. First consider the case when S contains an infinite number of points. Let t_2 be its least upper bound. Then for every $\epsilon > 0$, there exists a point t in S such that $t_2 - \epsilon < t \leq t_2$. Hence t_2 is an accumulation point of S. Since S is closed, t_2 is in S. Similarly, the greatest lower bound t_1 is in S. Next, consider the case when S is finite.

4. We may form a (bounded) sequence $\{z_n\}$ such that for $n = 1, 2, \cdots$, z_n is contained in R_n. Let z_0 be an accumulation point of $\{z_n\}$. Then, for each n, z_0 is an accumulation point of the subsequence $\{z_{n+1}, z_{n+2}, \cdots\}$ contained in R_n. (Why?) Thus z_0 is an accumulation point of R_n and consequently belongs to R_n. (Why?)

6. Apply Theorem 2.5.1 to the bounded closed set I.

7. Apply Exercise 2.4.5.

EXERCISES 2.7

2. Use Theorem 2.3.3.

3. Let $S = \sum_{n=1}^{\infty} z_n$, $S_N = \sum_{n=1}^{N-1} z_n$, $R_N = \sum_{n=N}^{\infty} z_n$. Let $\epsilon > 0$. For N sufficiently large we have $|S - S_N| = |R_N| < \epsilon$. (Why?) Hence

$$\left|\sum_{n=1}^{\infty} z_n\right| = |S| = |S_N + R_N| \leq |S_N| + |R_N| = \left|\sum_{n=1}^{N-1} z_n\right| + |R_N|$$

$$\leq \sum_{n=1}^{N-1} |z_n| + |R_N| < \sum_{n=1}^{\infty} |z_n| + \epsilon.$$

EXERCISES 2.8

2. Consider the upper limit $(-\alpha)$ of the sequence $\{-x_n\}$.

7. (a) No limit, since there are four accumulation points: ± 1, $\pm i$.
(b) 0. (c) No limit, since there are two accumulation points: $\pm 1 + i$.
(d) 0.   (e) $-1 - i$.   (f) 0.

8. (a) Divergent.   (b) Absolutely convergent.   (c) Convergent.
(d) Divergent.   (e) Convergent.   (f) Absolutely convergent.
(g) Absolutely convergent.   (h) Absolutely convergent.
(i) Divergent.   (j) Absolutely convergent.
(k) Absolutely convergent.   (l) Absolutely convergent.
(m) Divergent.   (n) Absolutely convergent.

EXERCISES 2.9

2. Use Theorem 2.9.2 and Exercises 2.4.7 and 2.4.2.

5. Use Exercises 2.9.3 and 2.9.4.

6. Apply Exercise 2.9.1 to the mappings T and T^{-1}.

7. Apply Theorem 2.9.2 to the mappings T and T^{-1}.

8. Apply Exercise 2.9.1 to the mapping T^{-1}.

9. Use Exercise 2.9.8.

11. Let $T(D_i)$ denote the image of D_i $(i = 1, 2)$ under T. By Theorem 2.9.2 $T(D_i)$ is connected, and consequently must be contained in D_1' or in D_2'. Also $T(D_1)$ and $T(D_2)$ cannot both be contained in the same D_i'. (Why?) Suppose, for example, that $T(D_1) \subset D_1'$ and $T(D_2) \subset D_2'$. Now apply Exercise 2.9.10.

12. Let S be a nonempty subset of a group G. First show that if S has the property that T_1^{-1} and $T_2 T_1$ are elements of S whenever T_1 and T_2 are elements of S, then S is a group. Now use Theorem 2.9.5.

EXERCISES 2.10

1. Use the fact that C is a continuous mapping.

2. The set of such points is the image of an interval under a continuous mapping. Now use Exercice 2.4.7 and Theorem 2.9.2.

4. The points z on the segment joining z_1 to z_2 are given by $z = z_1 + t(z_2 - z_1)$, $0 \leq t \leq 1$. Let the circle be given by $|z - z_0| = R$, and have z_1 and z_2 in its interior. Then

$$|z_1 + t(z_2 - z_1) - z_0| = |(z_1 - z_0)(1 - t) + t(z_2 - z_0)|$$
$$< R(1 - t) + Rt = R.$$

5. Use Exercise 2.10.4.

6. Since D is an open set, there exists a circle with center at z whose interior is in D. (a) Now apply Exercise 2.10.5. (b) Suppose that the conclusion is false. Use Exercise 2.10.5 to obtain a contradiction.

7. Use Theorem 2.9.3 together with the fact that the set of all t such that $\alpha \leq t \leq \beta$ is bounded and closed.

8. For each t, $\alpha \leq t \leq \beta$, let $N(t)$ be a neighborhood of t such that the image of $N(t)$ on the contour C given by $z = z(t)$ is contained in D_t. (For $t = \alpha$ or β, use half-neighborhoods.) By Theorem 2.5.1, a finite number $N(t_1), \cdots, N(t_k)$ of the $N(t)$ cover I. Let $D(t_1), \cdots, D(t_k)$ denote the corresponding domains. Let k be minimal. Clearly, if $k = 1, 2$, Lemma 2.10.1 holds. Suppose that $k \geq 3$. Let $N(t_j): \alpha_j < t < \beta_j$, be indexed so that $\alpha = \alpha_1 \leq \alpha_2 < \cdots < \alpha_k$. Then (a) $\beta_1 < \cdots < \beta_{k-1} \leq \beta_k = \beta$, (b) $\alpha_{j+1} < \beta_j$, $j = 1, 2, \cdots, k - 1$, (c) $\beta_j \leq \alpha_{j+2}$, $j = 1, 2, \cdots, k - 2$. Now, let $t'_j = (\alpha_{j+1} + \beta_j)/2$, $j = 1, 2, \cdots, k - 1$.

EXERCISES 2.11

1. Write $P = (x_1, x_2, \cdots, x_{k-1}, x_k)$ as (Q, x_k), where $Q = (x_1, x_2, \cdots, x_{k-1})$ Then following the proof of Theorem 2.3.3, show that $P^{(n)} = (Q^{(n)}, x_k^{(n)})$ converges to $P^{(0)} = (Q^{(0)}, x_k^{(0)})$ if, and only if, $Q^{(n)}$ converges to $Q^{(0)}$ and $x_k^{(n)}$ converges to $x_k^{(0)}$. Now use mathematical induction to complete the proof.

EXERCISES 2.12

2. (a) The equations of QN are given by $X = 0 + \xi t$, $Y = 0 + \eta t$, $Z = 1 + (\zeta - 1)t$. Setting $Z = 0$, we obtain $t = 1/(1 - \zeta)$. Hence $z = x + iy = (\xi + i\eta)t = (\xi + i\eta)/(1 - \zeta)$.

(b) By part (a), $\xi + i\eta = z(1 - \zeta)$. Thus $\xi - i\eta = \bar{z}(1 - \zeta)$. Therefore $\xi^2 + \eta^2 = z\bar{z}(1 - \zeta)^2$. Use Exercise 2.12.1 to obtain $\zeta = (1 - \zeta)z\bar{z}$. Solving for ζ and then using the above equations for $\xi + i\eta$ and $\xi - i\eta$, obtain the result.

3. Since (x_n, y_n) converges to (x_0, y_0), we have $x_n \to x_0$ and $y_n \to y_0$. (See Theorem 2.3.3.) It follows from Theorem 2.6.1 that

$$\frac{x_n}{x_n^2 + y_n^2 + 1} \to \frac{x_0}{x_0^2 + y_0^2 + 1}, \qquad \frac{y_n}{x_n^2 + y_n^2 + 1} \to \frac{y_0}{x_0^2 + y_0^2 + 1}$$

and

$$\frac{x_n^2 + y_n^2}{x_n^2 + y_n^2 + 1} \rightarrow \frac{x_0^2 + y_0^2}{x_0^2 + y_0^2 + 1}.$$

Apply now Exercise 2.11.1 to obtain the result.

4. Use the method given in the hint to Exercise 2.12.3.

5. Use Theorem 2.9.1 (see Remark 2.11.1) and Exercises 2.12.3 and 2.12.4.

6. Let the point in the plane and on the punctured sphere Σ' representing z_n, $n = 0, 1, \cdots$, be denoted by Q_n and P_n, respectively. Then $Q_n = T(P_n)$ and $Q_0 = T(P_0)$, where T is the mapping described in this section. It is required to show that $P_n \rightarrow P_0$ if, and only if, $Q_n \rightarrow Q_0$. The result now follows from Theorem 2.9.1 and Exercise 2.12.5.

7. Since (ξ, η, ζ) is on Σ, we have by Exercise 2.12.1 $\xi^2 + \eta^2 = \zeta(1 - \zeta)$. From Exercise 2.12.2.(a) we have $z = (\xi + i\eta)/(1 - \zeta)$. Hence

$$|z|^2 = \frac{\xi^2 + \eta^2}{(1 - \zeta)^2} = \frac{\zeta}{1 - \zeta} = \frac{1}{1 - \zeta} - 1,$$

from which the result may now be obtained.

8. The distance is given by $\sqrt{\xi^2 + \eta^2 + (\zeta - 1)^2}$. The result now follows from Exercise 2.12.1.

9. Use Exercises 2.12.7 and 2.12.8.

10. Use Exercise 2.12.9.

12. Use Exercises 2.12.5, 2.9.6 and 2.9.7.

CHAPTER 3

EXERCISES 3.3

1. All z.   **2.** All z, except $z = 4$.   **3.** All z, except $z = \pm i$.

4. All z.   **5.** All z.   **6.** All z, except $z = 1$, $z = \pm 3i$.

7. All z.   **8.** All z, except $z = -1$.

9. $w = u + iv = x^3 - 3xy^2 - 2x + i(3x^2y - y^3 - 2y)$.

10. $w = u + iv = xy + i(y + y^2)$.

11. $w = u + iv = \dfrac{x}{x^2 + y^2} - i\dfrac{y}{x^2 + y^2}$.

12. $w = u + iv = \dfrac{x + 1}{(x + 1)^2 + y^2} - i\dfrac{y}{(x + 1)^2 + y^2}$.

13. $w = u + iv = 2x^2 - 2y^2 - x + 1 + i(4xy - y)$.

14. $w = u + iv = \dfrac{x^2 + y^2 - 1}{(x + 1)^2 + y^2} + i\dfrac{2y}{(x + 1)^2 + y^2}$.

15. $w = u + iv = \dfrac{x^2 - y^2}{(x^2 + y^2)^2} - i\,\dfrac{2xy}{(x^2 + y^2)^2}$.

16. $w = u + iv = \dfrac{x^3 + xy^2 - x}{(x^2 - y^2 - 1)^2 + 4x^2y^2} - i\,\dfrac{y^3 + x^2y + y}{(x^2 - y^2 - 1)^2 + 4x^2y^2}$.

17. $\delta(\epsilon) = \dfrac{\epsilon}{8}$.   **18.** $\delta(\epsilon) = \epsilon$.   **19.** $\delta(\epsilon) = \dfrac{\epsilon}{27}$.

20. From (1.3.7), $|\mathscr{R}(z^2)| \leqq |z|^2$.

21. Choose $\epsilon = 1/10$, and suppose that a $\delta, 0 < \delta < 1$ can be found in accordance with Definition 3.3.3. Choose $z = 1 - \delta$ and $z_0 = 1 - 9\delta/10$. Then $|z - z_0| = \delta/10 < \delta$; however,

$$|f(z) - f(z_0)| = \left| \frac{1}{1 - (1 - \delta)} - \frac{1}{1 - (1 - 9\delta/10)} \right| = \frac{1}{9\delta} > \frac{1}{10}.$$

23. If $f(z)$ is uniformly continuous in D, then for every $\epsilon > 0$ there exists a $\delta > 0$, which depends only on ϵ, such that $|f(z) - f(z_0)| < \epsilon$ when $|z - z_0| < \delta$ and z and z_0 belong to D. Hence $\lim_{z \to z_0} f(z) = f(z_0)$.

24. Suppose to the contrary that there exists an $\epsilon > 0$, such that for every $\delta > 0$, there exists a z' such that $|z' - z_0| < \delta$, yet $|f(z') - f(z_0)| \geqq \epsilon$. Now, let $\delta = \delta_n = 1/n$ and let $z' = z_n$ $(n = 1, 2, \cdots)$. Thus we have constructed a sequence $\{z_n\}$ such that $|z_n - z_0| < \delta_n = 1/n$, yet $|f(z_n) - f(z_0)| \geqq \epsilon$. Clearly, the sequence $\{z_n\}$ converges to z_0. However, $|f(z_n) - f(z_0)| \geqq \epsilon$ for all n. But this is contrary to the original hypothesis [that $f(z_n) \to f(z_0)$ whenever $z_n \to z_0$]. Thus $f(z)$ is continuous at z_0.

25. Use Theorem 2.9.3.

26. Use Theorem 2.9.4.

27. (a) Let $g(z) = |z - \zeta_0|$. Then $g(z)$ is a continuous real-valued function on C. Now use Exercise 3.3.26.

(b) Use Exercise 2.10.7 and part (a).

(c) Use part (b).

28. By Theorem 2.9.2, the image of S under the mapping $w = g(z)$ is connected. Now, any set of integers containing more than one element is not connected. (Why?) Hence the image of S under the mapping $w = g(z)$ must contain only one integer.

29. Let z_1 and z_2 be any two points in the plane, and let ζ_1 and ζ_2 be any two points in Σ such that $\rho(z_1) = |z_1 - \zeta_1|$ and $\rho(z_2) = |z_2 - \zeta_2|$. Then $\rho(z_2) \leqq |z_2 - \zeta_1|$. (Why?) Consequently,

$$\rho(z_2) - \rho(z_1) \leqq |z_2 - \zeta_1| - |z_1 - \zeta_1| \leqq |z_2 - z_1|.$$

Similarly, $\rho(z_1) - \rho(z_2) \leqq |z_1 - z_2|$. Hence $|\rho(z_1) - \rho(z_2)| \leqq |z_1 - z_2|$.

30. Let $\rho(z)$ denote the (minimum) distance from z to Σ. By Exercise 3.3.29 $\rho(z)$ is continuous, and consequently by Exercise 3.3.26 there exists a point z_0 in S such that $\rho(z) \geqq \rho(z_0)$ for all z in S. Let ζ_0 be a point in Σ such that $\rho(z_0) = |z_0 - \zeta_0|$. Then, if z and ζ are any two points in S and Σ respectively, we have $|z - \zeta| \geqq \rho(z) \geqq |z_0 - \zeta_0|$.

31. Let ζ_1 and z_1 be any two points in Σ and S, respectively. Draw a circle C: $|z - \zeta_1| = R$ where $R = |z_1 - \zeta_1| + $ diameter (Σ). Hence $|z - \zeta| \geqq |z_1 - \zeta_1|$ for all z exterior to C and all ζ in Σ. Let S_1 be the intersection of S with the disk $|z - \zeta_1| \leqq R$. Then S_1 is bounded and closed. (Why?) By Exercise 3.3.30 there exists a point ζ_0 in Σ and a point z_0 in S_1 such that $|z - \zeta| \geqq |z_0 - \zeta_0|$ for all ζ in Σ and all z in S_1. Hence $|z - \zeta| \geqq |z_0 - \zeta_0|$ for all ζ in Σ and all z in S. (Why?)

32. Let $\{z_n\}$ be a sequence of points in S such that $z_n \to z_0$. Then $\{f(z_n)\}$ is a Cauchy sequence and by Theorem 2.4.1 has a limit, say w_0. Now $f(z_n) \to w_0$ and

$$\lim_{\substack{\eta \to z_0 \\ \zeta \to z_0}} [f(\eta) - f(\zeta)] = 0.$$

Thus, for each $\epsilon > 0$, there exists an $n_0 = n_0(\epsilon) > 0$ and a neighborhood $N = N(z_0, \epsilon)$ of z_0, such that for all $n > n_0$ and all z in N, we have

$$|f(z) - w_0| \leqq |f(z) - f(z_n)| + |f(z_n) - w_0| < \epsilon/2 + \epsilon/2 = \epsilon.$$

Therefore, $\lim_{z \to z_0} f(z) = w_0$.

33. Let the compact set be denoted by S and its image by Σ. Let w_0 be in Σ and let $\{w_n\}$ be any sequence in Σ such that $w_n \to w_0$. Then, since S is compact, the sequence $\{\zeta_n\} = \{f^{-1}(w_n)\}$ has an accumulation point ζ_0 in S. Hence, there exists a subsequence $\{\zeta_{n_j}\}$ of $\{\zeta_n\}$ such that $\zeta_{n_j} \to \zeta_0$. Since $f(z)$ is continuous, we have

$$f(\zeta_0) = \lim_{j \to \infty} f(\zeta_{n_j}) = \lim_{j \to \infty} w_{n_j} = w_0.$$

Therefore, $\zeta_0 = f^{-1}(w_0)$. Hence the bounded sequence $\{\zeta_n\}$ has ζ_0 as its only accumulation point. (Why?) Thus $\zeta_n \to \zeta_0$, that is, $f^{-1}(w_n) \to f^{-1}(w_0)$. Consequently (see Exercise 3.3.24), $f^{-1}(w)$ is continuous.

EXERCISES 3.5

1. $40z^3 + 2z^2 - 8.$

2. $5z^4 - 6z^2 + 1.$

3. $\dfrac{-z^4 + 14z^2 - 10z + 8}{(z^3 + 2z - 5)^2}.$

4. $\dfrac{2}{z^3}(z^4 - 1).$

5. $\dfrac{4}{27z^{13}}(z^6 - 1)^3(z^6 + 1).$

11. There exists an $\epsilon > 0$ such that $f(z)$ is continuous in the neighborhood given by $|z - z_0| < \epsilon$. Hence, $f(z)$ is continuous on the bounded closed set R given by $|z - z_0| \leq \epsilon/2$. Thus, by Exercise 3.3.25 there exists a constant M such that $|f(z)| \leq M$ when z is in R, and consequently $|f(z)| \leq M$ when $|z - z_0| < \epsilon/2$. [For another proof use (3.3.3).]

EXERCISES 3.6

1. Analytic everywhere.   2. Nowhere.   3. Nowhere.

4. Everywhere, except at $z = \pm 2i$.   5. Nowhere.   6. Nowhere.

7. Nowhere.   8. Nowhere.

9. Suppose that $f'(0)$ exists. Then

$$f'(0) = \lim_{z \to 0} \frac{f(z) - f(0)}{z - 0} = \lim_{z \to 0} \frac{xy^2}{x^2 + y^4} \, .$$

First, let $z \to 0$ along the line $y = x$. Next, let $z \to 0$ along the curve $y^2 = x$.

10. We shall indicate a proof of the necessity. Suppose that

$$w = f(z) = u(r, \theta) + iv(r, \theta)$$

is analytic in D, where $z = x + iy$, $x = r \cos \theta$ and $y = r \sin \theta$. Let us denote differentiation with respect to z by $'$ and partial derivatives by the usual subscript, that is, $dw/dz = w'$ .and $\partial w/\partial r = w_r$. Since $w = f(z)$ is analytic, $w' = (w')_\theta = w_r(r')_\theta$, where θ is held fixed, and $w' = (w')_r = w_\theta(\theta')_r$, where r is held fixed. Since $z = x + iy = r \cos \theta + ir \sin \theta$, we have $(r')_\theta = \cos \theta - i \sin \theta$, and $(\theta')_r = -(i/r)(\cos \theta - i \sin \theta)$. But $w_r(r')_\theta = w_\theta(\theta')_r$. Consequently, $w_r(\cos \theta - i \sin \theta) = w_\theta[-(i/r)(\cos \theta - i \sin \theta)]$. Therefore, $w_r = -(i/r) w_\theta$. Since $w = u(r, \theta) + iv(r, \theta)$, $w_r = u_r + iv_r$ and $w_\theta = u_\theta + iv_\theta$. Therefore, $u_r + iv_r = (1/r) v_\theta - (i/r) u_\theta$. Hence

$$\frac{\partial u}{\partial r} = \frac{1}{r}\frac{\partial v}{\partial \theta} \quad \text{and} \quad \frac{\partial v}{\partial r} = -\frac{1}{r}\frac{\partial u}{\partial \theta} \, .$$

[For another proof use equations (3.6.1).]

13. Use (3.6.9).

14. Let $F(z) = f(z) - g(z)$ with $f'(z) = g'(z)$. Apply Exercise 3.6.13 to $F'(z)$.

16. (b) Apply part (a) to the function $if(z)$.

17. Let $u^2 + v^2 = c$, where c is a constant different from zero. Since $f(z)$ is analytic, in view of (3.6.1), we then get $uu_x - vu_y = 0$ and $uu_y + vu_x = 0$. Solving these two equations simultaneously for u_x and u_y, we obtain $u_x = 0$ and $u_y = 0$. (If $c = 0$, then $u = v = 0$.)

18. $\lim_{z \to z_0} \dfrac{f(z)}{g(z)} = \lim_{z \to z_0} \left(\dfrac{f(z) - f(z_0)}{z - z_0} \Big/ \dfrac{g(z) - g(z_0)}{z - z_0} \right) = \dfrac{f'(z_0)}{g'(z_0)} \, .$

19. $|x^3 \pm y^3| \leq |x|^3 + |y|^3 = |x|\, x^2 + |y|\, y^2$
$\leq (x^2 + y^2)^{1/2}\, x^2 + (x^2 + y^2)^{1/2}\, y^2 = (x^2 + y^2)^{3/2}.$

20.
$$\frac{g(z) - g(z_0)}{z - z_0} = \frac{\overline{f(\bar{z})} - \overline{f(\bar{z}_0)}}{\bar{z} - \bar{z}_0} = \overline{\left[\frac{f(\zeta) - f(\zeta_0)}{\zeta - \zeta_0}\right]},$$

where $\zeta = \bar{z}$ and $\zeta_0 = \bar{z}_0$. Now, note that when z and z_0 are in $\bar{D}$, ζ and ζ_0 are in D. Hence $g'(z) = \overline{f'(\bar{z})}$ exists in $\bar{D}$.

EXERCISES 3.8

1. $v = -\dfrac{y}{x^2 + y^2} + c.$

2. $v = \tan^{-1}\dfrac{y}{x} + c.$

3. $v = 3x^2 y - y^3 + c.$

4. $v = \sinh x \sin y + c.$

5. $v = -\frac{1}{2}\ln\left[(x - a)^2 + (y - b)^2\right] + c.$

6. $u + iv = e^x x \cos y - e^x y \sin y + i(e^x x \sin y + e^x y \cos y + c) = z e^z + C.$

7. $u + iv = x^3 + 3x^2 - 3xy^2 - 3y^2 + 1 + i(3x^2 y - y^3 + 6xy + c) = z^3 + 3z^2 + C.$

8. $u + iv = (x - 1)^3 - 3xy^2 + 3y^2 + i[3y(x - 1)^2 - y^3 + c] = (z - 1)^3 + C.$

9. $u + iv = e^{x^2 - y^2}\cos 2xy + i(e^{x^2 - y^2}\sin 2xy + c) = e^{z^2} + C.$

10. The level curves $u = C_1$: $\left(x - \dfrac{1}{2C_1}\right)^2 + y^2 = \left(\dfrac{1}{2C_1}\right)^2$; and $v = C_2$:

$$x^2 + \left(y + \frac{1}{2C_2}\right)^2 = \left(\frac{1}{2C_2}\right)^2.$$

11. The level curves $u = C_1$: $\left(x + \dfrac{4C_1}{1 - C_1}\right)^2 + y^2 = \left(\dfrac{4}{1 - C_1}\right)^2$; and

$$v = C_2: (x - 4)^2 + \left(y + \frac{4}{C_2}\right)^2 = \left(\frac{4}{C_2}\right)^2.$$

12. $u_{1\zeta\zeta} + u_{1\eta\eta} = [(x_\zeta)^2 + (x_\eta)^2]\, u_{xx} + [x_{\zeta\zeta} + x_{\eta\eta}]\, u_x$
$\qquad\qquad + [(y_\zeta)^2 + (y_\eta)^2]\, u_{yy} + [y_{\zeta\zeta} + y_{\eta\eta}]\, u_y + 2[x_\zeta y_\zeta + x_\eta y_\eta]u_{xy}.$

13. Let $w = \mu - \lambda$, where $\mu = \log_e |f'|$ and $\lambda = \log_e (1 - |f|^2)$. Let Δ denote the Laplacian operator. Show that $\Delta\mu = 0$. Hence $\Delta w = -\Delta\lambda$. Also $|f|^2 = 1 - e^\lambda$. Take the Laplacian of both sides in the last equality, and use Exercise 3.6.12.(b) to obtain $4|f'|^2 = -e^\lambda(\lambda_x^2 + \lambda_y^2 + \Delta\lambda)$. Next use Exercise 3.6.12.(a) to find that $\lambda_x^2 + \lambda_y^2 = (4|f|^2|f'|^2)/(1 - |f|^2)^2.$

16. Concerning formula (b):

$$2u(x, y) = f(z) + \overline{f(z)} = \sum_{n=0}^{\infty} c_n z^n + \overline{\sum_{n=0}^{\infty} c_n z^n}$$

$$= \sum_{n=0}^{\infty} c_n(x + iy)^n + \sum_{n=0}^{\infty} \bar{c}_n(x - iy)^n.$$

Therefore

$$2u\left(\frac{z}{2},\frac{z}{2i}\right) = \sum_{n=0}^{\infty} c_n \left[\frac{z}{2} + i\left(\frac{z}{2i}\right)\right]^n + \overline{c_0} + \sum_{n=1}^{\infty} \overline{c_n}\left[\frac{z}{2} - i\left(\frac{z}{2i}\right)\right]^n$$

$$= \sum_{n=0}^{\infty} c_n z^n + \overline{c_0} = f(z) + \overline{c_0}.$$

Also note that

$$2u(0,0) = f(0) + \overline{c_0} = c_0 + \overline{c_0} = 2\mathscr{R}(c_0).$$

Hence

$$\overline{c_0} = \mathscr{R}(c_0) - i\mathscr{I}(c_0) = u(0,0) - ic,$$

where $c = \mathscr{I}(c_0)$ is a real number. Consequently, we have

$$f(z) = 2u\left(\frac{z}{2},\frac{z}{2i}\right) - u(0,0) + ic.$$

Concerning formula (a), we use the following relations

$$2u(x,y) = f(z) + \overline{f(z)} = \sum_{n=0}^{\infty} c_n(z - z_0)^n + \overline{\sum_{n=0}^{\infty} c_n(z - z_0)^n},$$

and then proceed as above with

$$\frac{z + \overline{z_0}}{2} = \frac{(x + x_0) + i(y - y_0)}{2}$$

and

$$\frac{z - \overline{z_0}}{2i} = \frac{(x - x_0) + i(y + y_0)}{2i}.$$

17. Utilize Exercise 3.6.10 and the fact that $\dfrac{\partial^2 v}{\partial r\, \partial\theta} = \dfrac{\partial^2 v}{\partial\theta\, \partial r}$.

CHAPTER 4

EXERCISES 4.2

5. Use (4.2.16).

6. Use (4.2.15).

14. $2n\pi \pm i \log_e (2 + \sqrt{3})$, $n = 0, \pm 1, \pm 2, \cdots$.

15. $(4n + 1)\dfrac{\pi}{2} \pm ik$, $n = 0, \pm 1, \pm 2, \cdots$. [Use (4.2.8).]

16. Use Exercise 4.2.6 and Theorem 4.2.2.

17. Use (4.2.17) and Exercise 4.2.16.

18. Use Exercise 4.2.17.

19. Use (4.2.15) and Theorem 4.2.2.

21. Utilize Exercise 4.2.20, and the equation $\tan z = cz$ to obtain $cx = \sin 2x/(\cos 2x + \cosh 2y)$, $cy = \sinh 2y/(\cos 2x + \cosh 2y)$. Thus $x/\sin 2x = y/\sinh 2y$, and consequently $x = k \sin 2x$, $y = k \sinh 2y$ (k is a real constant). If $z_0 = x_0 + iy_0$ ($x_0 \neq 0$, $y_0 \neq 0$) were a root of $\tan z = cz$, then we would have

$$k \sin 2x_0 = \int_0^{x_0} 2k \cos 2x \, dx = x_0.$$

Hence there exists a point, say x_1, lying between 0 and x_0 such that $|2k \cos 2x_1| > 1$. (Why?) Thus $|k| > 1/2$. Similarly, from $y = k \sinh 2y$ we obtain $|k| < 1/2$.

22. (b) Use part (a).

    (c) $(e^{iz} - e^{-iz})/2i = 2i/(e^{iw} - e^{-iw})$. Solve for e^{iz}.

    (d) Use Exercise 4.2.20 and part (c).

    (e) Use parts (b) and (d).

    (f) In (e) we may interchange x and u, y and v. (Why?)

EXERCISES 4.3

9. $(2n - \frac{1}{2}) \pi i$, $n = 0, \pm 1, \pm 2, \cdots$; $\log_e(-1 + \sqrt{2}) + 2n\pi i$ and

$\log_e(1 + \sqrt{2}) + (2n + 1) \pi i$, $n = 0, \pm 1, \pm 2, \cdots$.

EXERCISES 4.4

4. $\dfrac{1}{2} \text{Log } 2 - i \dfrac{\pi}{4}$.

5. $\text{Log } 3 + 2n\pi i$, $n = 0, \pm 1, \pm 2, \cdots$.

6. $e^{-(\pi/4)+(i/2)\text{Log } 2}$.

7. $\dfrac{1}{4} [2 \text{ Log } 2 + \pi + i(\pi - 2 \text{ Log } 2)]$.

8. $1 + i$.   **9.** $2i$.   **10.** $e^{-(3/4)\pi+(i/2)\text{Log } 2}$.   **11.** $e^{(\pi/4)+(i/2)\text{Log } 2}$.

15. Since $w = \text{Log } z$ is a single-valued continuous function of z in the domain D consisting of all points in the complex plane except $z = -|z|$, it follows that in D, $\Delta z \to 0$ implies $\Delta w \to 0$. Now, $z = e^w$. Consequently

$$\lim_{\Delta z \to 0} \frac{\Delta w}{\Delta z} = \lim_{\Delta w \to 0} \frac{\Delta w}{\Delta z} = \left(\lim_{\Delta w \to 0} \frac{\Delta z}{\Delta w} \right)^{-1} = \frac{1}{z}.$$

16. $-\pi < \theta \leq \pi$, where $\theta = \text{Arg } z$. For fixed n and θ, the integer k is given by

$$(-\pi - n\theta)/2\pi < k \leq (\pi - n\theta)/2\pi.$$

[See (4.4.13) and the definition of the bracket function found in Exercise 1.8.22.] Letting $n > 0$ and $\theta = -\pi + (2\pi\epsilon)/n$, with $\frac{1}{2} > \epsilon > 0$, we obtain

$$-\epsilon + \frac{(n-1)}{2} < k_{\max} < -\epsilon + \frac{(n+1)}{2}.$$

Thus $k_{max} = [n/2]$. Letting $n < 0$ and $\theta = \pi$, we obtain

$$\frac{(-n-1)}{2} < k_{max} \leqq \frac{(-n+1)}{2}.$$

Thus $k_{max} = [(-n+1)/2] = -[n/2]$. Clearly for, $n = 0$, $k_{max} = 0$. Hence for any integer n, $k_{max} = |[n/2]|$. Show, similarly, that $k_{min} = -[|n/2|]$.

17. Let $\theta = \text{Arg } z$. The principal argument of z^5 is given by $5\theta + 2k\pi$, where

$$-\pi < 5\theta + 2k\pi \leqq \pi$$

and

$k = -2$ when $\frac{3}{5}\pi < \theta \leqq \pi$, $k = -1$ when $\frac{1}{5}\pi < \theta \leqq \frac{3}{5}\pi$,
$k = 0$ when $-\frac{1}{5}\pi < \theta \leqq \frac{1}{5}\pi$, $k = 1$ when $-\frac{3}{5}\pi < \theta \leqq -\frac{1}{5}\pi$,
$k = 2$ when $-\pi < \theta \leqq -\frac{3}{5}\pi$.

18. $z = |z|e^{i\theta} = |z|e^{i\,\text{Arg } z} = |z|e^{i(\theta+2k\pi)}$, where k is to be chosen so that $-\pi < \theta + 2k\pi \leqq \pi$. Solving for k, we obtain

$$-\frac{1}{2} - \frac{\theta}{2\pi} < k \leqq \frac{1}{2} - \frac{\theta}{2\pi}. \quad \text{Hence} \quad k = \left[\frac{1}{2} - \frac{\theta}{2\pi}\right].$$

Exercises 4.5

4. Let $f(z) = \text{Log}\,(-z) + i\pi = \text{Log}\,\zeta + i\pi = g(\zeta)$, where $\zeta = -z$. Utilizing Theorems 3.5.2 and 4.4.3, we obtain

$$f'(z) = g'(\zeta)\frac{d\zeta}{dz} = -\frac{1}{\zeta} = \frac{1}{z}$$

for ζ in D_π or z in D_0.

5. It follows from Theorem 4.4.3 that $\text{Log}\,z + 2n\pi i$ is a branch of $\mathscr{W}$ in D_π, and from Exercise 4.5.4 that $\text{Log}\,(-z) + \pi i + 2n\pi i$ is a branch of $\mathscr{W}$ in D_0.

6. Since $\mathscr{W}$ is a continuous function of t, it follows that $\mathscr{W}$ is of the form $\mathscr{W} = \rho e^{i\theta/2}$. Now proceed as in text (Example 4.5.1).

7. $\mathscr{W}$ is a continuous function of t. It follows that $\mathscr{W}$ is of the form $\mathscr{W}(t) = \rho_1\rho_2 e^{i[(\theta_1+\theta_2)/2]}$, and $\mathscr{W}(t+2\pi) = \rho_1\rho_2 e^{i[(\theta_1+2\pi+\theta_2+2\pi)/2]} = \mathscr{W}(t)$, where $\rho_1, \rho_2, \theta_1, \theta_2$ are as in (4.5.6) and are continuous functions of t.

Exercises 4.7

1. Let $w = \text{arc sinh } z$, then $z = \sinh w$. From (4.3.10) we then have $z = \sinh w = (1/i)\sin(iw)$. Hence $w = -i\,\text{arc sin } iz$.

7. (a) $k\pi + (-1)^k[\pi - i\,\text{Log}\,(\sqrt{2}-1)]$, $k = 0, \pm 1, \cdots$.

(b) $2k\pi + (-1)^n i\,\text{Log}\,[2+\sqrt{3}]$, $k = 0, \pm 1, \cdots$, $n = 1, 2$.

8. (a) $k\pi + (1/4i)\,\text{Log}\,5 + \theta/2$, where $\theta = \text{Arc tan}\,(-\frac{1}{2})$, $k = 0, \pm 1, \cdots$.

(b) $k\pi + (1/4i)\,\text{Log}\,5 + \theta/2$, where $\theta = \text{Arc tan}\,(-2)$, $k = 0, \pm 1, \cdots$.

9. (a) $k\pi i - (-1)^k \left[\text{Log} \left(\dfrac{\sqrt{5}-1}{2} \right) + i\pi \right], \quad k = 0, \pm 1, \cdots.$

(b) $2k\pi i + (-1)^n i(\pi/3), \ k = 0, \pm 1, \cdots, \ n = 1, 2.$

CHAPTER 5

EXERCISES 5.1

1. Let $g(\tau) = f\left[\lambda + \dfrac{\mu - \lambda}{\delta - \gamma}(\tau - \gamma) \right], \gamma \leq \tau \leq \delta.$ Take $h(t) = \gamma + \dfrac{\delta - \gamma}{\mu - \lambda}(t - \lambda).$
Now, verify that (1) $h'(t)$ is continuous and positive on $\lambda \leq t \leq \mu$, (2) $h(\lambda) = \gamma$ and $h(\mu) = \delta$, and (3) $g[h(t)] = f(t).$

4. Let the relation between the new coordinate Z and the old coordinate z be given by $Z = e^{-i\theta}[z - f(t_0)]$, where $e^{i\theta} = f'(t_0)/|f'(t_0)|.$

5. Let us denote $f(t_0 + \epsilon)$ and $f(t_0 - \eta)$, $\epsilon > 0$, $\eta > 0$, by z_ϵ and z_η, respectively. Then

$$\frac{z_\epsilon - z_0}{|z_\epsilon - z_0|} = \frac{\dfrac{z_\epsilon - z_0}{\epsilon}}{\left| \dfrac{z_\epsilon - z_0}{\epsilon} \right|} \quad \text{and} \quad \frac{z_0 - z_\eta}{|z_0 - z_\eta|} = \frac{\dfrac{z_\eta - z_0}{-\eta}}{\left| \dfrac{z_\eta - z_0}{-\eta} \right|}.$$

Now observe that $\lim\limits_{\epsilon \to 0} \dfrac{z_\epsilon - z_0}{\epsilon} = \lim\limits_{\eta \to 0} \dfrac{z_\eta - z_0}{-\eta} = f'(t_0).$

EXERCISES 5.2

1. Let $z = \int_\alpha^\beta f(t)\, dt.$ Since $z = |z|\, e^{i\theta}$, we have $|z| = e^{-i\theta} z$, where $\theta = \arg z = \arg \left[\int_\alpha^\beta f(t)\, dt \right].$ Thus

$$\left| \int_\alpha^\beta f(t)\, dt \right| = e^{-i\theta} \int_\alpha^\beta f(t)\, dt = \int_\alpha^\beta e^{-i\theta} f(t)\, dt \geq 0.$$

Also we have

$$\int_\alpha^\beta e^{-i\theta} f(t)\, dt = \mathscr{R}\left[\int_\alpha^\beta e^{-i\theta} f(t)\, dt \right] = \int_\alpha^\beta \mathscr{R}[e^{-i\theta} f(t)]\, dt$$

$$\leq \int_\alpha^\beta |e^{-i\theta} f(t)|\, dt = \int_\alpha^\beta |f(t)|\, dt.$$

2. Let $z = f(t) = x(t) + iy(t).$ Then $|f'(t)| = \sqrt{[x'(t)]^2 + [y'(t)]^2}.$

3. (a) $-i.$ (b) $-1.$ (c) $2i.$
(d) $\pi i.$ (e) $\frac{3}{2} + \frac{1}{6} i.$ (f) $-\frac{2}{3} + \frac{4}{3} i.$

5. 0.   **6.** 0.   **7.** 0.   **8.** 0.

9. (a) $2\pi i.$
(b) Let the contour C be given by $z = f(t), \ \alpha \leq t \leq \beta.$

Since C is closed, $f(\alpha) = f(\beta)$. Hence

$$\int_C \frac{dz}{z^2} = \int_\alpha^\beta \frac{f'(t)\,dt}{[f(t)]^2} = 0. \text{ (Why ?)}$$

11. Use a method similar to the one given in hint to Exercise 5.2.9.(b).

12. 8.   **13.** (a) i.   **13.** (b) $2i$.

14. Since $z = f(t)$ and $z = g(t)$ represent the same contour C, there exists a continuously differentiable, strictly increasing function $h(t)$, $\alpha \leq t \leq \beta$ such that $g[h(t)] = f(t)$, $h(\alpha) = \gamma$ and $h(\beta) = \delta$. Hence, except for at most a finite number of points, we have $f'(t) = g'[h(t)]\,h'(t)$. Therefore

$$\int_\alpha^\beta G[f(t)]\,f'(t)\,dt = \int_\alpha^\beta G\{g[h(t)]\}\,g'[h(t)]\,h'(t)\,dt.$$

Setting $\tau = h(t)$, the last integral becomes $\int_\gamma^\delta G[g(\tau)]\,g'(\tau)\,d\tau$.

EXERCISES 5.3

1. Let $\lambda(t) = [\phi(t) - \psi(t)]/2\pi i$. Clearly, $\lambda(t)$ is continuous for $\alpha \leq t \leq \beta$. Moreover, for each t, $\lambda(t) = n$, where n is an integer. (Why?) Observe that n may depend on t. By Theorem 2.9.2 and Exercises 2.4.7 and 3.3.28, $\lambda(t)$ cannot assume a set of discrete values. Hence n is a constant, and consequently $\phi(\beta) - \phi(\alpha) = \psi(\beta) - \psi(\alpha)$.

2. Let $\phi(t)$ and $\psi(t)$ be continuous functions for $\alpha \leq t \leq \beta$ and such that

$$e^{\phi(t)} = f[z(t)] \quad \text{and} \quad e^{\psi(t)} = g[z(t)].$$

Let $\nu(t) = \phi(t) + \psi(t)$. Then $e^{\nu(t)} = f[z(t)]\,g[z(t)]$. Thus

$$\Delta_C \log [f(z)\,g(z)] = \nu(\beta) - \nu(\alpha) = \phi(\beta) - \phi(\alpha) + \psi(\beta) - \psi(\alpha).$$

EXERCISES 5.4

1. Observe that for n sufficiently large, ζ_n is exterior to C and

$$|\nu(C, \zeta_n)| \leq \frac{1}{2\pi} \int_C \frac{|dz|}{|z - \zeta_n|}.$$

There exists a constant M such that $|z| < M$ for all z on C. (Why?) For n sufficiently large we can make $|\zeta_n| > 2M$. Thus $|z| < |\zeta_n|/2$ and $|z - \zeta_n| \geq |\zeta_n| - |z| > |\zeta_n|/2$. For $|\zeta_n| > 2M$, we then have

$$|\nu(C, \zeta_n)| < \frac{L}{\pi\,|\zeta_n|},$$

where L is the length of C.

EXERCISES 5.5

1. Suppose to the contrary that both $S_1 = S \cap D_1$ and $S_2 = S \cap D_2$ are not empty. Then S_1 and S_2 contain no accumulation points of each other. (Why?) Hence S is not connected.

2. Let Q be a square containing C. The exterior S of Q is a connected set having no points in common with C. By Exercise 5.5.1 S is contained in one of the domains, say D_2. It follows that D_1 is contained in Q. Thus D_1 is bounded and D_2 is unbounded.

3. Since ζ is exterior to C, we have $0 = \nu(C, \zeta) = \nu(C_1, \zeta) + \nu(C_2, \zeta)$. Hence $\nu(C_1, \zeta) = -\nu(C_2, \zeta) = \nu(\bar{C}_2, \zeta)$.

4. Let the contour be given by C: $z = f(t), \alpha \leq t \leq \beta$, and let $Z = e^{-i\theta}(z - z_0)$ where z and Z are respectively the old and new coordinates of any point in the plane. Then the contour is also given by C: $Z = F(t), \alpha \leq t \leq \beta$, where $F(t) = e^{-i\theta}[f(t) - z_0]$. Let ω and Ω denote the old and new coordinates of any point not on C. Then

$$\frac{1}{2\pi i} \int_C \frac{dZ}{Z - \Omega} = \frac{1}{2\pi i} \int_\alpha^\beta \frac{F'(t)}{F(t) - \Omega}\, dt$$

$$= \frac{1}{2\pi i} \int_\alpha^\beta \frac{e^{-i\theta} f'(t)}{e^{-i\theta}[f(t) - z_0] - e^{-i\theta}(\omega - z_0)}\, dt = \frac{1}{2\pi i} \int_a^\beta \frac{f'(t)}{f(t) - \omega}\, dt$$

$$= \frac{1}{2\pi i} \int_C \frac{dz}{z - \omega}.$$

EXERCISES 5.7

1. Let D_Σ denote the set on the sphere projecting onto D under the stereographic projection of Section 2.12. Let E_Σ be the complement of D_Σ on the sphere. Then E_Σ is connected. Define the function $f(P)$ in E_Σ as follows:

$$f(P) = \begin{cases} \nu(\Gamma, z), & P \neq N, \\ 0, & P = N, \end{cases}$$

z being the point in the plane corresponding under the stereographic projection to the point P on the sphere Σ, and N is the point $(0, 0, 1)$ on Σ. (See Fig. 2.12.1.) Then $f(P)$ is continuous on E_Σ. (Why?) Since $f(P)$ takes on integral values and E_Σ is connected, it follows (see Exercise 3.3.28) that $f(P)$ is constant on E_Σ. Hence $f(P) = 0$ and $\nu(\Gamma, z) = 0$ for all finite z not in D.

2. If ζ is exterior to C, then for $|z|$ sufficiently large we may join ζ to z by means of a polygonal contour γ in the exterior of C. (See Theorems 5.5.1 and 2.10.1.) It follows that γ does not intersect C_1. Consequently $\nu(C_1, \zeta) = 0$. (Why?) By Theorem 5.6.1, ζ is exterior to C_1.

3. Let z_1 be any point on C_1. Then z_1 is in E_2. By Theorem 5.5.1, z_1 is an accumulation point of I_1. Hence, there is at least one point ζ_1 of I_1 in E_2. (Why?) By Theorem 5.5.2, $\nu(C_2, \zeta_1) = 0$. But I_1 is a connected set not intersecting C_2. Hence $\nu(C_2, \zeta) = 0$ for all ζ in I_1 (by Theorem 5.4.2). It follows from Theorem 5.6.1 that ζ is exterior to C_2 for every ζ in I_1.

EXERCISES 5.8

1. $|z_1 - z_2|$ does not exceed the length of the diagonal of the rectangle R, which in turn does not exceed the length of the largest side multiplied by $\sqrt{2}$.

2. Let $F(z) = u(x, y) + iv(x, y)$. Then $F'(z) = u_x + iv_x = v_y - iu_y$.

$$
\int_\alpha^\beta \frac{d\{F[z(t)]\}}{dt}\, dt = \int_\alpha^\beta F'[z(t)] \frac{dz}{dt}\, dt
$$

$$
= \int_\alpha^\beta (u_x + iv_x)\left(\frac{dx}{dt} + i\frac{dy}{dt}\right) dt
$$

$$
= \int_\alpha^\beta \left(u_x \frac{dx}{dt} + u_y \frac{dy}{dt}\right) dt + i \int_\alpha^\beta \left(v_x \frac{dx}{dt} + v_y \frac{dy}{dt}\right) dt
$$

$$
= u[x(t), y(t)]\Big|_\alpha^\beta + iv[x(t), y(t)]\Big|_\alpha^\beta = F[z(\beta)] - F[z(\alpha)],
$$

the next to the last equality following from a theorem on real functions.

EXERCISES 5.17

3. (a) $-\frac{1}{2}\cos i + \frac{1}{2} = -\frac{1}{2}(\cosh 1 - 1)$.   (b) $\frac{10}{3} i$.
    (c) $\frac{2}{3}\cosh 3\pi \sinh i = \frac{2}{3}i \cosh 3\pi \sin 1$.   (d) $-\frac{4}{3} i$.
    (e) $\frac{2}{3}i \sin 3$.   (f) $\frac{1}{3}\sin i\pi = (i/3)\sinh \pi$.

4. (a) 0.   (b) $2\pi i \cosh \pi$.   (c) 0.   (d) $-2\pi i$.
    (e) 0.   (f) 0.   (g) 0.   (h) $-2\pi \sinh(\pi/2)$.

5. (a) $(\pi/60) i$.   (b) $(8/15)\pi i$.   (c) $(8/3)\pi i \cosh \pi$.
    (d) $(\pi/3)\sinh \pi - (\pi/24) i \cosh (\pi/2)$.   (e) $2\pi i e^{2\pi}$.   (f) -24π.

6. Suppose that the formula is true for $n = k$. Then

$$
\frac{f^{(k)}(z_0 + h) - f^{(k)}(z_0)}{h} = \frac{k!}{2\pi i h} \int_C \frac{(z - z_0)^{k+1} - (z - z_0 - h)^{k+1}}{(z - z_0 - h)^{k+1}(z - z_0)^{k+1}} f(z)\, dz.
$$

By the binomial theorem,

$$
[(z - z_0) - h]^{k+1} = (z - z_0)^{k+1} - (k + 1) h(z - z_0)^k + h^2 F(z - z_0, h),
$$

where $F(z - z_0, h)$ is a polynomial in $(z - z_0)$ and h. Since $F(z - z_0, h)$ and $f(z)$ are continuous within and on C, there exists a constant M such that

$$
|f(z) F(z - z_0, h)| < M \text{ on } C.
$$

7. Suppose the result is true for $n = m$. Apply (5.13.6) and (5.13.7) to the analytic function $i^k f^{(m)}(z)$ to show that the result holds also for $n = m + 1$.

10. Draw a small circle C_{n+1} with center at z_0 lying interior to C and exterior to $C_1, C_2, \cdots, C_n$. The function $f(z)/(z - z_0)$ is analytic on $C, C_1, C_2, \cdots, C_{n+1}$ and at all points interior to C and exterior to $C_1, C_2, \cdots, C_{n+1}$. Apply Theorem 5.10.3 to obtain

$$
\int_{C_{n+1}} \frac{f(z)}{z - z_0}\, dz = \int_C \frac{f(z)}{z - z_0}\, dz - \sum_{j=1}^n \int_{C_j} \frac{f(z)}{z - z_0}\, dz.
$$

Now follow the method used to prove (5.12.1) and (5.13.5).

11. For $z_0 \neq 0$, let $z_1 = R^2 e^{i\theta_0}/r_0$. Then z_1 is exterior to Γ. Hence, the function $g(z) = f(z)/(z - z_1)$ is analytic within and on Γ, and consequently

$$\frac{1}{2\pi i} \int_\Gamma g(z)\, dz = \frac{1}{2\pi i} \int_\Gamma \frac{f(z)}{z - z_1}\, dz = 0.$$

Therefore

$$f(z_0) = \frac{1}{2\pi i} \int_\Gamma \frac{f(z)\, dz}{z - z_0} = \frac{1}{2\pi i} \int_\Gamma \frac{f(z)\, dz}{z - z_0} - \frac{1}{2\pi i} \int_\Gamma \frac{f(z)\, dz}{z - z_1}.$$

For $z_0 = 0$, we have

$$f(z_0) = \frac{1}{2\pi i} \int_\Gamma \frac{f(z)}{z}\, dz.$$

12. (b) Let $\phi(z) = \mathrm{Log}\, |f(z)|$, then $|f(z)| = e^{\phi(z)}$. Hence

$$\nabla^2 |f(z)| = e^{\phi(z)}(\nabla^2 \phi + \phi_x^2 + \phi_y^2).$$

13. Show that $\lim\limits_{z' \to z} \left[\dfrac{f(z') - f(z)}{z' - z} - \dfrac{1}{2\pi i} \int_C \dfrac{\phi(\zeta)\, d\zeta}{(\zeta - z)^2}\right] = 0$, for z not on C.

14. Show that $f(z) = 0$ for $|z| < 1$.

15. Choose $e^{i\alpha}$ so that $\left| \int_0^1 fg\, dt \right| = e^{i\alpha} \int_0^1 fg\, dt$. Then

$$\int_0^1 fg\, dt = e^{-i\alpha} \int_0^1 e^{i\alpha} fg\, dt = e^{-i\alpha} \int_0^1 \mathscr{R}(e^{i\alpha}g)\, f\, dt.$$

(Why?) By the mean value theorem for real-valued functions, the last expression is equal to $e^{-i\alpha} \mathscr{R}[e^{i\alpha}g(t_0)] \int_0^1 f\, dt$, for some t_0, $0 \leq t_0 \leq 1$. Now show that $e^{-i\alpha} \mathscr{R}[e^{i\alpha}g(t_0)] = \lambda g(t_0)$ for some λ, $|\lambda| \leq 1$.

16. Let $\mu(z) = e^{(1/k)\phi(z)}$, where $\phi(z)$ is the function given in Theorem 5.17.1.

17. Since $\lambda(z)$ is continuous and $\lambda(z_0) \neq 0$, there exists a circle Γ with center at z_0 such that $\lambda(z) \neq 0$ for all z interior to Γ. The interior of Γ is a simply connected domain. Now use Exercise 5.17.16.

18. Use Exercise 5.17.16.

19. Let $\mu(z) = iz\nu(1/z)$, where $\nu(z)$ is given in Exercise 5.17.18.

20. $[f(z)/g(z)]^k = 1$. Thus [see (1.8.1)], $h(z) \equiv f(z)/g(z) = e^{2\pi i m(z)/k}$. If k is odd, take $m(z) = (k/2\pi i)\, \mathrm{Log}\, h(z)$. If k is even, take $m(z) = (k/2\pi i)\, \mathrm{Log}\, [e^{\pi i/k}h(z)] - 1/2$. Using Theorems 3.3.1, 3.3.2, and Exercise 3.3.28, conclude that $m(z)$ is constant.

21. Let C be a circle interior to D with center at z_0; and let z_n and ζ_n be interior to C. Utilize Theorem 5.12.1 and equation (5.13.3) to obtain

$$\frac{f(\zeta_n) - f(z_n)}{\zeta_n - z_n} = \frac{1}{\zeta_n - z_n}\, \frac{1}{2\pi i} \int_C \left(\frac{1}{z - \zeta_n} - \frac{1}{z - z_n}\right) f(z)\, dz = f'(z_0) + \lambda_n,$$

where

$$\lambda_n = \frac{1}{2\pi i} \int_C \left[\frac{1}{(z - \zeta_n)(z - z_n)} - \frac{1}{(z - z_0)^2} \right] f(z)\, dz.$$

Now show that $\lambda_n \to 0$ as $n \to \infty$.

23. Suppose that the integral $F_0(z) = \int_{z_0}^{z} f(\zeta)\, d\zeta$ in (5.11.1) is multiple-valued. Let z_1 be a point in the given domain D, and let D_1 be a simply connected domain in D containing z_1. Let $G_1(z) = \int_{z_1}^{z} f(\zeta)\, d\zeta$, where z and the path of integration are in D_1. By Theorem 5.11.1, $G_1(z)$ is single-valued and analytic in D_1. Let $F_1(z_1)$ be one of the values of $F_0(z_1)$. Then $F_1(z) = F_1(z_1) + G_1(z)$ is single-valued and analytic in D_1. It can be shown that $F_0(z)$ is analytic, with $F_1(z)$ as a branch.

CHAPTER 6

Exercises 6.3

1. (a) 1.　　　　　(b) 1.　　　　　(c) $\frac{1}{4}$.　　　　(d) 1.　　　　　(e) infinity.
(f) e.　　　　　(g) e.　　　　　(h) e.　　　　(i) infinity.　　(j) 1.

2. (a) $|z| \leqq r < 1$.　　　(b) $|z| \leqq r < 1$.　　　(c) $|z - 2| \leqq r < \frac{1}{4}$.
(d) $|z| \leqq r < 1$.　　　(e) all z.　　　　　(f) $|z| \leqq r < e$.
(g) $|z| \leqq r < e$.　　　(h) $|z| \leqq r < e$.　　　(i) all z.
(j) $|z| \leqq r < 1$.

6. $z^n = \dfrac{z^{n+1} - z^n}{z - 1}, \quad z \neq 1.$

Hence, for all z, we have

$$(z - 1) \sum_{n=0}^{k} c_n z^n = c_k z^{k+1} - c_0 + \sum_{n=1}^{k} (c_{n-1} - c_n)\, z^n.$$

Since $c_n \geqq c_{n+1} > 0$ and $c_n \to 0$, we have for $|z| \leqq 1$, $\lim_{k \to \infty} c_k z^{k+1} = 0$ and

$$\sum_{n=1}^{\infty} |(c_{n-1} - c_n)\, z^n| \leqq \sum_{n=1}^{\infty} (c_{n-1} - c_n) = \lim_{k \to \infty} \left[\sum_{n=1}^{k} (c_{n-1} - c_n) \right]$$

$$= \lim_{k \to \infty} (c_0 - c_k) = c_0 - \lim_{k \to \infty} c_k = c_0;$$

thus the series $\sum_{n=1}^{\infty} (c_{n-1} - c_n)\, z^n$ converges (absolutely), and hence the series $\sum_{n=0}^{\infty} c_n z^n$ converges for $|z| \leqq 1$, $z \neq 1$.

7. Use Theorem 6.2.1.

8. S lies within some circle C_1 concentric with and interior to C. Now apply Theorems 6.2.1. and 6.3.1.

9. By Theorem 2.9.3, a contour is a compact set (why?). Now apply Exercise 6.3.8.

EXERCISES 6.4

1. (a) $e^z = \sum\limits_{n=0}^{\infty} \dfrac{z^n}{n!}$ when $|z| < \infty$.

(b) $\sin z = \sum\limits_{n=0}^{\infty} \dfrac{(-1)^n z^{2n+1}}{(2n+1)!}$ when $|z| < \infty$.

(c) $\cos z = \sum\limits_{n=0}^{\infty} \dfrac{(-1)^n z^{2n}}{(2n)!}$ when $|z| < \infty$.

(d) $\sinh z = \sum\limits_{n=1}^{\infty} \dfrac{z^{2n-1}}{(2n-1)!}$ when $|z| < \infty$.

(e) $\cosh z = \sum\limits_{n=0}^{\infty} \dfrac{z^{2n}}{(2n)!}$ when $|z| < \infty$.

(f) $\dfrac{1}{1+z} = \sum\limits_{n=0}^{\infty} (-1)^n z^n$ when $|z| < 1$.

(g) $\dfrac{z}{1-z} = \sum\limits_{n=1}^{\infty} z^n$ when $|z| < 1$.

(h) $\operatorname{Log}(1+z) = \sum\limits_{n=1}^{\infty} \dfrac{(-1)^{n-1}}{n} z^n$ when $|z| < 1$.

(i) $\tan z = z + \dfrac{1}{3} z^3 + \dfrac{2}{15} z^5 + \dfrac{17}{315} z^7 + \cdots$, when $|z| < \pi/2$.

2. (a) $\dfrac{1}{z} = \sum\limits_{n=0}^{\infty} (-1)^n (z-1)^n$, $R' = R = 1$.

(b) $\sqrt[3]{z} = (\sqrt{2})^{1/3} e^{i(\pi/12)} +$

$$\sum_{n=1}^{\infty} \frac{\{\prod_{k=1}^{n} [\frac{1}{3} - (k-1)]\} (\sqrt{2})^{[(1/3)-n]} e^{i(\pi/4)[(1/3)-n]}}{n!} (z-1-i)^n, R' = R = \sqrt{2}.$$

(c) $\sinh z = -\sum\limits_{n=1}^{\infty} \dfrac{(z-\pi i)^{2n-1}}{(2n-1)!}$, $R' = R = \infty$.

(d) $e^{z-1} = e \sum\limits_{n=0}^{\infty} \dfrac{(z-2)^n}{n!}$, $R' = R = \infty$.

(e) $\dfrac{1}{z-4} = -\sum\limits_{n=0}^{\infty} (z-3)^n$, $R' = R = 1$.

(f) $\dfrac{2z}{z-2} = -2 - 4\sum\limits_{n=1}^{\infty}(z-1)^n, \quad R' = R = 1.$

(g) $f(z) = 2\pi i, \ R' = \infty$ and $R = 1.$

3. Use Theorem 6.4.1.

4. Expand $\mathrm{Log}\,(1+z)$ and $\mathrm{Log}\,(1-|z|)$ in power series about $z_0 = 0.$

5. Consider the derivatives of $f(z)$ at $z = z_0.$

EXERCISES 6.5

1. (a) (1) $-\dfrac{1}{2z^2} - \dfrac{1}{4z} - \dfrac{1}{3}\sum\limits_{n=0}^{\infty}z^n - \dfrac{1}{24}\sum\limits_{n=0}^{\infty}(-1)^n\left(\dfrac{z}{2}\right)^n.$

(2) $-\dfrac{1}{2z^2} - \dfrac{1}{4z} + \dfrac{1}{3}\sum\limits_{n=0}^{\infty}\dfrac{1}{z^{n+1}} - \dfrac{1}{24}\sum\limits_{n=0}^{\infty}(-1)^n\left(\dfrac{z}{2}\right)^n.$

(3) $-\dfrac{1}{2z^2} - \dfrac{1}{4z} + \dfrac{1}{3}\sum\limits_{n=0}^{\infty}\dfrac{1}{z^{n+1}} - \dfrac{1}{12}\sum\limits_{n=0}^{\infty}(-1)^n\dfrac{2^n}{z^{n+1}}.$

(b) (1) $\dfrac{(2+i)}{10}\sum\limits_{n=0}^{\infty}(iz)^n + \dfrac{(2-i)}{10}\sum\limits_{n=0}^{\infty}(-1)^n(iz)^n + \dfrac{1}{10}\sum\limits_{n=0}^{\infty}(-1)^n\left(\dfrac{z}{2}\right)^n.$

(2) $\dfrac{(-1+2i)}{10}\sum\limits_{n=0}^{\infty}\dfrac{(-1)^n i^n}{z^{n+1}} - \dfrac{(1+2i)}{10}\sum\limits_{n=0}^{\infty}\dfrac{i^n}{z^{n+1}} + \dfrac{1}{10}\sum\limits_{n=0}^{\infty}(-1)^n\left(\dfrac{z}{2}\right)^n.$

(3) $\dfrac{(-1+2i)}{10}\sum\limits_{n=0}^{\infty}\dfrac{(-1)^n i^n}{z^{n+1}} - \dfrac{(1+2i)}{10}\sum\limits_{n=0}^{\infty}\dfrac{i^n}{z^{n+1}} + \dfrac{1}{5}\sum\limits_{n=0}^{\infty}(-1)^n\dfrac{2^n}{z^{n+1}}.$

(c) (1) $1 + \dfrac{3}{2}\sum\limits_{n=0}^{\infty}(-1)^n\left(\dfrac{z}{2}\right)^n - \dfrac{8}{3}\sum\limits_{n=0}^{\infty}(-1)^n\left(\dfrac{z}{3}\right)^n.$

(2) $1 + 3\sum\limits_{n=0}^{\infty}(-1)^n\dfrac{2^n}{z^{n+1}} - \dfrac{8}{3}\sum\limits_{n=0}^{\infty}(-1)^n\left(\dfrac{z}{3}\right)^n.$

(3) $1 + 3\sum\limits_{n=0}^{\infty}(-1)^n\dfrac{2^n}{z^{n+1}} - 8\sum\limits_{n=0}^{\infty}(-1)^n\dfrac{3^n}{z^{n+1}}.$

(d) (1) $\dfrac{1}{(-\lambda)^k}\left[1 + \sum\limits_{n=1}^{\infty}\dfrac{k(k+1)\cdots(k+n-1)}{n!}\left(\dfrac{z}{\lambda}\right)^n\right].$

(2) $\dfrac{1}{z^k} + \sum\limits_{n=1}^{\infty}\dfrac{k(k+1)\cdots(k+n-1)}{n!}\dfrac{\lambda^n}{z^{k+n}}.$

EXERCISES 6.8

1. (a) (1) $\sum\limits_{n=0}^{\infty} z^{n-4}$.

(2) $-\sum\limits_{n=0}^{\infty} \dfrac{1}{z^{n+5}}$.

(b) $\sum\limits_{n=0}^{\infty} \dfrac{z^{2n-4}}{(2n)!}$.

(c) $\sum\limits_{n=0}^{\infty} \dfrac{(-1)^n}{n!}(z-1)^{-n}$.

(d) $(1-z/\beta)^{-1/2}(1-\alpha/z)^{-1/2} = \left[\sum\limits_{m=0}^{\infty} \dfrac{(2m)!}{(2^m m!)^2}\dfrac{z^m}{\beta^m}\right]\left[\sum\limits_{n=0}^{\infty}\dfrac{(2n)!}{(2^n n!)^2}\dfrac{\alpha^n}{z^n}\right]$

$$= \sum\limits_{k=-\infty}^{\infty} C_k z^k,$$

where $C_k = \sum\limits_{\substack{m-n=k \\ m \geq 0 \\ n \geq 0}} \dfrac{(2m)!\,(2n)!}{(2^m m!)^2\,(2^n n!)^2}\dfrac{\alpha^n}{\beta^m}$.

2. (a) $\dfrac{1}{z^4} + \dfrac{1}{z^3} + \dfrac{3}{2}\dfrac{1}{z^2} + \dfrac{7}{6}\dfrac{1}{z} + \cdots$.

(b) $1 + \dfrac{1}{2}z^2 + \dfrac{5}{24}z^4 + \dfrac{61}{720}z^6 + \cdots$.

(c) $\dfrac{1}{z} - \dfrac{z}{3} - \dfrac{z^3}{45} - \dfrac{2}{945}z^5 - \cdots$.

3. (a) $3z + 6z^2 + \dfrac{3}{2}z^3 - 5z^4 + \cdots$.

(b) $1 - z + \dfrac{5}{2}z^2 - \dfrac{13}{6}z^3 + \cdots$.

4. (b) We have $(\text{Arc tan } z)^2 = \sum\limits_{n=1}^{\infty} c_n z^{2n}$. (Why?) Differentiating both sides and multiplying by $(1+z^2)/2$, we get

$$\text{Arc tan } z = c_1 z + \sum\limits_{n=2}^{\infty} [nc_n + (n-1)c_{n-1}] z^{2n-1}.$$

Comparing coefficients with the expansion of Arc tan z in part (a) we get

$$c_1 = 1, \quad nc_n = \dfrac{(-1)^{n-1}}{2n-1} - (n-1)c_{n-1}, \quad n = 2, 3, \cdots,$$

from which we deduce the value of c_n.

5. Use a method similar to the one given in the hint to Exercise 6.8.4.(b).

8. Use formulas (4.3.10) and (4.3.11).

10. Use Exercises 6.8.7, 6.8.8 and 6.8.9.(d).

11. $\tan z = \cot z - 2\cot 2z$. Now use Exercise 6.8.10.

12. $z/(\sin z) = z \cot z + z \tan z/2$. Now use Exercises 6.8.10 and 6.8.11.

13. Use Exercise 6.8.12.

14. Use Log $\sin z = \int \cot z \, dz$ and Exercise 6.8.10.

15. Use Log $\cos z = - \int \tan z \, dz$ and Exercise 6.8.11.

16. Use Log $\tan z = 2 \int \csc 2z \, dz$ and Exercise 6.8.13.

17. Use (4.3.10) and Exercise 6.8.14.

18. (d) From (4.3.11) sec $z = 1/\cos z = \text{sech } iz$.

19. (b) See proofs of Theorems 6.3.1, 6.4.1 and 6.5.1.

20. The average of $f_n(z)$ over the circle $C: \mid z \mid = r$ $(z = re^{i\theta})$ is

$$\frac{1}{2\pi} \int_0^{2\pi} f_n(re^{i\theta}) \, d\theta \quad \text{or} \quad \frac{1}{2\pi i} \int_C \frac{f_n(z)}{z} \, dz.$$

Now use (6.6.1) and (5.2.27).

21. Use an argument similar to the one used in proving Theorem 6.3.2.

22. Use Theorem 2.5.1.

CHAPTER 7

EXERCISES 7.1

1. Use equation (7.1.3).

2. Use Exercise 7.1.1.

3. Consider the function $g(z) = f(z) - \alpha$. Now use Theorem 7.1.2.

5. (a) Remove the singularity, and then use Theorems 3.4.1 and 2.9.3.
(b) See Remark 7.1.1, and then use part (a).

6. Suppose that the theorem is false. Then there exists a complex number α, an $\epsilon > 0$, and a $\delta > 0$ such that $\mid f(z) - \alpha \mid \geqq \epsilon$ whenever $\mid z - z_0 \mid \leqq \delta$. Thus $1/\mid f(z) - \alpha \mid$ is bounded for $\mid z - z_0 \mid \leqq \delta$. From this fact, and using the Laurent expansion of $1/[f(z) - \alpha]$ about the point $z = z_0$, deduce that $f(z)$ is either analytic or has a pole at z_0.

7. (a) $z = z_0$ is either a removable singularity, a pole of order k for some integer $k > 0$, or an essential singularity. If z_0 were a pole of order k, then by Exercise 7.1.5.(b) $(z - z_0)^{k-1} f(z)$, and consequently $f(z)$ would be unbounded in N. If $z = z_0$ were an essential singularity, then from Exercise 7.1.6, $f(z)$ would be unbounded in N. Consequently z_0 is a removable singularity of $f(z)$.
(b) If z_0 were a removable singularity, then in N_0 [see Exercise 7.1.5.(a)] $(z - z_0)^{m-1} f(z)$ would be bounded. If z_0 were an essential singularity, then the function $g(z) = (z - z_0)^m f(z)$ would also have an essential singularity at $z = z_0$, and hence by Exercise 7.1.6 would be unbounded. Consequently $f(z)$ has a pole. It is easy to show that the pole is necessarily of order m.

8. (a) Suppose to the contrary, that the number of singularities in S is infinite. Then by Theorem 2.5.2 the singularities have an accumulation point ζ_0 in S. But then ζ_0 is not an isolated singularity.

(b) By Theorem 7.1.2 each zero is isolated. Hence each point z_0 in S is the center of a circle containing at most one zero of $f(z)$ in S. (Why?) By Theorem 2.5.1 a finite number of these circles covers S.

9. Show that S is bounded and closed. Then use Exercise 7.1.8.

10. Since in the neighborhood of a pole $f(z)$ is unbounded, it follows that all the poles of $f(z)$ lie in the set S consisting of the points of R with $|z| \leq M$. The set S is bounded and closed. (Why?) Now use Exercise 7.1.8.

Exercises 7.2

1. (a) All poles are simple; Res $(2) = \frac{13}{20}$, Res $(-2) = \frac{3}{20}$, Res $(i) = $ Res $(-i) = -\frac{2}{5}$.

(b) All poles are of order two; Res $(i) = (1+2i)/2$, Res $(-i) = (1-2i)/2$.

(c) All poles are simple; Res $(n\pi i) = 1$, $n = 0, \pm 1, \cdots$.

(d) All poles are simple; Res $(n\pi) = (-1)^n (n\pi - 1)$, $n = 0, \pm 1, \cdots$.

(e) All poles are simple; Res $[(n + \frac{1}{2})\pi] = -1$, $n = 0, \pm 1, \cdots$.

(f) All poles are simple; Res $[(n + \frac{1}{2})i] = [(-1)^n/\pi i]\, e^{a(n+1/2)i}$, $n = 0, \pm 1, \cdots$.

(g) All poles are of order two; Res $(i) = -i/2e$, Res $(-i) = 0$.

(h) At $z = 0$ pole is of order three, at $z = \pm 1$ poles are simple; Res $(0) = 3$, Res $(1) = $ Res $(-1) = -\frac{3}{2}$.

(i) All poles are simple; Res $(n\pi) = 1$, $n = 0, \pm 1, \cdots$.

(j) All poles are simple; Res $(n\pi i) = (-1)^n$, $n = 0, \pm 1, \cdots$.

(k) At $z = 0$ pole is of order three, at $z = n\pi$, $n = \pm 1, \pm 2, \cdots$, poles are simple; Res $(0) = \dfrac{1}{6}$, Res $(n\pi) = \dfrac{(-1)^n}{(n\pi)^2}$, $n = \pm 1, \pm 2, \cdots$.

(l) All poles are simple; Res $\left(\dfrac{\sqrt{2}}{2} + i\dfrac{\sqrt{2}}{2}\right) = -\dfrac{\sqrt{2}}{8}(1 - i)$,

Res $\left(-\dfrac{\sqrt{2}}{2} + i\dfrac{\sqrt{2}}{2}\right) = \dfrac{\sqrt{2}}{8}(1 + i)$, Res $\left(-\dfrac{\sqrt{2}}{2} - i\dfrac{\sqrt{2}}{2}\right) = \dfrac{\sqrt{2}}{8}(1 - i)$,

Res $\left(\dfrac{\sqrt{2}}{2} - i\dfrac{\sqrt{2}}{2}\right) = -\dfrac{\sqrt{2}}{8}(1 + i)$.

(m) All poles are simple; Res $(-a^2) = \dfrac{e^{-ia^3}}{b^2 - a^2}$, Res $(-b^2) = \dfrac{e^{-iab^2}}{a^2 - b^2}$.

2. (a) (1) $6\pi i$.   (2) $2\pi i$.

(b) (1) $4\pi i$.   (2) $4\pi i$.

(c) (1) $2\pi i$.   (2) $2\pi i$.

(d) $(\pi/3)\, i$.   (e) $2\pi i$.

(f) (1) $2\pi i(e^4 + 10i)$.   (2) 0.

(g) π/e.   (h) 0.

(i) (1) 0.   (2) $\pi/5$.   (3) $-\pi/5$.   (4) $-\frac{2}{5}\pi i$.   (5) $\frac{2}{5}\pi i$.

3. Consider the case when $\alpha \neq 0$. Let $F(z) = z/f(z)$. Since $f(z)$ has a simple zero at $z = \alpha$, $F(z)$ has a simple pole at $z = \alpha$. From Theorem 7.2.3, we obtain

$$\int_C F(z)\, dz = 2\pi i \operatorname{Res}[F(z), \alpha] = \frac{2\pi i \alpha}{f'(\alpha)}.$$

EXERCISES 7.3

1. Let $z = 1/w$ and $F(w) = f(1/w)$. Then $F(w)$ is analytic in the interior of the circle $|w| = R_1 = 1/\rho_1$. Hence by Theorems 6.4.1 and 6.2.1 we have

$$F(w) = a_0 + a_1 w + a_2 w^2 + \cdots,$$

and the convergence is uniform and absolute for $|w| < r < R_1$. Substituting $1/z$ for w, the result now follows.

2. See proof of Theorem 6.6.1. Let L denote the length of Γ. Then since $f(z)$ is uniformly continuous on Γ, given an $\epsilon > 0$, there exists a positive integer $M(\epsilon)$ such that for $N \geq M(\epsilon)$ and all z on Γ, $|R_N(z)| < \epsilon/L$, where

$$R_N(z) = \sum_{n=N}^{\infty} \frac{a_n}{z^n}.$$

$$\left| \int_\Gamma f(z)\, dz - \sum_{n=0}^{N-1} \int_\Gamma \frac{a_n}{z^n}\, dz \right| = \left| \int_\Gamma R_N(z)\, dz \right| \leq L \frac{\epsilon}{L} = \epsilon$$

for $N \geq M(\epsilon)$, from which the result now follows.

3. (c) Let $z = 1/w$ and let $f(w) = F(1/w)$. Then to the neighborhood M_0 of $z = \infty$ there corresponds a neighborhood N_0 of $w = 0$. Now use Exercise 7.1.7.(c) for the case when $z_0 = 0$.

4. Use Exercise 7.3.3.(a).

5. Use Exercise 7.3.3.(a).

EXERCISES 7.4

1. Let $g(z) = -z$. Then for all z on C, $|f(z)| < 1 = |z| = |-z| = |g(z)|$. Let $H(z) = f(z) + g(z) = f(z) - z$. Now apply Theorem 7.4.3 to conclude that $H(z)$ has only one zero in the interior of C.

2. Let $S_n(z) = \sum_{k=0}^{n} z^k/k!$ and $g_n(z) = \sum_{k=n+1}^{\infty} z^k/k!$. Take $n \geq N$, where N is sufficiently large so that for all z on C, $|g_n(z)| < |S_n(z)|$. Now apply Theorem 7.4.3 to conclude that $S_n(z)$ has as many zeros as $g_n(z) + S_n(z) = e^z$ in the interior of C.

3. Write $ze^{a-z} = 1$ as $z = 1/e^{a-z}$. Let $H(z) = f(z) - g(z)$, where $f(z) = z$ and $g(z) = 1/e^{a-z}$. Since $a > 1$, we have for all z on C, $|g(z)| < 1 = |z| = |f(z)|$. Now apply Theorem 7.4.3 to conclude that $H(z)$ has only one zero in the interior of C.

4. Since C is compact, $|f(z)|$ has a minimum $m > 0$ in C. Take $\epsilon = m/2$ in (6.8.17). Write $f_n(z) = f(z) - [f(z) - f_n(z)]$. Deduce an inequality so that Theorem 7.4.3 may be applied. (The interior of C is assumed to be in D.)

EXERCISES 7.8

2. (a) Use Theorem 7.8.1.
    (b) Use Theorem 7.8.2.

17. Integrate $\cos tz \, \mathrm{sech} \, az$ around the rectangle with corners at $\pm R$ and $\pm R + i(\pi/a)$, $a = \sqrt{\pi/2}$. Then let $R \to \infty$.

18. Use Exercise 7.8.14.(c).

EXERCISES 7.9

1. Use (7.9.13).

2. $\left(\dfrac{d}{dz}\right)(\pi \tan \pi z) = \dfrac{\pi^2}{(\cos \pi z)^2}$. Now use Exercise 7.9.1.

3. $-\pi \cot \pi z = \displaystyle\int \dfrac{\pi^2 \, dz}{(\sin \pi z)^2}$. Now use (7.9.13).

4. $2\pi/\sin 2\pi z = \pi(\tan \pi z + \cot \pi z)$. Now use Exercises 7.9.2 and 7.9.3.

5. Choose a positive number R and positive integer N, such that $|z_0| < R < N/2$. Then for $|z| < R$ and $|n| > N$, we have $|z - n| > |n| - R > |n|/2$. It follows that given an $\epsilon > 0$, we have for $|z| < R$ and k a sufficiently large integer

$$\sum_{n=-k}^{-\infty} \frac{1}{|z - n|^2} + \sum_{n=k}^{\infty} \frac{1}{|z - n|^2} < 2\sum_{n=k}^{\infty} \frac{4}{n^2} < \epsilon.$$

EXERCISES 7.10

2. Use Theorem 2.5.1.

3. Let z_0 be a point in D_0 and let z_1 be any other point in D. Let $f_1(z_1)$ be any one of the values of $f(z)$ at the point $z = z_1$, and let $G_1(z)$ be a branch of $f(z)$ defined over a neighborhood D_1 of z_1, $D_1 \subset D$, such that $G_1(z_1) = f_1(z_1)$. Then in accordance with Definition 4.5.4, there exists a curve Γ in D joining z_0 to z_1 such that the branch $G_0(z)$ may be continued analytically along Γ into the branch $G_1(z)$. Utilizing Lemma 2.10.1 and Theorem 7.10.4 we obtain $G_1(z_1) = G_0(z_0)$. Thus $f_1(z_1) = c$. Hence $f(z) = c$ for all z in D.

4. Use Exercises 3.6.13 and 7.10.3.

5. Apply Exercise 7.10.4 to $H(z) - F(z)$.

6. Let z_0 be a point in D, $N(z_0)$ a neighborhood of z_0 and $G_0(z)$ a branch of $H(z)$ in $N(z_0)$. Then, since $G_0(z)$ is single-valued and analytic in $N(z_0)$, by Exercise 3.6.16, $G_0(z)$ is constant in $N(z_0)$. Now apply the result of Exercise 7.10.3.

7. Suppose that $u = \mathscr{R}[f(z)]$, where $f(z)$ is single-valued and analytic in D. But we also have that $u = \mathscr{R}[\log z]$. Therefore, $\mathscr{R}[f(z) - \log z] = 0$. Now use Exercise 7.10.6 to show that $\log z$ must be single-valued in D contradicting Theorem 4.4.1.

8. (a) For $z \neq 0$, let $F_1(z) = \log z$ and $F_2(z) = -\log z$. Then $F(z) = F_1(z) + F_2(z) = 2\pi i k$, $k = 0, \pm 1, \pm 2, \pm \cdots$. In view of Exercise 7.10.3, $F(z)$ is not analytic.

CHAPTER 8

EXERCISES 8.3

1. Use formulas (5.12.1) and (5.13.3).

2. Use Exercise 8.3.1.

3. Use Exercise 8.3.2 and (1.3.11).

EXERCISES 8.4

1. (a) Use Lemma 8.2.1.

(b) Use Lemma 8.2.2 and Exercise 2.9.9.

(c) Let $z_0 = g(w_0)$. Let w be any other point in D_w and let $z = g(w)$ be its image point. By part (b) if $\Delta w = w - w_0 \to 0$, then also $\Delta z = z - z_0 \to 0$.

Hence

$$\lim_{\Delta w \to 0} \frac{\Delta z}{\Delta w} = \lim_{\Delta z \to 0} \frac{\Delta z}{\Delta w} = \frac{1}{\displaystyle\lim_{\Delta z \to 0} \frac{\Delta w}{\Delta z}} = \frac{1}{f'(z_0)}.$$

Since by part (a), $f'(z) \neq 0$ for all z in D_z, we see that $g'(w)$ exists (and is finite) for all w in D_w.

2. (b) Consider the inverse mapping $z = f(w)$ of D_w onto D_z. This mapping, by Exercise 8.4.1, is one-to-one and analytic. The inverse image under $w = F(z)$ is the same as the image under $z = f(w)$.

EXERCISES 8.6

1. $\left| \dfrac{Re^{i\theta} - \rho e^{i\lambda}}{Re^{i\theta} - (R^2/\rho) e^{i\lambda}} \right| = \dfrac{\rho}{R} \left| \dfrac{1 - (\rho/R) e^{i(\lambda-\theta)}}{(\rho/R) e^{-i(\lambda-\theta)} - 1} \right|.$

Now use Exercise 1.3.6.

2. Suppose that $(p - z_0)(\bar{q} - \bar{z}_0) = R^2$. Let $r = |p - z_0|$ and $\rho = |q - z_0|$. Since $(p - z_0)(\bar{q} - \bar{z}_0) = R^2$, we have $\arg(p - z_0) = -\arg(\bar{q} - \bar{z}_0) = -\arg(\overline{q - z_0}) = \arg(q - z_0)$. Thus the points z_0, p and q are collinear. Also $|\bar{q} - \bar{z}_0| = |q - z_0| = \rho$; hence $r\rho = R^2$.

EXERCISES 8.10

6. The equation of the circle C is given by $|z - z_0|^2 = r^2$, which can also be written in the equivalent form

$$z\bar{z} + \delta z + \bar{\delta}\bar{z} + \gamma = 0,$$

where $\bar{\delta} = -z_0$ and $\gamma = \delta\bar{\delta} - r^2$ is a real number. Note that the center of the circle is equal to the negative of the coefficient of $\bar{z}$ and the radius $r^2 = \delta\bar{\delta} - \gamma$. If we subject this circle to the transformation $w = 1/z$, we obtain

$$w\bar{w} + \frac{\bar{\delta}}{\gamma}w + \frac{\delta}{\gamma}\bar{w} + \frac{1}{\gamma} = 0.$$

Thus

$$\rho^2 = \frac{\bar{\delta}}{\gamma}\frac{\delta}{\gamma} - \frac{1}{\gamma}, \qquad w_0 = -\frac{\delta}{\gamma},$$

from which the results now follow.

8. Write the transformation $w = (az + b)/(cz + d)$ as three successive transformations:

(1) $z' = z + \dfrac{d}{c}$,   (2) $z'' = \dfrac{1}{z'}$,   (3) $w = \dfrac{a}{c} + \dfrac{bc - ad}{c^2}z''$.

Apply Exercise 8.10.7 to (1), then apply Exercise 8.10.6 to (2) and finally apply again Exercise 8.10.7 to (3).

9. It is sufficient to take the center of inversion at the origin. Then the inversion may be considered as the result of the transformations

(1) $z' = \dfrac{R^2}{z}$,   (2) $w = \bar{z'}$.

Apply Exercise 8.10.8 and the fact that the reflection $w = \bar{z'}$ (into the reals) leaves distance unchanged.

10. Use Exercise 8.10.8.

11. (g) $\dfrac{w - r}{w - s} = \left(\dfrac{-4 + 3i}{5}\right)\left(\dfrac{z - r}{z - s}\right)$, where $r = 4 + 3i$, $s = -4 + 3i$.

12. (a) $1, -1$.   (b) $\dfrac{1}{2} + \dfrac{1}{2}i\sqrt{3}, \dfrac{1}{2} - \dfrac{1}{2}i\sqrt{3}$.   (c) $0, 2$.

(d) $1 + \sqrt{2}, 1 - \sqrt{2}$.   (e) $\dfrac{(1 + i)(1 + \sqrt{3})}{2}, \dfrac{(1 + i)(1 - \sqrt{3})}{2}$.

(f) ∞.   (g) $5, 5$.   (h) $\dfrac{1 + i}{2}, \dfrac{-1 + i}{2}$.

(i) $2i, -2i, i, -i$.

13. (a) $w = -\dfrac{z+i}{3z-i}$.   (b) $w = \dfrac{3z+2i}{iz+6}$.   (c) $w = -\dfrac{z-1}{(2i-1)z+1}$.

(d) $w = \dfrac{i}{z}$.   (e) $w = \dfrac{(z_2-z_3)z - z_1(z_2-z_3)}{(z_2-z_1)z - z_3(z_2-z_1)}$.

(f) $w = \dfrac{2\sqrt{3}iz - 2\sqrt{3}i}{(\sqrt{3}i-3)z - (\sqrt{3}i+3)}$.

16. (b) Let $F_1(w) = (w_1, w_2, w_3, w)$ and $F_2(z) = (z_1, z_2, z_3, z)$. By part (a), $F_1(w)$ and $F_2(z)$ are linear fractional transformations. Since $F_1(w) = F_2(z)$, and the linear fractional transformations form a group, $w = F_1^{-1} F_2(z)$ is also a linear fractional transformation, and consequently $\alpha\delta - \beta\gamma \neq 0$.

17. $z = \lambda$ is on the straight line determined by $0, 1, \infty$ if, and only if, λ is real. Now see Remark 8.9.2 and Theorems 8.10.1 and 8.10.2.

18. Consider the linear fractional transformation $T(z) = (z_1, z_2, z_3, z)$. Then $T(z_1) = 0$, $T(z_2) = 1$ and $T(z_3) = \infty$. Let $T(z_4) = \lambda$. Thus $\lambda = (0, 1, \infty, \lambda) = (z_1, z_2, z_3, z_4)$. By Exercise 8.10.17, λ is real. To show that λ is negative, consider the image of the arc $z_4 z_1 z_2$ under the transformation $T(z)$.

21. It is sufficient to consider the case where C is a circle with center at the origin and z_2 and z_4 are on the real axis. (See Section 8.5 and Theorem 8.10.1.) [C could be taken to be the unit circle (see Theorems 8.11.1 and 8.11.2).]

22. Again we prove only the necessity. (See Exercise 1.6.18.) Suppose that z_1, z_2, z_3, z_4 are arranged in the given order around the circle. By Exercise 8.10.18 $(z_1, z_2, z_3, z_4) < 0$. Thus $|(z_1, z_2, z_3, z_4)| = -(z_1, z_2, z_3, z_4)$. By Exercise 8.10.19 $(z_1, z_2, z_4, z_3) = 1 - (z_1, z_2, z_3, z_4) > 0$. Hence $|(z_1, z_2, z_4, z_3)| = (z_1, z_2, z_4, z_3)$. Therefore

$$|(z_1, z_2, z_4, z_3)| = 1 + |(z_1, z_2, z_3, z_4)|,$$

from which the result now follows.

23. (c) Any circle passing through z_1 and $\overline{z_1}$ is perpendicular to the real axis. Now use parts (a) and (b), and the fact that angles are preserved under conformal mapping. (See Theorem 8.9.2.)

(e) Use Theorem 8.9.2; parts (b), (d), and (a).

26. The exterior of C is a domain. The exterior and interior of Γ are disjoint domains. If the image of the exterior of C were partly interior and partly exterior to Γ, it would be disconnected, contradicting Theorem 2.9.2. A similar result holds for the interior of C. Now use Exercise 2.9.10.

Exercises 8.12

2. Since $F(z_1) = 0$ and $F(z_2) = \infty$, the images L_1' of C_1 and L_2' of C_2 are straight lines passing through the origin $w = 0$. Since $F(\zeta_1) \equiv w_1 > 0$, it follows that $L_1' = L_1$. Since $\angle(C_1, C_2) = \angle(L_1, L_2)$, it follows that $L_2' = L_2$. Let z_3 be any point interior to the crescent (C_1, C_2), and let C_3 be a circle passing through z_1, z_2, z_3. The image L_3 of C_3 is a straight line passing through the origin. (Why?) Let w_3, the image point of z_3, be any point on L_3. Show that w_3 lies in the interior of the angle formed by L_1 and L_2.

3. Show that the linear fractional transformation mapping the interior of the circle $|z| = \rho$ onto the exterior of the circle $|\zeta| = \rho$ has the form

$$\zeta = \rho^2 e^{i\beta} \frac{z - z_1}{\bar{z}_1 z - \rho^2}, \qquad \beta \text{ real}, \qquad |z_1| > \rho.$$

To establish this result, consider the transformation

$$\zeta = \frac{\rho^2}{w} = \frac{\rho^2}{e^{i\alpha}} \cdot \frac{\bar{z}_0}{z_0} \cdot \frac{z - \rho^2/\bar{z}_0}{(\rho^2/z_0)z - \rho^2},$$

where w is given in (8.12.8).

5. $w = \rho \dfrac{1 - z}{1 + z}$, $\rho > 0$. [To obtain this result, use (8.12.12).]

7. $w = -\dfrac{z - 1}{z + 2}$. [To obtain this result, use the transformation in Exercise 8.12.6 with w replaced by $w - 1$.]

9. The product of the particular transformation $z' = iz$, taking the imaginary z axis onto the real z' axis, followed by the general transformation

$$w = e^{i\alpha} \frac{z' - z_0}{z' - \bar{z}_0}, \qquad \alpha \text{ real and } \mathscr{I}(z_0) \neq 0,$$

[see (8.12.5)] taking the real z' axis onto the unit circle, yields the general transformation taking the imaginary axis onto the unit circle.

10. From (8.12.2) it follows that the sets $\mathscr{I}(z) > 0, \mathscr{I}(z) = 0$ and $\mathscr{I}(z) < 0$ are mapped respectively into $\mathscr{I}(w) > 0, \mathscr{I}(w) = 0$ and $\mathscr{I}(w) < 0$. Now use Exercise 2.9.10.

EXERCISES 8.15

2. The point $-k$ is mapped into 0. Now use Exercise 8.15.1.

3. By Exercise 8.15.2, the image of the circle is a straight line, thus passing through the point $w = \infty$.

4. $z_1 + k^2/z_1 = z_2 + k^2/z_2$.

5. Suppose that two distinct points z_1, z_2 on the circle were mapped by (8.13.1) into the same point. Use now Exercises 8.15.3 and 8.15.4 to obtain a contradiction.

6. Compute $a^2 - b^2$ with a and b as in (8.13.4).

9. As $|z_0| \to \infty$, Arg z_0 fixed, the arc ABC approaches coincidence with the chord joining $-k$ to $ke^{i\theta}$.

10. Denote by P the point whose coordinate is z. Let Q be the inverse of P with respect to the circle $|\zeta| = k$, and Q' the conjugate of Q. Then the coordinate of Q' is k^2/z. (Why?) Denote by S the midpoint of the line segment $Q'P$. Then the coordinate of S is $\frac{1}{2}(z + k^2/z) = \frac{1}{2}w$.

12. Let $z' = iz$, $w' = z' + k^2/z'$ and $w = -iw'$.

15. Let $z' = (1/4)z$. Then $w = z' + m^2/z'$, where $m = k/2$.

16. (a) It is sufficient to draw the image of the line $x = -k$, since the circle Γ_2 is the image of the line $x = -k$ under the transformation $z' = k^2/z$. (c) For the case $0 < a < k/2$. The interior of Γ_1 has the same image as the exterior of Γ_3, where Γ_3 is the image of Γ_1 under the transformation $z' = k^2/z$. The circle Γ_3 passes through the point $-k$ and contains k in its interior. Now see Theorem 8.15.1.

17. Find the image in the z' plane of the sector $|z| \leq 1$, $0 \leq \theta \leq \pi/n$, under the transformation $z' = z^n$. Then find the image in the w plane of the semicircle $|z'| \leq 1$, $\mathscr{I}(z') \geq 0$, under the transformation

$$w = \left(\frac{z'+1}{z'-1}\right)^2.$$

18. (b) Use part (a).

19. Use the method for obtaining the cusp of the Joukowski airfoil.

EXERCISES 8.16

6. $u + iv = w = x + iy + e^{x+iy}$. Thus $u = x + e^x \cos y$ and $v = y + e^x \sin y$. The image is the w plane slit along the two half-lines $u \leq -1$, $v = \pm \pi$.

EXERCISES 8.17

5. Use (4.2.8).

6. Use (4.2.8) to obtain $u^2/\sin^2 p - v^2/\cos^2 p = 1$.

8. $w = \tan^2 \frac{1}{2}z = (1 - \cos z)/(1 + \cos z)$. The mapping is a product of the mapping (1) $z' = \cos z$ followed by the mapping (2) $w = (-z' + 1)/(z' + 1)$.

11. The given transformation may be obtained by applying successively the transformations (1) $z' = 2z$, (2) $z'' = e^{z'}$, and (3) $w = (z'' - 1)/(z'' + 1)$.

12. See Exercise 8.17.11. The circle is $|w - \coth 2c| = |\operatorname{csch} 2c|$.

13. $e^w = (z - 1)/(z + 1)$. Hence $z = -(e^w + 1)/(e^w - 1)$. Consider the product mapping $z' = e^w$ followed by $z = -(z' + 1)/(z' - 1)$, of the strip $-\infty < u < \infty$, $0 \leq v \leq \pi$. The product mapping is one-to-one.

15. The upper half of the w plane slit along the half line $u \geq 1$, $v = \pi$.

16. Utilizing (4.3.6) and (4.3.1), we have $\coth \frac{1}{2}z = (e^z + 1)/(e^z - 1)$. Thus the given transformation may be obtained by applying successively the transformations:

(a) $z' = e^z$,   (b) $z'' = (z' + 1)/(z' - 1)$,   (c) $w = \operatorname{Log} z''$.

EXERCISES 8.19

3. By Exercise 8.19.1, $u(z) = \mathscr{R}[f(z)]$, where $f(z)$ is an analytic function (not necessarily single-valued). Let z_0 be any point in D_0, and let $N(z_0)$ in D_0 be a neighborhood of z_0 over which there is defined a branch $G(z)$ of $f(z)$. Then $\mathscr{R}[G(z)] = 0$ in $N(z_0)$. Hence by Exercise 3.6.16.(b), $G(z) = ic$ in $N(z_0)$. Thus by Exercise 7.10.3, $f(z) = ic$ in D. Therefore $u(z) = \mathscr{R}[f(z)]$ is identically zero in D.

4. Apply Exercise 8.19.3 to the function $u(z) = u_1(z) - u_2(z)$.

6. See Theorem 8.19.3.

7. Consider the linear fractional transformation $z = [i(1 + w)]/(1 - w)$. This transformation maps the unit circle $|w| = 1$ and its interior $|w| < 1$ respectively onto the line $\mathscr{I}(z) = 0$ and the domain $\mathscr{I}(z) > 0$. The function

$u(z)$ on R induces a function $U(w) = u\left[\dfrac{i(1 + w)}{1 - w}\right]$ which is continuous

on the region $|w| \leq 1$, harmonic in $|w| < 1$ and constant on the circle $|w| = 1$. By Theorem 8.19.4, $U(w)$ is constant in the region $|w| \leq 1$. [For another proof use Theorem 8.19.3.]

8. Suppose that $|f(z)| \leq |f(z_0)| = M$. Let $f(z_0) = Me^{i\alpha}$. Let $g(z) = f(z) e^{-i\alpha}$ and let $u(z) = \mathscr{R}[g(z)]$. It follows that

$$u(z) \leq |u(z)| \leq |g(z)| = |f(z)| \leq |f(z_0)| = u(z_0).$$

Thus $u(z)$ is constant in D. Hence $g(z)$ is also constant in D. [See Exercise 3.6.16.(b).]

9. Laplace's equation in polar coordinates is (see Exercise 3.8.17)

$$\frac{\partial}{\partial r}\left(r\,\frac{\partial u}{\partial r}\right) + \frac{1}{r}\,\frac{\partial^2 u}{\partial \theta^2} = 0.$$

Since $u = u(r)$, we have $\partial^2 u/\partial \theta^2 = 0$. Consequently

$$\frac{d}{dr}\left(r\,\frac{du}{dr}\right) = 0.$$

Hence $u = A \operatorname{Log} r + B$.

10. See Exercise 5.17.12 and Remark 5.13.1.

EXERCISES 9.2

1. To prove that $\phi_x = q_1$, let (x, y) be any point in D. Then if h is sufficiently small, the segment C joining (x, y) to $(x + h, y)$ lies in D. Thus

$$\phi_x(x, y) = \lim_{h \to 0}\frac{1}{h}\left[\int_{(x_0, y_0)}^{(x+h, y)} q_1\,dx + q_2\,dy - \int_{(x_0, y_0)}^{(x, y)} q_1\,dx + q_2\,dy\right]$$

$$= \lim_{h \to 0}\frac{1}{h}\int_{(x, y)}^{(x+h, y)} q_1\,dx + q_2\,dy = \lim_{h \to 0}\frac{1}{h}\int_C q_1\,dx + q_2\,dy.$$

Since $dy = 0$ along C, we have

$$\phi_x(x, y) = \lim_{h \to 0} \frac{1}{h} \int_C q_1 \, dx = \lim_{h \to 0} \frac{1}{h} \int_x^{x+h} q_1(\zeta, y) \, d\zeta = q_1(x, y).$$

To prove that $\phi_y = q_2$, we use a segment C joining (x, y) to $(x, y + h)$. The proof that $\psi_x = -q_2$ and $\psi_y = q_1$ is similar.

2. Suppose to the contrary, that there is a point z_0 on C such that $q_n = \alpha$, $\alpha \neq 0$. For definiteness, assume $\alpha > 0$. Then there exists a neighborhood $N(z_0)$ on C such that $q_n > \frac{1}{2}\alpha$ in $N(z_0)$. Let z_1 and z_2 be any two distinct points in $N(z_0)$. Then

$$\psi(z_2) - \psi(z_1) = \int_{z_1}^{z_2} q_n \, ds > 0,$$

thus contradicting the assumption that $\psi(z)$ is constant on C.

EXERCISE 9.3

1. Let

$$G_1(z) = \int_{z_0}^{z_1} (q_t + iq_n) \, ds + \int_{z_1}^{z} (q_t + iq_n) \, ds$$

and

$$G_2(z) = \int_{z_0}^{z_2} (q_t + iq_n) \, ds + \int_{z_2}^{z} (q_t + iq_n) \, ds,$$

be given over $N(z_1)$ and $N(z_2)$ respectively, where the integrals $\int_{z_0}^{z_1}$, $\int_{z_0}^{z_2}$ are taken respectively along paths γ_1 and γ_2, while the integrals $\int_{z_1}^{z}$, $\int_{z_2}^{z}$ are taken along any path lying respectively in $N(z_1)$ and $N(z_2)$. Referring to Definition 4.5.3, let $C: z = z(t)$, $a \leq t \leq b$, be composed of the path γ_1 reversed (that is, from z_1 to z_0), followed by the path γ_2 (from z_0 to z_2), and take $g(z) = G_1(z_1) + \int_{z_1}^{z(t)} (q_t + iq_n) \, ds$ with the path of integration along C. [It can be shown that $G_1(z)$ and $G_2(z)$ have the above form.]

EXERCISES 9.4

1. By conditions (a) and (b), the velocity vector is given by $q = f(r) e^{i\theta}$, where $f(r) > 0$ and $z - \alpha = re^{i\theta}$. Let C be a circle of radius r and center at $z = \alpha$. Then by (c), we have

$$m = \int_C q_n \, ds = \int_0^{2\pi} f(r) \, r \, d\theta = 2\pi r f(r).$$

Hence $f(r) = m/2\pi r$, and consequently $q = me^{i\theta}/2\pi r$. It follows that

$$F'(z) = \bar{q} = \frac{m}{2\pi r e^{i\theta}} = \frac{m}{2\pi(z - \alpha)},$$

and

$$F(z) = \frac{m}{2\pi} \log (z - \alpha).$$

2. Use a method similar to that employed in Exercise 9.4.1.

EXERCISES 9.5

2. Draw a circle Γ_3 containing C, Γ_1 and Γ_2 in its interior. Then apply Exercise 9.5.1.

3. Let $G'(z) = g(z) - i\gamma(z), F_1'(z) = f_1(z) - i\lambda_1(z)$ and $F_2'(z) = f_2(z) - i\lambda_2(z)$. Hence $g(z) = f_1(z) - f_2(z)$, and $\gamma(z) = \lambda_1(z) - \lambda_2(z)$. The stream function $\psi(z)$ of the complex potential $G(z)$ is given by

$$\psi(z) = \int_{z_0}^{z} (-\gamma \, dx + g \, dy) = \int_{z_0}^{z} -(\lambda_1 - \lambda_2) \, dx + (f_1 - f_2) \, dy$$

$$= \int_{z_0}^{z} -\lambda_1 \, dx + f_1 \, dy - \int_{z_0}^{z} -\lambda_2 \, dx + f_2 \, dy = \psi_1(z) - \psi_2(z).$$

4. (a) Let $\psi(z)$, $\psi_1(z)$ and $\psi_2(z)$ be the stream functions of the flows determined by $F(z)$, $F_1(z)$ and $F_2(z)$, respectively. Then as in Exercise 9.5.3, $\psi(z) = \psi_1(z) + \psi_2(z)$. Since $\psi_1(z)$ and $\psi_2(z)$ are constant on C, so is $\psi(z)$.
(b) Use Theorem 9.3.2.

6. Setting (9.5.16) equal to zero and simplifying, we get

$$(ze^{-i\lambda})^2 - \frac{\mathscr{C}i}{2\pi A} (ze^{-i\lambda}) - k^2 = 0.$$

Set $\mathscr{C}/2\pi A = 2t$ and solve for $ze^{-i\lambda}$.

7. Use Exercise 9.5.6.

8. Set $t/k = \cos \theta$ and $\dfrac{\sqrt{k^2 - t^2}}{k} = \sin \theta$ in the expression for the stagnation points given in Exercise 9.5.6.

9. By Theorem 9.2.1, there exists a single-valued and analytic function $F(z)$ in D such that $F'(z) = q_1 - iq_2$. Now use Exercise 7.10.5.

EXERCISES 9.6

2. We first consider the case when Γ_w is in D_w. Let Γ_w be given by the equation $w = w(t)$, $t_1 \leq t \leq t_2$. Then Γ_z will be given by the equation $z = z(t)$, $t_1 \leq t \leq t_2$, where $z(t) = g[w(t)]$. We have in view of (9.6.3)

$$\int_{\Gamma_w} H'(w) \, dw = \int_{\Gamma_w} F'[g(w)] \, g'(w) \, dw = \int_{t_1}^{t_2} F'[z(t)] \, g'(w) \frac{dw}{dt} \, dt.$$

But $g'(w)\, dw/dt = dz/dt$. Hence

$$\int_{\Gamma_w} H'(w)\, dw = \int_{t_1}^{t_2} F'[z(t)] \frac{dz}{dt}\, dt = \int_{\Gamma_z} F'(z)\, dz.$$

In case Γ_w is in R_w but not entirely in D_w, then it is known that for any $\epsilon > 0$, there exists a closed contour γ_w in D_w such that

$$\left| \int_{\gamma_w} H'(w)\, dw - \int_{\Gamma_w} H'(w)\, dw \right| < \frac{\epsilon}{2} \ \text{and} \ \left| \int_{\gamma_z} F'(z)\, dz - \int_{\Gamma_z} F'(z)\, dz \right| < \frac{\epsilon}{2},$$

where γ_z is the image of γ_w under the mapping $z = g(w)$. Since

$$\int_{\gamma_z} F'(z)\, dz = \int_{\gamma_w} H'(w)\, dw,$$

it follows that

$$\left| \int_{\Gamma_z} F'(z)\, dz - \int_{\Gamma_w} H'(w)\, dw \right| < \epsilon.$$

4. By Exercise 9.6.3 we have $\mathscr{C} = 4\pi A\rho \sin(\sigma - \lambda)$, where $-k - z_0 = \rho e^{i\sigma}$. Therefore $\rho = |k + z_0|$ and $\sigma = \arg(k + z_0) + \pi$. The result now follows.

7. By Theorem 8.14.1, the transformation (9.6.10) maps the domain $E(\gamma)$ in the z plane one-to-one onto the domain $E(\gamma')$ in the w plane. By Exercise 8.4.1.(c), the inverse function is analytic in $E(\gamma')$. Furthermore, from (9.6.10) we obtain $w^2 - 4k^2 = (2z - w)^2$. Hence

$$\lim_{w \to -2k} g(w) = \lim_{w \to -2k} z = -k.$$

8. Let $\delta > 0$ be the (minimum) distance from the origin to the circle Γ. Then $|z| > \delta$ for all z in D_z. Let L be any number such that $L > k^2/\delta$. Then by (9.6.10), $|w| < 2L$ for z in D_z and $|z| < L$. Hence, for w in D_w and $|w| \geq 2L$, we have $|z| = |g(w)| \geq L$.

EXERCISES 9.9

1. If $\alpha_1 < 0$, then both $g(z)$ and $h(z)$ are continuous at $z = x_1$. If $\alpha_1 > 0$, then write

$$\phi(z) = \frac{[(z - x_2)^{-\alpha_2} \cdots (z - x_n)^{-\alpha_n}] - [(x_1 - x_2)^{-\alpha_2} \cdots (x_1 - x_n)^{-\alpha_n}]}{(z - x_1)^{\alpha_1}}$$

and apply L'Hospital's rule (see Exercise 3.6.18).

2. Let the path of integration for $\int_{z_1}^{z_2} \phi(\zeta)\, d\zeta$ consist of an arc of the circle $|z - x_1| = |z_1 - x_1|$ and a segment of the line $z - x_1 = t(z_2 - x_1)$.

3. Let $\Psi(z) = (1 - x_1/z)^{-\alpha_1} \cdots (1 - x_n/z)^{-\alpha_n}$, $\mathscr{I}(z) \geq 0$, $z \neq x_j$. Then we have $g(z) = z^{\alpha}\Psi(z)$, where $\alpha = -\sum_{j=1}^{n} \alpha_j < -1$. We readily see that $\lim_{z \to z_\infty} \Psi(z) = 1$. Now, $f(z_2) - f(z_1) = A \int_{z_1}^{z_2} g(\zeta) \, d\zeta$. Let the path of integration for $\int_{z_1}^{z_2} g(\zeta) \, d\zeta$ consist of an arc of the circle $|z| = |z_1|$ and a segment of the line $z = tz_2$. Show that

$$\lim_{\substack{z_1 \to \infty \\ z_2 \to \infty}} [f(z_2) - f(z_1)] = 0.$$

Now use Exercise 3.3.32.

4. For an indentation about a point x_j, decompose $g(z)$ as in the proof of Lemma 9.9.1. For the indentation about z_∞, express $g(z)$ as in the hint to Exercise 9.9.3.

5. Show that if the exterior angles of a closed polygonal line Γ are all positive and less than π, with sum equal to 2π, then Γ is a polygon. (Use the definition of exterior angle given in Remark 9.9.5.)

6. Let $g(\zeta)$ be the integrand in (9.9.22). Then $g(\zeta) = (\zeta - x_j)^{-\alpha_j} h_j(\zeta)$, $j = 1, 2, \cdots, n$; and for $\alpha = \sum_{j=1}^{n} \alpha_j$, $g(\zeta) = \zeta^{-\alpha} h_{n+1}(\zeta)$; where $\lim_{\zeta \to x_j} h_j(\zeta)$ is finite and nonzero, $j = 1, 2, \cdots, n + 1$.

7. Let z_1 be a point in the extended half plane $\mathscr{I}(z) \geqq 0$. Show that $f(z) = A \int_{z_1}^{z} g(\zeta) \, d\zeta + B'$, where $B' = f(z_1)$.

8. Consider the transformation $f(-1/\zeta)$, $\mathscr{I}(\zeta) \geqq 0$ or $\zeta = \zeta_\infty$.

10. $(1 - \zeta^2)^{2/3} = C(\zeta + 1)^{2/3} (\zeta - 1)^{2/3}$, where C is constant. Use Lemma 9.9.8, Theorem 9.9.1 and Exercise 9.9.5.

11. $w = \int_0^z \dfrac{d\zeta}{(1 - \zeta^2)^{3/4}}$ is a solution. (See hint to Exercise 9.9.10.)

12. See hint to Exercise 9.9.10.

13. Show that $|w(0) - w(1)| = |w(1) - w(\infty)|$.

17. We may take $\operatorname{Arg} \zeta_j < \arg (\zeta - \zeta_j) < 2\pi + \operatorname{Arg} \zeta_j$. Let [see (8.12.5)]

$$z = g(\eta) = \frac{\eta - i}{\eta + i}, \qquad \mathscr{I}(\eta) \geqq 0, \qquad \text{or } \eta = \eta_\infty.$$

Show that the transformation $f[g(\eta)]$ is of the form (9.9.20). For the bicontinuity use Exercise 3.3.33.

19. It follows from Coulomb's law that $V(x, y) = -2q \operatorname{Log} |z - z_0| + H(x, y)$, where $H(x, y)$ is harmonic in D, is continuous on R, and is equal to $2q \operatorname{Log} |z - z_0|$ on B;

$$V_1(u, v) = -2q \operatorname{Log} |w - w_0| + H_1(u, v),$$

where $H_1(u, v)$ is harmonic in D_1, is continuous on R_1, and is equal to $2q \operatorname{Log} |w - w_0|$ on B_1. For z on B, $V_1[f(z)] = \mathscr{I}\{F_1[f(z)]\} = 0$. Since the mapping $f(z)$ is analytic in D and one-to-one on R,

$$f(z) - w_0 = (z - z_0) f_1(z),$$

where $f_1(z) \neq 0$ for z in R. Hence $\text{Log} \, |f_1(z)|$ is continuous on R and harmonic in D. (See Exercise 8.19.10.) Now,

$$
\begin{aligned}
V_1[f(z)] &= -2q \, \text{Log} \, |\, (z - z_0)f_1(z) \,| + H_1[f(z)] \\
&= -2q \, \text{Log} \, |\, z - z_0 \,| - 2q \, \text{Log} \, |f_1(z)\,| + H_1[f(z)] \\
&\equiv -2q \, \text{Log} \, |\, z - z_0 \,| + H_2(x, y),
\end{aligned}
$$

where $H_2(x, y)$ is continuous on R and harmonic in D. (See Lemma 8.19.1.) Since $H_2 = H$ on B, it follows that $H_2 = H$ on R. (See Theorem 8.19.4.) Consequently $V(x, y) = V_1[f(z)]$.

Using bounded domains, which in the limit become the domains of Example 9.9.3, it can be shown that $V(x, y) = V_1[f(z)]$ also when B, B_1, and $F(z)$ are as in Example 9.9.3.

Index

Numbers in parentheses refer to exercises.

INDEX